Parcel, Mauro
Hultin & Spaendra

11/89

ECONOMIC EVALUATION AND INVESTMENT DECISION METHODS

Sixth Edition

FRANKLIN J. STERMOLE
COLORADO SCHOOL OF MINES
AND
JOHN M. STERMOLE
INVESTMENT EVALUATIONS CORP.

INVESTMENT EVALUATIONS CORPORATION
2000 Goldenvue Drive
Golden, Colorado 80401

Franklin J. Stermole, B.S., M.S., Ph.D, Chemical Engineering, Iowa State University, is Professor of Mineral Economics and Chemical and Petroleum Refining Engineering at Colorado School 'of Mines where he has taught since 1963. He has taught economic evaluation techniques for 25 years to undergraduate and graduate students and has done economic evaluation consulting for numerous mineral and non-mineral companies. Since 1970 he has taught more than 350 "Economic Evaluation" one-week short courses to over 10,000 persons from mineral and non-mineral industry companies and government organizations in the U.S and abroad, with many of the courses presented in Australia, Canada, Colombia, Germany, France, Indonesia, Mexico, Norway, Saudi Arabia, South Africa, Trinidad, and Venezuela for industry and government organizations. This domestic and foreign industrial consulting and teaching experience has had a direct effect on the applications-oriented content and organization of the text.

John M. Stermole, B.S.B.A., Finance, University of Denver, and M.S., Mineral Economics, Colorado School of Mines is Vice-President of Investment Evaluations Corporation where he has developed personal computer software with economic evaluation applications for general and natural resource industries. He has done economic evaluation consulting intermittently for the past ten years and has assisted in the presentation of dozens of domestic and foreign country "Economic Evaluation" one-week short courses. Prior to joining Investment Evaluations Corporation full time, he gained three years of industry experience applying engineering economy applications to heavy construction projects related to mine site and highway development.

ISBN 0-9603282-8-9
Library of Congress Catalog Card Number 86-083278

Printed in the U.S.A.

TABLE OF CONTENTS

iv

CHAPTER 8: INCOME TAX, CASH FLOW, WORKING CAPITAL AND DISCOUNTED CASH FLOW ANALYSIS

CHAPTER 9: AFTER-TAX INVESTMENT DECISION METHODS AND APPLICATIONS

CHAPTER 10: REPLACEMENT ANALYSIS

CHAPTER 11: EVALUATIONS INVOLVING BORROWED MONEY

CHAPTER 12: VALUATION OF PROPERTY, PROJECTS AND BUSINESSES

PREFACE

This textbook is an introduction to the concepts of the time value of money and the application of time value of money considerations to the after-tax evaluation of virtually all types of investment situations. The text presents the development and application of economic evaluation techniques that can be used to compare systematically and quantitatively the relative economic merits of investment alternatives. The Chase Manhattan bank has projected that 4-5 trillion dollars must be spent on capital investment in the U. S. in the next ten years to maintain a satisfactory rate of economic growth and they say this is more investment dollars than were spent cumulatively in the first 200 years of our history. The growing need for systematic methods to enhance economic decision-making seems evident.

Dual objectives in the initial writing and revision of this text were first, to present valid economic decision methods as clearly as possible and second, to show the application of these economic evaluation methods using investment evaluation illustrations that are as meaningful and realistic as possible. The text content is organized in a manner that presumes this is the reader's first encounter with economic evaluation techniques and applications. However, the textbook has been designed with heavy emphasis on the use of example case studies that together with in-depth discussions on various subjects serve as excellent review material for experienced economic evaluation personnel as well as being the best way to introduce the subject to new students. People with broadly differing economic evaluation backgrounds can benefit from a course or self-study using this textbook.

This textbook has been designed for use in three basic ways. First, it can serve as a university textbook for undergraduate or graduate students. The material covered is applicable for students of engineering, science, economics, accounting, business, finance, management, and other disciplines that relate to economic evaluation work. Second, it can be used for continuing education courses for industry and government personnel with backgrounds and interests just mentioned. Third, it can be used for self-study to teach one's self economic evaluation techniques and applications. This latest text revision has placed special emphasis on strengthening the text discussions and examples for this use, which also makes the text better for use as a course text.

The primary goal of this textbook is to provide the reader with the economic evaluation tools needed to carry out properly the economic evaluation of any type of investment situation on an after-tax basis. To achieve this goal the first 6 chapters in the text present time value of money and economic decision-making techniques on a before-tax basis so the reader is not confused with tax considerations while he is being introduced to the basic time value of money concepts and general economic evaluation methods and applications. From Chapter 7 on the evaluation concepts developed in the first 6 chapters are applied after-tax. The emphasis on after-tax analysis considerations is considered to be a major strength of this text. Tax effects are a major factor for most investment situations so valid economic analyses must be done after-tax. The experience of having the opportunity to teach more than 4 dozen university courses and more than 300 one-week courses for industry and government personnel in the U. S. and many foreign countries using previous versions of this text material has enhanced the organization, content, and illustrations presented in this revised edition to make it as succinctly readable and practical as possible.

Finally, it is important to emphasize that correct economic evaluation of any type of project whether mineral or non-mineral in any country of the world requires the same basic economic evaluation concepts applied after-tax for the tax considerations that are relevant to the type of project being evaluated for the tax laws of the country in which the project is proposed. Although the after-tax illustrations in this text are based on existing U. S. tax law, the text content generally is applicable to the evaluation of any type of project anywhere in the world if the proper tax considerations are applied.

Good luck in your study of the text content and even more luck in finding many potentially profitable investment ventures to which you can apply the concepts presented. In most investment decision-making situations, you will find that application of the concepts and techniques presented in the text together with common sense and good management judgment will enable you to do a better job of economic investment decision-making than you can achieve without using these methods.

Frank and John Stermole

CHAPTER 1

INVESTMENT DECISION MAKING

1.1 Introduction to Investment Analysis

Economic evaluation of investment alternatives relates to systematically evaluating the relative profit potential of investment alternatives. If systematic, quantitative methods are not used to compare the economic considerations of investment alternatives, it seems evident that in certain investment decision making situations the wrong choices may be made from an economic viewpoint. For example, in the analysis of investment alternatives for a given investment situation, the alternatives under consideration may have differences with respect to costs and profits or savings and the timing of costs and profits or savings. Differences may also exist in project lives, tax considerations, and the effects of escalation and inflation on projected costs and revenues. If a systematic approach is not used to quantify the economic effects of these factors, it is very difficult to correctly assess which alternatives have the best economic potential.

Since the days of the writings of economist Adam Smith it has been recognized that capital accumulation has been the primary investment objective of capitalistic individuals, companies and societies to enable them to improve their standard of living. It is emphasized later in this chapter that factors other than economic considerations enter into most investment decisions, but from an economic viewpoint it is assumed that maximizing capital accumulation (or the value of assets that could be converted to capital) is the economic objective of investments. During the ten year period between the late 1980's and late 1990's, it is estimated that more capital investment dollars will be spent in the United States than were spent cumulatively in the past 200 years of U.S. history. The importance of proper economic evaluation techniques in determining the most economically effective way to spend this money seems evident whether you analyze it from an individual, company or government viewpoint.

This text presents the development and application of economic evaluation techniques that can be used to enhance your ability to make correct investment decisions from an economic viewpoint. Note that it is not purported that the use of these techniques will enable you to make correct economic decisions all the time. Because of the effects of risk and uncertainty including escalation and inflation of costs and revenues, it is not possible to develop evaluation techniques that guarantee investment decision making success. However, by using one or more of the economic evaluation techniques presented and recommended in this text, you should be able to do a consistently better job of economic decision making than you can do without using these techniques. Obviously a given analysis is only as good as the input cost and revenue data that go into it. Risk and uncertainty effects make it impossible to know for certain that a given set of data for a proposed investment situation are correct. This, of course, means we cannot be certain of the economic analysis results based on the data. Even when probabilities of success and failure are incorporated into the analyses as is introduced in Chapter 6, we do not have analysis results that are certain for any given investment situation. However, even under evaluation conditions of great uncertainty, the use of formal economic evaluation techniques presented in this text will give the decision maker a much better feeling for the relative risks and uncertainties between alternatives. This information together with the numerical economic evaluation results usually will put the decision maker in a better position to make a correct decision than he would be in if systematic evaluation procedures were not used.

Evaluation of investment alternatives to select project investments that will maximize profit per dollar invested is a key goal of every successful corporate manager or individual investor. To fully achieve this goal, managers or individuals should be familiar with the principles of economic evaluation and investment decision methods which provide the basis for quantified economic evaluation of alternative engineering projects and general investment opportunities.

Most business decisions are made by choosing what is believed to be the best alternative out of several courses of action. Problems in this area are therefore called "alternative choice problems". In many business situations, the decisions are made intuitively, because systematic, quantified decision methods are not available to weigh the alternatives. This should not be the case for weighing the economic considerations related to most investment decisions. Systematic economic decision methods are available for evaluating individual investment projects and for comparing alternative investment projects. The "whims of management" should not be the basis for reaching decisions concerning economic differences between investment alternatives. In this age of increasingly complex investment situations, to be successful over the long run it is imperative that a primary economic evaluation criterion be selected and applied to compare alternative investment choices. This text presents economic evaluation criteria which are based on the premise that profit maximization is the investment objective; that is, maximization of the future worth of available investment dollars. In other words, methods are developed and illustrated in this text to enable a person to determine the courses of action that will make best economic use of limited resources. In general, this involves answering the question, "Is it better to invest cash in a given investment situation or will the cash earn more if it is invested in an alternative situation?".

1.2 "Engineering Economy" and "Economic Evaluation"

Engineering and science technology in one way or another provide the basis for most of the investment opportunities in this world today. Even the economic desirability of investments in land often relates to engineering technology that may make the land more valuable several years from now for apartments, a park or some industrial plant utilization. In a capitalistic society it is imperative that engineering proposals as well as all other types of investment proposals be evaluated in terms of worth and cost before they are undertaken. Even in public activities, benefits must be greater than costs before expenditures normally are approved. Thus, the term "engineering economy" which is used widely in literature and texts applies in general to the "economic evaluation" of all types of investment situations. The terms "economic evaluation" and "engineering economy" are considered to have the same meaning in this text. A person does not need to be an engineer to be proficient in the application of engineering economy (or economic evaluation) principles to evaluate investment alternatives. The well known prerequisite of successful engineering ventures is economic feasibility. This prerequisite applies to both engineering and non-engineering investment situations, so the terms "economic evaluation" and "engineering economy" have valid meaning and importance not only to engineers, but also to bankers, accountants, business managers and other personnel in a wide variety of job descriptions where they are concerned with economic evaluation of investment alternatives. This text is written for people with these kinds of backgrounds or interest.

1.3 Making Decisions

Peter Drucker, in his management texts, has stated that decision making has five distinct phases:

1. Defining the problem
2. Analyzing the problem
3. Developing alternate solutions
4. Deciding upon the best solution
5. Converting the decision into effective action

These decision making phases apply to economic evaluation decision making as well as general managerial decision making. Defining economic evaluation problems clearly is as important in economic analysis as any other situation that requires a decision. In any situation requiring decision making it is necessary to ask the right questions before one can expect to get the answers that are needed. Analysis of the problem or questions is the next step in the decision making process for economic analysis as well as general managerial decisions. This leads to the third phase of decision making concerning whether alternative approaches or investments might not be better. Analysis of these alternative investments then leaves us in a position to decide upon the best economic choice and to take action to implement the best choice.

This text, and the concept of economic decision making, is primarily concerned with the three middle phases defined by Drucker. Again, this includes presenting and illustrating methods that can be used to analyze correctly, various investment situations, developing alternative solutions and the economic analysis of these solutions. Emphasis is directed toward the fact that economic analysis always involves comparison of alternatives, and determining the best way to invest available capital. From an economic viewpoint this means we want to maximize the future profit that can be accumulated from the available investment dollars.

Economic evaluation decision making relates to two basic classifications of projects or investments:

1. Revenue producing investments
2. Service producing investments

Sometimes people think a third investment classification might be, savings producing projects, but it will be illustrated in Chapter 3 that looking at differences between the costs of providing a service by alternative methods, gives the savings that incremental investments in the more costly initial investment alternatives will generate. Analysis of these savings and incremental costs is just one of several valid ways of evaluating general service producing projects.

Many analysis techniques are presented and illustrated in this text. However, emphasis is placed on compound interest rate of return analysis and net present value analysis, properly applied on an after tax basis. A large majority of individuals, companies and government organizations that use formal evaluation techniques use rate of return analysis as their primary decision making criterion with net present value the second most used technique. There are other correct techniques for evaluating various investment situations including future and annual value, and several ratios. These techniques are presented in the text. It is necessary in economic evaluation work to be familiar with many different approaches to economic analysis because eventually you will interact with people that have a wide variety of evaluation backgrounds who use or advocate widely varying economic evaluation techniques. Familiarity with different evaluation techniques enhances communication with these people. Also, it will be shown in Chapter 4 that in certain evaluation situations, methods such as net present value have significant advantages over rate of return analysis. To communicate effectively with different evaluation people you must be familiar with the principles and advantages or disadvantages associated with different evaluation techniques. Also, beware that when you discuss rate of return analysis with different people, the chances are that the term, "rate of return" may mean something very different to the other person than it does to you. Many different rates of return are defined in the literature, some of which follow; return on initial investment, (ROI) which may be defined as being based on initial investment, average investment or some other investment, return on assets (ROA) which is also called accounting rate of return and generally is based on the non-depreciated asset value, return on equity (ROE) which refers to return on individual or stockholder equity capital as the basis of the calculation, return on sales (ROS), which is not an investment rate of return at all, and the compound interest rate of return (ROR) or discounted cash flow rate of return on an after tax basis (DCFROR) which is analogous to a bank account or mortgage interest rate and is the interest rate that makes project costs and revenues equivalent at a given point in time. Only this latter rate of return, DCFROR, is valid consistently for analyzing alternative investments. The other rates of return may have use in certain analysis or accounting situations but they should not, in general, be used to evaluate the relative economic merits of alternative investments because they do not account for the time value of money properly over the project evaluation life. In general these other rates of return look at project rate of return at a specific point in time, or for some kind of average profit and cost considerations.

It is imperative that the time value of money be handled correctly in all valid economic evaluation methods. Also, since taxes are a cost relevant to most evaluation situations, economic analyses must be done after-tax. To omit a major project cost such as taxes may be more important than omitting operating costs and few people would think we should leave operating costs out of an analysis. In certain government project evaluations of projects where taxes do not apply, it is of course proper to neglect taxes. In general you should think in terms of doing all analyses after-tax, omitting tax considerations only when appropriate. In Chapters 2 through 6 of the text, evaluation techniques and illustrations are presented primarily on a before-tax basis to avoid confusing the reader with significant tax considerations at the same time various evaluation techniques and the time value of money are being introduced. Starting in Chapter 7 everything is presented on an after-tax analysis basis and this is the way all evaluations should be done for decision making purposes.

1.4 Definition of Discounted Cash Flow Analysis

In all industries, whether for corporations or individuals, economic analysis of potential investment projects is done to select the investment project or projects that will give maximum value from the investment of available capital. Investors usually use economic analysis techniques based on either rate of return, present value, annual value, future value, or various breakeven analyses to reach economic analysis decisions. When the techniques just mentioned are based on handling the time value of money with a compound interest rate, these techniques are all referred to as "Discounted Cash Flow Analysis Techniques". Understanding this concept requires definition of terms "discounted" and "cash flow".

The term "discount" is generally considered to be synonymous with "present worth" in economic evaluation work. In handling the time value of money, investors want to account for the fact that a dollar in hand today, has greater value than a dollar at some future time because a dollar in hand today, can be put to work now in a bank account or other investments, to accrue interest, or return on investment. Compound interest is the generally accepted approach today for calculating accrued interest, or return on investment, in time value of money calculations. The future value that is projected to be accrued from the investment of dollars today at a specified compound interest rate is equal to the sum of the accrued interest and the initial dollars (principal) invested. The concept of present worth is just the opposite of compounding. The present worth of a future value is the sum of money that invested today, at a specified compound interest rate, would grow to the given future value. When you are working with positive interest rates, present values are always less than future values. Since the term "discounting" implies reducing the value of something, the use of the terms "discounting" and "present worth" have equivalent meaning because they both relate to reducing the value of assets or dollars.

The term "cash flow" is used to refer to the net inflow or outflow of money that occurs during a specified operating period such as a month or year.

Gross Revenue, or Savings
– Operating Expenses
– Tax Costs
– Capital Costs
————————————
= Cash Flow   1-1

Inflows of money from revenues and savings, minus outflows of money for expenditures such as operating costs, income taxes and capital expenditures, equal the project cash flow for a given period. If outflows exceed inflows of money, then cash flow is negative for that period. Of course, it follows that if inflows of money exceed outflows, then cash flow will be positive. Sometimes investors look at project evaluations on a before-tax basis, so they omit income tax costs and savings from economic analyses and define cash flow on a before-tax basis. Generally, it is undesirable to evaluate investments on a before-tax basis, unless the investor is not subject to income taxation. As previously mentioned, Chapters 2 through 6 do not directly address "after-tax" cash flow calculations. The reader can use Equation 1-1 to help visualize the after-tax cash flow values that are illustrated in more detail in Chapter 7 through 12 examples.

The term "discounted cash flow" evolved from the fact that investors most often handle the time value of money using present value calculations so they "present worth" or "discount", positive and negative "cash flow" anticipated from an investment to evaluate the project economic potential.

Discounted cash flow analysis forces an investor to think systematically and quantitatively about all the relevant economic factors that may affect the economic potential of investments. In the past, successful entrepreneurs "intuitively" took into account investment economic analysis factors such as the magnitude and relative timing of investment costs and revenues, the effects that inflation and escalation may have on costs and revenues, the risk of failure involved with the overall investment, the uncertainty associated with projection of specific investment analysis parameters, the tax effects relevant to a proper after-tax evaluation for the financial situation of the investor, and finally, how to assimilate these considerations in a manner that enabled fair, consistent comparison of alternative investments. As investors have become more diversified, it has become more difficult to use entrepreneurial judgments consistently and correctly in analyzing the economic potential of different investments. Discounted cash flow analysis has provided a systematic approach to quantitatively take into account the factors that are relevant in all industries for the proper economic analysis of investments.

Examples of the use of discounted cash flow analysis today are innumerable. Income and service producing project investments of all types are analyzed using discounted cash flow analysis. Investors in minerals, petroleum, timber, real estate, manufacturing, leasing, etc., use discounted cash flow analysis to determine the upper limit that they could be willing to pay for mineral rights, land or assets to generate projected negative and positive cash flows over future years that yield a specified return on invested capital. Major companies use discounted cash flow analysis to evaluate the economic value of other companies. In a simplified form, by evaluating the value of individual properties and businesses that make up a company, the overall company value may be considered to be the cumulative sum of the value of individual properties or businesses that make up the company. The acquisition bids for companies in recent years are situations where discounted cash flow analysis by major investors has indicated the value of companies to be considerably different than the value common stock shareholders had been placing on the companies utilizing net income approaches. Sometimes the discounted cash flow analysis will give a higher indicated value of a project or company than other evaluation approaches might give. Sometimes the discounted cash flow value may be less. The advantage of discounted cash flow analysis is that in all cases the assumptions on which the analysis is based can be explicitly stated and understood by all. If you do not like the input assumptions they can be changed to what you consider more realistic. The non-discounted cash flow, older economic analysis methods have various implicit assumptions built in that may or may not be correct in different analysis situations and therefore, often lead to incorrect economic evaluations. In particular, the older evaluation techniques do not properly account for the time value of money. This is the single most important consideration that has caused companies and investors in most industries to shift to discounted cash flow analysis since the mid 1960's.

The real utility of discounted cash flow analysis is that it puts all investments on a common evaluation basis of handling the time value of money with compound interest rate of return. In all industries, we are concerned with analyzing inflows of money (such as revenues and savings) and outflows of money (such as operating costs, capital expenditures and income tax costs). Discounted cash flow analysis enables investors to fairly and properly account for the magnitude and timing of these dollar value considerations regardless of the type of investment.

1.5 Example of Discounted Cash Flow

Remembering that investment cash flow in any year represents the net difference between inflows of money from all sources minus investment outflows of money from all sources, consider the cash flow diagram presented in thousands of dollars:

Year	0	1	2	3	4	5	6
Revenue			170	200	230	260	290
− Operating Cost			− 40	− 50	− 60	− 70	− 80
− Capital Costs	− 200	− 100					
− Tax Costs			− 30	− 40	− 50	− 60	− 70
Project Cash Flow	− 200	− 100	+ 100	+ 110	+ 120	+ 130	+ 140

The negative cash flows incurred during years 0 and 1 will be paid off by the positive cash flows in year 2 through 6, very much like loans of $200 and $100 thousand today and one year from today respectively, would be paid off by mortgage payments in amounts equal to the positive cash flow in years 2 through 6. What after-tax rate of return (DCFROR), or mortgage compound interest rate, would an investor be receiving, if he incurs the negative cash flows in years 0 and 1 to generate the positive cash flow from revenue in years 2 through 6? The compound interest rate that makes the present worth positive cash flow plus the present worth negative cash flow equal to zero is the desired rate of return, compound interest rate, or DCFROR, using those terms interchangably. This value is 20.8% for this stream of positive and negative cash flows.

Net present value (NPV) is the cumulative present worth of positive and negative investment cash flow using a specified discount rate to handle the time value of money. In general, the discount rate represents the minimum acceptable investment DCFROR. For this example a discount rate of 15% is used. Positive net present value represents the present worth positive cash flow that is above what is needed to cover the present worth negative cash flow for the discount rate used. In other words, positive NPV represents additional costs that could be incurred in the year NPV is calculated, and allow the project to still have a DCFROR equal to the discount rate. Remember that rate of return (or DCFROR) is the discount rate that makes NPV equal to zero. For the 15% discount rate, the NPV for the above values is +$54.75 thousand. This represents the additional negative cash flow that could be incurred in year 0 (in addition to the -$200 thousand cash flow in year zero) and have the project yield a 15% DCFROR.

Sensitivity analyses can be made to see how the acquisition cost of $54.75 thousand is affected by changing the relative timing of when the costs and revenues are to be incurred. First, instead of incurring the cumulative positive investment cash flow of $600 thousand over years 2 through 6, assume the same cumulative positive cash flow will be realized over years 2 and 3 with +$280 thousand in year 2 and +$320 thousand in year 3.

Project Cash Flow	-200	-100	+280	+320
Year	0	1	2	3

For this case the DCFROR will increase to 37.1% and the NPV grows to +$135.2 thousand. Accounting for the time value of money and realizing positive cash flow much quicker enhances the economics of a project significantly. Second, if we slow down the receipt of positive cumulative cash flow of $600 thousand so that the cash flow is realized more slowly over years 2 through 9 with +$55, +$60, +$65, +$70, +$75, + $85, +$90, and +$100 thousand per year respectively, what is the effect on the project economics?

Project Cash Flow	-200	-100	+55	+60	+65	+70	+75	+85	+90	+100
Year	0	1	2	3	4	5	6	7	8	9

Deferring positive cash flow into the future drops the NPV to -$11.7 thousand and the DCFROR to 14%. Both values indicate that the project is unsatisfactory compared to other opportunities thought to exist at a 15% rate of return, and in fact the NPV indicates that we would have to be paid $11.7 thousand to take this project and receive a 15% return on invested capital.

Summary of Findings

Investment Life	3 Years	6 Years	9 Years
Project DCFROR	37%	21%	14%
Project NPV @ 15%	+$135.2	+$54.7	-$11.7
Cumulative +CF, Thousands	$600.0	$600.0	$600.0
Cumulative -CF, Thousands	$300.0	$300.0	$300.0

In this example we have looked at three different evaluations of the same cumulative negative cash flow (investment dollars) of $300 thousand and cumulative positive cash flow of $600 thousand. If we neglect the time value of money, we would consistently determine that the project yields $300 thousand in profits. Yet the economic conclusions that account for the time value of money indicate a range of NPV's for these three cases from −$11.7 thousand to +$135.2 thousand. Obviously, project economics properly accounting for the time value of money can be very sensitive to the relative timing of investment capital costs and revenues over the expected project life.

The discount rate selected can also have a very significant effect on economic evaluation results. To illustrate this concept we will analyze the NPV of the six year life analysis for discount rates of 10 and 20 percent, as well as 15 percent. The results are presented below;

Discount Rate	NPV
10%	+$116.1
15%	+$ 54.8
20%	+$ 6.8

NPV results vary by a factor of 17 from + $116.1 to +$6.8 thousand as the discount rate is increased by a factor of two from 10 to 20 percent. In the following section, discussion is related to determining the appropriate discount rate.

1.6 Minimum Rate of Return/Opportunity Cost of Capital/Discount Rate

In most cases the interest rate that should be used in non-rate of return economic evaluation calculations is not the cost of borrowed money, but is instead *the minimum rate of return which reflects the rate of return that the investor feels represents other opportunities in which to invest available investment capital with a reasonable level of risk.* This minimum rate of return should reflect the minimum expected growth rate for capital. For example, if an investor's alternative to investing in a project is leaving the money in a bank at 6% interest, the minimum rate of return that should be used in a before-tax analysis is 6% while the minimum rate of return that should be used in an after-tax analysis is 6%, multiplied by one minus the tax rate, since interest is taxable as ordinary income. This is probably less than the cost of borrowed money. If the investor's alternative to investing in a project is to forgo investment in an apartment house projected to yield a 20% after-tax rate of return, the minimum rate of return that should be used is 20%. The 20% rate probably is greater than the cost of borrowed money. Only if borrowed money is unlimited, that is, if there is a sufficient supply of borrowed money to invest in all projects under consideration, should the cost of borrowed money be used as the minimum rate of return in economic evaluation calculations. Usually, the unlimited borrowed money case is a hypothetical situation for an individual or corporation. Use of the cost of borrowed money as the minimum rate of return tells an investor whether borrowing is economically desirable or undesirable for various alternative investments. However, it does not enable the investor to determine which alternative investments are the optimum economic investment choices or choice. The minimum rate of return must represent other opportunities for the investment of capital to determine optimum investment decisions from an economic viewpoint.

The term "opportunity cost of capital" often is used interchangeably with "minimum rate of return" because both terms represent the other opportunities for the investment of capital that are considered to exist and must be passed by if we invest available capital somewhere else. For example, neglecting taxes, if we pass up an opportunity to invest $1000 for 1 year at a 10% annual interest rate, we incur an opportunity cost of $100 which corresponds to a 10% rate of return on the $1000. From an economic evaluation viewpoint we would not want to incur that opportunity cost unless other alternative uses for the investment of capital looked better, that is, show promise of giving a rate of return greater than 10%. Some investors refer to the minimum rate of return or opportunity cost of capital as the hurdle rate since an economical project must have a rate of return that hurdles that minimum rate of return. Other investors use the term discount rate or minimum discount rate in referring to the minimum rate of return.

Understanding the minimum rate of return concept is an extremely important point that is fundamental to almost all economic evaluations. However, it is a concept that often is not understood and illustrations in numerous places of the early chapters of this text should help clarify the minimum rate of return concept. Chapter 3 contains a section specifically devoted to discussion of the minimum rate of return in more detail.

1.7 Investment Analysis

Before proceeding to the development of the compound interest formulas in the next chapter, it should be pointed out that this text is concerned primarily with decision methods for "economic analysis" of alternative investment opportunities. An overall investment analysis should, and usually does involve three analyses:

1. Economic Analysis
2. Financial Analysis
3. Intangible Analysis

Economic analysis involves evaluation of the relative merits of investment situations from a profit and cost (or economic) viewpoint. *Financial analysis* refers to where the investment funds for proposed investments will be obtained. Some alternate methods of financing investments include use of personal or corporate funds, borrowing from a bank, having a corporate funded debt offering of bonds or debentures, or going to the public with a new common stock offering. *Intangible analysis* involves consideration of factors that affect investments but which cannot be quantified easily in economic terms. Typical intangible factors are legal and safety considerations, public opinion or goodwill, political considerations in foreign ventures, ecological and environmental factors, uncertain regulatory or tax law conditions, and many others.

Often times an alternative that looks best economically may be rejected for financial or intangible reasons. For instance, attractive projects may have to be rejected for financial reasons if internal funds are not available to finance the projects and outside financing cannot be obtained at attractive interest rates. Intangible factors that may cause rejection of economically sound projects are innumerable, but high on the list of importance are potential public opinion and legal problems from possible air, land, or water pollution. The importance of financial and intangible analysis factors in relation to economic factors must never be underestimated in management investment decision making. They often are as important as economic considerations.

There is a tendency in the literature and practice to interchange the use of the terms "economic analysis" and "financial analysis". This often leads to confusion and improper use of investment decision methods. It is important to recognize that, as used in this text, "economic analysis" relates to evaluation of the profitability of a proposed project and "financial analysis" relates to how the project will be financed. This text primarily is concerned with the development and illustration of economic analysis techniques.

Concerning questions that may arise in your mind about the meaning of various investment terms as you proceed through the text, note that Appendix D is a glossary of investment terminology that may contain the definition of terms which are unfamiliar to you. Whether your background is engineering, accounting, business, geology, science, liberal arts, law or some other academic discipline, it is likely that from time to time you will develop questions about the meaning of certain terms. The use of the systematic quantitative economic evaluation techniques developed and illustrated in the following chapters, of necessity, requires the use of some terms that may be new to you, but economic evaluation experience will reduce this problem as you progress through the text.

CHAPTER 2

COMPOUND INTEREST FORMULAS AND EQUIVALENCE APPLICATIONS

2.1 Introduction to Equivalence

Economic evaluation of investment alternatives requires that the alternatives be evaluated on the same basis and that the time value of money be accounted for properly. When alternate sources of loan money are available with different payment schedules that make it difficult or impossible to determine intuitively the source that is least expensive, it is necessary to convert the alternatives to an "equivalent" basis that permits comparison of the alternatives. This necessitates correct accounting for the time value of money. For example, would you rather have $100 now or $102 a year from now? A majority of people would take $100 now because they intuitively know that putting the $100 in a bank at 4% or 5% interest will give them more than $102 a year from now. Would you rather have $100 now or $150 a year from now? A majority of people would probably take $150 a year from now because they intuitively know that they probably do not have other places to invest $100 where it will earn $50 profit or a 50% rate of return in one year. Now if you are asked whether you would rather have $100 now or $150 five years from now, the problem is more difficult to evaluate intuitively. What compound interest rate will cause $100 now to grow to $150 in 5 years? Do you have alternative places to invest the $100 where it will grow to more than $150 in 5 years? These questions must be answered by using one of several possible "equivalence" methods to compare the relative economic merits of $100 today with $150 five years from today. In the following section the compound interest formulas that provide the basis for equivalence calculations are developed and illustrated.

2.2 Compound Interest Formula Derivations and Illustrations

This section presents the derivation of the six basic compound interest formulas commonly needed to apply engineering economy decision methods for proper comparison of investment alternatives. To develop general formulas, the following letter symbols will be used throughout the remainder of this text:

P: Present single sum of money; normally refers to a sum of money at time zero, but may represent a sum of money at any point from which we choose to measure time.

F: A future single sum of money at some designated future date.

A: The amount of each payment in a uniform series of equal payments made at each period. When the periods are years, "A" refers to annual payments or value.

n: The number of interest compounding periods in the project evaluation life.

i: The period compound interest rate (may refer to either the cost of borrowed money, the rate of return on invested capital, or the minimum rate of return, depending on the situation).

To assist in understanding these letter symbols and their relationship to investment evaluation problems, refer to the following horizontal time line diagram shown in Figure 2-1.

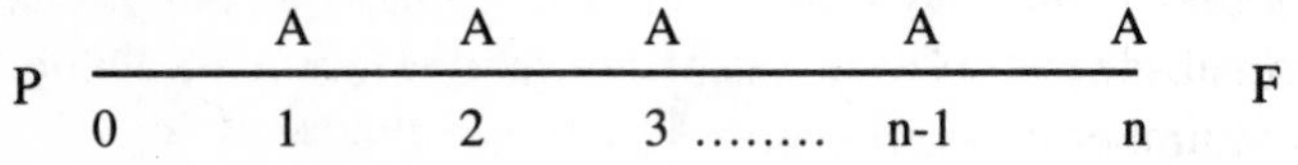

$$
\begin{array}{ccccccc}
 & A & A & A & A & A & \\
\hline
P & & & & & & F \\
0 & 1 & 2 & 3 & \dots\dots & n\text{-}1 & n
\end{array}
$$

Figure 2-1 A Time Diagram Illustrated

The interest compounding periods are designated 1, 2, 3, ... n, below the horizontal line. At time zero, "P" designates a present single sum of money; "A" designates a uniform series of equal payments at each compounding period; and "F" designates a future sum of money at the end of period "n". It usually is desirable to put the monetary numbers from economic evaluation problems on this type of time diagram to reduce confusion that creeps into problem statements before attempting to calculate the desired quantities. Once you have determined what monetary values are given, where they occur on the time diagram, what increment of time designates a period, what the interest rate per period is, and what you want to calculate, the problem is essentially solved. It is then just a matter of putting the information into the appropriate equation that will calculate the desired quantity.

On the following pages the compound interest formula factors are developed to mathematically relate "P", "F", and "A". In developing and discussing the application of these factors, you will note that the terms "worth" and "value" are used interchangeably to refer to either cost or income quantities and calculations.

There are six different two variable relationships that can be developed between "P", "F", and "A", as follows:

Calculated Quantity	=	Given Quantity	X	Appropriate Factor
F	=	P	X	$F/P_{i,n}$
F	=	A	X	$F/A_{i,n}$
P	=	F	X	$P/F_{i,n}$
P	=	A	X	$P/A_{i,n}$
A	=	F	X	$A/F_{i,n}$
A	=	P	X	$A/P_{i,n}$

Table 2-1 Variable Relationships Between "P", "F", and "A" and the Appropriate Factors

To reduce the need to memorize the verbal names of the time value of money factors, *the factor symbolism given here and used throughout the text is based on the first letter in each factor designating the quantity that the factor calculates while the second letter designates the quantity that is given.* The two subscripts on each factor are the period interest rate, "i", followed by the number of interest compounding periods, "n".

You should note that there are only three basic types of time value of money calculations: 1) calculation of future value, "F", from either "P" or "A"; 2) calculation of uniform and equal annual (or period) values, "A", from either "F" or "P"; 3) calculation of present value, "P", from either "F" or "A". All time value of money calculations involve writing an equation or equations to calculate either "F", "P", or "A" so familiarity with the development and application of the factors needed to make these calculations is very important.

SINGLE PAYMENT COMPOUND-AMOUNT FACTOR. When you desire to calculate the future worth, "F", "n" periods from now, of a present sum of money, "P", with compounded interest at i% per period, the calculations are made as shown on the time diagram in Figure 2-2.

Principal $\quad P \atop Pi$ $\left.\right\}P(1+i)$ $\quad {P(1+i) \atop P(1+i)i}$ $\left.\right\}P(1+i)^2$ $\qquad {P(1+i)^{n-1} \atop P(1+i)^{n-1}i}$ $\left.\right\}P(1+i)^n = F$
Interest

P ——

$\quad 0 \qquad\qquad 1 \qquad\qquad\qquad 2\ldots\ldots\ldots\ldots\ldots\ldots n$

Figure 2-2 Time Diagram Illustration of Calculation of the
Single Payment Compound-Amount Factor.

Interest is paid each year on the principal in the account at the beginning of the year. For year one the principal is P and interest is Pi which gives $P(1+i)$ accumulated at the end of year one. Therefore, in year two, the principal $P(1+i)$ draws interest of $P(1+i)i$, which gives a total value of $P(1+i)^2$ accumulated at the end of year two. The final value accrued at the end of year "n" is given in Equation 2-1.

$$F = P(1+i)^n \qquad\qquad\qquad\qquad\qquad 2\text{-}1$$

The factor $(1+i)^n$ is called the "single payment compound-amount factor". Because we are calculating a future single sum of money, "F", from a present single sum of money, "P", we will designate the factor $(1+i)^n$ as $F/P_{i,n}$. *The $F/P_{i,n}$ factor is used to calculate a future sum, "F", that is equivalent to a present sum, "P".* We will use this type of symbolism to designate all six compound interest formulas to be developed here. In each case, *for the symbolism used, the first letter in the symbol designates what we are calculating, and the second letter designates the given quantity from which we are calculating. As previously described, the first subscript "i" always designates the period interest rate and the second subscript "n" always designates the number of interest compounding periods.* Use of this symbolism eliminates the confusion of trying to memorize the name of each factor and when to use each factor until you are more familiar and at ease with the use of each factor. The common names of the different factors should be learned eventually, since the literature commonly uses name terminology rather than symbolism. However, for the student initially learning time value of money calculations, the symbolism is a great help in becoming familiar with the application of compound interest formulas to solve problems. Following is an example illustrating the use of the $F/P_{i,n}$ factor.

EXAMPLE 2-1 Single Payment Compound-Amount Factor Illustration

Calculate the future worth that $1,000 today will have six years from now if interest is 10% per year compounded annually.

Solution:

$$P = \$1,000 \quad \frac{\quad\quad\quad\quad\quad\quad\quad}{0 \quad\quad 1 \quad\quad 2 \quad \ldots\ldots\ldots\ 6}$$

$$\overset{1.772}{F} = \$1,000(F/P_{10\%,6}) = \$1,772$$

The $F/P_{i,n}$ factor is found in the tables in Appendix A, or it can be calculated mathematically to be $(1 + .10)^6 = 1.772$.

SINGLE PAYMENT PRESENT-WORTH FACTOR. If we are given the value of a future sum, "F", and wish to calculate its present value, "P", we can do this solving Equation 2-1 for "P" as follows:

$$P = F [1/(1 + i)^n] \qquad\qquad 2\text{-}2$$

The factor $1/(1 + i)^n$ is called the "single payment present-worth factor", and we designate it by $P/F_{i,n}$. This factor is used to calculate a present single sum, "P", that is equivalent to a future single sum, "F".

Note that $P/F_{i,n} = 1/F/P_{i,n}$. Although one factor can be calculated from the other, the tables of compound interest formulas (Appendix A in the back of the text) give both factors for convenience.

EXAMPLE 2-2 Single Payment Present-Worth Factor Illustration

Calculate the present value of a $1,000 payment to be received six years from now if interest is 10% per year compounded annually.

Solution:

$$P = \$1,000 \overset{.5645}{(P/F_{10,6})} = \$564.50$$

$$\frac{\quad\quad\quad\quad\quad\quad\quad\quad\quad\quad\quad}{0 \quad\quad\quad\quad\quad\quad\quad\quad\quad\quad 6}$$

$$F = \$1,000$$

The $P/F_{10,6}$ factor was taken from the Appendix A tables. The result shows that $564.50 invested today at 10% interest per year would grow to $1,000.00 in six years.

UNIFORM SERIES COMPOUND-AMOUNT FACTOR. Uniform series of equal investments are encountered frequently in economic evaluation problems, and it often is necessary to calculate the future worth, "F", of these payments. Derivation of the equation to do this follows. Each equal single investment, "A", draws compound interest for a different number of periods as illustrated in Figure 2-3. The investment, "A", at the end of period "n" draws no interest. The investment, "A", at the end of period "n-1" draws interest for one period, and so forth. Writing the information given in Figure 2-3 into an equation to determine the cumulative future

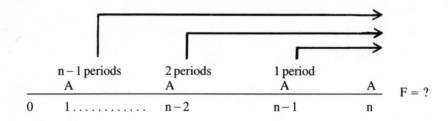

Figure 2-3 Time Diagram Development of Equation 2-3.

worth of these equal investments for a compound interest rate of i% per period gives Equation 2-3. Note that each "A" value in this equation corresponds to a present single sum "P" as used in Equation 2-1 which describes the single payment compound amount factor.

$$F = A(1) + A(1+i) + A(1+i)^2 + \ldots + A(1+i)^{n-1}$$ 2-3

Multiplying both sides of Equation 2-3 by $1+i$ yields:

$$F(1+i) = A(1+i) + A(1+i)^2 + A(1+i)^3 + \ldots + A(1+i)^n$$ 2-4

Subtracting 2-3 from 2-4 gives:

$$F(1+i) - F = A(1+i)^n - A$$

or

$$F = A\,[(1+i)^n - 1]/i$$ 2-5

The factor $[(1+i)^n - 1]/i$ is called the "uniform series compound-amount factor" and we designate it by $F/A_{i,n}$. This factor is used to calculate a future single sum, "F", that is equivalent to a uniform series of equal end of period payments, "A".

EXAMPLE 2-3 Uniform Series Compound-Amount Factor Illustration

Calculate the future value six years from now of a uniform series of $1,000 investments made at the end of each year for the next six years if interest is 10% per year compounded annually.

Solution:

```
    A=$1,000   A=$1,000        A=$1,000              7.716
_____  F = $1,000(F/A_{10,6}) = $7,716
 0        1           2 ........... 6
```

SINKING-FUND DEPOSIT FACTOR. To determine the amount of money, "A", that must be sunk into a fund at the end of each period for n periods at i% interest per period to accumulate "F" dollars, we can solve

Equation 2-5 for "A".

$$A = F \{i/[(1 + i)^n - 1]\} \qquad 2\text{-}6$$

The factor $i/[(1+i)^n - 1]$ is called the "sinking-fund deposit factor" and we designate it by $A/F_{i,n}$. The factor is used to calculate a uniform series of equal end period payments, "A", that are equivalent to a future sum, "F".

Note that, $A/F_{i,n} = 1/(F/A_{i,n})$

EXAMPLE 2-4 Sinking-Fund Deposit Factor Illustration

Calculate the uniform series of equal payments made at the end of each year for the next six years that are equivalent to a $1,000 payment six years from now, if interest is 10% per year compounded annually.

Solution:

$$\underset{0 \quad 1 \;\ldots\ldots\ldots\ldots\ldots\ldots\; 5}{\overset{.12961}{\underline{A = \$1,000(A/F_{10,6}) = \$129.61}}} \quad \begin{matrix} A \\ 6 \end{matrix} \quad \begin{matrix} A \\ \\ F = \$1,000 \end{matrix}$$

CAPITAL-RECOVERY FACTOR. To relate a uniform series of end of period payments, "A", to a present sum, "P", we can combine Equations 2-6 and 2-1 as follows:

$$A = (P(1+i)^n)[i/(1+i)^n - 1] = P[i(1+i)^n]/[(1+i)^n - 1] \qquad 2\text{-}7$$

The factor $i(1+i)^n/[(1+i)^n - 1]$ is called the "capital-recovery factor" and we designate it by $A/P_{i,n}$. This factor is used to calculate a uniform series of end of period payments, "A", that are equivalent to a present single sum of money, "P".

EXAMPLE 2-5 Capital-Recovery Factor illustration

Calculate the uniform series of payments at the end of each year for six years that are equivalent to a present sum of $1,000 if interest is 10% per year compounded annually. (This is the calculation of six end-of-year mortgage payments to pay off a $1,000 loan at 10% interest.)

Solution:

$$P = \$1,000 \quad \underset{0 \quad 1 \;\ldots\ldots\ldots\ldots\ldots\ldots\; 6}{\overset{.22961}{\underline{A = \$1,000(A/P_{10,6}) = \$229.61}}} \quad A$$

UNIFORM SERIES PRESENT-WORTH FACTOR. To determine the present single sum of money, "P", that is equivalent to a uniform series of equal payments, "A", for n periods, at i% interest per period, we can solve Equation 2-7 for "P".

$$P = A[(1+i)^n - 1]/i(1+i)^n \qquad\qquad 2\text{-}8$$

The factor $[(1+i)^n - 1/i(1+i)^n]$ is called the "uniform series present-worth factor" and we designate it by $P/A_{i,n}$. This factor is used to calculate the present sum, "P", that is equivalent to a uniform series of equal end of period payments, "A".

Note that $A/P_{i,n} = 1/(P/A_{i,n})$

EXAMPLE 2-6 Uniform Series Present-Worth Factor Illustration

Calculate the present value of a series of $1,000 payments to be made at the end of each year for six years if interest is 10% per year compounded annually.

Solution:

```
          -   A=$1,000                      A=$1,000
P = ?    _____
          0          1 . . . . . . . . . . . . . . . . . . . . 6
```

$$\text{where at time zero, } P = \$1,000(P/A_{10,6}) = \$4,355.00$$
$$\overset{4.355}{}$$

Note that the uniform series present worth factor $P/A_{10,6}$ brings the six equal $1,000 values at periods 1 through 6 to time zero (which is the beginning of period one), and not to time one, which is the end of period one.

SUMMARY OF COMPOUND INTEREST FORMULAS

Name, Formula and Symbol Designation	Illustration
Single Payment Compound-Amount Factor $= (1+i)^n = F/P_{i,n}$	$\dfrac{P_{given}}{0 \ldots\ldots\ldots\ldots n}$ $F = P(F/P_{i,n})$
Single Payment Present-Worth Factor $= 1/(1+i)^n = P/F_{i,n}$	$\dfrac{P = F(P/F_{i,n})}{0 \ldots\ldots\ldots\ldots\ldots n}$ F_{given}
Uniform Series Compound Amount Factor $= [(1+i)^n - 1]/i = F/A_{i,n}$	$\dfrac{A_{given} \quad A}{0 \ 1 \ldots\ldots n}$ $F = A(F/A_{i,n})$
Sinking-Fund Deposit Factor $= i/[(1+i)^n - 1] = A/F_{i,n}$	$\dfrac{A = F(A/F_{i,n}) \ A}{0 \qquad 1 \ldots\ldots\ldots n}$ F_{given}
Capital-Recovery Factor $= i(1+i)^n/[(1+i)^n - 1] = A/P_{i,n}$	$P_{given} \quad A = P(A/P_{i,n}) \quad A$ $0 \qquad\qquad 1 \ldots\ldots\ldots\ldots n$
Uniform Series Present-Worth Factor $= [(1+i)^n - 1]/i(1+i)^n = P/A_{i,n}$	$P = A(P/A_{i,n}) \quad A_{given} \qquad A$ $0 \qquad\qquad\qquad 1 \ldots\ldots\ldots n$

Note that in applying the formula's as shown in the illustration column, the symbol letters always alternate in each equation. Knowing this may assist the reader in remembering the correct factor to use for various applications of the formulas.

2.3 Period, Nominal, Effective, and Continuous Interest Rates

Interest rates are normally specified by financial agencies on a nominal annual basis with interest compounded a specified number of times per year. For example, if a bank pays 5.0% interest compounded daily this means that the nominal annual interest rate is 5.0% and the daily period interest rate is 5.0% divided by 365 days which is 0.0137% per day. With daily compounding a depositor would receive interest on the principal in his account at the end of each daily period. Relating this to our compound interest formulas, there would be 365 periods per year with the period interest rate $i = 0.0137\%$. Due to the effect of compounding, with more than one interest compounding period per year, the total amount of interest paid per year is greater than the nominal interest rate, r, times initial principal. The term "annual percentage rate", which the common bank acronym "APR" represents, is interchangeable with "nominal" interest rate.

Period interest rate $= i = r/m$
where; m = number of compounding periods per year
$\qquad$ r = nominal interest rate = mi

An effective interest rate is the interest rate that when applied once per year to a principal sum will give the same amount of interest equal to a nominal rate of r% per year compounded "m" times per year. The development of the formula for an effective interest rate, "E", follows:

The future worth "F_1" of P dollars invested at 1% per period for "m" periods is

$$P \text{ —————————————— } \quad F_1 = P(F/P_{i,m}) = P(1+i)^m$$
$$0 \qquad 1 \qquad 2\ldots\ldots\ldots m \quad \text{periods/year}$$

If we apply an effective interest rate, E, once per year we get a future worth, "F_2", from investing "P" dollars.

$$P \text{ —————————————— } \quad F_2 = P(F/P_{E,1}) = P(1+E)^1$$
$$0 \qquad\qquad\qquad\qquad 1 \quad \text{period/year}$$

Since the initial principal, P, is the same in each case, we must set $F_1 = F_2$ to make the total annual interest the same for both cases. This gives the result shown in Equation 2-9 for E:

Effective Annual Interest, $E = (1+i)^m - 1$ 2-9

where $i = r/m$,

Note that $E = F/P_{i,m} - 1$

If we let the number of compounding periods, "m", per year become very large, the period interest rate, r/m, becomes very small. In the limit as "m" approaches infinity, period interest "i" approaches zero and we have the continuous interest situation. Skipping mathematical details, the development of the effective annual continuous interest rate formula results in the following equation where "e" is the natural log base e:

$$E_{continuous} = limit_{m \to \infty} [1+(r/m)]^m - 1 = e^r - 1 \qquad 2\text{-}10$$

To illustrate the different types of interest rates just discussed, consider the 1.5% monthly period interest charged on some credit card accounts. This period interest rate corresponds to a monthly compounded nominal rate of 18.0%. Using Equation 2-9, the effective annual interest rate that is equivalent to a nominal rate of 18% compounded monthly is $E = (1+.015)^{12} - 1 = 0.1956$ in decimal form or 19.56% per year on any unpaid credit card account balance. If the nominal rate of 18.0% were compounded continuously instead of monthly, we would use equation 2-10 to get an effective annual interest rate, $E = 19.72\%$ from $E = e^{.18} - 1$. Exponential factors given in Appendix B enhance this calculation if you do not have a calculator that calculates them directly.

EXAMPLE 2-7 Effective Interest Rate Illustration

What effective annual interest rate is equivalent to the following?
a) A nominal interest rate of 8% compounded quarterly
b) A nominal interest rate of 8% compounded continuously
c) A nominal interest rate of 8% compounded daily

Solution:
a) $E = (1+.08/4)^4 - 1 = 0.82432$ or 8.2432%
b) $E = e^{.08} - 1 = 0.083287$ or 8.3287%
c) $E = (1+.08/365)^{365} - 1 = 0.83277$ or 8.3277%

2.4 Other Bases for Compound Interest Formulas

Compound interest formulas can be developed for a number of different assumptions that differ from the assumptions of discrete period compounding and end of period values used to develop the formulas in this chapter. Three common variations that have useful practical applications are:

1. Mid-period value assumption
2. Continuous interest for end of period values
3. Continuous interest for continuous period values (commonly known as "funds flow" formulas in the literature).

The compound interest formulas for continuous interest are developed in Appendices B and C, respectively. The fact that the development is given later rather than in this section is not meant to reflect the lack of importance of these factors for use in economic evaluation decision methods. On the contrary, although a large majority of people and companies use discrete period compounding with end of period payments as previously discussed in this chapter, many companies use one of the continuous interest approaches and the corresponding compound interest formulas in the evaluation of alternative investments. Investment decision method calculations and evaluation results are similar regardless of the type of compounding and period payments used as is illustrated in the following two examples.

EXAMPLE 2-8 Mid-Period vs. End or Beginning of Period Timing

Calculate the present value of $100 to be received between five and six years from now using a discrete compound interest rate of 15% per year assuming the money is received either at the beginning of year 6, the middle of year 6, or the end of year of year 6.

Beginning of Period Assumption

P = ?   - $100   -
_____
0   1 5   6
              .4972
P = 100(P/F$_{15\%,5}$) = 100{$1/(1+.15)^5$} = $49.72

End of Period Assumption

P = ? $100
_____
0   1 5   6
              .4323
P = 100(P/F$_{15\%,6}$) = 100{$1/(1+.15)^6$} = $43.23

Mid-Period Assumption

P = ?   -   - $100   -
_____
0   1 5   5.5   6
              .4636
P = 100(P/F$_{15\%,5.5}$) = 100{$1/(1+.15)^{5.5}$} = $46.36

Split Period Assumption

P = ?   -   - $50 $50

0   1 4   5   6

.4323   .4972
$$P = 50(P/F_{15\%,6}) + 50(P/F_{15\%,5}) = \$46.47$$

The present worth results differ for these different timing assumptions. However, *the key to correct analysis is putting costs and revenues into an analysis as close as possible to the period when they are actually expected to be incurred. Whether you use mid-period values or beginning or end of period values is not critically significant.* For example, the end of any year is the same time as the beginning of the next year. Relating these comments to Example 2-8, if you expect the $100 value to be realized closer to year 5 than to year 6, or 5.5, then the $100 should be treated as a year 5 value, which may be thought of either as an end of year 5 value, or a beginning of year 6 value. If the mid-period assumption is used, a value of $100 incurred uniformly during year 6 can be treated as a mid-year 6 value at period 5.5. With end of period values, this same $100 value incurred uniformly during year 6 can be treated as a split value with the $50 value incurred during the first half of year 6 treated as a year 5 value (the closest point in time) and the $50 value incurred in the last half of year 6 treated as a year 6 value. Note the similar present values of mid-period and split-period values in Example 2-8. A majority of evaluation persons in industry tend to prefer to use whole number evaluation periods rather than fractional periods associated with mid-period timing of values so end of period compounding is emphasized throughout this text.

EXAMPLE 2-9 Illustration of Continuous Interest Factors

Calculate the present value of $100 to be received in the future assuming a continuous compound interest rate of 15% per year for the following timing assumptions:

A) The $100 is a discrete sum received once at the end of year six.
B) The $100 is a discrete sum received once at the beginning of year six, which is the end of year 5.
C) The $100 is received uniformly during year six.

Solution:

A) P = ?

-	-	-	-	F=$100

    0   1 4   5   6

$$P = 100(P/F_{15\%,6}) = 100(1/e^{.15(6)}) = \$40.66$$

with .4066 above $P/F_{15\%,6}$

(See Appendix B for the continuous interest factor development for discrete values.)

B) P = ?

-	-	-	F=$100	-

    0   1 4   5   6

$$P = 100(P/F_{15\%,5}) = 100(1/e^{.15(5)}) = \$47.23$$

with .4723 above $P/F_{15\%,5}$

(See Appendix B for the continuous interest factor development for discrete values.)

C) P = ?

-	-	-	—— F=$100 ——

    0   1 4   5   6

$$P = 100(P/F^*_{15\%,6}) = \$43.86$$

with .4386 above $P/F^*_{15\%,6}$

(See the table at the end of Appendix C for continuous interest, continuous flow of money, single payment present worth factors.)

The continuous interest present values are smaller than the corresponding discrete interest present values in Example 2-8 for the similar value assumptions. However, note the same relative differences exits between the discrete and continuous interest results for beginning of period, end of period, and mid-period or continuous flow of money assumptions. *As long as you are consistent in your use of either discrete or continuous interest results (and do not mix comparison of discrete interest results with continuous interest results), you get the same economic conclusions in evaluating projects using either discrete or continuous compounding of interest.* Since a majority of industry uses discrete interest compounding, it is emphasized in this text.

2.5 Applications of Compound Interest Formulas

EXAMPLE 2-10 F/P$_{i,n}$ Factor Illustration With Interpolation

What is the future worth six years from now of a present sum of $1,000 if:
a) the interest rate is 8% compounded quarterly?
b) the interest rate is 7.5% compounded annually?

Solution:

a) 8% interest compounded quarterly

$$P = \$1,000 \quad \overline{} \quad \begin{array}{c} 1.608 \\ F=\$1,000(F/P_{2,24})=\$1,608 \end{array}$$
$$ \quad 0 \quad 1 \quad 2 \ldots\ldots\ldots 24 \text{ quarterly periods}$$

b) 7.5% interest compounded annually

$$P = \$1,000 \quad \overline{} \quad \begin{array}{c} 1.545 \\ F=\$1,000(F/P_{7.5,6}) = \$1,545 \end{array}$$
$$ \quad 0 \quad 1 \quad 2 \ldots\ldots 6$$

See the following for interpolation to obtain F/P$_{7.5,6}$, using the 7% and 8% factors available in the Appendix A Tables.

Interpolation for F/P$_{7.5\%,6}$

$$F/P_{7.5\%,6} = \$1.501 + .5(1.587 - 1.501)$$
$$= 1.544$$

In general, $F/P_{7.5\%,6} = 1.501 + \text{"a"}$

and a/b = c/d so a = (b/d)(c)
$$= (.5/1)(1.587 - 1.501)$$
$$= (.5)(.0860)$$
$$= .0430$$

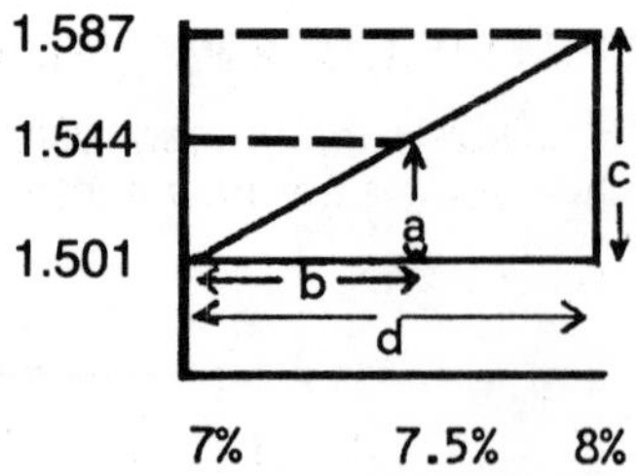

Figure 2-4
Interpolation Illustration

Mathematically $F/P_{7.5\%,6} = (1 + 0.75)^6 = 1.543$

The difference in the 1.543 mathematical result and the $1.544 interpolation result is due to interpolation error.

EXAMPLE 2-11 F/P$_{i,n}$ Factor Illustrated With Interpolation

How many years will it take for a present sum of $1,000 to grow to $2,000 if interest is 10% compounded annually? (Or in general, how long does it take to double your money invested at 10% per annum?)

Solution:

$$P = \$1,000 \overline{} \qquad F = \$2,000 = \$1,000(F/P_{10\%,n})$$
$$\ 0 \qquad\qquad\qquad\qquad n$$

Go into the 10% tables in the $F/P_{i,n}$ column to find $F/P_{10,n} = 2.000$.
Linear interpolation between $F/P_{10,7} = 1.949$ and $F/P_{10,8} = 2.144$ gives:
n = 7 years + (1) [(2.000 – 1.949)/(2.144 – 1.949)] = 7.26 years

    A general rule of thumb follows that can be used to obtain the approximate period of time required to double your money at a given compound interest rate per period. This rule often is called the "Rule of 72" for an obvious reason.

$$\text{Number of Periods} \atop \text{to double money} = \frac{72}{\text{Compound Interest Rate per Period}} \qquad\qquad 2\text{-}11$$

    In Example 2-11 note that 72/10, (where 10 equals 10%) gives 7.2 years needed to double your money, which is very close to the 7.26 year result calculated. To double money at 6% interest per year takes 72/6 = 12 years, while to double money at 12% per year takes only 6 years. Approximation error is very significant for 3 or less compounding periods, or interest rates above 30%.

EXAMPLE 2-12 $P/F_{i,n}$ Factor Illustration

    What is the present value of two $1,000 payments to be made three and five years from now if interest is 8% compounded semi-annually?

Solution:

$$\quad \overline{}\quad\quad\quad \$1,000 \quad\quad\quad\quad\quad \$1,000$$
$$P = ?$$
$$\quad 0\quad 1\quad 2\quad 3\quad 4\quad 5\quad 6\quad 7\quad 8\quad 9\quad 10$$

Note: In this example, "n" is expressed in semi-annual periods. Therefore, the appropriate compound interest rate "i" is 4% per period.

$$\overset{0.7903}{P = \$1,000(P/F_{4\%,6})} + \overset{0.6756}{\$1,000(P/F_{4\%,10})} = \$1,465.90$$

EXAMPLE 2-13 $P/A_{i,n}$ Factor Illustration

    What is the present value of a series of $100 payment to be made at the end of each month for the next five years if interest is 12% compounded monthly?

Solution:

$$\frac{\text{\$100 \$100} \hspace{10em} \text{\$100}}{}$$

P = ?   0   1   2 .... 60 months

i = 1% per month

$$P = \$100(P/A_{1\%,60}) = \$4,495$$
(over the factor: 44.95)

EXAMPLE 2-14 Factor Illustration for Multiple Uniform Series

Calculate the present, future and equivalent annual end of period values for the series of incomes presented in the following time line diagram. Assume an interest rate of 15%.

$$\frac{A_1=\$100 \hspace{3em} A_1=\$100 \hspace{1em} A_2=\$150 \hspace{3em} A_2=\$150 \hspace{1em} A_3=\$200 \hspace{3em} A_3=\$200}{}$$

P=?   F=?

0   1..........5   6..........10   11..........15

Solutions:

Present Value

$$P = 100(P/A_{15,5}) + 150(P/A_{15,5})(P/F_{15,5}) + 200(P/A_{15,5})(P/F_{15,10})$$
(over factors: 3.352 ; 3.352 .4972 ; 3.352 .2472)

$$= \$751$$

$$\text{or} = 100(P/A_{15,5}) + 150(P/A_{15,10}-P/A_{15,5}) + 200(P/A_{15,15}-P/A_{15,10})$$
(over factors: 3.352 ; 5.019 3.352 ; 5.847 5.019)

$$= \$751$$

Future Value:

$$F = 200(F/A_{15,5}) + 150(F/A_{15,5})(F/P_{15,5}) + 100(F/A_{15,5})(F/P_{15,10})$$
(over factors: 6.742 ; 6.742 2.011 ; 6.742 4.046)

$$= \$6,110, \quad \text{or} \quad 751(F/P_{15,15}) = \$6,110$$
(over factor: 8.137)

Equivalent Annual Value

$$A = 751(A/P_{15,15}) = \$128 \quad \text{or} \quad 6,110(A/F_{15,15}) = \$128$$
(over factors: .17102 ; .02102)

EXAMPLE 2-15 A/F$_{i,n}$ Factor Illustration

What uniform annual cost for ten years is equivalent to a single $10,000 cost ten years from now if interest is 8% per year?

Solution:

$$\overset{0.06903}{A = \$10,000(A/F_{8,10})} = \$690.30 \qquad A$$

$$F = \$10,000$$

0   1   10

EXAMPLE 2-16 Equivalent Annual Payments Illustration

What payments each year are equivalent to $3000 payments at the end of years three, six and nine from now if interest is 10% compounded annually? Determine the future worth of these payments at the end of year nine.

Solution:

		$3,000			$3,000			$3,000	

0   1   2   3   4   5   6   7   8   9

Equivalent Annual Payments $= \$3,000(A/F_{10,3})\overset{.30211}{=} \$906.33$ each year for nine years. Spreading the $3,000 at the end of year three uniformly over years one, two and three gives the same equivalent annual cost as spreading the $3,000 at the end of year six uniformly over years four, five and six. The argument is similar for years seven, eight and nine.

Future Worth $= \$906.33(F/A_{10,9})\overset{13.579}{=} \$12,308$

or $= \$3,000(F/P_{10,3})\overset{1.331}{} + \$3,000(F/P_{10,6})\overset{1.772}{} + \$3,000 = \$12,308$

Note that you cannot take $3,000 times a uniform series compound amount factor for the 10% interest rate because the equal payments do not occur at the end of every annual compounding period. You must make the calculation as shown unless you determine an effective interest rate per three year period and work the problem with three periods of three years each. The effective interest rate approach to this type of problem is based on using Equation 2-9 presented earlier in this chapter.

EXAMPLE 2-17 A/P$_{i,n}$ Factor Illustration

What annual end of year mortgage payments are required to pay off a $10,000 mortgage in five years if interest is 10% per year?

Solution:

$$P = \$10,000 \quad \begin{array}{ccccc} \underline{A = ?} & & & & \underline{A = ?} \\ 0 & 1 & \cdots\cdots\cdots\cdots\cdots\cdots & 5 \end{array}$$

$$.2638$$
$$A = \$10,000(A/P_{10,5}) = \$2,638/year$$

The following table shows how these payments amortize the mortgage.

END OF YEAR	PRINCIPAL OWED DURING YEAR	MORTGAGE PAYMENT	INTEREST = .10 (PRINCIPAL)	AMOUNT APPLIED TO REDUCE PRINCIPAL	NEW PRINCIPAL OWED
1	10,000	2,638	1,000	1,638	8,362
2	8,362	2,638	836	1,802	6,560
3	6,560	2,638	656	1,982	4,578
4	4,578	2,638	458	2,180	2,398
5	2,398	2,638	240	2,398	0
TOTALS		13,190	3,190	10,000	

Figure 2-5 Mortgage Amortization Schedule

2.6 "Loan Points" and Buying Down Interest

Lending organizations such as banks, savings and loans, and insurance companies charge "points" on loans as a way of indirectly increasing the effective interest rate being charged on loans. Points are a percentage of loan value and vary widely at different times. In a related way, developers who want to sell assets sometimes "buy-down" interest rates on loan money by paying an up front lump-sum to lending agencies so that the lending agencies can loan to persons at a lower rate. However, the developer typically adds the buy-down charge to the price of the property being sold. The buyer needs to understand the economic principles related to "points" and "buying down" interest to make valid investment decisions that involve these considerations.

EXAMPLE 2-18 Illustration of "Loan Points" and "Buying Down" Interest Rates.

If a lender receives "six points" (a fee of 6% of loan value) to make a $100,000 loan at a 12% interest rate per year with uniform and equal annual mortgage payments over twenty years, what actual interest rate is the lender receiving?

Solution:

The mortgage payments are based on the $100,000 loan value at 12% interest per year over twenty years.

$$A = \$100,000 \ (\overset{0.13388}{A/P_{12,20}}) = \$13,388 \text{ per year payments}$$

From the lender viewpoint, the actual net loan amount is $100,000—$6,000 point fee = $94,000.

Net loan = $94,000   Payments/year = $13,388 $13,338

    0   1 20

Annual Worth Equation: $94,000(A/P_{i,20}) = \$13,338$

where "i" is the actual net loan interest rate for the lender

$A/P_{i,20} = 13,388/94,000 = .14243$

by interpolation:

$A/P_{15,20} = .15976$
$A/P_{12,20} = .13388$

$i = 12\% + 3\%[(.15976 - .13388)/(.14243 - .13388)] = 12.99\%$

12.99% is the interest rate actually being realized on the net loan by the lender. If the borrower is paying the points, borrower is paying 12.99% interest on the actual net loan amount. If someone else is paying the points, such as the seller of a house to be financed by an FHA loan in the United States, then the borrower is really only paying 12% annual interest.

The concept of "buying down interest rates" involves similar calculations. To illustrate, consider a realtor who would like to "buy down" the interest rate on $100,000 of twenty year loan money from 12% to 10%. What up-front lump sum payment, similar to points in the previous calculations, will enable the lender to loan $100,000 at 10% instead of 12% with uniform and equal mortgage payments over twenty years?

let X = buy-down payment at time of loan, so net loan = $100,000 – X

$$(\$100,000 \ \text{-} \ X)(\overset{.13388}{A/P_{12,20}}) = \$100,000(\overset{.11746}{A/P_{10,20}})$$

$(13,388 \ \text{-} \ 11,746)/.13388 = X = \$12,265$

Equivalently, we could have discounted the actual mortgage payments to be received, (based on 10% interest) at the desired yield, (which in this example is 12%) and subtracted that amount from the loan value to determine the required up-front payment.

$$\text{Actual Payments to be Received} = \$100,000(\overset{.11746}{A/P_{10,20}}) = \$11,746$$

$$\text{Required Buy-Down Payment} = \$100,000 - \$11,746(\overset{7.469}{P/A_{12,20}})$$
$$= \$100,000 - \$87,731 = \$12,269$$

$12,269 is within round-off error accuracy of the previous method of explicitly solving for the payment which was $12,265. The $12,265 up-front payment makes the lender net loan of $100,000 − $12,265 = $87,735 at 12% interest which enables the lender equivalently to loan $100,000 at 10% interest.

2.7 Simple Interest (Also Called "Add-On" or "Flat" Interest)

While compound interest is applied to unpaid investment principal and accrued interest each interest compounding period, *a simple interest rate is applied to the initial investment principal each interest compounding period.* This means that the cumulative interest paid or received by a borrower or lender on a simple interest loan is proportional to the length of the loan period and not affected by the payment schedule. If P = initial investment principal, i = simple interest rate per period, and n = number of interest paying periods,

$$\text{Cumulative Simple Interest for "n" Periods} = (P)(i)(n) \qquad 2\text{-}12$$

Be aware that bankers often use the term "simple" interest to refer to period interest as defined in section 2.3 rather than the common engineering economy use of simple interest defined here.

Note that the interest paying periods are not necessarily years but may be days, weeks, months, or other periods. When it is necessary to calculate the interest due for a fraction of a year or period, it is common practice to take loan principal, "P", times the simple interest rate, "i", times the fraction of the year, or applicable period. For example, $1,000 principal at simple interest of 9% per annum for 100 days gives simple interest = (.09)($1,000)(100/365) = $24.66.

It is best to always state explicitly the type of interest and compounding you are using in financial calculations, otherwise, confusion about the meaning of the results can occur. It is completely legitimate and ethical to use either simple interest or compound interest in financial dealings, but if simple interest loans are made, the U.S. Truth and Lending Law requires lenders to state the nominal annual compound interest rate (often called annual percentage rate, or APR) that is equivalent to the simple interest rate.

2.8 Arithmetic Gradient Series

In many economic evaluation situations, revenues and costs increase or decrease from period to period in an arithmetic gradient series. For example, escalation to de-escalation of projected incomes and operating costs from period to period including the effects of inflation and supply/demand considerations often may be approximated by an arithmetic gradient series of values.

Figure 2-6 illustrates a general arithmetic gradient series, where the first term in the gradient series is "B" and the constant gradient between period terms is "g".

B	B+g	B+2g	B+(n−2)g	B+(n−1)g
0	1	2	3.............n−1	n

Figure 2-6 A General Arithmetic Gradient Series

Computing the present worth or future worth of the series of values shown in Figure 2-6 requires "n" separate calculation terms using the single payment present worth or future worth techniques. To reduce the labor involved in these calculations, it is desirable to be able to convert this arithmetic gradient series of payments to a uniform series of equal payments which can then be converted to present or future worth single sums with $P/A_{i,n}$ or $F/A_{i,n}$ factors.

The uniform series of equal payments which is equivalent to an arithmetic gradient series of payments may be found with Equation 2-13 in which the sign on "g" is plus for an increasing gradient and minus for a decreasing gradient series:

$$A = B + g(A/G_{i,n}) \hspace{3cm} 2\text{-}13$$

where $A/G_{i,n} = (1/i) - n/[(1+i)^n - 1]$ is a factor tabulated in Appendix A for various interest rates, "i", and project lives, "n". The derivation of this factor is presented in the Appendix E. To illustrate the $A/G_{i,n}$ factor consider an example where the first term in the gradient series, $B = \$1,100$, the arithmetic gradient, $g = \$100$, the interest rate, $i = 8\%$ per period and project life, $n = 10$ periods. The series of equal payments or incomes that is equivalent to the gradient series of values may be found by using Equation 2-13.

$$\overset{3.871}{\text{Uniform Equal Payments, } A = \$1,100 + \$100(A/G_{8,10}) = \$1,487.10}$$

This result tells us that if money is valued at 8% per period, the uniform series of ten equal end of period payments of $1,487.10 is exactly equivalent to the original gradient series. To illustrate this on the following time diagrams, the uniform series of payments

	$1,487.10	$1,487.10		$1,487.10
0	1	2............................10		

is equivalent to the gradient series

	$1,100.00	$1,200.00		$2,000.00
0	1	2...........................10		

Note two things about the gradient series calculations. First, the gradient, "g", is plus or minus depending on whether the gradient series is increasing or decreasing. Second, the arithmetic series factor is calculated for the "n" period project life, not the $n - 1$ periods the gradient is applied. This is due to the way the gradient factor derivation works out as developed in Appendix E for readers interested in the mathematical development of the factor. In other words, always include the base value period in determining the appropriate value of "n" for the $A/G_{i,n}$ factor. A geometric gradient series factor for constant percent variation in values from period to period also is developed and illustrated in Appendix F.

EXAMPLE 2-19 Arithmetic Gradient Series Factor Illustration

A man expects to invest $1,000 in common stock this year, $1,100 next year and to continue making each years investment $100 greater than the previous year, for twenty years. If he earns a 10% rate of return on his investments, what will the investment value be twenty years from now? Assume end of year investments.

Solution:

	$1000	$1100	$2900		6.508	57.27
0	1	2 20				

$$F = [\$1,000 + \$100(A/G_{10,20})](F/A_{10,20})$$

$$= \$94,500$$

EXAMPLE 2-20 A Uniform Series With an Arithmetic Gradient Series

Find the present worth of the series of payments shown on the diagram if interest is 10% per period.

	$500	$500	$500	$600	$700	-- gradient series --$1,700
P=?						
	0	1	2	3	4	5 15

Solution:

Conversion of the series of gradient terms to a uniform series of equal payments from years three to fifteen yields:

$$\text{Years 3 to 15; } A = \$500 + \$100(A/G_{10,13}) = \$969.90$$
$$4.699$$

This gives the following equivalent time diagram:

```
          $500  $500  $969.90  $969.90              $969.90
P=?      _____
          0     1     2        3        4 ................. 15
```

Present Worth:

$$P = 500(P/A_{10,2}) + 969.90(P/A_{10,13})(P/F_{10,2}) = \$6,561$$
$$\quad\quad 1.736 \quad\quad\quad\quad 7.103 \quad .8264$$

$$\text{or } = 500(P/A_{10,2}) + 969.90(P/A_{10,15} - P/A_{10,2}) = \$6,561$$

2.9 Alternative Time Line Diagram and the Concept of Cash Flow

An alternative time line diagram that often is used to more graphically illustrate the concept of inflows and outflows of money is presented in Figure 2-4. *The key consideration to any time line diagram is allocating outflows and inflows of money at the point in time closest to when dollar amounts are actually expected to be incurred.* When we speak of inflows and outflows of money, on a before-tax basis, we are referring to revenues and capital or operating costs associated with a particular investment. However, only if your projects are tax-free should you consider making economic evaluations on a before-tax basis. In general, economic evaluations are made on an after-tax basis utilizing cash flow generated from a project for the investor's unique tax position. In Chapters 2 through 6 of this text the dollar value per period generated by adding revenue and capital or operating costs in a time period, should really be thought of as representing positive and negative cash flow in that period. As mentioned in Chapter 1, these first six chapters ignore the specifics of tax considerations to reduce confusion while gaining an important understanding of the basic concepts of time value of money. If we had a specified investment "P" at time zero that was expected to generate equal annual revenues "A" over years 1 through 4, the modified time line diagram may appear as follows:

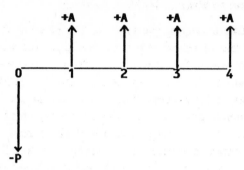

Figure 2-7 Alternative Time Line Diagram Approach

EXAMPLE 2-21 Illustration of the Modified Time Line Diagram

Investments at time zero of $5,000 and time one of $10,000 are expected to generate revenues of $7,500 each year, for three years, beginning in year 2. Draw the modified time line diagram for this proposed investment and then calculate the net present value of future revenues and costs associated with this project for a minimum discount rate of 15%.

Solution:

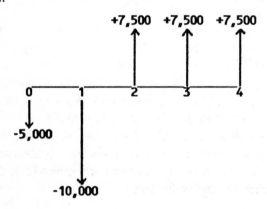

Net Present Value @ 15% =

$$\overset{2.283}{7,500(P/A_{15,3})}\overset{.8696}{(P/F_{15,1})} - 10,000\overset{.8696}{(P/F_{15,1})} - 5,000 = +\$1,193.7$$

The alternative time line approach is not utilized extensively in this textbook because of the author's preference for a straight line time diagram. However, this approach may be preferred by the reader in laying out solutions to problems in the text.

2.10 Introduction to Rate of Return Analysis

In the illustrative examples presented to this point in the text the period interest rate (or rate of return) has been specified and we have calculated equivalent present worth, future worth, or annual quantities for given values of incomes or costs. If we change any of these example problems by specifying both the costs and revenues while leaving the period interest rate, "i", unknown, we generate a rate of return calculation type problem. To illustrate this concept, consider changing Example 2-17 to read "What borrowed money annual compound interest rate is being paid on a $10,000 mortgage that will be paid off in five years with five equal end of year mortgage payments of $2,638?" The annual mortgage interest rate that the borrower is paying is the annual rate of return that the lender or investor is receiving on the unamortized mortgage investment principal each year. To determine this rate of return we must write an equation comparing costs and revenues at the same point in time or on an equivalent annual or period basis using an unknown rate of return per period, "i". For example, for an unknown "i", we can equate the annual mortgage payment of $2,638 to the equivalent annual investor cost as we did in Example 2-17 to calculate the mortgage payments for a given interest rate.

$$\$10,000(A/P_{i,5}) = \$2,638$$

$$(A/P_{i,5}) = 2,638/10,000 = 0.2638$$

By trial and error procedures we can check the factor $A/P_{i,5}$ in the tables for different interest rates until we find in the 10% tables that $A/P_{i,5}$ gives the desired value of 0.2638. Therefore, the rate of return, i = 10% per year. Usually the "i" value we are looking for occurs between interest rates given in the tables and we must use linear interpolation to calculate the "i" value. The details of this interpolation procedure and general rate of return calculations are illustrated in the next chapter.

2.11 Summary

In summary of the material presented in this chapter, note that factors have been developed and illustrated for three basic types of calculations as follows:

Calculation	Factors to Use
Present Worth	$P/F_{i,n}$ or $P/A_{i,n}$
Future Worth	$F/P_{i,n}$ or $F/A_{i,n}$
Annual Worth	$A/P_{i,n}$, $A/F_{i,n}$ or $A/G_{i,n}$

Familiarity with the use of these seven factors in present worth, future worth, and annual worth equations is a prerequisite to a general understanding of investment decision methods which are developed and illustrated in the remainder of this text. The following example illustrates the use of all these factors.

EXAMPLE 2-22 Illustration of the Use of All Factors

An investor is to make the following payments for a parcel of land: $5,000 down payment at time zero, a gradient series of payments starting at $2,000 at the end of year one and increasing by a constant gradient of $500 per year in years two through eight plus a lump sum "balloon" payment of $10,000 at the end of year eight. For an interest rate of 12% compounded annually, calculate:

a) the present worth of the payments, i.e. the single time zero payment that would be equivalent to the given series of payments.
b) the future worth of the payments, i.e. the single end of year eight payment that would be equivalent to the given series of payments.
c) the equivalent annual payments, i.e. the uniform annual payments at the end of each year that would be equivalent to the given series of payments.

Solution:

```
                                                            $10,000
  $5,000  $2,000   $2,500    --  gradient series   --        $5,500
  ─────────────────────────────────────────────────────────────────
    0       1        2  ....................................... 8
```

$$\underset{2.913}{} \quad \underset{4.968}{} \quad \underset{.4039}{}$$

a) $P = 5,000 + [2,000 + 500(A/G_{12,8})](P/A_{12,8}) + 10,000(P/F_{12,8}) = \$26,211$

$$\underset{2.476}{} \quad \underset{2.913}{} \quad \underset{12.300}{}$$

b) $F = 5,000(F/P_{12,8}) + [2,000 + 500(A/G_{12,8})](F/A_{12,8}) + 10,000 = \$64,895$

$$\underset{.2013}{} \quad \underset{2.913}{} \quad \underset{.0813}{}$$

c) $A = 5,000(A/P_{12,8}) + 2,000 + 500(A/G_{12,8}) + 10,000(A/F_{12,8}) = \$5,276$

PROBLEMS

2-1. What future amount of money will be accumulated 10 years from now by investing $1,000 now plus $2,000 5 years from now at 6% interest compounded semi-annually?

2-2. What is the present value of $500 payments to be made at the end of each 6 month period for the next 10 years if interest is 8% compounded semi-annually?

2-3. What equivalent annual end-of-year payments for the next 6 years are equivalent to paying $5,000 now and $10,000 6 years from now if interest is 6% compounded annually?

2-4. What monthly car mortgage payments for the next 36 months are required to amortize a present loan of $3,000 if interest is 12% compounded monthly?

2-5. What amount of money must be deposited in a savings account at the end of each quarter for the next 5 years to accumulate $10,000 in 5 years if interest is 6% compounded quarterly?

2-6. What is the present value of $1,000 payments to be made at the end of each year for the next 10 years if interest is 8% compounded semi-annually?

2-7. What is the present worth of prospective $2,000 payments to be made at the end of 2 years, 4 years and 6 years from now if interest is 8% compounded quarterly? What quarterly payments are equivalent to the $2,000 payments every 2 years?

2-8. An investor plans to invest $1,000 at the end of every year for 20 years at 10% interest compounded annually. What is the expected value of this investment 20 years from now? What single sum of money invested now at 10% compounded annually would generate the same expected future worth?

2-9. What is the future value 5 years from now of a present amount of $2,000 and end-of-year payments of $1,000 for each of the next 5 years if interest is 20% compounded annually? What semi-annual payments are equivalent to the $1,000 payments each year if the 20% interest is compounded semi-annually? What is the future worth 5 years from now of the $2,000 plus $1,000 annual payments for semi-annual compounding?

2-10. What effective annual interest rate is equivalent to 20% compounded quarterly?

2-11. What nominal annual interest rate is equivalent to an effective annual interest rate equal to 20% if interest is compounded quarterly?

2-12. What sum of money will be accumulated in 40 years if:

A) $1,000 is invested at the end of each of the next 40 years at a 15% rate of return compounded annually?

B) $1,000 is invested at the end of the first year, $1,100 is invested at the end of the second year and each succeeding year's investment is $100 higher than the previous year's investment for 40 years at 15% compounded annually.

C) What single investment at time zero would generate the part 'A' future worth?

2-13. It is estimated that a mineral deposit will produce 20,000 tons of ore this coming year and that production will decrease 500 tons per year each year thereafter until the end of 20 years from now. It is estimated that profit after mining expenses will be $6 per ton for the next 9 years and $8 per ton the remaining 11 years. What is the present value of future profit from this mine for an interest rate of 8%? For an interest rate of 20%?

2-14. Company A owns a patent with 15 years of remaining life. Company B is paying royalties to Company A for a license to the patent. It is estimated that royalty payments for the next 15 years will be $6,000 per year for the first 5 years, $8,000 per year for the next 4 years and $10,000 per year for the last 6 years. Company B offers to prepay the expected royalty payments for $70,000 now. If Company A considers 10% per year to be its minimum acceptable return on investment, should it accept the prepayment offer for $70,000 now or take the royalty payments year by year?

2-15. What uniform annual payments for the next 15 years are equivalent to the non-uniform series of royalty payments described in Problem 2-14?

2-16. A machine which has a 10 year life will cost $11,000 now with annual operating costs of $500 the first year and increasing $50 per year each of the next 9 years. If the salvage value is estimated to be $2,000 at the end of the 10th year, what is the equivalent annual cost of operating this machine for the next 10 years if other opportunities exist to have the investment dollars invested where they would earn an 8% annual rate of return?

2-17. A person engaged in making small loans offers to lend $2,000 with the borrower required to pay $89.30 at the end of each month for 30 months in order to extinguish the debt. By appropriate use of your time value of money factor tables, find the approximate period interest rate per month. What is the equivalent nominal interest rate per annum? What is the effective interest rate per annum?

2-18. For the series of incomes shown on the following time diagram, if 12% per year is the minimum rate of return find:

600	700	800	900	1000	1100	1200	1200	1200	1200
0	1	2	3	4	5	6	7	8	9	10

A) the present worth of income at year 0.
B) the future worth of income at the end of year 10.

2-19. Determine the sum of money that must be invested today at 9% interest compounded annually to give an investor annuity (annual income) payments of $5,000 per year for 10 years starting 5 years from now.

2-20. Determine the monthly mortgage payments that will pay off a $6,000 car loan with 36 equal end-of-month payments for a:
A) 10% per year simple or add-on interest rate.
B) 10% per year compound interest rate.

CHAPTER 3

PRESENT WORTH, ANNUAL WORTH, FUTURE WORTH, RATE OF RETURN, AND BREAKEVEN ANALYSIS DECISION METHODS

3.1 Introduction

The five economic decision method approaches in the title of this chapter are the basis of virtually all economic analysis decision methods used today. When applied properly, any of these approaches leads to exactly the same economic conclusion. Proper application of these different approaches to analyzing the relative economic merit of alternative projects depends on the type of projects being evaluated and the evaluation situation. As was mentioned in Chapter 1, there are two basic classifications of investments that are analyzed:

1) Revenue producing investment alternatives
2) Service producing investment alternatives

The application of present worth, future worth, annual worth and rate of return analysis techniques differs for revenue and service producing projects. In addition, there are a variety of different breakeven analysis approaches that can be applied to analyze both income producing and service producing investment alternatives. In this chapter we will concentrate on the application of present worth, annual worth, future worth and rate of return techniques. Variations in the application of present worth analysis techniques using either net present value, present worth cost, present value ratio or benefit cost ratio will be addressed. Breakeven analyses of various types are also discussed in this chapter and subsequent chapters of the text. These techniques are presented here on a before-tax analysis basis to avoid confusing the reader with tax considerations at the same time new evaluation techniques are introduced. Starting in Chapter 8, these techniques are applied after-tax, to varying evaluation situations. Valid analyses must be done after-tax unless taxes are not relevant or significant.

3.2 Breakeven and Rate of Return (ROR) Calculations Using Present, Annual, and Future Worth Equations

In Chapter 2, several examples and end of chapter problems relate to calculating the present worth of a future stream of revenue for a given interest rate or desired rate of return. This calculation gives the initial cost that can be incurred for the future stream of revenue if you want to receive the specified rate of return on your investment dollars. This really is a breakeven type of calculation involving calculation of the initial investment cost that will enable you to breakeven with a specified rate of return on your invested dollars. Example 3-1 illustrates this type of breakeven calculation for different conditions, to emphasize the importance and effect of the time value of money. Example 3-1 is indicative of breakeven calculations. Breakeven calculations can be made for any single project parameter such as initial cost, annual revenue, salvage value or project life to name common breakeven parameters. One equation can always be solved for one unknown, either explicitly or by trial and error. The evaluator has a choice of letting the unknown be any desired breakeven parameter or evaluation criterion.

EXAMPLE 3-1 Present Worth Revenue Equals Breakeven Acquisition Cost

Determine the present worth of the revenue streams, I, given in alternatives "A" and "B" for minimum rates of return of 10% and 20%. This gives the initial cost that can be incurred to breakeven with the 10% or 20% rate of return. Note that the cumulative revenues are the same for the A and B alternatives but the timing of the revenues is very different.

A)	P=?	I=$200	I=$300	I=$400	I=$500
	0	1	2	3	4

B)	P=?	I=$500	I=$400	I=$300	I=$200
	0	1	2	3	4

·

Solution:

$$i = 10\%, \quad P_A = 200\overset{.9091}{(P/F_{10,1})} + 300\overset{.8264}{(P/F_{10,2})} + 400\overset{.7513}{(P/F_{10,3})}$$

$$+ 500\overset{.6830}{(P/F_{10,4})} = \$1{,}071.76$$

or $$P_A = \{200 + 100\overset{1.381}{(A/G_{10,4})}\}\overset{3.170}{(P/A_{10,4})} = \$1{,}071.78$$

$$i = 20\%. \quad P_A = \{200 + 100\overset{1.274}{(A/G_{20,4})}\}\overset{2.589}{(P/A_{20,4})} = \$847.64$$

Note that to get a 10% rate of return you can afford to pay $224 more than the $847 you would pay to get a 20% rate of return.

$$i = 10\%, \quad P_B = \{500-100\overset{1.381}{(A/G_{10,4})}\}\overset{3.170}{(P/A_{10,4})} = \$1{,}147.22$$

$$i = 20\%, \quad P_B = \{500-100\overset{1.274}{(A/G_{20,4})}\}\overset{2.589}{(P/A_{20,4})} = \$964.66$$

Note that in Example 3-1, while you still pay more to get a 10% rate of return than to get a 20% rate of return, the cost that you can incur for the "B" stream of income for a given rate of return is greater than the corresponding cost that you can incur for the "A" income stream. Since the cumulative revenue is identical for "A" and "B", the difference is due to the time value of money. Getting the revenue more quickly in "B" enables us to economically justify paying more for it initially. It is important in evaluation work to account for the time value of money correctly by treating costs and revenues on the time diagram in the amounts and at the points in time most expected. If you think of the incomes in "A" and "B" as being analogous to mortgage payments that will pay off an investor's loan, you will note that the bigger payments in early years for "B" amortize the investor's principal more rapidly than in "A". Compound interest rate of return is directly analogous to the interest rate you receive on money in the bank, or to the interest rate you pay on a loan. In all cases rate of return refers to the interest rate that the investor will receive on unamortized investment principal each interest compounding period. *The term "unamortized investment principal" refers to the investment principal and accrued interest that have not been recovered through profits, salvage, savings, mortgage pay-ments, withdrawals from a bank account, or other revenue forms, depending on the investment situation.* It is important that you recognize that the rate of return which banks pay as interest on a savings account is exactly analogous to the interest rate charged on compound interest mortgage loans which in turn is analogous to the rate of return that we will be using to evaluate different types of investments where costs and revenues are known or pro-jected.

In the next example it is shown that results such as those calculated in Example 3-1, can be obtained using other types of calculations such annual or future worth equations. When we talk about writing an equation in economic analysis work, this usually means we are going to equate costs and revenue terms on an equivalent basis. However, sometimes we write an equation to equate the costs of alternative service producing projects. By revenue terms we mean all incomes, profits, savings, salvage or other receipts of revenue. On an after-tax basis, revenues reduced by operating costs and income taxes are represented by positive cash flow. Costs refer to all expen-ditures or outflows of money and are represented on an after-tax basis by negative cash flow. It also is possible to refer to before-tax positive and negative cash flow if income tax considerations are neglected. Following are the three basic equations used in economic evaluation work:

Present Worth Equation: Present Worth Costs = Present Worth Revenues
Annual Worth Equation: Equivalent Annual Costs = Annual Revenues
Future Worth Equation: Future Worth Costs = Future Worth Revenue

In economic evaluations, whether you are making rate of return analysis, breakeven or net value calculations, you can compare costs and revenues at any desired point in time. You are not limited to present worth, annual worth and future worth equations, although they are most commonly used.

Consider the Example 3-2 to illustrate the application and equivalence of present worth, future worth and annual worth equations.

EXAMPLE 3-2 Illustration of Present Worth, Future Worth and Annual Worth Equations

A rental housing investment is expected to yield $2,000 per year income after all expenses, for each of the next ten years and it is expected to have a resale value of $25,000 in ten years. How much can be paid for this property now, if a 12% rate of return before taxes is desired? Note that you could change the wording of this example to describe a mineral, petroleum, chemical plant or other general investment project and the solution would be identical if you leave the costs, revenues, salvage, and life the same.

Solution:

C = Cost,   I = Income,   L = Salvage Value and i = 12%.

```
C=?   I=$2,000   I=$2,000          I=$2,000
                                              L=$25,000
0      1          2 ................ 10
```

Present Worth Equation:

Equate costs and income at time zero. The present worth of income and salvage at a ROR of 12% is the breakeven cost that can be paid at time zero; PW Cost = PW Income and Salvage at 12%.

$$C = PW \text{ Cost} = 2,000(P/A_{12,10}) \overset{5.650}{} + 25,000(P/F_{12,10}) \overset{.3220}{} = \$19,350$$

$$C = PW \text{ Cost} = 2,000\underset{5.650}{(P/A_{12,10})} + 25,000\underset{.3220}{(P/F_{12,10})} = \$19,350$$

If $19,350 is paid for the property at time zero, a 12% rate of return per year on the unamortized investment will be realized. It is instructive to note the same result could have been obtained by writing a future worth equation or an annual worth equation.

Future Worth Equation:

Equate cost and income at end of year ten.

$$C(F/P_{12,10}) \underset{3.106}{} = 2,000(F/A_{12,10}) \underset{17.55}{} + 25,000$$

$$C = [2,000(17.55) + 25,000] / 3.106 = \$19,350$$

Annual Worth Equation:

Equate equivalent annual cost to equivalent annual income.

$$C(A/P_{12,10}) \underset{.1770}{} = 2,000 + 25,000(A/F_{12,10}) \underset{.0570}{} \quad \text{so} \quad C = \$19,350$$

It should be noted in Example 3-2 that although a present worth quantity, "C", was to be calculated, it could be obtained from a future worth or annual worth equation as well as a present worth equation. In fact, an equation could be written to equate costs and income at any point in time and the same result, C = $19,350, would be obtained.

Now consider the use of present, future and annual worth equations to determine project rate of return. This requires writing the equations with the unknown rate of return, "i", in evaluation situations where both the costs and revenues are specified but the rate of return, "i", is unknown. A trial and error solution generally is required to calculate "i" as illustrated in the following examples.

EXAMPLE 3-3 Rate of Return (ROR) Illustration

If you pay $20,000 for the housing investment in Example 3-2, what compound interest rate of return on investment dollars will be received?

Solution:

C = Costs, I = Incomes, L = Salvage Value, i = ?

```
C=$20,000    I=$2,000    I=$2,000       I=$2,000
                                                   L=$25,000
  0            1           2 ........... 10
```

The only unknown in this problem is the rate of return, i. A present worth, future worth or annual worth equation may be used to obtain "i" by trial and error calculation. In fact, an equation may be written setting costs equal to income at any point in time (the beginning or end of any period), to determine the project rate of return, "i". The result is the same regardless of the point in time chosen to write the cost equals income equation.

Present Worth Equation at Year 0 to Determine "i"

PW Cost = PW Income + PW Salvage Value

$20,000 = 2,000(P/A_{i,10}) + 25,000(P/F_{i,10})$

Mathematically the equation is;

$$20,000 = 2,000[(1+i)^{10}-1]/(1+i)^{10}i + 25,000[1/(1+i)^{10}]$$

There is no mathematical way to explicitly solve this equation for "i". A trial and error solution is required and this is more easily done using the equation in factor form, rather than mathematical form. By trial and error we want to find the "i" that makes the right side of the equation equal to the left side, which is $20,000. This is done by picking an "i" value, then looking up the factors from the tables in Appendix A. To approximate an "i" value in the correct rate of return range, the following approximation is good for fairly long lives of 8 to 10 periods or more.

$$\text{Approximate i} = \frac{\text{Arithmetic Average Income}}{\text{Cumulative Initial Costs}} = \frac{2,000}{20,000} = 0.10$$

Salvage value is neglected in this approximation because it is far enough into the future for lives of 8 to 10 periods or more that, due to time value of money, it has little effect on analysis results. That is why this approximation is only valid for relatively long lives of 8 to 10 periods or more.

i = 10% = 2000(6.145) + 25,000(.3855) = \$21,930
i = ?   = \$20,000
i = 12% = 2000(5.650) + 25,000(.3220) = \$19,350

Because there are no 11% tables in Appendix A, we must interpolate between the 10% and 12% values:

i = 10% + 2%[(21,930 − 20,000) / (21,930 − 19,350)] = 11.5%

Note that although the present worth equation used to calculate the rate of return, "i", has two unknown present worth factors, each factor is a function of only the single variable, "i". There is no limit to the number of unknown factors that can be in an equation used to calculate rate of return as long as all factors are a function of the same variable, "i".

Future Worth Equation to Determine "i"

$20,000(F/P_{i,10})$ = $2,000(F/A_{i,10})$ + $25,000$

Trial and error solution of this equation gives the same result: i = 11.5%. Details are left to the reader. Only interpolation error will cause the result to be slightly different from the present worth equation result.

Annual Worth Equation to Determine "i"

$20,000(A/P_{i,10})$ = $2,000$ + $25,000(A/F_{i,10})$

Trial and error solution of this equation gives the same result: i = 11.5%. Details are left to the reader.

The "i" value of 11.5% in this example is the rate of return per year that the investor would receive on unamortized investment principal. In this text, rate of return often is referred to as "ROR". Other authors sometimes use the term "return on investment" or "ROI" to refer to the same quantity. Whatever it is called, it is helpful and important to note the exact analogy between rate of return on investments in general, and rate of return on mortgage investments or bank account deposits. In each case the ROR to the investor is calculated each year (or period) based on unamortized investment, which is the investment value that remains to be recovered. Project ROR is not the return received on initial investment each year or period, it is the return received on unamortized investment each year or period. Example 2-17 illustrated this point. That example is presented again from a different viewpoint in Example 3-5, in Section 3.3 to relate it to rate of return meaning using a graphical approach.

To relate the meaning and calculation of rate of return to discrete and continuous interest concepts discussed in Chapter 2, consider the following example.

EXAMPLE 3-4 Rate of Return for Discrete or Continuous Interest

For the cash flows presented below calculate rate of return for the following assumptions regarding the type of compounding and flow of funds in a project.

A) Assume discrete end of period dollar values and discrete compounding of interest.
B) Assume a continuous flow of dollar values with continuous compounding of interest.
C) Relate the solutions from A & B to show that they are equivalent and interchangeable.

CF=-21	CF=+13	CF=+13	CF=+14	CF=+15	CF=+19
0	1	2	3	4	5

Solution:

A) ROR PW Eq (Discrete Cash Flow, Discrete Compounding):

PW Eq: $19(P/F_{i,5}) + 15(P/F_{i,4}) + 14(P/F_{i,3}) + 13(P/F_{i,2})$

$+ 13(P/F_{i,1}) - 21 = 0$

i=50% $19(.1317) + 15(.1975) + 14(.2963) + 13(.4444)$

$+ 13(.6667) - 21 = +3.06$

i=70% $19(.0704) + 15(.1197) + 14(.2035) + 13(.3468)$

$+ 13(.5882) - 21 = -2.87$

By Interpolation; $i = 50\% + 20\%[(3.06-0)/(3.06-(-2.87))] = 60.3\%$

Eliminating interpolation error by interpolating over much smaller increments of "i", the true ROR is 59.05%.

B) ROR PW Eq (Continuous Cash Flow, Continuous Compounding):
(Factors are from Appendix C Table C-1)

$$19(P/F^*_{r,6}) + 15(P/F^*_{r,5}) + 14(P/F^*_{r,4}) + 13(P/F^*_{r,3})$$
$$+ 13(P/F^*_{r,2}) - 21(P/F^*_{r,1}) = 0$$

r=40%

19(.1115) + 15(.1664) + 14(.2482) + 13(.3703) + 13(.5525)

- 21(.8242) = +2.78

r=50%

19(.0646) + 15(.1065) + 14(.1756) + 13(.2895) + 13(.4773)

- 21(.7869) = -1.27

By Interpolation;

i = 40% + 10%[(2.78-0)/(2.78-(-1.27))] = 46.9%

Eliminating interpolation error by interpolating over much smaller increments of "i", the true ROR is 46.4%.

C) Equivalence of Discrete and Continuous Compounding Results
   Given E = e^r − 1, From Eq. 2-10.

where; "E" is effective discrete compound interest per year. This is the Part
       A result.
       "r" is the nominal period interest compounded continuously. This is
       the Part B result. "e" is the natural log base e.

       E = $e^{.464}$ − 1 = .5904 or 59.04%

The equivalence of the discrete and continuous interest rate of return results is demonstrated. Once you have either result (discrete or continuous), you can calculate the other using Eq. 2-10.

3.3 Rate of Return and Cumulative Cash Position

The cumulative cash position diagram is a graphical means of explaining the meaning of rate of return that gives results that are analogous to the tabular results presented in Chapter 2 for Example 2-17, to explain the meaning of the 10% interest rate or rate of return in that example. The advantage of the cumulative cash position diagram is that a picture is often better than a lot of words or tabular figures to clearly explain something. By definition, *cumulative cash position is the investment principal and accrued interest that has not been amortized by revenue such as profits, salvage value, savings, mortgage payments or other inflows of money. Letting revenue terms have a positive sign gives costs a negative sign, so in investment situations, the cumulative cash position starts in a negative position and works back to zero at the end of a project life when the time value of money is handled at the project rate of return.* Each compounding period the cumulative cash position is adjusted in the negative direction for new investments and accrued interest and in the positive direction for revenues received. Unamortized investment is another term with a meaning synonymous with cumulative cash position. When we speak of cumulative cash diagrams, it is important to recognize that we are not referring to a plot of individual project cash flows, but rather, are monitoring the overall cash position of an investment opportunity. The following four examples illustrate rate of return calculations and explanation of their meaning using the cumulative cash position concept.

EXAMPLE 3-5 Illustration of ROR and Cumulative Cash Diagram

For a $10,000 investment now, an investor is to receive $2,638 income at the end of each of the next five years and zero salvage value. Calculate the rate of return and diagram the investor's cumulative cash position for the project life. Note the identity between this problem and Example 2-17.

Solution: Writing an annual worth equation as we did in Example 2-17 gives:

$$10,000(A/P_{i,5}) = \$2,638, \text{ so } i = 10\%$$

The calculation of "i" would be by trial and error if we had not already determined the result in Example 2-17.

Plotting the cumulative cash position for the 10% project rate of return in Figure 3-1, we start out in a $-\$10,000$ cash position at time zero. During each year we expect to receive a 10% rate of return on unamortized investment at the beginning of that year, so the negative cumulative cash position is increased each year by 10% of the unamortized investment at the beginning of the year. For example, if the investor wanted to terminate this investment at the end of year one, he would need to receive a total of $11,000 at year 1 to realize a 10% ROR on the initial $10,000 investment. If he wanted to terminate it at the end of year two, the cumulative cash position diagram shows that he would need to receive $9,198 at the end of year two in addition to the $2,638 received at the end of year one. The cumulative cash position diagram shows that the investors rate of return of 10% makes the cumulative cash position zero at the end of the project life. Any other interest rate makes the final cash position either positive for "i" less than 10% or negative for "i" greater than 10%. In other words, for "i" less than 10% the $2,638 annual payments are more than enough to pay i% interest on the unamortized investment each year, with money left over at the end of the fifth year. The opposite, of course, is true for "i" greater than 10%. Note in the cumulative cash position diagram that the rate of return of 10% is applied to the unamortized investment each year, a declining amount of money each year in this problem. It is not applied each year to the initial investment and it is not applied to the income each year. On the contrary, the income each year is used to reduce the amount of principal that the rate of return is applied to in the following year.

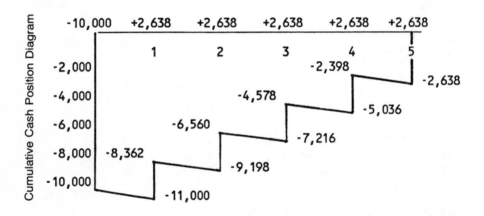

Figure 3-1 Cumulative Cash Position Diagram

EXAMPLE 3-6 Rate of Return When Salvage Equals Initial Cost

Work Example 3-4 with a salvage value of $10,000.

Solution:

Intuitively you can determine the rate of return in your head when initial cost and final salvage value are equal with uniformly equal revenues each period. Regardless of the physical investment, you can always think of this analysis situation as being equivalent to putting the investment dollars in the bank at an interest rate equal to the project rate of return, withdrawing the interest each period, (which is equivalent to the period revenue), and withdrawing the investment principal from your account at the end of the evaluation life (which is equivalent to salvage value). The project interest rate, or rate of return per period, in this situation, where initial investment cost equals salvage, is always equal to the period revenue divided by the initial investment (or salvage value since they are equal). Using the following present worth equation you can verify that the rate of return is 26.38% for this example.

PW Equation: $10,000 = 2,638(P/A_{i,5}) + 10,000(P/F_{i,5})$
$\quad\quad\quad\quad\quad i = 26.38\%$ by trial and error

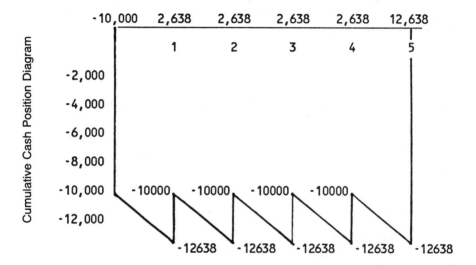

Figure 3-2 Cumulative Cash Position Diagram

The cumulative cash position diagram shown in Figure 3-2 illustrates that when salvage value equals the initial investment and annual incomes are uniform, the investors rate of return is applied to unamortized investment value equal to the initial investment each year ($10,000 in this case).

EXAMPLE 3-7 Rate of Return for Initial Cost and a Single Revenue

Evaluate the rate of return an investor will receive if he invests $10,000 at time zero and this investment generates a future lump sum income of $16,105 five years later. Develop the cumulative cash position diagram at the project rate of return.

Solution:

C=10,000   -   -   -   -   -
_____   I=16,105
      0   1   2   3   4   5

PW Equation: $10{,}000 = 16{,}105(P/F_{i,5})$ so $P/F_{i,5} = 0.62093$
              $i = 10\%$ per year by trial and error

Notice that the unamortized investment get larger each year when no annual revenues are received to offset the accrued interest. Also note that the Examples 3-5 and 3-6 both involve 10% rate of return projects with a $10,000 initial investment and a five year evaluation life. However, the unamortized investments that the 10% rate of return relates to in Examples 3-5 and 3-6 are very different after the first year for each of these projects. The cumulative cash position diagrams clearly show this.

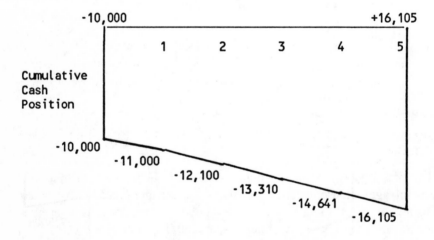

Figure 3-3 Cumulative Cash Position Diagram

The next example illustrates a rate of return problem with costs at two points in time.

EXAMPLE 3-8 Rate of Return With More Than One Cost

Consider the investment of $10,000 at time zero and $5,000 at the end of year one to generate incomes of $9,000 at the end of year two and $9,500 at the end of each of years three, four and five. What is the annually compounded project rate of return? Develop the cumulative cash position diagram at the project rate of return.

Solution:

C=$10,000	C=$5,000	I=$9,000	I=$9,500	I=$9,500	I=$9,500
0	1	2	3	4	5

PW Eq:

$$10,000+5,000(P/F_{i,1}) = 9,000(P/F_{i,2})+9,500(P/A_{i,3})(P/F_{i,2})$$

Rearrange:

$$0 = -10,000-5,000(P/F_{i,1})+9,000(P/F_{i,2})+9,500(P/A_{i,3})(P/F_{i,2})$$

i = 30%

-10,000-5,000(.7692)+9,000(.5917)+9,500(1.816)(.5917) = +$1,687

i = 40%

-10,000-5,000(.7143)+9,000(.5102)+9,500(1.589)(.5102) = -$1,278

By interpolation;
i = ROR = 30% + (40%-30%)[(1,687-0)/(1,687+1,278)] = 35.69%

Eliminating interpolation error by interpolating over smaller ranges of "i" than 30% to 40% gives 35.254% as the correct ROR result.

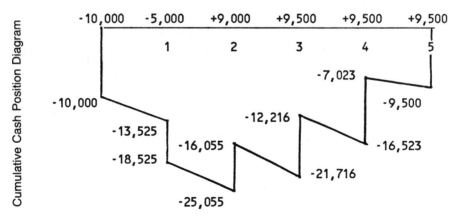

Figure 3-4 Cumulative Cash Position Diagram at ROR = 35.254%.

3.4 Alternative Methods to Obtain Annual Cost From Initial Cost, C, and Salvage Value, L.

Determination of the rate of return for problems such as Example 3-6 where initial cost equals salvage, and income is uniform each period can be simplified by introduction of another method to obtain annual cost from an initial investment, C, and a salvage value, L. Until now the normal way to obtain annual cost for given initial cost, C, and salvage value, L, has been:

$$C(A/P_{i,n}) - L(A/F_{i,n}) = \text{Equivalent Annual Cost} \qquad 3\text{-}1$$

for cost, C, and salvage, L, shown on the following time diagram.

C = Investment $\overline{}$ L = Salvage Value
0   n

An alternate method to convert an initial investment, C, and a salvage value, L, into equivalent annual cost is:

$$(C-L)(A/P_{i,n}) + Li = \text{Equivalent Annual Cost} \qquad 3\text{-}2$$

It may not be immediately evident that Equations 3-1 and 3-2 are equivalent so the proof follows:

Working only with Equation 3-2:

$(C-L)(A/P_{i,n}) + Li =$

$C(A/P_{i,n}) + L(i - A/P_{i,n}) =$

$C(A/P_{i,n}) + L(i - [(i(1+i)^n)/((1+i)^n - 1)]) =$

$C(A/P_{i,n}) + L\{ [(i(1+i)^n - i) - (i(1+i)^n]/(1+i)^n - 1\}$

$C(A/P_{i,n}) - L(A/F_{i,n})$

This completes the proof showing that Equation 3-1 is equal to Equation 3-2. Either equation may be used to reduce a first cost, C, and salvage, L, to an equivalent annual cost. One situation where the use of Equation 3-2 is very useful occurs when salvage value equals the investment. Writing the annual cost equation for Example 3-6 in the form of Equation 3-2 yields the annual worth equation shown:

From Ex 3-6:   C = $10,000   I = $2,638 $\overline{}$ I = $2,638   L = $10,000
                 0   1 5

AW Eq: $(10,000 - 10,000)(A/P_{i,5}) + 10,000i = \$2,638$

Therefore, $i = .2638$ or 26.38% explicitly, without trial and error. Note that this rate of return result is the ratio of average annual income ($2,638) divided by initial investment cost ($10,000). That is the approximate ROR calculation introduced in Example 3-3. When initial cost and salvage value are equal, and income is uniform and equal, the ROR obtained from the Example 3-3 ROR approximation given earlier is always the exact project ROR. Writing an annual worth equation using Equation 3-2 instead of a present worth equation makes this intuitively evident. An example illustrating that Equation 3-1 and 3-2 give the same equivalent annual cost follows.

EXAMPLE 3-9 Illustration of Two Equivalent Annual Cost Calculation Methods

Determine the equivalent annual cost for equipment with an estimated ten year life having initial cost of $30,000, estimated salvage value in ten years of $10,000 for a minimum ROR of 15% per year. Use both Equation 3-1 and Equation 3-2 to show that they give the same result. See Example 3-10 to illustrate another application of Equation 3-2 to rate of return calculations.

Solution:

Using Equation 3-1:

$$A = 30,000(A/P_{15,10}^{.19925}) - 10,000(A/F_{15,10}^{.04925}) = \$5,485$$

Using Equation 3-2:

$$A = (30,000 - 10,000)(A/P_{15,10}^{.19925}) + 10,000(.15) = \$5,485$$

3.5 Rate of Return on Bond Investments

Bond and debenture offerings are very popular ways for companies and governments to raise debt capital. Implicitly then, the analysis of bond and debenture investments is an important investment analysis for potential investors. *Bonds and debentures are similar debt paper except bonds are backed by the assets of the issuing organization as collateral whereas debentures are only backed by the name and general credit of the issuing organization.* These types of investments are really very straightforward to evaluate but people often get confused between new bond interest rates (or rates of return) which fix the dividends for the life of bonds and old bond rates of return. Another factor that adds to bond analysis confusion is that bond interest usually is paid semi-annually which means you must work with semi-annual periods and a semi-annual period rate of return to handle the time value of money properly in bond yield calculations. *Three other important factors to remember in bond evaluations are: 1) at the maturity date of a bond, the holder of the bond will receive its face value as a salvage or terminal value, 2) bond cost or value will vary between the initial offering date and the maturity date as interest rates fluctuate up and down in general money markets and 3) bond call privileges are written into most bond offerings to give bond issuers the right to pay off a bond issue early (before the maturity date) at any date after the call date.* Early payoff of bonds is desirable for the bond issuer if interest rates have dropped significantly (by several percentage points) so the old bonds can be refinanced with new bonds at a lower rate. Bond call privileges often affect the value of old bonds significantly. Examples follow to illustrate bond analysis considerations.

EXAMPLE 3-10 New Bond Rate of Return Analysis Using Eq. 3-2

Calculate the new bond rate of return for a new issue of $1,000 bonds with a maturity date twenty years after the issuing date, if the new bond pays dividends of $40 every six month period.

Solution:

C = Cost, I = Dividend Income, L = Maturity Value

C = $1,000   I=$40   I=$40   I=$40
  ───   L=$1,000
  0   1   2 .... 40 semi annual

Since initial cost equals salvage (maturity) value, and period income is uniform and equal, use Equation 3-2 to simplify the rate of return calculations:

Annual Worth Eq: $(C - L)(A/P_{i,n}) + Li = I$
$(1,000 - 1,000)(A/P_{i,40}) + 1,000i = 40$
$i = .04$ or 4% per semi-annual period

Nominal rate of return equals 8% per year compounded semi-annually which, in stock and bond broker terminology, often is called "yield to maturity".

EXAMPLE 3-11 Old Bond Rate of Return Analysis

If the bond described in Example 3-10 was initially offered six years ago and now sells for $800, what rate of return would an investor who holds the bond to maturity receive? Note that only the cost and evaluation life are different from the Example 3-10 new bond evaluation. Fourteen years (28 semi-annual periods) of life remain from the original 20 year life.

Solution:

C = Cost, I = Dividend Income, L = Maturity Value

```
C=$800        I=$40        I=$40              I=$40
_____       L=$1,000
0             1            2 ................. 28
```

When initial cost does not equal salvage value there is no advantage in writing an annual worth equation over a present worth equation to calculate rate of return

Present Worth Eq: $800 = 40(P/A_{i,28}) + 1,000(P/F_{i,28})$

In selecting the initial trial and error "i" value, remember that "i" is a semi-annual period rate of return. If we paid $1,000 for the bond we know i = 4%, so try a higher value:

$i = 6\% = 40(13.406) + 1000(.1956) = \$731.84$
$i = 5\% = 40(14.898) + 1000(.2551) = \$851.02$

By interpolation i = 5.43% per semi-annual period. The nominal (annual) rate of return is 10.86% per year compounded semi-annually, which is the "yield to maturity". Another broker term, "current yield" is defined as annual dividends divided by bond cost. For this example old bond current yield is 80/800 equaling .10 or 10%, which compares to the previously calculated yield to maturity of 10.86% compounded semi-annually.

EXAMPLE 3-12 Old Bond Rate of Return With and Without Call Privileges

Consider that the bond described in Example 3-10 was initially offered 6 years ago and now sells for $1,200 (interest rates have dropped so the bond price has increased). The bond is callable 10 years after the initial offering date (which is 4 years from now) at par value (the original $1,000 value). Calculate the rate of return that an investor paying $1,200 for this bond would receive if the bond is not called early and is held until normal maturity 14 years from now. Then calculate the rate of return that the investor would receive if the bond is called 4 years from now.

Solution:

No early call privileges, so use a 14 year (28 semi-annual periods) life.

C = Cost, I = Dividend Income, L = Maturity Value

```
C=$1,200      I=$40        I=$40              I=$40
_____       L=$1,000
0             1            2 ................. 28 semi-annual
```

Present Worth Eq: 1,200 $= 40(P/A_{i,28}) + 1,000(P/F_{i,28})$

The semi-annual period rate of return is 2.98%, and the annual rate of return (yield to maturity) is 5.96% compounded semi-annually.

Call privilege exists and can be expected to be exercised since interest rates have dropped, so use a 4 year (8 semi-annual periods) life to the call date.

```
C=$1,200      I=$40       I=$40                    I=$40
                                                        L=$1,000
0             1           2 ..............  8 semi-annual
```

Present Worth Eq: 1,200 $= 40(P/A_{i,8}) + 1,000(P/F_{i,8})$

The semi-annual period rate of return is 1.35%, and the annual rate of return (yield to call date maturity) is 2.70% compounded semi-annually. If you pay $1,200 for this bond and it is called 4 years later, your rate of return is considerably less than the 5.96% annual rate of return to maturity at year 14. If an investor wants to receive a 6% rate of return compounded semi-annually to the call date, the present worth of dividends and maturity "call" value for 8 semi-annual periods at 6.0%/2, or 3.0% interest per semi-annual period gives the bond value:

$$\overset{7.020}{} \qquad \overset{.7894}{}$$
$$\text{Value of Callable Bond} = 40(P/A_{3\%,8}) + 1,000(P/F_{3\%,8}) = \$1,070$$

to yield 6.0% compounded semi-annually.

3.6 Rate of Return Related to T-Bill Discount Rates

U.S. Treasury Bill (T-Bill) discount rates are not the same as compound interest rate of return because T-bill interest is paid at the beginning of compounding periods instead of at the end. T-bills are sold at U.S. Federal Reserve Banks each Monday morning in denominations of $10,000, or $5,000 increments above $10,000 with maturity lives of 3 months, 6 months or 1 year. Generally within 10 days of purchasing a T-bill, an investor receives a check for the full interest. Getting the interest up-front, instead of at the end of compound interest evaluation periods as with bond, debenture or certificate of deposit investments means the investor in T-bills is receiving a compound interest rate of return greater than the T-bill discount rate. The following example illustrates the relationship between T-bill discount rates and compound interest.

EXAMPLE 3-13 T-Bill Discount Rates and Rate of Return

A $10,000, 6 month T-bill with a 10% discount rate can be purchased. What is the equivalent compound interest rate of return on this investment?

Solution:

Discount rates are always given on an annual basis, so 10.0%/2 = 5.0% per 6 months. The 5% interest is paid up front a week or so after the T-bill is purchased. The face value of the T-bill is paid as maturity value at the six month maturity date.

Interest $500 = .05(10,000)

Cost = $10,000   Maturity Value = $10,000

0   6 months

PW Eq: $10,000 = 500 + 10,000(P/F_{i,1})$

Trial and Error, i = 5.263% per 6 months

Doubling this six month period rate gives an annual rate of return of 10.526% compounded semi-annually as being equivalent to a 10%, six month T-bill discount rate.

3.7 Minimum Rate of Return, i*

The rate of return that can be obtained by investing in alternative projects often is referred to as the minimum rate of return, interchangeably it is also referred to as hurdle rate, opportunity cost of capital or minimum discount rate in practice. If alternative investments exist that will yield the minimum rate of return on capital available to invest, from an economic viewpoint, we do not want to accept any other project investments that will not yield a rate of return greater than or equal to the minimum rate of return. A common investment analysis error is to use the cost of borrowed money or the "cost of capital" as the minimum rate of return. *Only if borrowed money is unlimited is the cost of capital a valid minimum rate of return. Whether investment dollars are to be cash equity or borrowed does not change the fact that we want to get optimum results (maximum profit) from the investment of these dollars. Therefore, in the economic evaluation of any investment, to make valid decisions with rate of return analysis, the investment rate of return must be compared to a minimum rate of return that reflects the return that can be achieved from other alternate uses of the capital that are thought to exist. Present worth, future worth, annual worth, and breakeven investment analysis calculations must be made at this minimum rate of return for valid economic decision making.*

In some cases it is easy to determine the return that will be achieved from alternative uses of capital, such as when the decision involves whether to leave money in a bank at a given compound interest rate of return or withdraw the money and invest it in a project or in stocks or bonds. Often, in project evaluations, the alternative uses of capital are not clear cut, and a minimum rate of return is used that reflects a combination of past and projected future rate of return performance on similar projects. It should be mentioned that the cost of capital plus allowances for risk may be an appropriate minimum rate of return for bankers to use in evaluating the economic merits of projects if the banker's primary concern is that a project generate sufficient cash flow to pay off loan value. However, this approach is appropriate from a company viewpoint only if borrowed money in unlimited quantities is available to invest in all projects with rate of return potential greater than the minimum rate of return. This evaluation situation does not occur very often. Sometimes it is proper for a company using its own cash for investment purposes to use a minimum rate of return that is less than the cost of borrowed money, if this rate truly reflects the rate of return that can be received on alternative investments. (Normally, treasury bill or short term paper interest rates set the floor for the minimum rate of return and this rate generally is less than borrowed money interest rates.) An example to illustrate some of these minimum rate of return considerations follows. Consider a new investment project that has been evaluated to yield a 15% annual rate of return on invested capital. The project would be financed with a combination of cash equity and borrowed money at a 10% annual interest rate. Should this project be accepted if other opportunities exist to invest all equity and borrowed dollars at a 20% rate of return? Any investor who uses the cost of borrowed money of 10% as the minimum rate of return would conclude that accepting the project is the economic choice. However, accepting a 15% rate of return project and having to forego investing capital elsewhere in projects expected to yield a 20% rate of return obviously results in sub-optimal use of investment capital. Whether borrowed funds or cash equity is used to finance investments, the proper minimum rate of return for correct economic decisions must represent other opportunities for investing capital and not the cost of borrowed money.

Using the cost of borrowed money as the minimum rate of return will tell an investor whether or not it is desirable to borrow money to finance a particular project, but it will not enable the investor to determine whether investing in that project is more or less desirable than investing in another project. However, it is important to note that if the minimum rate of return representing other investment opportunities is less than the cost of borrowed money, it is necessary to compare the minimum rate of return to the cost of borrowed money to conclude the obvious, that it is not desirable to borrow money to invest at a rate of return less than the borrowed dollar interest rate (or the cost of capital for funds raised from bond, debenture or new common stock issue financing). For example, say other opportunities are available to invest money in 10 year treasury bonds at 7% interest per year while the cost of borrowed money is 10% per year. Neglecting any possible tax consideration differences, it should be obvious to all investors that it is not desirable to borrow money at 10% per year to invest in bonds or projects of any type yielding an annual rate of return such as 7% that is less than the cost of capital. Determining whether or not it is desirable to borrow money is a different question from the common evaluation problem of determining which of several alternatives is better or best from an economic viewpoint. This is the type of question that requires using opportunity cost of capital as a minimum rate of return to reach correct economic conclusions.

A question sometimes asked is, "what do I use as a minimum rate of return for a large investment project, say $1 billion, to be financed primarily with borrowed money, when no other alternative projects exist? In considering the answer to this question you should be aware that other investment opportunities always do exist if you are willing to broaden the realm of investment fields to be considered. However, neglecting this consideration leads us to the combined economic and financial conclusion that the project must be good enough to convince both the investor and his bankers that it will have satisfactory annual cash flow to cover the debt payments and leave a satisfactory margin of profit under the poorest project conditions envisioned. Depending on the risks and uncertainties associated with the project, this may mean the minimum acceptable project ROR is anywhere from slightly greater than the cost of capital to much greater. Note again, however, that it is easy to say that other opportunities do not exist for the use of capital but most of the time other opportunities do exist if you look for them and they fix the minimum rate of return.

Some companies use a weighted average compound interest ROR on historical invested capital as a minimum ROR. This may not be an unreasonable approach to the subject if the future is projected to be similar to the past. For example, a 12% minimum ROR may result from weighted averaging of past projects with rates of return from 5% to 20%. If you think other opportunities will exist to earn at least the average ROR on invested dollars in the future, this is considered by some people to be a reasonable approach to determining minimum ROR. However, as it relates to discounted cash flow analysis of investments, always remember that the minimum rate of return reflects future investment opportunities thought to exist rather than past opportunities already realized.

3.8 Net Present Value, Net Annual Value and Net Future Value Methods of Analysis

It will have occurred to many readers before now that to determine if a given project is satisfactory by using rate of return analysis, it really is not necessary to go through the trial and error calculations required to obtain the project ROR. Depending on the type of equation you have written, comparison of present, annual or future revenues and costs calculated at the minimum rate of return, i*, tells you if there is more or less than enough revenue to cover costs at the minimum rate of return.

Net value analysis is based on formally looking at the difference between revenues and costs on an equivalent basis (at the same point in time or an annual or period basis) with time value of money calculations made at the minimum rate of return, i. A positive difference between equivalent revenues and costs means that an investment will earn a rate of return equal to i* plus generate additional revenue equal to the positive net value.* For all net value analyses, the "i" value that makes net present value, net annual value or net future value equal to zero is the project rate of return. Most commonly we work with present, annual or future net value analyses (with net present value the most commonly used method of all) and these methods are defined as follows in terms of revenues and costs. *The term "revenue" as used in these definitions refers to positive cash flow or inputs to positive cash flow such as income, profits, savings, salvage values or other inflows of money. The term "costs" refers to negative cash flow.*

Net Present Value (NPV) = Present Worth Revenues @ i*
                                            - Present Worth Costs @ i*
Net Annual Value (NAV) = Equivalent Annual Revenues @ i*
                                            - Equivalent Annual Costs @ i*
Net Future Value (NFV) = Future Worth Revenues @ i*
                                            - Future Worth Costs @ i*

A positive net value indicates a satisfactory investment.

To illustrate the application of NPV, NAV and NFV to evaluate projects consider the following example.

EXAMPLE 3-14 Net Present, Annual and Future Value Analysis

Using Example 3-3 where Rate of Return was introduced, calculate the project net present, net annual and net future values. Assume the minimum ROR, i^*, was given as 10%. The time diagram is reproduced below:

C = Costs, I = Incomes, L = Salvage Value, i^* = 10%

```
C=$20,000    I=$2,000    I=$2,000              I=$2,000
                                                          L=$25,000
   0            1           2 ................ 10
```

Solution:

Net Present Value
Present Worth Revenues @ i^* − Present Worth Cost @ i^*

$$2,000(P/A_{10,10}) \overset{6.144}{} + 25,000(P/F_{10,10}) \overset{.3855}{} - 20,000 = +\$1,925$$

1,925 > 0, so accept.

Net Annual Value
Annual Worth Revenues @ i^* − Annual Worth Cost @ i^*

$$2,000 + 25,000(A/F_{10,10}) \overset{.06275}{} - 20,000(A/P_{10,10}) \overset{.16275}{} = +\$314$$

314 > 0, so accept.

Net Future Value
Future Worth Revenues @ i^* − Future Worth Cost @ i^*

$$2,000(F/A_{10,10}) \overset{15.937}{} + 25,000 - 20,000(F/P_{10,10}) \overset{2.594}{} = +\$4,994$$

4,994 > 0, so accept.

You can convert between NPV, NAV and NFV as follows; so of course you get the same conclusion using any of these techniques.

$$NPV = NAV(P/A_{i^*,n}) = NFV(P/F_{i^*,n})$$

$$NPV = 314(P/A_{10,10}) \overset{6.144}{} = 1,929 \quad \text{within round-off error.}$$

$$NPV = 4,994(P/F_{10,10}) \overset{.3855}{} = 1,925$$

The absence of the need to make trial and error calculations, as is required for rate of return analysis, is a major advantage of net value analysis. The time value of money is accounted for properly and analogously by both rate of return and net value analysis. The meaning of the minimum ROR, i*, is identical for both rate of return and net value analysis as well as all other valid discounted cash flow methods of analysis. Net value analysis provides a quick, easy and therefore very useful way of screening mutually exclusive alternatives to determine which is best as discussed in detail in Chapter 4. Finally, remember that a project earning a rate of return equal to the minimum ROR, i*, has a zero net value, so projects with a positive net value are better than investing money elsewhere at i*.

An important consideration to be aware of when applying NAV or NFV to analyze unequal life income producing alternatives is that you must use a common evaluation life for all alternatives. Normally the life of the longest life alternative is selected but any common life may be used. If you use unequal lives for different alternatives, the time value of money considerations are different in annual value and future value calculations and you may choose the wrong alternative as being best. This means that you must calculate NFV at the same future point in time for all alternatives, or you must calculate NAV by spreading costs and revenues over the same number of years for all alternatives. Analysis related to comparison of unequal life income producing alternatives is presented in Chapter 4.

EXAMPLE 3-15 NPV Applied to Project Valuation

Determine the maximum cost that an investor can incur to acquire land for an industrial development (or mineral rights for petroleum or mining development) and realize a 12% rate of return on invested dollars. If the land is acquired, development is expected to occur two years later for a cost of $1,700,000. Development is projected to generate net revenues after operating costs (before-tax positive cash flow) of $200,000 at year three, $225,000 at year four, $250,000 at year 5, with a $2,000,000 sale value also expected to be realized at year 5.

Solution: (All Values in Thousands of Dollars)

```
Land Cost = ?      -      C=$1,700    I=$200     I=$225     I=$2,250

     0             1          2          3          4          5
```

On a before-tax analysis basis, positive NPV represents additional cost that can be incurred at the point in time where NPV has been calculated and give the investor the minimum rate of return on investment capital. It will be illustrated later in the text that on an after-tax basis, NPV represents additional after-tax cost (which is negative cash flow) that can be incurred and give the investor the after-tax minimum rate of return on invested capital. Because of tax savings from the tax deductions related to additional costs, this generally causes the breakeven acquisition cost to be bigger than after-tax NPV.

NPV at the 12% minimum rate of return equals:

$$-\$1,700(P/F_{12\%,2})\overset{.7972}{}+200(P/F_{12\%,3})\overset{.7118}{}+225(P/F_{12\%,4})\overset{.6355}{}+2,250(P/F_{12\%,5})\overset{.5674}{}$$

$$= +\$206,758$$

$206,758 is the breakeven time zero land acquisition cost that could be incurred, and still have the project generate a 12% rate of return.

EXAMPLE 3-16 Comparison of NPV and Rate of Return Analysis

A three year project requires an investment of $12,000 to generate revenues of $6,000 at the end of year 1, $8,000 at the end of year 2 and $10,000 at the end of year 3. The minimum rate of return is 15%. Use NPV and ROR to determine if this project is economically acceptable.

```
C=$12,000     I=$6,000      I=$8,000     I=$10,000

    0            1             2            3
```

Net Present Value (NPV) @ i* 15%:

$$= 6,000(P/F_{15,1})\overset{.8696}{}+8,000(P/F_{15,2})\overset{.7561}{}+10,000(P/F_{15,3})\overset{.6575}{}-12,000$$

$$= +\$5,841 > 0, \text{ so accept project.}$$

Rate of Return (ROR) PW Eq:

$$6,000(P/F_{i,1})+8,000(P/F_{i,2})+10,000(P/F_{i,3}) - 12,000 = 0$$

By trial and error;

ROR, i = 40% > 15% accept project.

Since the present worth equation to calculate rate of return is in the NPV format of present worth revenue minus present worth cost equals zero, it becomes evident that project ROR is the compound interest rate, "i", that makes NPV equal to zero.

By substituting values of "i" ranging between 0% and 60%, into this equation, we can more specifically illustrate the relationship between NPV and ROR.

"i" Value	Net Present Value
0%	12,000
15%	5,841
30%	1,901
35%	898
40%	0
45%	(777)
50%	(1,481)
60%	(2,684)

For decision-making purposes, NPV must be calculated at the minimum rate of return that represents other opportunities for investing capital. The tabular data here show that for any minimum rate of return less than 40%, NPV is positive and the project economics are satisfactory. For a minimum rate of return equal to 40%, NPV is zero and project economics are a breakeven with investing elsewhere at a 40% ROR. For any minimum rate of return greater than 40%, NPV is negative and project economics are unsatisfactory. The NPV versus "i" data often are presented graphically as follows to illustrate that project rate of return is the compound interest rate "i" that makes NPV equal to zero.

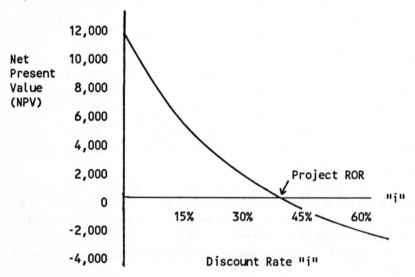

Figure 3-5 NPV vs Discount Rates

This figure shows the non-linear relationship between NPV and the discount rate "i", and the fact that when the project ROR is inserted into the NPV equation, NPV is exactly equal to zero.

3.9 Benefit-Cost Ratio and Present Value Ratio

Instead of looking at the difference in present worth revenues and present worth costs to analyze projects with net present value calculation results, some people prefer to look at the ratio of present worth revenues to present worth costs for economic decision-making. This ratio is commonly called the benefit-cost ratio.

$$\text{Benefit-Cost Ratio} = \frac{\text{Present Worth Revenues @ i*}}{\text{Present Worth Net Costs @ i*}}$$

To calculate correct ratios you must first net together all costs and revenues at the same points in time. The present worth net costs in the denominator of correct ratios represent the present worth of net costs of all types not covered by project revenues, handling the time value of money at the minimum ROR. Generally the net costs involved in the denominator occur in the early development years of a project. If downstream costs are offset by revenues either in the year costs are incurred or in earlier years, those down stream costs do not affect ratio denominators.

A benefit-cost ratio (B/C Ratio) greater than 1 indicates a satisfactory project, a B/C Ratio equal to 1 is a breakeven with investing elsewhere at an ROR equal to the minimum ROR, i*, and a B/C Ratio less than 1 is an unsatisfactory project compared to investing elsewhere at i*.

A variation of benefit-cost ratio often used in industry practice is present value ratio.

$$\text{Present Value Ratio} = \frac{\text{Net Present Value @ i*}}{\text{Present Worth Net Costs @ i*}}$$

The denominators of Benefit/Cost Ratio and Present Value Ratio are the same.

A present value ratio (PVR) greater than zero indicates a satisfactory project, a PVR equal to zero is a breakeven with investing elsewhere at an ROR of i*, and a PVR less than zero is an unsatisfactory project compared to investing elsewhere at i*.

The mathematical relationship between PVR and B/C Ratio may be shown as follows;

$$\text{PVR} = \frac{\text{NPV @ i*}}{\text{PW Net Costs @ i*}} = \frac{\text{PW Revenue @ i*} - \text{PW Net Costs @ i*}}{\text{PW Net Costs @ i*}}$$

$$= \frac{\text{PW Revenues @ i*}}{\text{PW Net Costs @ i*}} - \frac{\text{PW Net Costs @ i*}}{\text{PW Net Costs @ i*}}$$

$$\text{PVR} = \text{B/C Ratio} - 1 \text{ or PVR} + 1 = \text{B/C Ratio}$$

This explains why the ratios differ by unity with the PVR breakeven criterion equal to zero and the B/C Ratio breakeven criterion equal to one.

B/C Ratio and PVR are simple to calculate and apply to economic decision-making, but using the correct present worth costs in the denominator of either ratio is the key to the correct application of either ratio. The proper denominator in either ratio is the present worth of net equity investment costs not covered by project revenues (which is net negative cash flow) in either the year the costs are incurred or earlier years. B/C Ratio gives you dollars of present worth revenue generated per present worth out-of-pocket equity investment dollars spent. PVR gives you dollars of NPV generated per present worth out-of-pocket equity investment dollars spent. If you put costs that are offset by project revenues into the denominator of either ratio, you get ratios that can be misleading and can give incorrect economic decisions in certain evaluation situations discussed in Chapter 4. The denominator of correct ratios for projects in any industry is "the present worth of maximum invested dollars at risk". Keep in mind that it does not make any difference whether investment costs are for equipment, research, development, energy, labor operating costs, or other type costs, or whether revenues are from sale of product, liquidation of assets, tax deduction benefits or tax credits. Only income tax deduction considerations are affected by the type of costs or revenues involved. In all ratio calculations the present worth of net investment costs not covered by revenues in the year costs are incurred, or earlier years is the correct ratio denominator. The following example more specifically illustrates this consideration.

EXAMPLE 3-17 Calculation of Correct PVR and B/C Ratios

To illustrate correct ratio denominator calculations for both PVR and B/C Ratio, consider the following four cases which cover all the different situations that occur in determining correct ratio denominators. Calculate the proper denominator, PVR and B/C Ratio for each case, given a minimum rate of return of 15%.

Case 1

C=100	Rev=50	Rev=50	Rev=50	Rev=50
0	1	2	3	10

Correct Ratio Denominator = 100

$$\text{B/C Ratio} = 50(P/A_{15,10}^{5.019}) / 100 = 2.5045 > 1, \text{ so satisfactory}$$

$$\text{PVR} = [50(P/A_{15,10}^{5.019}) - 100] / 100 = 1.5045 > 0, \text{ so satisfactory}$$

Note, PVR + 1 = B/C Ratio for all the cases.

	C=90			
C=100	Rev=50	Rev=50	Rev=50	Rev=50

Case 2

0	1	2	3 10

Correct Ratio Denominator = $100 + (90-50)(P/F_{i}^{*},_{n})$

$$\text{B/C Ratio} = 50(\overset{4.772}{P/A_{15,9}})(\overset{.8696}{P/F_{15,1}}) \;/\; 100+40((\overset{.8696}{P/F_{15,1}})$$
$$= 1.5394 > 1, \text{ so satisfactory}$$

$$\text{PVR} = [50(\overset{4.772}{P/A_{15,9}})(\overset{.8696}{P/F_{15,1}})-40(\overset{.8696}{P/F_{15,1}})-100] \;/\; 100+40((\overset{.8696}{P/F_{15,1}})$$
$$= .5394 > 0, \text{ so satisfactory}$$

	C=190			
C=100	Rev=50	Rev=50	Rev=50	Rev=50

Case 3

0	1	2	3 10

Correct Ratio Denominator = $100+[(190-50)(P/F_{i}^{*},_{n})-50](P/F_{i}^{*},_{n})$

B/C Ratio

$$= 50(\overset{4.487}{P/A_{15,8}})(\overset{.7561}{P/F_{15,2}}) \;/\; 100+\{140(\overset{.8696}{P/F_{15,1}})-50\}(\overset{.8696}{P/F_{15,1}})$$
$$= 1.044 > 1, \text{ so marginally satisfactory}$$

PVR

$$= \{50(\overset{5.019}{P/A_{15,10}})-190(\overset{.7561}{P/F_{15,2}})-100\} \;/\; 100+\{140(\overset{.8696}{P/F_{15,1}})-50\}(\overset{.8696}{P/F_{15,1}})$$
$$= 0.044 > 0, \text{ so marginally satisfactory}$$

	C=90			
C=100	Rev=50	Rev=50	Rev=50	Rev=50

Case 4

0	1	2	3 10

Correct Ratio Denominator = 100

$$\text{B/C Ratio} = \frac{50(\overset{4.487}{P/A_{15,8}})(\overset{.7561}{P/F_{15,2}}) - 40(\overset{.7561}{P/F_{15,2}}) + 50(\overset{.8696}{P/F_{15,1}})}{100}$$

$$= 1.829 > 1, \text{ so satisfactory}$$

$$\text{PVR} = \frac{50(\overset{4.487}{P/A_{15,8}})(\overset{.7561}{P/F_{15,2}}) - 40(\overset{.7561}{P/F_{15,2}}) + 50(\overset{.8696}{P/F_{15,1}}) - 100}{100}$$

$$= 0.829 > 0, \text{ so satisfactory}$$

EXAMPLE 3-18 Illustration of Ratios, NPV and ROR Analysis

An investment project will involve spending $200,000 at year 0 and $350,000 at year 1 to generate net revenues after operating costs (before-tax positive cash flow) of $100,000 at year 1 and $180,000 per year at years 2 through 8 with zero salvage value. Make NPV, ROR, PVR and Benefit/Cost Ratio analysis of the economic potential of this project compared to investing the money elsewhere at a 15% rate of return.

Solution: (All Values in Thousands of Dollars)

C = Cost, I = Income, L = Salvage

```
            I=100
C=200       C=350        I=180                      I=180
                                                          ──── L=0
0           1            2 ....................  8
```

$$NPV = -200 - \overset{.8696}{250(P/F_{15,1})} + \overset{4.160}{180(P/A_{15,7})}\overset{.8696}{(P/F_{15,1})} = +\$233.8$$

$233.8 > 0, so project economics are satisfactory.

Project ROR is the "i" value that makes NPV = 0

$$0 = -200 - 250(P/F_{i,1}) + 180(P/A_{i,7})(P/F_{i,1})$$

By trial and error with interpolation;

i = ROR = 29.6% > i^* = 15%, so the project is satisfactory

$$PVR = \frac{NPV \text{ @ } i^*}{PW \text{ Net Cost @ } i^*} = \frac{233.8}{200 + 250((P/F_{15,1})} = 0.56$$

0.56 > 0, so satisfactory

$$B/C \text{ Ratio} = \frac{PW \text{ Revenues @ } i^*}{PW \text{ Net Costs @ } i^*} = \frac{180(P/A_{15,7})(P/F_{15,1})}{200 + 250((P/F_{15,1})} = 1.56$$

1.56 > 1.0, so satisfactory

Note that PVR + 1 = B/C Ratio. Also note that all four evaluation criteria give the same economic conclusion of very satisfactory economics compared with investing elsewhere at a 15% rate of return.

3.10 ROR, NPV and PVR Analysis of Service Producing Investments With Equal Lives

In comparing alternative ways of providing a service, it is common to have only costs and maybe some salvage value given for each alternative being considered. This means that rate of return for individual alternative ways of providing a service is usually negative, and often minus infinity if no net revenue is involved in the analysis. Therefore, rate of return analysis of the individual investments to provide a service does not give useful information for economic decision making. Similar considerations relate to NPV and ratio analysis of service alternatives. In providing a service, the most common situation is that you know the service is needed and from an economic viewpoint you want to provide it as cheaply as possible. *For rate of return, net value, or ratio analysis of alternatives that provide a service you must analyze the incremental differences between the alternatives to determine if the incremental investments in the more costly initial investment alternatives are justified by incremental savings.* If the rate of return on incremental investment is greater than the minimum rate of return, or if net value is greater than zero, or if PVR is greater than zero, then the incremental investment is satisfactory from an economic viewpoint and selecting the larger investment alternative is economically justified. The following example illustrates ROR, NPV and Ratio analysis of this type of service producing evaluation problem for equal life alternatives. The analysis of unequal life service producing alternatives is addressed in Section 3.16 and Examples 3-27 and 3-28.

EXAMPLE 3-19 ROR, NPV and PVR Analysis of Service Producing Alternatives with Equal Lives

A company is considering the installation of automated equipment in a processing operation to reduce labor operating costs from $300,000 to $220,000 in year one, from $330,000 to $240,00 in year two, from $360,000 to $260,000 in year three and from $400,000 to $290,000 in year four. The automated equipment will cost $200,000 now with an expected salvage value of $50,000 in four years. The minimum rate of return, i*,is 20%. Use ROR, NPV and PVR analysis to determine if the equipment should be installed from an economic viewpoint. Then consider an increase in the minimum ROR to 40% from 20% and re-evaluate the alternatives.

Solution: (All Values in Thousands of Dollars)
C = Cost, OC = Operating Cost, L = Salvage

A)   C=200   OC=220   OC=240   OC=260   OC=290
       ─── L=50
        0   1   2   3   4

B)   C=0   OC=300   OC=330   OC=360   OC=400
       ─── L=0
        0   1   2   3   4

A-B)   C=+200   OC=-80   OC=-90   OC=-100   OC=-110
       ─── L=+50
        0   1   2   3   4

Incremental Rate of Return (ROR) Analysis

Negative incremental operating costs are the same as positive savings as shown in the following present worth equations.

$$200 - 80(P/F_{i,1}) - 90(P/F_{i,2}) - 100(P/F_{i,3}) - 110(P/F_{i,4}) = 50(P/F_{i,4})$$

Rearranging this equation to put the incremental operating cost terms on the right side of the equation shows that they are effectively equivalent to positive savings or revenue terms:

$$200 = +80(P/F_{i,1}) + 90(P/F_{i,2}) + 100(P/F_{i,3}) + 160(P/F_{i,4})$$

or using the arithmetic gradient factor:

$$200 = 80 + 10(A/G_{i,4})(P/A_{i,4}) + 50(P/F_{i,4})$$

Now, by trial and error:

for $i = 30\%$, right side of equation $= \$216$

for $i = 40\%$, right side of equation $= \$181$

Interpolating:

$$i = 30\% + 10\% (216 - 200)/(216 - 181) = 34.6\%$$

The incremental investment rate of return of 34.6% is greater than the 20% minimum rate of return and therefore satisfactory, so accept the $200,000 investment in automated equipment.

Incremental Net Present Value (NPV) Analysis

$$\overset{.8333}{} \qquad \overset{.6944}{} \qquad \overset{.5787}{} \qquad \overset{.4823}{}$$
$$NPV = -200 + 80(P/F_{20,1}) + 90(P/F_{20,2}) + 100(P/F_{20,3}) + 160(P/F_{20,4})$$

$$= +64.2 > 0, \text{ so accept automated equipment.}$$

Incremental Present Value Ratio Analysis (PVR)

$$PVR = +64.2 / 200 = 0.32 > 0, \text{ so accept automated equipment.}$$

In this case and in general, ROR, NPV and PVR (or B/C Ratio) give the same economic conclusions if the techniques are used properly. Chapter 4 emphasizes the proper use of these techniques in different analysis situations. It is not always as simple and straight forward as in this example.

Changing the Minimum Rate of Return, i*

Changing the minimum ROR to 40% from 20% changes the economic conclusion to rejection of the automated equipment investment with all evaluation criteria per the following discussion and calculations.

Comparing the incremental investment ROR of 34.6% to i* of 40% indicates reject the automated equipment investment with ROR analysis.

Recalculating incremental NPV for i* of 40% gives:

$$NPV = -200 + 80 \overset{.7143}{(P/F_{40,1})} + 90 \overset{.5102}{(P/F_{40,2})} + 100 \overset{.3644}{(P/F_{40,3})} + 160 \overset{.2603}{(P/F_{40,4})}$$

$$= -18.8 < 0, \text{ so reject automated equipment.}$$

Incremental Present Value Ratio

$$PVR = -18.8 / 200 = -0.094 < 0, \text{ so reject automated equipment}$$

Consistently with all analysis techniques the economic choice has shifted to rejecting the automated equipment investment. For a 40% minimum ROR all methods show that it is economically better to invest your money elsewhere at 40% than to invest in the automated equipment. For this to be a valid conclusion note that other opportunities must really exist to invest at the 40% minimum ROR.

3.11 Present, Annual and Future Cost Analysis of Service Producing Investments With Equal Lives

Instead of evaluating the incremental differences in service producing alternatives using incremental rate of return, net value, or ratios, it is equally valid to analyze the present, annual and future cost of providing a service for a common evaluation life. With any of these methods, economic selection is based on the alternative that provides the service for the minimum cost. *The "minimum cost" analysis decision criteria is based on using the cost and revenue sign convention where costs are positive and revenues negative. Note that this is the opposite of net value sign convention where revenues are positive and costs negative.* In cost analysis calculations, if you let costs be negative and revenues such as salvage be positive (the net value sign convention), you are looking for the least negative cost alternative, which is the maximum value alternative. It does not make any difference which sign convention you use as long as you understand whether it relates to selecting the minimum or maximum present, annual, or future cost or value.

When the evaluation life used represents the expected useful life of the asset, this type of analysis is often referred to as "life cycle cost analysis". Example 3-20 illustrates these cost analysis techniques.

EXAMPLE 3-20 Present, Annual and Future Cost Analysis of Service Producing Alternatives With Equal Lives

Evaluate alternatives A and B from Example 3-19 shown on the following time diagrams using present worth cost analysis, annual cost analysis and future worth cost analysis for a minimum rate of return $i^* = 20\%$. Then re-evaluate for changing i^* to 40%.

All Values in Thousands of Dollars

```
    C=200        OC=220       OC=240       OC=260       OC=290
A)  ──────────────────────────────────────────────────────── L=50
    0            1            2            3            4

    C=0          OC=300       OC=330       OC=360       OC=400
B)  ──────────────────────────────────────────────────────── L=0
    0            1            2            3            4
```

Solution:

Present Worth Cost (PWC$_A$)

$$\overset{.8333}{200+220(P/F_{20,1})}+\overset{.6944}{240(P/F_{20,2})}+\overset{.5787}{260(P/F_{20,3})}+\overset{.4823}{(290-50)(P/F_{20,4})}$$

$$= \$816.2$$

Present Worth Cost (PWC$_B$)

$$\overset{.8333}{300(P/F_{20,1})}+\overset{.6944}{330(P/F_{20,2})}+\overset{.5787}{360(P/F_{20,3})}+\overset{.4823}{400(P/F_{20,4})} = \$880.39$$

Select "A" with the minimum present worth cost of $816.2.

Annual Cost (AC$_A$)

$$(PWC_A)(A/P_{20,4}) = \overset{.38629}{816.2(.38629)} = \$315.29$$

Annual Cost (AC_B)

$$(PWC_B)(A/P_{20,4}) = 880.39(.38629) = \$340.086$$
$$\phantom{(PWC_B)(A/P_{20,4}) = 880.39(}.38629$$

Select "A" with the minimum annual cost of \$315.29. Annual cost analysis sometimes is referred to as "annual revenue requirement" analysis since equivalent annual cost on a before-tax analysis basis represents the annual revenues needed to cover costs at the minimum rate of return.

Future Worth Cost (FWC_A)

$$FWC_A = (PWC_A)(F/P_{20,4}) = 816.2(2.074) = \$1,692.8$$

Future Worth Cost (FWC_B)

$$FWC_B = (PWC_B)(F/P_{20,4}) = 880.39(2.074) = \$1,825.9$$

Select "A" with the minimum future worth cost of \$1,692.8 as the economic choice. With cost analysis of the individual alternatives on a present, annual or future cost basis, we get the same economic conclusions obtained in Example 3-18 using incremental ROR, NPV and PVR.

Changing the minimum ROR to 40% from 20% changes the economic choice to rejecting the automated equipment with all cost analysis criteria, just like it changed the economic choice with ROR, NPV and PVR analysis in the previous example.

$i^* = 40\%$:

(PWC_A):

$$200+220\underset{.7143}{(P/F_{40,1})}+240\underset{.5102}{(P/F_{40,2})}+260\underset{.3644}{(P/F_{40,3})}+(290-50)\underset{.2603}{(P/F_{40,4})}$$

$$= \$636.8$$

(PWC_B)

$$300\underset{.7143}{(P/F_{40,1})}+330\underset{.5102}{(P/F_{40,2})}+360\underset{.3644}{(P/F_{40,3})}+400\underset{.2603}{(P/F_{40,4})} = \$618.0$$

Select "B" with the minimum present worth cost of \$618.0

(AC_A): $(PWC_A)(A/P_{40,4}) = 636.8(.54077) = \$344.4$

(AC_B): $(PWC_B)(A/P_{40,4}) = 618.0(.54077) = \$334.2$

Select "B" with the minimum annual cost of \$334.2.

$(FWC_A) = (PWC_A)(F/P_{40,4}) = 636.8(3.842) = \$2,446.6$

$(FWC_B) = (PWC_B)(F/P_{40,4}) = 618.0(3.842) = \$2,374.4$

Select "B" with the minimum future cost of $2,374.4. For the same set of evaluation costs, revenue, life and minimum ROR data, all discounted cash flow criteria give the same economic conclusions.

This example and the previous example illustrate that the minimum rate of return is a significant evaluation parameter that has a definite effect on economic conclusions with all evaluation criteria. It must be selected carefully to represent the attainable rate of return thought to exist from investing in other alternatives. The minimum rate of return must not be an arbitrarily determined "hoped for" number.

3.12 Effect of Income Producing Project Life on Project Economics

Because of the time value of money, costs and revenues that occur more than ten years from now are not nearly as important to project economics as the costs and revenues that will occur within the first ten years of project life. However, it is important for persons doing economic analyses to recognize that the investment evaluation situation significantly affects the sensitivity that project life has on evaluation results such as rate of return. In general, the rate of return for a project with relatively good profitability will be helped much less by lengthening project life beyond 10 years compared to a project with marginal profitability. The effects of investment profitability and project life on project rate of return are illustrated in the following example.

EXAMPLE 3-21 Rate of Return Affected by Investment Size and Life

To illustrate the effect of investment profitability and project life on project rate of return, consider rate of return analysis of a project that may have an initial cost of either $20 million or $36 million depending on final engineering considerations and which is expected to generate profits of $6 million per year for either 5, 10 or 20 years with zero salvage value.

Solution: (All values are in millions of dollars.)

5 Year Evaluation Life:

```
C=$20         I=$6                 I=$6
                                           L=0
0              1 .............. 5
```

PW Eq: $20 = 6(P/A_{i,5})$ so i = ROR = 15.2%

```
C=$36         I=$6                 I=$6
                                           L=0
0              1 .............. 5
```

PW Eq: $36 = 6(P/A_{i,5})$ so i = ROR = -5.8%

10 Year Evaluation Life:

C=$20   I=$6   I=$6
——— L=0
0   1 10

PW Eq: 20 = 6(P/A$_{i,10}$) so i = ROR = 27.3%

C=$36   I=$6   I=$6
——— L=0
0   1 10

PW Eq: 36 = 6(P/A$_{i,10}$) so i = ROR = 10.6%

The effect on ROR results from doubling the evaluation life from 5 to 10 years has been very significant for both cases. When the evaluation life is less than 10 years, the life used has a very significant effect on evaluation results for both economically good and marginal projects. Now double the evaluation life from 10 to 20 years:

20 Year Evaluation Life:

C=$20   I=$6   I=$6
——— L=0
0   1 20

PW Eq: 20 = 6(P/A$_{i,20}$) so i = ROR = 29.5%

C=$36   I=$6   I=$6
——— L=0
0   1 20

PW Eq: 36 = 6(P/A$_{i,20}$) so i = ROR = 15.9%

The effect on ROR results from doubling evaluation life from 10 to 20 years has been relatively insignificant for the economically better $20 million cost project (the ROR change from 27.3% to 29.5% is only a percent change of about +8%), while the effect on the economically more marginal $36 million cost project is greater (the ROR change from 10.6% to 15.9% is a percent change of +50%).

In general, economic evaluation results of economically good projects are affected little by lengthening evaluation life beyond 10 years while economic evaluation results of economically marginal projects are affected more significantly by changes in evaluation lives up to 15 or 20 years. Increasing evaluation life beyond 20 years has little effect on a large majority of good or bad projects.

3.13 Mineral and Petroleum Project Analyis

Mineral and petroleum projects are evaluated in the same manner using the same evaluation techniques applicable for evaluating non-mineral/petroleum projects. Only income tax considerations differentiate the analysis of mineral, petroleum, real estate, chemical plant or other non-mineral/petroleum type of projects. On a before-tax analysis basis, in all industries, all types of costs are outflows of money and revenues for all sources are inflows of money. When you lay out a time diagram with costs, revenues and salvage value at different times, except for tax considerations, economic analysis of a project is not affected by the industry source of the costs and revenues. Analyses should be done after-tax in all situations where income tax considerations are relevant, but the details of proper after-tax analysis of mineral, petroleum, and general investment projects are presented in Chapters 7 through 12.

Although evaluation considerations are the same for analyzing projects in all industries on a before-tax basis, there are significant differences in common terminology used to refer to costs, revenues and ownership interests in different industries. The petroleum industry especially tends to use unique terminology. Mineral and petroleum rights acquisition costs are analogous to land and patent acquisition costs in general industry analyses. Research costs in all industries are equivalent to exploration costs incurred in searching for petroleum and minerals. Project development costs in all non-mineral/petroleum industries are equivalent to development costs in petroleum and mineral projects. However, in the petroleum industry, exploration or development well costs are often broken into two components and referred to as intangible drilling costs (the cost of drilling oil and gas wells to the point of completion) and tangible well costs (the costs for tubing, producing equipment, tank batteries, separators and gathering pipelines necessary to "complete" bringing a well into production. The acronym "IDC" often is used to refer to "intangible drilling costs" in petroleum drilling projects. Tax deduction considerations are the primary differences in tangible and intangible well costs as discussed in detail for different types of investors in Chapters 7 and 8.

Joint ventures to finance projects are common in all industries. The terms "farm-out" and "farm-in" are unique petroleum industry joint venture terms. To get development money, the owner of petroleum mineral rights may "farm-out" his mineral rights to another investor or group of investors who will put up development cost money to receive a specified percentage of revenues. The investors who put up the development money to receive a percentage of revenues are the "farm-in" joint venture partners. The term "working interest" primarily is used in petroleum and refers to ownership interest of each joint venture partner in terms of responsibility for project costs. A 40% working interest owner generally incurs 40% of all project costs. "Royalty interest" owners in both petroleum and minerals receive the royalty percentage of project revenues before any deductions, without any obligation to incur any of the project costs. Finally, the term "net revenue interest" or "net interest" is another petroleum term that refers to the revenue minus royalty interest of a working interest owner. In a project involving a 15% royalty rate, a 100% working interest owner would receive 85% of total revenues since royalty owners receive 15% of total revenues. The term "net interest" or "net revenue interest" commonly is used to refer to the 85% of total revenues that go to the 100% owner. With a 15% royalty interest, a 40% working interest owner would receive a 34% net revenue interest (40% x 85%).

There are many other investment analysis terms unique to petroleum and mineral project evaluations but the terms described give the reader sufficient background to understand many mineral or petroleum project evaluation statements and solutions.

EXAMPLE 3-22 A Mineral Project Analysis

An investor has requested that you evaluate the economic potential of purchasing a gold property now (at year 0) for a $1 million mineral rights acquisition cost. Mining equipment costs of $3 million will be incurred at year 0. Mineral development costs of $2 million will be incurred at year 0 and mineral development costs of $1.5 million will be incurred at year 1. Production is projected to start in year 1 with the mining of 150,000 tons of gold ore, with uniform production of 250,000 tons gold ore per year in each of years 2, 3 and 4. Gold ore reserves are estimated to be depleted at the end of year 4. Reclamation costs of $0.5 million will be incurred at the end of year 4 when $1.0 million is projected to be realized from equipment salvage value. All gold ore is estimated to have an average grade of 0.1 ounces of gold per ton of ore with metallurgical recovery estimated to be 90%. The price of gold is estimated to be $300 per ounce in year 1 and to escalate 15% in year 2, 20% in year 3 and 10% in year 4. Operating costs are estimated to be $20 per ton of ore produced in year 1, and to escalate 8% per year. Calculate the project ROR, NPV and PVR for a minimum rate of return of 15%.

Solution: (All values in millions of dollars)

C = Costs, I = Income, OC = Operating Costs, L = Salvage Value,
Net Cash Flow (CF) = Income and Salvage − All Costs

```
                    I=4.05                                    L= 1.0
                    OC=3.00                            C_Rec |= 0.5
C_Dev    =2.0    C_Dev=1.50    I=7.763    I=9.315    |=10.246
C_Min.Rts=1.0    C_Eq =3.00    OC=5.400    OC=5.832    OC= 6.298
```

Year	0	1	2	3	4
Before-Tax Net CF	-3.0	-3.45	+2.363	+3.483	+ 4.448

Production/Yr x Ounces/Ton x Ounces Recovered x Price = Revenue

Year 1 Revenue, (Revenues in Millions of Dollars).

150,000 tons/yr x 0.1oz/ton x 0.9oz recovered x $300/oz = $4.05

Year 2 Revenue at the Year 1 Selling Price

250,000 tons/yr x 0.1oz/ton x 0.9oz recovered x $300/oz = $6.75

Now account for selling price escalation of 15% in year 2, 20% in year 3, and 10% in year 4.

Year 2 Revenue = $6.750 x 1.15 = $7.763

Year 3 Revenue = $7.763 x 1.20 = $9.315

Year 4 Revenue = $9.315 x 1.10 = $10.246

Year 1 Operating Costs (Operating Costs in Millions of Dollars).

150,000 tons/yr x $20/ton = $3.0

Year 2 Operating Cost at the Year 1 Cost Rate

250,000 tons/yr x $20/ton = $5.000

Year 2 Operating Cost = $5.000 x 1.08 = $5.400

Year 3 Operating Cost = $5.400 x 1.08 = $5.832

Year 4 Operating Cost = $5.832 x 1.08 = $6.298

NPV @ 15% Using the before-tax net cash flows on the time diagram.

$-3.0-3.45(P/F_{15,1})+2.363(P/F_{15,2})+3.483(P/F_{15,3})+4.448(P/F_{15,4})$
$= +\$0.620$

Rate of Return (ROR) = 19.4% is the "i" value that makes NPV = 0.

Present Value Ratio (PVR) = $0.620/(3.0+3.45(P/F_{15,1})) = +0.103$

NPV and PVR greater than zero and ROR greater than $i^* = 15\%$ all consistently indicate economic acceptability of this project compared to investing elsewhere at a 15% rate of return.

EXAMPLE 3-23 A Petroleum Project Analysis

Analyze the economics of the following petroleum project in which an investor has a 100% working interest. Costs are in thousands of dollars, production is in thousands of barrels and crude price is in dollars per barrel.

Production	-	80	45	20	10	5
Crude Oil Price/Bbl	-	20	21	22	23	24
Intangibles (IDC's)	900	-	-	-	-	-
Tangible Compl Cost	300	-	-	-	-	-
Min Rights Acq Cost	200	-	-	-	-	-
Operating Costs	-	50	55	60	65	70
Year	0	1	2	3	4	5

Royalties are 16% of revenues. Net salvage and abandonment value at the end of year 5 is estimated to be zero. Determine the investment ROR, NPV and PVR for a 12% minimum rate of return.

Solution: (All values in thousands of dollars)

Revenue	-	1,600	945	440	230	120
-Royalties	-	-256	-151	-70	-37	-19
-Operating Costs	-	-50	-55	-60	-65	-70
Intangibles (IDC's)	-900	-	-	-	-	-
Tangible Compl Cost	-300	-	-	-	-	-
Min Rights Acq Cost	-200	-	-	-	-	-
Before-Tax Net Cash Flow	-1,400	+1,294	+739	+310	+128	+31

Where Net Cash Flow equals Revenues minus all Costs.

NPV @ 12% = $-1{,}400 + 1{,}294(P/F_{12,1}) + 739(P/F_{12,2}) + 310(P/F_{12,3})$

$$+ 128(P/F_{12,4}) + 31(P/F_{12,5})$$

$$= +\$664.0$$

ROR = 43.5% is the "i" value that makes NPV = 0.

PVR = 664.0 / 1,400 = +0.474

NPV and PVR greater than zero and ROR greater than i* = 12% all consistently indicate economic acceptability of this project compared to investing elsewhere at a 12% ROR.

3.14 Rate of Return and the Revenue Reinvestment Question

Is reinvestment of project revenue or positive cash flow related to the physical meaning of project compound interest rate of return? This is a question that has confused many knowledgeable investment analysts for many years. Let's address answering the question by looking at rate of return analysis of a simple project described in the next example.

EXAMPLE 3-24 Rate of Return Meaning

Consider the investment of $100,000 at year 0 to generate five uniform and equal revenues of $37,185 at each of years 1 through 5 with zero salvage at year 5. Calculate the project rate of return and discuss the meaning of the result.

Solution:

```
Cost = $100,000      Rev = $37,185      Rev = $37,185
                                                        Salv = 0
0                         1 ............... 5
```

PW Eq: $0 = -100,000 + 37,185(P/A_{i,5})$

Trial and Error, i = ROR = 25.0%

The rate of return on this investment is 25%. *Is reinvestment of year 1 through 5 revenues at 25% tied into the meaning of the 25% rate of return? That is the classical rate of return revenue reinvestment question. Many analysts have said yes, but the answer is no. Reinvestment of revenues is not tied to the meaning of any ordinary compound interest rate of return and that answer can and will be explained in several different ways.* First, an intuitive approach is used. If you consider the $100,000 investment in our example to be a loan that would be paid off by five equal mortgage payments of $37,185 at years 1 through 5, the compound mortgage interest rate received by the lender and paid by the borrower would be 25%. Intuitively you know that the meaning of the 25% compound interest rate, from the viewpoint of either the borrower or lender, is unaffected by what the lender does with the mortgage payments as they are received. The economic welfare of the lender will certainly be affected by what the lender does with the mortgage payments as they are received, but the physical meaning of the 25% rate of return is not affected by what is done with the revenue each year. A second intuitive explanation can be made of why reinvestment of revenues is not related to the meaning of ordinary rate of return by thinking of project investments as being analogous to deposits in a bank account. Then consider that the bank interest rate equals the project ROR with project revenues being equivalent to withdrawals from the bank account each year with the last withdrawal reducing the account balance to zero. Any reasonable person knows that what an investor does with money taken from a bank account each year has no effect on the physical meaning of the bank account compound interest rate of return. Similar rationale applies to compound interest project rates of return in general.

If you look at the cumulative cash position diagram illustration of project ROR, this is a more explicit way of showing that compound interest rates of return in general, relate to remaining unamortized investment each period and have nothing to do with reinvestment of revenue at any rate of return. For this example the cumulative cash position diagram is shown in Figure 3-6.

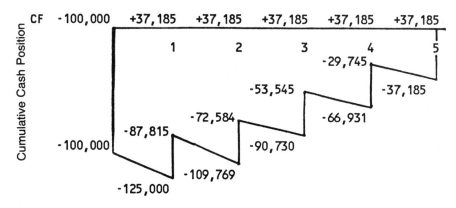

Figure 3-6 Cumulative Cash Position Diagram for 25% ROR Project

You can see by analyzing Figure 3-6 that the 25% ROR applies to remaining investment value to be paid off (amortized) each year and that interest from reinvestment of revenues at any rate of return is not related to the diagram in any way. Only if an investor is interested in calculating the rate of growth of investment dollars does reinvestment of revenues affect the calculations and meaning of rate of return results. This relates to the concept of growth rate of return that is introduced and illustrated in the next section.

3.15 Growth Rate of Return

Growth rate of return is the compound interest rate at which investment dollars grow. All compound interest rates of return, however, are not growth rates of return. To determine the compound interest rate at which investment dollars will grow requires making an assumption concerning the rate of return that will be received from the reinvestment of project revenues (or positive cash flow) as they are received. The minimum rate of return reflects other opportunities that exist for the investment of capital now and in the future, so the minimum rate of return is the reinvestment rate that should be used in growth rate of return calculations. Note that you do not assume that you will be able to reinvest initial project revenues at a rate of return equal to initial project ROR. You assume that your reinvestment rate represents other opportunities for the investment of capital thought to exist now and in the future over the project life. That is exactly what the minimum rate of return represents as it relates to all discounted cash flow analysis calculations and the proper application of discounted cash flow analysis results for economic decision purposes. With some analysis techniques such as NPV, the meaning of minimum rate of return just described is implicitly built into the calculations, but with growth rate of return the minimum rate of return revenue reinvestment meaning is explicitly built into the analysis calculations.

To illustrate specific growth rate of return calculations, Example 3-25 considers an extension of $100,000 investment case study used in Example 3-24 as the basis for discussing rate of return and the revenue reinvestment question.

Example 3-25 Growth Rate of Return Analysis

Consider the investment of $100,000 at year 0 to generate five uniform and equal revenues of $37,185 at each of years 1 through 5, with zero salvage value at year 5. The rate of return on this investment was shown in the previous section to be 25% and discussion was given in several different ways to emphasize that the reinvestment of the $37,185 revenue each year has nothing to do with the meaning of the 25% ROR. However, the 25% ROR does not represent the rate of growth of investment dollars (Growth ROR). To calculate Growth ROR reinvestment of revenues as they are received must be tied into the analysis calculations. Assume that the investor minimum ROR is 12% over the 5 year project life, which means other opportunities for investing capital at a 12% ROR are thought to exist both now and in the future over the next 5 years. Calculate the investment Growth ROR and develop the cumulative cash position diagram showing its meaning.

Solution:

C = Cost, R = Revenue, L = Future Terminal Value

```
                 C=$100,000    R=$37,185              R=$37,185
Initial Project  ─────────────────────────────────────────── L=0
                 0             1 ............... 5
```

```
                 -            C=$37,185            C=$37,185
Revenue Reinvest ─────────────────────────────────────────── L=$236,236
                 0             1 ............... 5
```

$$\text{where, Future Terminal Value, L} = \$37,185(F/A_{12,5}^{6.353})$$

```
Total            C=$100,000       -                  -
Initial+Reinvest ─────────────────────────────────────────── L=$236,236
                 0             1 ............... 5
```

PW Eq: $-100,000 + 236,236(P/F_{i,5}) = 0$

Trial and Error, i = Growth ROR = 18.76%

The growth ROR of 18.76% is the compound interest ROR on the combination of the initial and revenue reinvestment project. However, it is a special rate of return that has rate of growth on investment dollar meaning since a single future revenue at year 5 is generated by the initial investment. Whenever a single future revenue is generated by earlier cost or costs, the meaning of project ROR is Growth ROR.

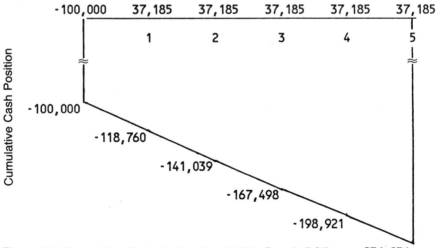

Figure 3-7 Cumulative Cash Position for 18.76% Growth ROR

The Growth ROR of 18.76% relates to larger and larger unamortized investment values each year whereas the initial project ROR of 25% relates to smaller and smaller unamortized investment values each year as was illustrated in Figure 3-6 in Example 3-24. The initial project ROR of 25% and the Growth ROR of 18.76% not only differ in magnitude but they relate to completely different investment values each year after the first year. A question that often occurs to people at this time is "why isn't the Growth ROR bigger than the initial project ROR since future value from reinvestment of revenues is being added to the initial project?" The answer relates to the fact that reinvestment costs as well as the revenue reinvestment future value are added to the initial project to get Growth ROR, and the reinvestment costs and future value correspond to a 12% project ROR. Adding the revenue reinvestment 12% project to the initial project which has a 25% ROR, the combination of the two projects will have a weighted average rate of return between 12% and 25%. In this case the weighted average ROR is 18.76%, the project Growth ROR.

A majority of investors do not utilize Growth ROR for evaluating the economic potential of investment projects. However, it will be shown in Chapter 4 that there are two evaluation situations where if you want to make rate of return analysis of projects, using Growth ROR is either necessary or a desirable alternative to ordinary ROR analysis. Remember, however, that there are no evaluation situations where it is necessary to use rate of return analysis. You always have the alternative choice of using present, annual or future value, or breakeven analysis to analyze the economic potential of either income or service-producing alternatives.

A second Growth ROR example will now be presented to re-emphasize Growth ROR concepts and additional related considerations.

EXAMPLE 3-26 Growth Rate of Return With Multiple Costs

Consider the year 0 initial investment of $55,000 and a year 1 investment of $45,000 in project A, to generate incomes of $30,000 per year for years two through ten with zero salvage. Determine project ROR. Then assume that each year incomes are reinvested in other investment opportunities yielding a 12% ROR. Refer to revenue reinvestment at a 12% ROR as project B. Determine the overall growth rate on the year 0 and 1 investments by combining the initial and revenue reinvestment projects A and B.

Solution:

```
        C=55,000      C=45,000      I=30,000          I=30,000
A)                                                                    L=0
          0             1             2 ............... 10
```

PW Eq: $0 = -55,000-45,000(P/F_{i,1})+30,000(P/A_{i,9})(P/F_{i,1})$

i = 25%: $-55,000-45,000(.8000)+30,000(3.463)(.8000) = -\$7,800$

i = 20%: $-55,000-45,000(.8333)+30,000(4.031)(.8333) = +\$8,272$

i = $.20 + .05[(8,272-0)/(8,272+7,800)] = .226$ or 22.6%

Without interpolation error, the ROR is 22.37% No reinvestment assumption or requirement is associated with the meaning of the initial project rate of return. Reinvestment of revenues only relates to growth rate of return calculations. Reinvestment of revenues at 12% is project B.

```
                -     -    C=$30,000              C=$30,000
B)             ─────────────────────────────────────────── F=$443,280
               0    1        2..................... 10
```

$$\text{where, Future Reinvestment Value, } F = 30,000(F/A_{12,9}^{14.776})$$
$$= \$443,280$$

The overall growth rate over ten years on the initial project A year 0 and 1 investments of $55,000 and $45,000 respectively can be found by combining the cost and revenue numbers on the project A and B time diagrams by adding them together. Combining project A with a 22.37% ROR and project B with a 12% ROR must give an ROR between 12% and 22.37% on the combination of the projects.

```
       C=$55,000   C=$45,000        -              -
A+B)   ──────────────────────────────────────────── F = $443,280
       0            1           2 .......... 10
```

PW Equation: $0 = -55,000-45,000(P/F_{i,1})+443,280(P/F_{i,10})$

By trial and error:

i = 15% = $-55,000-45,000(.8696)+443,280(.2472) = +15,447$

i = 20% = $-55,000-45,000(.8333)+443,280(.1615) = -20,909$

therefore, i = $15\% + 5\%[(15,447-0)/(15,447+20,909)] = 17.1\%$

The rate of return on the combined projects A and B is 17.1%. This 17.1% ROR is a compound interest rate of return, but it is a special compound interest ROR that represents rate of growth of investment dollars. Whenever a single revenue (such as $443,288 at year 10) is generated by costs at an earlier point in time, the project ROR is Growth ROR.

A variation of this Growth ROR calculation used by some people is to bring any costs at periods forward of period zero back to time zero at the minimum ROR instead of at the unknown project ROR, "i". This gives Growth ROR on the period zero equivalent present worth investment cost instead of Growth ROR on the costs from the points in time where they actually are incurred. This modified present worth cost Growth ROR calculation for Example 3-26 follows:

Modified PW Eq: $0 = -55,000 - 45,000(P/F_{i^* = 12,1}) + 443,280(P/F_{i,10})$

or $0 = -95,180 + 443,280(P/F_{i,10})$

By trial and error, i = Growth ROR $= 16.7\%$

This Growth ROR is slightly different (lower) in magnitude from the 17.1% result because it is based on different (bigger) initial investment value due to the modification in the handling of the year 1 cost. This result is equivalent to the non-modified 17.1% result and therefore is equally valid. Although both types of results are useful in some analysis situations, it will be introduced later in Chapter 4 that in using Growth ROR to rank independent income-producing alternatives, it is necessary to use Growth ROR results based on the modified present worth cost.

3.16 Comparison of Unequal Life Alternatives that Provide the Same Service

In this section we introduce and illustrate methods that may be used to compare unequal life alternatives that provide the same service. In general, the methods presented here are not valid for comparing unequal life income producing alternatives, or for comparing service producing projects that do not result in the same service. Assumptions for the evaluation of unequal life income producing projects are presented and illustrated in Chapter 4, while analysis of service alternatives that provide different service is addressed in Section 3.17.

To get a meaningful comparison of unequal life alternatives that provide the same service, assumptions or estimates must be made to permit comparison of the alternatives on an equal life or equal study period basis. You are comparing different total service if you compare project costs for unequal time periods. Three methods will be presented that cover the possible ways of comparing unequal life projects. Combinations of these methods may also be used. The methods are not listed in their order of importance or validity. It is impossible to say that one method is best for all situations.

Project circumstances usually dictate the method that is best for given evaluation conditions. However, method 1 is seldom a desirable or valid approach to use. You should be familiar with it because many textbook and literature authors have advocated its use. *Methods 2 and 3 are the approaches that in general should be used to obtain a common study period for unequal life projects that provide the same service.* The three methods for obtaining a common study period for unequal life service producing alternatives are now described and illustrated using the following two unequal life alternatives A and B.

C = Cost, OC = Operating Cost, L = Salvage Value

A)
$$\frac{C_A \qquad OC_{A1} \qquad OC_{A2}}{0 \qquad\quad 1 \qquad\quad 2} \; L_A$$

B)
$$\frac{C_B \qquad OC_{B1} \qquad OC_{B2} \qquad OC_{B3}}{0 \qquad\quad 1 \qquad\quad 2 \qquad\quad 3} \; L_B$$

Remember, once you get a common study period using one of the following methods, you are then comparing equal life alternatives and you use the five basic approaches presented earlier in this chapter which are present worth, annual worth, future worth, ROR or breakeven analysis. However, for the results from any of these calculation procedures to be valid for economic decision-making, you must be looking at the costs for each alternative to provide the same service per day, week or yearly period as well as for a common evaluation life.

Method 1: Replacement In-Kind

This method of getting a common study period for unequal life alternatives is based on the assumption that projects A and B can be replaced in-kind for the same initial costs, operating costs and salvage values until a common study period equal to the lowest common denominator between the project lives is attained. For alternatives A and B replacement in-kind gives a six year study period as follows:

A)
$$\frac{C_A \; OC_{A1} \; OC_{A2}}{0 \quad 1 \quad 2} L_A \frac{C_A \; OC_{A1} \; OC_{A2}}{2 \quad 3 \quad 4} L_A \frac{C_A \; OC_{A1} \; OC_{A2}}{4 \quad 5 \quad 6} L_A$$

B)
$$\frac{C_A \; OC_{B1} \; OC_{B2} \; OC_{B3}}{0 \quad 1 \quad 2 \quad 3} L_B \frac{C_B \; OC_{B1} \; OC_{B2} \; OC_{B3}}{3 \quad 4 \quad 5 \quad 6} L_B$$

The obvious shortcoming of this method is that escalation of values is neglected from year to year. Experience of recent decades emphasizes the fact that costs can, and generally do escalate as time goes by. To assume replacement in-kind involves closing our eyes to the true situation that costs change. Economic analysis is only valid when you use actual expected costs and revenues and actual timing of costs and revenues. A method such as replacement in-kind that does not project actual expected costs should not be used. As mentioned earlier in this section, replacement in-kind is presented here to familiarize the reader with the disadvantages of the method since it is mentioned and advocated widely in other texts and journal literature.

Methods 2: Neglect Extra Life to Longer Life Alternatives

This method of getting a common study period for unequal life alternatives is based on neglecting the extra life of longer life alternatives over shorter life alternatives and letting salvage values at the end of the shorter life reflect remaining estimated value of the assets from sale or use of the assets elsewhere. This often is a valid assumption if the service provided is only expected to be needed for the short alternative life. Applying this method to alternatives A and B gives a two year study period as follows:

A) $\dfrac{C_A \qquad OC_{A1} \qquad OC_{A1}}{0 \qquad 1 \qquad 2} L_A$

B) $\dfrac{C_B \qquad OC_{B1} \qquad OC_{B2}}{0 \qquad 1 \qquad 2} L'_B$

Note that the salvage value of B is designated L'_B at the end of year 2 to designate it differently from L_B. Normally we would expect L'_B to be greater that L_B, since the asset will have been used for a shorter time at year 2 compared to year 3.

Method 2 is a valid method of obtaining a common study period in many physical evaluation situations.

Method 3: Estimate Actual Costs to Extend Shorter Life Alternatives to a Longer Life Common Study Period

This method of getting a common study period for unequal life alternatives is based on extending the life of the shorter life alternatives by estimating actual replacement or major repair and operating costs needed to extend the service life of an alternative. This method may result in a study period equal to the longest life alternative or it may result in a study period unrelated to the alternative lives. If we apply this method to alternatives A and B for a common study period of three years we get the following:

A) $\dfrac{C_A \quad OC_{A1} \quad OC_{A2}}{0 \qquad 1 \qquad 2}\, L_A \quad \dfrac{C'_A \quad OC_{A3}}{2 \qquad 3}\, L'_A$

B) $\dfrac{C_B \quad OC_{B1} \quad OC_{B2} \quad OC_{B3}}{0 \qquad 1 \qquad 2 \qquad 3}\, L_B$

Note that at the end of year two the replacement cost C'_A is not assumed to be the same as the initial cost, C_A. C'_A may be greater or less than C_A depending on whether it is new or used equipment. At the end of year three note that the operating cost, OC_{A3}, and the salvage value, L'_A, are designated differently than earlier values to emphasize that they probably will not be the same as the corresponding values for earlier years.

Engineering and business judgement is required on the part of the investment analyst to use correct assumptions in different analysis situations. In many cases the correct assumptions to use are not clear cut and it may be best to look at a problem from several analysis assumption points of view. It is very important to get into the habit of clearly stating all assumptions used in making an analysis so that the person with the responsibility of evaluating analysis calculations, assumptions and economic conclusions has the necessary information to make his or her evaluation properly. Economic analyses involve intangible considerations (such as the best assumptions to use to convert unequal life projects to equal life projects) and the decision-making manager must know the basis on which an analysis has been made before analysis results can be utilized to reach valid economic decisions.

Once again, before illustrating these three methods, it is important to re-emphasize that these methods or combinations of these methods are valid only for alternatives that provide the same service and not for income producing projects. Methods 1,2 and 3 are almost never valid for the comparison of income or service producing projects that provide different services or benefits.

EXAMPLE 3-27 Comparison of Unequal Life Service Alternatives

All values are in dollars:

A) $\dfrac{C=6{,}000 \qquad OC_1=1{,}500 \qquad OC_2=2{,}000}{0 \qquad\qquad 1 \qquad\qquad 2}\, L=1{,}000$

B)
$$\overline{\text{C=10,000 \quad OC}_1\text{=1,000 \quad OC}_2\text{=1,400 \quad OC}_3\text{=1,800 \quad OC}_4\text{=2,200}}$$ L=2,000

0   1   2   3   4

C)
$$\overline{\text{C=14,000 \quad OC}_1\text{=500 \quad OC}_2\text{=600 \quad OC}_3\text{=700 \quad OC}^4\text{=800 \quad OC}_5\text{=900}}$$ L=5,000

0   1   2   3   4   5

Three alternative methods A, B and C with costs, salvage values and lives given on the time diagrams are being considered to carry out a processing operation for the next three years. It is expected that the process will not be needed after three years. A major repair costing $3,000 at the end of year two would extend the life alternative A through year three with a third year operating cost of $2,500 and the salvage value equal to $1,000 at the end of year three instead of year two. The salvage value of alternative B is estimated to be $3,000 at the end of year three and the salvage value of alternative C is estimated to be $7,000 at the end of year three. For a minimum rate of return of 15%, which alternative is economically best? Use equivalent annual cost analysis for a three year study period.

Solution, The three year study period time diagrams follow with all values in dollars:

A)
$$\overline{\text{C=6000 \quad OC=1500 \quad \begin{array}{c}C=3000\\OC=2000\end{array} \quad OC=2500}}$$ L=1000

0   1   2   3

B)
$$\overline{\text{C=10,000 \quad OC=1000 \quad OC=1400 \quad OC=1800}}$$ L=3000

0   1   2   3

C)
$$\overline{\text{C=14,000 \quad OC=500 \quad OC=600 \quad OC=700}}$$ L=7000

0   1   2   3

The annual cost calculations follow:

$$AC_A = 6000\overset{.43798}{(A/P_{15,3})} + 1500 + 500\overset{.907}{(A/G_{15,3})} - 1000\overset{.28798}{(A/F_{15,3})}$$

$$+ 3000\overset{.7561}{(P/F_{15,2})}\overset{.43798}{(A/P_{15,3})} = \$5,287$$

$$AC_B = 10,000\overset{.43798}{(A/P_{15,3})} + 1000 + 400\overset{.907}{(A/G_{15,3})} - 3000\overset{.28798}{(A/F_{15,3})}$$

$$= \$4,897$$

$$AC_C = 14,000\overset{.43798}{(A/P_{15,3})} + 500 + 100\overset{.907}{(A/G_{15,3})} - 7000\overset{.28798}{(A/F_{15,3})}$$

$$= \$4,706$$

Select alternative C with the smallest equivalent annual cost. This problem is presented again on an after-tax evaluation basis in Chapter 10 and we then find alternative A is best, B next best and C the poorest choice which emphasizes the importance of tax considerations and that analyses must be done after-tax to be valid. Once again, taxes are being omitted in the early chapters of this text to avoid confusing the reader with tax considerations at the same time evaluation concepts are being developed.

3.17 Comparison of Service Producing Alternatives that Provide Different Service

If different service producing alternatives are projected to give different service per operating period, and if the extra service produced by the more productive alternative can be utilized, then it is necessary to get the alternatives on a common service producing basis per operating period as well as for a common evaluation life. This simply means that if two old assets are required to do the job of one new asset and service provided by two old assets is needed, then you must either compare the cost of service for two old assets to one new asset, or one old asset to one-half of a new asset, or some other 2 to 1 ratio of old to new assets. Differences in annual operating hours of service as well as volume of work differences per year between alternatives must be taken into account to get all alternatives on a common service basis before making economic comparisons.

EXAMPLE 3-28 Comparison of Alternatives that Provide Different Service

Three used machines can be purchased for $45,000 each to provide a needed service for the next three years. It is estimated that the salvage value of these machines will be zero in three years and that they will need to be replaced at year 3 with two new machines that each give 150% of the productivity per machine being realized with each old machine. The new machines would cost $145,000 each at year 3. The service of the old and new machines is needed for the next 5 years, so use a 5 year evaluation life assuming the salvage value of the new machines will be $50,000 per machine at year 5. Operating costs per machine for the old machines are estimated to be $30,000 in year 1, $35,000 in year 2, and $40,000 in year 3. Operating costs per new machine are estimated to be $33,000 in year 4 and $36,000 in year 5. Another alternative is to buy the two new machines now for a cost of $125,000 per machine to provide the needed service for the next 5 years with annual operating costs per machine of $25,000 in year 1, $30,000 in year 2, $35,000 in year 3, $40,000 in year 4, and $45,000 in year 5. Salvage value at year 5 would be $15,000 per machine. For a minimum ROR of 15%, use present worth cost analysis to determine the most economical alternative way of providing the needed service. Then determine the uniform and equal revenues for each alternative that would be required at each of years 1 to 5 to cover the cost of service at the 15% before-tax minimum ROR.

Solution: (All values in thousands of dollars)

Compare the economics of 3 used machines with 2 new machines for a 5 year life to get the alternatives on a common service basis for a 5 year common study period.

```
                                            C=290
                 C=135      OC=90   OC=105   OC=120   OC=66   OC=72
A)  "3 Used"    ─────────────────────────────────────────────────── L=100
                   0         1        2        3        4       5
```

```
                 C=250      OC=50   OC=60    OC=70    OC=80   OC=90
B)  "2 New"     ─────────────────────────────────────────────────── L=30
                   0         1        2        3        4       5
```

$$\text{PW Cost}_A = 135 + 90\overset{.8696}{(P/F_{15,1})} + 105\overset{.7561}{(P/F_{15,2})} + 410\overset{.6575}{(P/F_{15,3})}$$

$$+ 66\overset{.5718}{(P/F_{15,4})} + (72-100)\overset{.4972}{(P/F_{15,5})} = \$586$$

$$\text{PW Cost}_B = 250 + 50\overset{.8696}{(P/F_{15,1})} + 60\overset{.7561}{(P/F_{15,2})} + 70\overset{.6575}{(P/F_{15,3})}$$

$$+ 80\overset{.5718}{(P/F_{15,4})} + (90-30)\overset{.4972}{(P/F_{15,5})} = \$460 \quad \text{select min. cost}$$

Alternative B with the minimum present worth cost is the economic choice.

On a before-tax analysis basis, equivalent annual cost represents the equivalent annual revenues required to cover cost of service at a specified minimum ROR as the following calculations illustrate.

$$\text{Annual Revenues} = \text{Annual Cost} = (\text{PW Cost})(A/P_{i,n}^{*})$$

$$\text{Annual Revenues}_A = AC_A = 586\overset{.29832}{(A/P_{15,5})} = 174.8$$

$$\text{Annual Revenues}_B = AC_B = 460\overset{.29832}{(A/P_{15,5})} = 137.2 \quad \text{select minimum}$$

The alternative with the minimum revenue requirement is the economic choice. This is alternative B which in this case and in general, always agrees with the cost analysis results.

3.18 Summary

Methods have been presented and illustrated in this chapter to compare investment alternatives by seven economic analysis methods:

1. Present Worth Cost Analysis
2. Annual Cost Analysis
3. Future Worth Cost Analysis
4. Rate of Return Analysis
5. Net Value Techniques
6. Benefit Cost and Present Value Ratios
7. Breakeven Analysis

These seven methods with many variations provide the basis of most valid investment decision methods for both before-tax and after-tax analysis. The net value and ratio techniques are variations of the basic present, annual and future cost or value analysis methods. Familiarity with all of these methods is desirable for correct economic evaluation of investment alternatives of different types, in different situations. When the inter-relationships between these methods are understood it becomes evident that each of these seven methods leads to the same economic analysis decision if the methods are applied correctly. In Chapter 3 we have discussed and illustrated how to apply these techniques to analyze service producing alternatives. In Chapter 4, the use of these techniques will be related to the evaluation of income producing alternatives.

PROBLEMS

3-1. A subdivider offers lots for sale at $2,500, with $500 to be paid down now and $500 to be paid at the end of each year for the next 4 years with 'no interest' to be charged. In discussing a possible purchase you will find that you can get the same lot for $2,250 cash. You also find that on a time purchase there will be a service charge of $50 at the date of the purchase to cover legal and administrative expenses. What rate of interest will actually be paid if the lot is purchased on this time plan? This is "what incremental rate of return will be received on the incremental purchasing investment compared to time payments?" Draw the cumulative cash position diagram for your ROR result.

3-2.   The owner of a patent is negotiating a contract with a corporation that will give the corporation the right to use the patent. The corporation will pay the patent owner $3,000 a year at the end of each of the next 5 years, $5,000 at the end of each year for the next 8 years and $6,000 at the end of each year for the final 3 years of the 16-year life of the patent. If the owner of this patent wants a lump sum settlement 3 years from now in lieu of all 16 payments, at what price would he receive equivalent value if his minimum rate of return is 8% before income taxes?

3-3.   Machine A has an initial cost of $50,000, an estimated service period of 10 years and an estimated salvage value of $10,000 at the end of the 10 years. Estimated end-of-year annual disbursements for operation and maintenance are $5,000. A major overhaul costing $10,000 will be required at the end of 5 years. An alternate Machine B has an initial cost of $40,000 and an estimated zero salvage value at the end of the 10-year service period with estimated end-of-year disbursements for operation and maintenance of $8,000 for the first year, $8,500 for the second year and increasing $500 each year thereafter. Using a minimum ROR of 10%, compare the equivalent annual costs of 10-year service from Machines A and B.

3-4.   A project has an initial cost of $120,000 and an estimated salvage value after 15 years of $70,000. Estimated average annual receipts are $25,000. Estimated average annual disbursements are $15,000. Assuming that annual receipts and disbursements will be uniform, compute the prospective rate of return before taxes.

3-5.   A man plans to purchase a home for $50,000. Property taxes are expected to be $900 a year and insurance about $200 a year. Annual repair and maintenance is estimated at about $400. An alternative is to rent a house of about the same size for $400 a month. (Approximate the rent as $4,800 end of year payments.) If 6% before taxes is the minimum attractive rate of return on the investment in the house, what must the resale value be 10 years hence for the equivalent annual cost of ownership to equal the equivalent annual cost of renting?

3-6.   An old 30 year life $1000 bond matures in 20 years and pays semi-annual dividends of $40. What rate of return compounded semi-annually does the bond yield if you pay $800 for it and hold it until maturity assuming the analysis is made on the first day of a new semi-annual dividend period? If the bond is callable 8 years from now at face value, what could an investor pay for the bond and be assured of receiving annual returns of 6% compounded semi-annually? Neglect the possibility of bankruptcy by the bond issuer.

3-7.   What can be paid for the bond in problem 3-6 if a 10% return compounded semi-annually is desired and a bond call is considered a negligible probability?

3-8.   An investor has $5,000 in a bank account at 7% interest compounded annually. She can use this sum to pay for the purchase of a plot of land. She expects that in 10 years she will be able to sell the land for $13,000. During that period she will have to pay $200 a year in property taxes and insurance. Should she make the purchase? Base your decision on a rate of return analysis and verify your conclusion with future value analysis.

3-9.   A new project will require development costs of $60 million at time zero and $100 million at the end of 2 years from time zero with incomes of $40 million per year at the end of years, 1, 2 and 3 and incomes of $70 million per year at the end of years 4 through 10 with zero salvage value predicted at the end of year 10. Calculate the rate of return for this project.

3-10. Equipment is being leased from an equipment manufacturer for $500,000 per year beginning of year payments and the lease expires 3 years from now. It is estimated that a new lease for the succeeding 4 years on similar new equipment will provide the same service and will cost $750,000 per year with beginning of year payments. The equipment manufacturer is offering to terminate the present lease today and to sell the lessee new equipment for $2 million now which together with a major repair cost of $600,000 4 years from now should provide the needed equipment service for the next 7 years when salvage value is estimated to be 0 for both the purchase and leasing options. Use equivalent annual cost analysis for a minimum rate of return of 20% to determine if leasing or purchasing is economically the best approach to provide the equipment service for the next 7 years. Verify your conclusion with ROR and NPV analysis.

3-11. A person is considering an investment situation that requires the investment of $100,000 now and $200,000 a year from now to generage profits of $90,000 per year starting at year 2 and running through year 10 (a 9 year profit period) with projected salvage value of $150,000 at the end of year 10. Determine the rate of return for this investment and draw the cumulative cash position diagram for year 0 through 3.

3-12. A firm is evaluating whether to lease or purchase a fleet of 4 heavy trucks. The trucks can be purchased for a cost of $240,000 and operated for maintenance, insurance and general operating costs of $20,000 at year 0, $40,000 at year 1, $50,000 at year 2 and $30,000 at year 3 (putting operating costs at the closest points in time to where they are incurred) with an expected salvage value of $100,000 at the end of year 3. The trucks could be leased for $120,000 per year, for the 3 years, with monthly payments, so consider $60,000 lease cost at year 0, $120,000 per year at years 1 and 2 and $60,000 at year 3, putting lease costs at the closest point in time to where they are incurred. The lease costs include maintenance costs but do not include insurance and general operating costs of $10,000 at year 0, $20,000 per year at years 1 and 2 and $10,000 at year 3. If the minimum rate of return is 15% before tax considerations, use present worth cost analysis to determine if economic analysis dictates leasing or purchasing. Verify your conclusion with ROR, NPV and PVR analysis.

3-13. 500,000 lbs. per year of raw material are needed in a production operation (treat as end-of-year requirements). This material can be purchased for $0.24 per pound or produced internally for operating costs of $0.20 per pound if a $40,000 machine is purchased. A major repair of $10,000 will be required on the machine after 3 years. For a 5 year project life, zero salvage value and a 30% minimum rate of return before tax considerations, determine whether the company should purchase the equipment to make the raw material.
A) Use Incremental ROR, NPV and PVR analysis.
B) Verify your result from "A" with present worth cost analysis.

3-14. Development of a new oil field will require capital cost expenditures of $10 million at time zero and $20 million at year 1 to cover costs for lease acquisition, drilling, well completion, pipeline, roads and other contingencies. Production will start in year 2 and is estimated to yield annual net revenues (revenues after operating costs and royalties) of $12 million at the end of years 2, 3 and 4 with revenues declining by an arithmetic gradient of $1 million per year starting in year 5 until the project terminates at the end of year 15 when salvage value is estimated to be 0. Calculate the rate of return for this project. If the net revenues are reinvested at a 15% annually compounded rate of return as they are received, what will be the growth rate of return on invested dollars over the 15 year project life? Also calculate NPV and PVR for the 15% minimum ROR.

3-15. A corporation has invested $250,000 in a project that is expected to generate $100,000 profit per year for years 1 through 5 plus a $150,000 salvage value at the end of year 5. It is proposed that the profits and salvage value from this investment will be reinvested immediately each year in real estate that is projected to have a $2,000,000 value at the end of 6 years from now. From the combination of these two projects, what is the growth rate of return on the $250,000 initial investment? What is the rate of return on the initial project investment? What is the real estate reinvestment project rate of return?

3-16. A heavy equipment manufacturer plans to lease a $100,000 machine for 30 months with an option to buy at the end of that time. The manufacturer wants to get 1% per month compound interest on the unamortized value of the machine each month and wants the unamortized value of the machine to be $25,000 at the end of the 30th month. What uniform monthly beginning-of-month lease payments must the company charge for each of the 30 months so that these payments plus a $25,000 option to buy payment at the end of 30 months will recover the initial $100,000 value of the equipment plus interest? What interest is paid by the lessee during the third month of the lease? What is the unamortized investment principal after the fourth payment is made?

3-17. A 20-year loan is being negotiated with a savings and loan company. $50,000 is to be borrowed at 8% interest compounded quarterly with mortgage payments to be made at the end of each quarter over a 20-year period. To obtain the loan the borrower must pay "2 points" at the time he takes out the loan. This means the borrower must pay 2% of $50,000 or a $1,000 fee at time zero to obtain the $50,000 loan. If the borrower accepts the loan under these conditions determine the actual nominal interest rate compounded quarterly that he will pay.

3-18. Two development alternatives exist to bring a new project into production. The first development approach would involve equipment and development expenditures of $1 million at year 0 and $2 million at year 1 to generate incomes of $1.8 million per year and operating expenses of $0.7 million per year starting in year 1 for each of years 1 through 10 when the project is expected to terminate with zero salvage value. The second development approach would involve equipment and development expenditures of $1 million at year 0 and expenses of $0.9 million at year 1 to generate incomes of $2 million per year and operating expenses of $0.9 million per year starting in year 2 for each of years 2 through 10 when the project is expected to terminate with zero salvage value. For a minimum rate of return of 15%, evaluate which of the alternatives is economically better using (a) ROR analysis, (b) NPV analysis, (c) PVR analysis.

3-19. An investor is interested in purchasing a company and wants you to determine the maximum value of the company today considering the opportunity cost of capital is 20%. The company assets are in two areas. First, an existing production operation was developed by the company over the past two years for equipment and development costs of $100,000 two years ago, $200,000 one year ago and costs and revenues that cancelled each other during the past year. It is projected that revenue minus operating expense net profits will be $120,000 per year at the end of each of the next 12 years when production is expected to terminate with a zero salvage value. The second company asset is a mineral property that is projected to be developed for a $350,000 future cost one year from now with expected future profits of $150,000 per year starting two years from now and terminating 10 years from now with a zero salvage value.

3-20. A company is considering replacement of an existing natural gas boiler system with a coal fired boiler system that would cost $5 million at time zero. The value of the existing natural gas boiler system is estimated to be nil at time zero. Natural gas energy, maintenance and labor operating costs in year 1 are estimated to be $2.5

million with the natural gas boiler system and to escalate by a constant arithmetic gradient of plus $0.4 million per year in years 2 through 20 with a zero salvage value at the end of year 20. Coal energy, maintenance and labor operating costs in year 1 are estimated to be $2 million for the coal boiler system and to escalate by a constant arithmetic gradient of plus $0.2 million per year in years 2 through 20 with a $1 million salvage value at the end of year 20. If the minimum rate of return is 15%, determine the most economical boiler system using (a) present worth cost analysis, (b) incremental ROR analysis, (c) NVP analysis and (d) PVR analysis.

3-21. Based on the following data for a petroleum project, calculate the before tax annual cash flow, ROR, NPV and PVR for a 15% minimum ROR. Then calculate the breakeven crude oil price that, if received uniformly from years 1 through 5, would give the project a 15% ROR. Cost dollars and production units in thousands.

Year	0	1	2	3	4	5
Production, bbls		62	53	35	24	17
Price, $ per bbl		26.0	26.0	26.0	27.3	28.7
Intangible (IDC)	750	250				
Tangible		670				
Mineral Rights Acq.	100					
Operating costs		175	193	212	223	256

Royalties are 14% of revenues.
Liquidation value in year 5 is zero.

3-22. The following data relates to a mining project with increasing waste rock or overburden to ore ratio as the mine life progresses, giving declining production per year. Calculate the before tax annual cash flow, ROR, NPV, and PVR for a 15% minimum ROR. Then calculate the breakeven price per ton of ore that, if received uniformly from years 1 through 5, would give the project a 15% ROR.

Cost dollars and ore production in thousands.

Year	0	1	2	3	4	5
Production, tons of ore		62	53	35	24	17
Price, $ per ton		26.0	26.0	26.0	27.3	28.7
Mineral development	750	250				
Mining equipment		670				
Mineral rights acquisition	100					
Operating costs		175	193	212	233	256

Royalties are 14% of revenues.
Liquidation value in year 5 is zero.

3-23. A machine in use now has a zero net salvage value and is expected to have an additional two years of useful life but its service is needed for another 6 years. The operating costs with this machine are estimated to be $4,500 for the next year of use at year 1 and $5,500 at year 2. The salvage value will be 0 in two years. A replacement machine is estimated to cost $25,000 at year 2 with annual operating costs of $2,500 in its first year of use at year 3, increased by an arithmetic gradient series of $500 per year in following years. The salvage value is estimated to be $7,000 after 4 years of use (at year 6). An alternative is to replace the existing machine now with a new machine costing $21,000 and annual operating costs of $2,000 at year 1, increasing by an arithmetic gradient of $500 each following year. The salvage value is estimated to be $4,000 at the end of year 6. Compare the economics of these alternatives for a minimum ROR of 20% using a 6 year life by:

A) Present worth cost analysis.
B) Equivalent annual cost analysis.
C) Incremental NPV analysis.

3-24. Discount rates on U.S. treasury bills (T-bills) are different from normal compound interest discount rates because T-bills interest effectively is paid at the time T-bills are purchased rather than at the maturity date of the T-bills. Calculate the nominal annual rate of return compounded semi-annually to be earned by investing in a 6-month $10,000 T-bill with a 15% annual discount rate.

3-25. A company wants you to use rate of return analysis to evaluate the economics of buying the mineral rights to a mineral reserve for a cost of $1,500,000 at year 0 with the expectation that mineral development costs of $5,000,000 and tangible equipment costs of $4,000,000 will be spent at year 1. The mineral reserves are estimated to be produced uniformly over an 8 year production life (evaluation years 2 through 9). Since escalation of operating costs each year is estimated to be offset by escalation of revenues, it is projected that profit will be constant at $4,000,000 per year in each of evaluation years 2 through 9 with a $6,000,000 salvage value at the end of year 9. Calculate the project rate of return, then assume a 15% minimum rate of return and calculate the project growth rate of return, NPV and PVR.

3-26. A company is evaluating the economics of whether to purchase a coal mining property now at year 0 for a $10 million acquisition cost with plans to spend a significant amount of capital for development during year 1 to start producing coal in year 2. It is estimated annual profit will be $20 million at year 2 (assume end of year 2) and that profit will escalate by $2 million per year through year 7 and then remain constant through year 15 when coal reserves will be depleted and the project terminated with an estimated zero salvage value. In addition to the $10 million year 0 acquisition cost, what total capital cost can be incurred at year 0 and at year 1 (with 30% at year 0 and 70% at year 1) to develop the coal mine and breakeven with receiving a 20% rate of return on invested dollars over the 15 year project life?

3-27. To achieve a 20% rate of return on invested capital, determine the maximum cost that can be incurred today to acquire oil and gas mineral rights to a property that will be developed 3 years from now for estimated escalated dollar (actual) drilling and well completion costs of $2,500,000 with an expected net profit of $1,500,000 projected to be generated at year 4 and declining by an arithmetic gradient of $200,000 per year in each year after year 4 for eight years of production (evaluation years 4 through 11). Salvage value is estimated to be zero. If the oil and gas mineral rights are already owned by an investor whose minimum ROR is 20%, what range of sale values for these mineral rights would make the owner's economics of selling better than holding the property for development 3 years from now for the stated profits?

CHAPTER 4

INCOME PRODUCING PROJECT ANALYSIS

Economic analysis involves comparison of alternatives and explicitly or implicitly this often requires looking at differences between alternatives. The words incremental, difference, and marginal are used interchangeably by persons involved in evaluation work when referring to changes in costs or revenues that are incurred in going from one alternative to another or from one level of operation to another. The time value of money concepts and basic economic evaluation techniques were developed and illustrated in Chapters 2 and 3. Incremental costs and rate of return, net present value and ratios on incremental levels of investment were introduced in Chapter 3 for the analysis of service producing alternatives providing the same service. In this chapter we want to expand the application of present worth, annual worth, future worth, ratio and rate of return decision making techniques by applying them to different income producing investment situations. It will be shown that incremental analysis plays a key role in analyzing mutually exclusive income producing alternatives just as it was shown in Chapter 3 to be important in the analysis of mutually exclusive service producing alternatives. Then it will be shown how these same techniques are applied in very different ways to properly analyze non-mutually exclusive alternatives.

For economic analysis purposes, *income producing alternatives must be broken into two sub-classifications which are: (1) comparison of mutually exclusive alternatives, which means making an analysis of several alternatives from which only one can be selected, such as selecting the best way to improve an existing operation or the best way to develop a new process, product, mining operation or oil/gas reserve; (2) comparison of non-mutually exclusive alternatives which means analyzing several alternatives from which more than one can be selected depending on capital or budget restrictions, such as ranking research, development, an exploration projects to determine the best projects to fund with available dollars.* Analysis of mutually exclusive alternatives will be presented first in this chapter with non-mutually exclusive alternative analysis discussed in the latter pages of the chapter.

4.1 Analysis of Mutually Exclusive Income Producing Alternatives Using Rate of Return, Net Value and Ratios.

In any industry, classic illustration of mutually exclusive alternative analysis often involves evaluation of whether it is economically desirable to improve, expand or develop investment projects. Whenever you must make an economic choice between several alternative investment choices, and selecting one of the choices excludes in the foreseeable future being able to invest in the other choices, you are involved with mutually exclusive alternative analysis. It will be illustrated in the following examples that incremental analysis is the key to correct analysis of mutually exclusive alternatives with all discounted cash flow analysis techniques.

EXAMPLE 4-1 Analysis of Mutually Exclusive Income Producing Alternatives

Consider the analysis of two different ways, "A" and "B", of improving an existing process. As shown on the following time diagrams, "A" involves a small change costing $50,000 with savings and salvage as illustrated. "B" involves a much larger change costing $500,000 which includes the "A" changes with savings and salvage as shown. Assume $500,000 is available to invest and that other opportunities exist to invest any or all of it at a 15% ROR. Which, if either, of the mutually exclusive alternatives "A" and "B" should we select as our economic choice? Use ROR analysis, then verify your economic conclusions with NPV, NAV, NFV and PVR analysis.

Solution, All Values in Thousands of Dollars:

ROR Analysis of Mutually Exclusive Alternatives "A" and "B"

C = Cost, I = Savings, L = Salvage Value

```
A)   C=50        I=50             I=50
     ──────────────────────────────────     L=50
     0           1 ............. 5
```

PW Eq. $0 = -50 + 50(P/A_{i,5}) + 50(P/F_{i,5})$

$i = ROR_A = 100\%$ by trial and error, $> i^* = 15\%$, so satisfactory

B)   C=500   I=250   I=250
    ───   L=500
      0   1 5

PW Eq.   0 = -500 + 250(P/A$_{i,5}$) + 500(P/F$_{i,5}$)

i = ROR$_B$ = 50% by trial and error, > i*=15%, so satisfactory

The ROR results can also be obtained by dividing annual savings by initial cost and multiplying by 100, since initial cost equals salvage.

Many people think in terms of the project with the largest rate of return on total investment as always being economically best, but in fact, the largest rate of return project is not always the best economic choice. In this case, although "A" has a total investment rate of return of 100%, which is twice as large as the "B" rate of return, the investments differ in magnitude by a factor of ten. A smaller ROR on a bigger investment often is economically better than a bigger ROR on a smaller investment. Incremental analysis must be made to determine if the extra, (or incremental) $450,000 that will be invested in "B" over the required "A" investment, will be generating more or less profit (or savings), than the $450,000 would earn if invested elsewhere at the minimum rate of return of 15%. The incremental analysis is made for the bigger project "B" minus the smaller project "A" so that incremental cost is followed by incremental income giving:

B-A) C=450   I=200   I=200
    ───   L=450
      0   1 5

PW Eq.   0 = -450 + 200(P/A$_{i,5}$) + 450(P/F$_{i,5}$)

i = ROR$_{B-A}$ = 44.4%

It should be clear from an economic viewpoint that if $500,000 is available to invest, we would better off with all of it invested in project "B". Our incremental analysis has broken project "B" into two components, one of which is like project "A", and the other is like the incremental project. Selecting project "B" effectively is equivalent to having $50,000 of the capital invested in project "A" earning a 100% ROR and $450,000 incremental investment earning a 44.4% ROR. Surely selecting "B" is better than selecting "A" which would give a 100% ROR on the $50,000 capital invested in A and require investing the remaining $450,000 elsewhere at the 15% minimum ROR. Incremental analysis is required to come to this correct conclusion and notice that it requires rejecting alternative "A" with the largest ROR of 100% on total investment.

Evaluation of mutually exclusive multiple investment alternatives (the situation where only one alternative may be selected from more than one invest-

ment choice) by rate of return analysis requires both total investment and incremental investment rate of return analysis. The rate of return analysis concept for mutually exclusive alternatives is based on testing to see that each satisfactory level of investment meets two requirements as follows: 1) The rate of return on total investment must be greater than or equal to the minimum rate of return, i*. 2) The rate of return on incremental investment compared to the last satisfactory level of investment must be greater than or equal to the minimum ROR, i*. The largest level of investment that satisfies both criteria is the economic choice. Analysis of total investment rate of return alone will not always lead to the correct economic choice because the project with the largest total investment rate of return is not always best. It is assumed that money not invested in a particular project can be invested elsewhere at the minimum rate of return, i*. Therefore, it is often preferable to invest a large amount of money at a moderate rate of return rather than a small amount at a large return with the remainder having to be invested elsewhere at a specified minimum rate of return. *These evaluation rules and concepts apply to growth rate of return analysis as well as regular rate of return analysis, since growth rate of return is just a special type of regular return.*

Net Value Analysis (Present, Annual, Future) of Mutually Exclusive Alternatives "A" and "B"

To illustrate the application of NPV, NAV and NFV to evaluate mutually exclusive investment alternatives these techniques will now be applied to evaluate alternatives "A" and "B" for the previously stated 15% minimum ROR.

A)   C=50   I=50   I=50

        0   1 5   L=50

B)   C=500   I=250   I=250

        0   1 5   L=500

B-A)   C=450   I=200   I=200

        0   1 5   L=450

$$\text{NPV}_A = 50 \overset{3.352}{(P/A_{15,5})} + 50 \overset{0.4972}{(P/F_{15,5})} - 50 = +\$142.5$$

$$\text{NPV}_B = 250(P/A_{15,5}) + 500(P/F_{15,5}) - 500 = +\$586.6$$

$$\text{NAV}_A = 50 + 50 \overset{0.14832}{(A/F_{15,5})} - 50 \overset{0.29832}{(A/P_{15,5})} = +\$42.5$$

$$\text{NAV}_B = 250 + 500(A/F_{15,5}) - 500(A/P_{15,5}) = +\$175.0$$

$$\text{NFV}_A = 50 \overset{6.742}{(F/A_{15,5})} + 50 - 50 \overset{2.011}{(F/P_{15,5})} = +\$286.5$$

$$\text{NFV}_B = 250(F/A_{15,5}) + 500 - 500(F/P_{15,5}) = +\$1,180.0$$

We see that all the net value results are positive which consistently indicates that both alternatives "A" and "B" are satisfactory since they generate sufficient revenue to more than pay off the investments at the minimum ROR of 15%. To determine which alternative is best we must make incremental net value analysis just as we did for ROR analysis. We can get the incremental net value results either by looking at the differences between the total investment net values for the bigger investment minus the smaller, which is "B-A" in this case, or by working with the incremental costs, savings, and salvage. Exactly the same incremental net values are obtained either way.

$$NPV_{B-A} = NPV_B - NPV_A = 586.6 - 142.5 = +\$444.1$$

$$\text{or} \quad = 200(P/A_{15,5}) + 450(P/F_{15,5}) - 450 = +\$444.1$$
$$\phantom{\text{or} \quad = 200(P/A_{}} 3.352 \phantom{(P/A_{15,5})} 0.4972$$

directly from the incremental data;

$$NAV_{B-A} = NAV_B - NAV_A = 175.0 - 42.5 = +\$132.5$$

$$NFV_{B-A} = NFV_B - NFV_A = 1,180.0 - 286.5 = +\$893.5$$

In each case the incremental net value results are positive, indicating a satisfactory incremental investment. The reason it is satisfactory can be shown by looking at the net value that would be received from investing the $450,000 incremental capital elsewhere at $i^* = 15\%$.

$$C = 450 \text{ at } i^* = 15\%.$$

0	1 5	

$$F = 450(F/P_{15,5}) = +\$904.95$$

$$NPV = 904.95(P/F_{15,5}) - 450 = 0$$
$$\phantom{NPV = 904.95(P/F_{}} 0.4972$$

Similarly, NAV = 0 and NFV = 0.

Money invested at the minimum ROR, i^*, always has a zero net value. Obviously the positive incremental net value results for "B-A" are better than the zero net value that would be obtained by investing the money elsewhere at i^*.

In summary, the net value analysis concept for evaluating mutually exclusive alternatives is based on two tests: 1) the net value on total investment must be positive, 2) the incremental net value obtained in comparing the total investment net value to the net value of the last smaller satisfactory investment level must be positive. The largest level of investment that satisfies both criteria is the economic choice. This is always the alternative with the largest positive net value. This means, if you have a dozen mutually exclusive alternatives and calculate NPV, or NAV, or NFV for each, the economic choice will always be the alternative with the largest net value. When you select the mutually exclusive investment alternative with the largest net value as the economic choice, you are not omitting incremental analysis. Experience shows that incremental analysis always leads to selection of the project with the biggest net value on total investment as the economic choice. You can mathematically convert between NPV, NAV and NFV and therefore you must get the same economic conclusion using any of these techniques.

$$NPV = NAV(P/A_{i^*,n}) = NFV(P/F_{i^*,n})$$

Ratio Analysis of Mutually Exclusive Alternatives A and B

A) C=50   I=50   I=50
    ──────────────────────────────────── L=50
    0   1 5

B) C=500   I=250   I=250
    ──────────────────────────────────── L=500
    0   1 5

PVR_A = NPV_A / PW Cost = 142.5/50 = 2.85 > 0, so satisfactory

PVR_B = NPV_B / PW Cost = 586.6/500 = 1.17 > 0, so satisfactory

Project "A" has the bigger total investment ratio but the smaller project "B" ratio relates to ten times larger investment value. Incremental analysis is the optimization analysis that answers the question concerning which of mutually exclusive alternatives "A" and "B" is the better investment. This is true with ratios the same as was illustrated earlier for ROR and net value analysis.

B-A) C=450   I=200   I=200
      ────────────────────────────────── L=450
      0   1 5

PVR_{B-A} = NPV_{B-A} / PW Investment = 444/450 = 0.99 > 0 satisfactory

Accepting the incremental "B-A" investment indicates accepting project "B" over "A", even though the total investment ratio on B is less than A. *As with ROR analysis, the mutually exclusive alternative with bigger ROR, PVR or Benefit Cost Ratio on total investment often is not the better mutually exclusive investment. Incremental analysis along with total investment analysis is the key to correct analysis of mutually exclusive choices.*

Since benefit cost ratio equals PVR plus one, it should be evident to the reader that either PVR or Benefit Cost Ratio analysis give the same conclusions, as long as the correct breakeven ratios of zero for PVR and one for Benefit Cost Ratio are used.

4.2 Unequal Life Mutually Exclusive Income Producing Alternative Analysis

As was mentioned in Chapter 3, it is important to recognize that when using ROR, NAV or NFV techniques to analyze unequal life alternatives, you must use a common evaluation life for all alternatives, normally the life of the longest life alternative. Unequal life alternatives are not a problem with NPV or ratio analysis because time zero is a common point in time for calculating NPV of either equal or unequal life alternatives. If you have unequal lives for different alternatives, the time value of money considerations are different in rate of return, annual value and future value calculations and you may choose the wrong alternative as being best, if you do not get a common evaluation life. This merely means that you must calculate NFV at the same future point in time for all alternatives, or you must calculate NAV by spreading costs and revenues over the same number of years for all alternatives. *For ROR, Net Value or Ratio analysis of unequal life income producing alternatives, treat all projects as having equal lives which are equal to the longest life project with net revenues and costs of zero in the later years of shorter life projects.* Note that this is not the same technique presented in Chapter 3 to convert unequal life service producing alternatives to equal life alternatives using either Method 1, 2 or 3.

EXAMPLE 4-2 Net Value, ROR and PVR Analysis of Unequal Life Income Producing Investments

Use NPV, NAV, NFV, ROR and PVR analysis to evaluate the following two unequal life income producing alternatives, considering the minimum rate of return to be 20%

All Values in Thousands of Dollars,
C = Cost, I = Profit, L = Salvage Profit

A)   C=88   I=35   I=35
    ───   L=0
       0   1 5

B)   C=50   I=30   I=30
    ──────────────────────────────────   L=0
       0   1 3

Solutions:

Extend the life of project "B" to 5 yrs with net revenues and costs of zero in years 4 and 5.

Net Value Analysis

$$\text{NPV}_A = 35(\overset{2.991}{P/A_{20,5}}) - 88 = +\$16.69 \qquad \text{Select Largest}$$

$$\text{NPV}_B = 30(\overset{2.106}{P/A_{20,3}}) - 50 = +\$13.18$$

NAV calculations must be based on a 5 year life for both alternatives "A" and "B".

$$\text{NAV}_A = 35 - 88(\overset{.33438}{A/P_{20,5}}) = +\$5.57 \qquad \text{Select Largest}$$

$$\text{NAV}_B = 30(\overset{2.106}{P/A_{20,3}})(\overset{.33438}{A/P_{20,5}}) - 50(\overset{.33438}{A/P_{20,5}}) = +\$4.41$$

If you incorrectly use a 3 year life for alternative "B", you get;

$$\text{Incorrect NAV}_B = 30 - 50(\overset{.4747}{A/P_{20,3}}) = +\$6.27$$

which is greater than NAV_A and you would select "B" incorrectly. Similarly, NFV calculations must be based on a common 5 year life.

$$\text{NFV}_A = 35(\overset{7.442}{F/A_{20,5}}) - 88(\overset{2.488}{F/P_{20,5}}) = +\$41.53 \qquad \text{Select Largest}$$

$$\text{NFV}_B = 30(\overset{3.640}{F/A_{20,3}})(\overset{1.440}{F/P_{20,2}}) - 50(\overset{2.488}{F/P_{20,5}}) = +\$32.85$$

Alternative "A" with the largest total investment NPV, NAV and NFV is the economic choice because it has positive incremental net value when compared to alternative "B". Check the interchangeable character of net value results within the accuracy of significant figures;

$$\text{NPV}_A = 16.69 = \text{NAV}_A(\overset{5.57(2.991)}{P/A_{20,5}}) = \text{NFV}_A(\overset{41.53(.4019)}{P/F_{20,5}}) \qquad \text{ok}$$

$$\text{NPV}_B = 13.18 = \text{NAV}_B(\overset{4.41(2.991)}{P/A_{20,5}}) = \text{NFV}_B(\overset{32.85(.4019)}{P/F_{20,5}}) \qquad \text{ok}$$

Rate of Return Analysis

A) PW Eq: $0 = -88 + 35(P/A_{i,5})$

   $i = ROR_A = 28.36\%$ by trial and error, this is greater than the minimum rate of return of 20%, so satisfactory.

B) PW Eq: $0 = -50 + 30(P/A_{i,3})$

   $i = ROR_B = 36.31\%$ by trial and error, this is greater than the minimum rate of return of 20%, so satisfactory.

The bigger ROR on total investment "B" does not necessarily indicate that project "B" is better than "A", because the "B" ROR relates to smaller investment value. A smaller ROR on bigger investment value may be the better investment. Incremental ROR analysis is the optimization calculation that tells us which project is better. Always look at the incremental difference of the bigger initial investment project "A" minus the smaller initial investment project "B" so that incremental investment cost is followed by incremental revenue or savings.

```
         C=38      I=5           I=5        I=35        I=35
A-B) ─────────────────────────────────────────────────────── L=0
         0         1 .......... 3          4           5
```

A-B) PW Eq: $0 = -38 + 5(P/A_{i,3}) + 35(P/A_{i,2})(P/F_{i,3})$

$i = ROR_{A-B} = 22.81\%$ by trial and error, this is greater than the minimum rate of return of 20%, so select A. This conclusion is consistent with net value analysis.

PVR Analysis

$PVR_A = NPV_A / PW\ Cost_A = 16.69/88 = 0.19 > 0$, so acceptable

$PVR_B = NPV_B / PW\ Cost_B = 13.18/50 = 0.26 > 0$, so acceptable

The bigger ratio on total investment "B" does not necessarily make "B" preferable to "A" for the same logic described with the ROR analysis. Incremental PVR analysis is the necessary optimization calculation.

$PVR_{A-B} = NPV_{A-B} / PW\ Cost_{A-B} = 3.51/38 = 0.09 > 0$, so select "A".

EXAMPLE 4-3 Mutually Exclusive Project Analysis Case Study

An existing production facility must be shut down unless an environmental capital cost of $150 million is incurred now at year 0. This improvement will enable production to continue and generate estimated profits of $60 million per year for each of the next 8 years when salvage value of the facility is projected to be zero. An alternative under consideration would combine process improvement and expansion with an environmental cost change for a cost of $200 million now at year 0, plus $150 million cost at year 1 to generate estimated project profits of $60 million in year 1 and $120 million profit per year in each of years 2 through 8 when salvage value is estimated to be $100 million. The minimum ROR is 20%. Evaluate which of these alternatives is better using ROR, NPV and PVR analysis.

Solution, all values in millions of dollars:

```
     C=150    I=60    I=60    I=60    I=60              I=60
A)   ─────────────────────────────────────────────────────        L=0
      0        1       2       3       4 ............ 8
```

```
              I= 60
     C=200   C=150   I=120   I=120   I=120            I=120
B)   ─────────────────────────────────────────────────────        L=100
      0        1       2       3       4 ............ 8
```

ROR Analysis

A) PW Eq: $150 = 60(P/A_{i,8})$, $i = ROR_A = 37.2\% > i^* = 20\%$

B) PW Eq: $200 = -90(P/F_{i,1}) + 120(P/A_{i,7})(P/F_{i,1})$

$$+ 100(P/F_{i,8}), \quad i = ROR_B = 30\% > i^* = 20\%$$

Both projects have acceptable economics, but incremental rate of return analysis is required to determine if the extra incremental investment in B generates sufficient incremental revenues to justify the additional $50 million cost at time zero and the additional $150 million cost at year one.

```
       C=50    C=150   I=60    I=60    I=60            I=60
B-A)   ─────────────────────────────────────────────────────      L=100
        0        1       2       3       4 ........ 8
```

B-A) PW Eq: $50 = -150(P/F_{i,1}) + 60(P/A_{i,7})(P/F_{i,1})$

$$+ 100(P/F_{i,8}), \quad i = ROR_{B-A} = 25\% > i^* = 20\%$$

so select B.

Note that once again, the project with biggest ROR on total investment is not the economic choice.

NPV Analysis

$$\overset{3.837}{\text{NPV}_A)\quad 60(P/A_{20,8})} - 150 = +\$80.2$$

$$\overset{3.605\qquad .8333\qquad\qquad\quad .2326\qquad\qquad\quad .8333}{\text{NPV}_B)\quad 120(P/A_{20,7})(P/F_{20,1}) + 100(P/F_{20,8})} - 90(P/F_{20,1}) - 200$$

$$= +\$108.5$$

Incremental analysis verifies the selection of the project with the largest total investment NPV which is "B".

$$\text{NPV}_{B-A})\quad \text{NPV}_A - \text{NPV}_B = 108.5 - 80.2 = +\$28.3 > 0,\ \text{so select B.}$$

Incremental analysis of mutually exclusive alternatives always leads to selection of the investment project with largest NPV on total investment. Often this is not the project with the largest ROR or PVR on total investment. However, incremental analysis gives the same economic conclusion with all techniques of analysis.

PVR Analysis

$$\text{PVR}_A = \frac{\text{NPV}_A}{\text{PW Cost}_A} = \frac{80.2}{150} = 0.53 > 0$$

$$\text{PVR}_B = \frac{\text{NPV}_B}{\text{PW Cost}_B} = \frac{108.5}{200 + 90(P/F_{20,1})} = 0.39 > 0$$

Which alternative is better, "A" or "B"? A is not necessarily preferred just because it has the largest ratio on total investment. As with ROR and NPV, incremental analysis must be made.

$$\text{PVR}_{B-A} = \frac{\text{NPV}_A - \text{NPV}_B}{\text{PW Cost}_A - \text{PW Cost}_B} = \frac{108.5 - 80.2}{150 + 50(P/F_{20,1})}$$

$$= 0.16 > 0,\ \text{so select B, consistent with the}\\ \text{ROR and NPV results.}$$

See the incremental time diagram for verification that the incremental costs are 50 in year 0 and 150 in year 1.

Benefit cost ratio analysis gives the same conclusions following the PVR analysis procedure. Remember that benefit cost ratio equals PVR plus one, and one is the breakeven ratio with benefit cost ratio analysis while zero is the breakeven ratio with PVR analysis.

4.3 Mutually Exclusive Investment Analysis Using Growth Rate of Return and Future Worth Profit Methods

It was mentioned in the summary of the Example 4-1 ROR analysis that Growth ROR analysis is applied to evaluate mutually exclusive alternatives in the same way regular ROR analysis is applied. This means calculating Growth ROR on both total investments and incremental investments to verify that both are greater than the minimum ROR, i*.

Looking at future worth profit for decision purposes is just a variation of the Growth ROR or Net Future Value evaluation techniques. *The objective of all investments from an economic viewpoint is to maximize the profit that can be accumulated at any specified future point in time from a given amount of starting capital.* Instead of using analysis methods such as ROR, Growth ROR, NPV, NAV, NFV or PVR to achieve that investment objective, another valid evaluation approach is to directly calculate the future worth profit (future value) that can be generated by investing a given amount of capital in different ways and assuming the profits can be reinvested at the minimum ROR, i*, when the profits are received. The investment choice that gives the maximum future worth profit is the same choice we would get using ROR, Growth ROR, NPV, NAV, NFV or PVR analyses. The following example illustrates the Growth ROR and future worth profit techniques.

EXAMPLE 4-4 Growth ROR and Future Worth Profit Analysis

Use Growth ROR analysis for a minimum rate of return of 15% to determine which of the following mutually exclusive alternatives, "A" or "B", is best. Verify the result with future worth profit analysis.

All Values in Thousands of Dollars, C = Cost, I = Income, L = Salvage

```
      C=200       I=80                        I=80
A)    ─────────────────────────────────────────────        L=200
      0           1 ........................ 8


      C=300       I=150   I=140   Declining Gradient
B)    ─────────────────────────────────────────────        L=0
      0           1       2 ................ 8
```

Solution:

Both Growth ROR and Future Worth Profit analysis, as well as NPV, NAV, NFV and regular ROR analysis assume that residual capital not invested in one of the projects and incomes as they are received can be invested elsewhere at the minimum ROR, which is $i^* = 15\%$ for this analysis. This gives the following Growth ROR and future worth income (profit) calculations:

Growth Rate of Return Analysis

Alternative A

```
     C=200        I=80                     I=80
A)   ─────────────────────────────────────────        L=200
     0            1  ..................... 8
```

Reinvest "I" and "L" at $i^* = 15\%$

```
                                          C=200
     C=80                                 C=80
     ─────────────────────────────────────────  F=1,298
     0            1  ..................... 8
```

where $F = 80(F/A_{15,8}) + 200 = +\$1,298$

A + Reinvestment of Income

```
     C=200
     ─────────────────────────────────────────  F=1,298
     0            1  ..................... 8
```

Growth ROR_A PW Eq: $200 = 1,298(P/F_{i,8})$

Growth ROR_A $i = 26.5\% > i^* = 15\%$, so satisfactory

Alternative B

```
     C=300        I=150    I=140 Declining Gradient
B)   ───────────────────────────────────────────      L=0
     0            1        2 ............. 8
```

Reinvest "I" at $i^* = 15\%$

```
                  C=150    C=140  Declining Gradient
                  ─────────────────────────────────  F=1,677
     0            1        2 ............. 8
```

where $F = \{150 - 10(A/G_{15,8})\}(F/A_{15,8}) = 1,677$

B + Reinvestment of Income

```
     C=300
     ───────────────────────────────────────────  F=1,677
     0            1        2 ............. 8
```

Growth ROR_B PW Eq: $300 = 1,677(P/F_{i,8})$

Growth ROR_B, $i = 24.1\% > i^* = 15\%$, so satisfactory

Incremental Growth ROR Analysis

$$
\begin{array}{c}
\text{C=100} \\
\overline{\rule{6cm}{0.4pt}} \quad \text{F=379}
\end{array}
$$

(B-A)

    0   1   2 8

Growth ROR_{B-A} PW Eq: $100 = 379(P/F_{i,8})$

Growth ROR_{B-A} = i = 18.4% > i^* = 15%, indicating select B

Project "B" does not have the largest Growth ROR on total investment but incremental analysis indicates that "B" is the economic choice.

Future Worth Profit Analysis

Future worth profit analysis uses the future worth profit calculations from the Growth ROR analyses. If $300 thousand is available to invest, putting $200 thousand of it into alternative "A" and reinvesting the profits at $i^* = 15\%$ will generate a future value of $1,298 thousand in 8 years. Investing elsewhere the $100 thousand of our $300 thousand that is not needed if we choose "A" gives:

$$
\begin{array}{c}
\text{C=100} \qquad\qquad - \qquad\qquad - \qquad\qquad 3.059 \\
\overline{\rule{6cm}{0.4pt}} \qquad F = 100(F/P_{15,8}) \\
\end{array}
$$

(B-A)

    0   1 8   = 305.9

Therefore, the total future value 8 years from now of $200 thousand invested in project "A" and $100 thousand elsewhere is $1,298 thousand plus $305 thousand or $1,603 thousand. This is not as great as the future worth of "B" calculated to be $1,677 thousand, so select "B". This is the same conclusion reached with Growth ROR analysis. The reader can verify that NPV_A = $224 thousand and NPV_B = $248 thousand, also indicating select "B" with NPV analysis.

Ordinary compound interest ROR analysis cannot be used on this problem and many similar problems because of difficulties encountered with the incremental ROR analysis. Evaluation of ordinary compound interest ROR on total investment shows that the rates of return on projects "A" and "B" are satisfactory. Incremental analysis gives the following time diagram:

$$
\begin{array}{c}
\text{C=100} \qquad \text{I=70} \qquad \text{I=60} \;\ldots\ldots\; \text{I=0} \\
\overline{\rule{6cm}{0.4pt}} \qquad\qquad \text{L=-200}
\end{array}
$$

(B-A)

    0   1   2 8

This time diagram has incremental cost followed by incremental income followed by negative incremental salvage value which is the same as incremental cost. This is the type of analysis situation that generates the dual ROR problem discussed later in this chapter. Regular ROR analysis cannot be used in this situation for reasons that will be given later. This is why it is important to be familiar with other techniques of analysis such as Growth ROR, Future Worth Profit, NPV, NAV, NFV or PVR.

4.4 Changing the Minimum Rate of Return with Time

The minimum rate of return represents the rate of return that we think we could get by investing our money elsewhere, both now and in the future for the period of time covered by the project evaluation life. There is little reason to expect that our other opportunities will remain uniformly the same over a long period of time. While other opportunities for the investment of capital now may be at i* = 10%, we may expect a major project with a projected 20% ROR to be developed starting three years from now which could absorb all of our available capital and raise i* to 20%. For analyses with minimum rates of return that change with time, NPV, NFV, PVR and Future Worth Profit analysis are recommended as the best and really the only usable analysis methods. Regular ROR and Growth ROR are not good if you do not have a single minimum ROR to which you can compare them. Similarly, you cannot calculate NAV with different minimum rate of return values at different points in time. For analysis simplification reasons, most investors, including major companies assume their minimum ROR is uniform and equal over project evaluation lives. However, changing the minimum rate of return is illustrated in the following example to demonstrate proper economic analysis techniques for this situation.

EXAMPLE 4-5 Multiple Minimum Rates of Return Illustrated

Compare mutually exclusive alternatives A and B if the minimum rate of return is considered to be 15% through the end of year 3 and 25% for years 4 through 10. Use NPV, NFV, PVR and FW Profit analysis. Then try to use regular ROR analysis.

Solution, All Values Are in Thousands of Dollars:

```
     C=20    I=10    I=10    I=10    I=10           I=10
A)   ─────────────────────────────────────────────────── L=20
     0       1       2       3       4  .........  10
         *
     ROR_A = 50% > i  = 15% or 25%, so satisfactory


     C=30    I=12    I=12    I=12    I=12           I=12
B)   ─────────────────────────────────────────────────── L=30
     0       1       2       3       4  .........  10
         *
     ROR_B = 40% > i  = 15% or 25%, so satisfactory
```

Incremental Rate of Return Analysis

Incremental ROR analysis is needed now to determine the optimum choice, since both "A" and "B" have satisfactory rates of return on total investment compared to either $i^* = 15\%$ or $i^* = 25\%$.

$$
\begin{array}{c}
\text{C=10 \quad I=2 \quad I=2 \quad I=2 \quad I=2 \qquad\qquad I=2} \\
\text{B-A)} \overline{\rule{0pt}{1em}\hspace{14em}} \text{L=10} \\
\text{0 \quad\quad 1 \quad\quad 2 \quad\quad 3 \quad\quad 4 \ldots\ldots\ldots\ 10}
\end{array}
$$

$$\text{ROR}_{B-A} = 20\% > i^* = 15\%, \text{ but } < i^* = 25\%$$

Is a 20% incremental ROR satisfactory? It is during the first 3 years when $i^* = 15\%$, but it is unsatisfactory during evaluation year 4 through 10 when $i^* = 25\%$. It seems evident that ROR analysis is not an adequate decision method in this situation.

Net Present Value Analysis

$$
\text{NPV}_A = 10(\overset{2.283}{P/A_{15,3}}) + 10(\overset{3.161}{P/A_{25,7}})(\overset{.6575}{P/F_{15,3}})
$$

$$
+ 20(\overset{.2097}{P/F_{25,7}})(\overset{.6575}{P/F_{15,3}}) - 20 = +\$26.37
$$

$$
\text{NPV}_B = 12(\overset{2.283}{P/A_{15,3}}) + 12(\overset{3.161}{P/A_{25,7}})(\overset{.6575}{P/F_{15,3}})
$$

$$
+ 30(\overset{.2097}{P/F_{25,7}})(\overset{.6575}{P/F_{15,3}}) - 30 = +\$26.47
$$

The NPV results indicate the two alternatives are a breakeven since the NPV results are equal for "A" and "B".

Present Value Ratio Analysis

$$\text{PVR}_A = 26.37 \ / \ 20 = 1.32 > 0, \text{ so satisfactory.}$$

$$\text{PVR}_B = 26.47 \ / \ 30 = 0.88 > 0, \text{ so satisfactory.}$$

$$\text{PVR}_{B-A} = 0.10 \ / \ 10 = 0.01, \text{ similar to zero, so a breakeven.}$$

Net Future Value Analysis

$$\text{NFV}_A = 10(F/A_{15,3})(F/P_{25,7}) + 10(F/A_{25,7}) + 20$$
$$\quad\quad\quad\;\; \overset{3.472}{}\;\;\overset{4.768}{}\quad\quad\quad\overset{15.073}{}$$

$$\;\;- 20(F/P_{15,3})(F/P_{25,7}) = +\$191.23$$
$$\quad\quad\;\; \overset{1.521}{}\;\;\overset{4.768}{}$$

$$\text{NFV}_B = 12(F/A_{15,3})(F/P_{25,7}) + 12(F/A_{25,7}) + 30$$
$$\quad\quad\quad\;\; \overset{3.472}{}\;\;\overset{4.768}{}\quad\quad\quad\overset{15.073}{}$$

$$\;\;- 30(F/P_{15,3})(F/P_{25,7}) = +\$191.97$$
$$\quad\quad\;\; \overset{1.521}{}\;\;\overset{4.768}{}$$

The NFV results also indicate the alternatives are economically a breakeven.

Future Worth Profit Analysis of the Same Initial Investment of 30 Thousand Dollars

$$\text{FW}_A = 10(F/A_{15,3})(F/P_{25,7}) + 10(F/A_{25,7}) + 20$$
$$\quad\quad\quad\;\; \overset{3.472}{}\;\;\overset{4.768}{}\quad\quad\quad\overset{15.073}{}$$

$$\quad\quad + 10(F/P_{15,3})(F/P_{25,7}) = +\$408.8$$

$$\text{FW}_B = 12(F/A_{15,3})(F/P_{25,7}) + 12(F/A_{25,7}) + 30$$
$$\quad\quad\quad\;\; \overset{3.472}{}\;\;\overset{4.768}{}\quad\quad\quad\overset{15.073}{}$$

$$\quad\quad = +\$409.5$$

The Future Worth Profit results which are effectively equal also indicate that the alternatives are economically a breakeven. The following example illustrates how changing the minimum rate of return can change evaluation results.

EXAMPLE 4-6 Illustration of Minimum ROR Significance to Investment Decisions

Improvement and expansion of a production facility are under consideration. At the present time profits are $450,000 per year, and in the future escalation of operating costs each year is expected to exactly offset escalation of revenue, so profit margins are projected to remain constant at $450,000 per year for each of the years 1 through 10. Two alternatives for improvement and improvement combined with expansion are being considered with projected costs and revenues as shown on the time diagrams following this problem statement, with all dollar values expressed in thousands of dollars.

```
       -          I=450        I=450                    I=450
A) ────────────────────────────────────────────────────────  L=0
       0            1            2  . . . . . . . . . . . . . 10


    C=800          I=700        I=700                    I=700
B) ────────────────────────────────────────────────────────  L=0
       0            1            2  . . . . . . . . . . . . . 10

                   I=850
    C=1,300        C=900        I=1,050                  I=1,050
C) ────────────────────────────────────────────────────────  L=0
       0            1            2  . . . . . . . . . . . . . 10
```

For a minimum rate of return of 15%, and considering the alternatives to be mutually exclusive, determine whether the present "A", improvement "B", or improvement plus expansion project "C" is economically best using ROR, NPV and PVR. Then increase the minimum ROR to 25% from 15% over the entire 10 year evaluation life and re-evaluate the alternatives using both ROR and NPV analysis. Then assume that the minimum ROR is increased from 15% to 25% for evaluation years one and two and then, starting in year three, the minimum ROR reverts to 15% again through year 10.

Solution, All Values in Thousands of Dollars:

```
      C=800         I=250        I=250                   I=250
B-A) ────────────────────────────────────────────────────────  L=0
       0             1            2  . . . . . . . . . . . . . 10

      C=500         C=750        I=350                   I=350
C-B) ────────────────────────────────────────────────────────  L=0
       0             1            2  . . . . . . . . . . . . . 10
```

Rate of Return Analysis

ROR_A $0 = 450(P/A_{i,10})$ $i = \infty$ $> i^* = 15\%$

ROR_B $800 = 700(P/A_{i,10})$ $i = 87.34\% > i^* = 15\%$

ROR_C $1,300 = 1,050(P/A_{i,9})(P/F_{i,1}) - 50(P/F_{i,1})$

          $i = 50.9\% > i^* = 15\%$

ROR_{B-A} $800 = 250(P/A_{i,10})$

          $i = 28.8\% > 15\%$, Accept B over A

ROR_{C-B} $500 = \{350(P/A_{i,9}) - 750\}(P/F_{i,1})$

          $i = 21.25\% > i^* = 15\%$, Accept C over B

Selecting alternative "C" is the economic choice.

Net Present Value Analysis

NPV_A $450(P/A_{15,10}) = +2,259$

NPV_B $700(P/A_{15,10}) - 800 = +2,713$

NPV_C $1,050(P/A_{15,9})(P/F_{15,1}) - 50(P/F_{15,1}) - 1,300$

$= +3,013$, Maximum, so select C.

Alternative "C" is the economic choice. Since NPV_{C-B} and NPV_{C-A} are positive, "C" with maximum NPV is the economic choice. The mutually exclusive alternative with maximum NPV on total investment always turns out to be the economic choice from incremental NPV analysis.

Present Value Ratio

PVR_A $2,259 / 0 = \infty > 0$

PVR_B $2,713 / 800 = 3.39 > 0$

PVR_C $3,013 / \{50(P/F_{15,1}) + 1,300\} = 2.24 > 0$

PVR_{B-A} $(2,713-2,259) / 800 = 0.57 > 0$, select B over A

PVR_{C-B} $(3,013-2,713) / 500 + 750(P/F_{15,1}) = .26 > 0$

Choose "C" over "B"

Alternative "C" is the economic choice. ROR, NPV and PVR analyses all agree that "Improve and Expand", "C" is the economic choice for $i^* = 15\%$.

Change the Minimum Rate of Return from 15 Percent to 25 Percent.

ROR_{C-B} $500 = \{350(P/A_{i,9}) - 750\}(P/F_{i,1})$

$i = 21.25\% < i^* = 25\%$, Accept B over C

NPV_A $450(P/A_{25,10}) = 1,607.0$

NPV_B $700(P/A_{25,10}) - 800 = 1,699.7$ Maximum, so select B.

NPV_C $1,050(P/A_{25,9})(P/F_{25,1}) - 50(P/F_{25,1}) - 1,300$

$= 1,568.9$

Increasing the minimum ROR to 25% from 15% changes the economic choice to selecting "B" with both ROR and NPV analysis. PVR would select "B" also.

Change the Minimum Rate of Return to 25 Percent for the Next Two Years, Then Back to 15 Percent for the Next Eight Years.

With ROR analysis, we can't tell if ROR_{C-B} = 21.25% is satisfactory or not. Therefore, we have to go to another evaluation technique such as net present value.

NPV_A $450(P/A_{15,8})(P/F_{25,2})$ + $450(P/A_{25,2})$ = +1,940

NPV_B $700(P/A_{15,8})(P/F_{25,2})$ + $700(P/A_{25,2})$ - 800 = +2,218

NPV_C $1,050(P/A_{15,8})(P/F_{25,2})$ + $1,050(P/F_{25,2})$ - $50(P/F_{25,1})$

- 1,300 = +2,347   Maximum, so select C.

Changing the minimum ROR with time gives the economic choice of selecting project "C". This is not the same result achieved by changing the minimum ROR to 25% over the entire evaluation life. The minimum ROR is a very significant evaluation parameter and must represent other opportunities for investing capital both now and in the future over the evaluation life of projects. If the minimum ROR is projected to change with time, that change must be built into evaluation calculations as illustrated to achieve valid economic analysis results.

4.5 Differences Between Net Value Analysis and Cost Analysis

There is a tendency for people to get confused concerning the difference between Present Worth (PW), Annual Worth (AW), or Future Worth (FW) cost analysis and Net Present Value (NPV), Net Annual Value (NAV) and Net Future Value (NFV) analysis. They are similar but very different, because *with cost analysis, you are looking for the alternative way of providing a service for the minimum present, annual or future cost, while with net value analysis you are looking for the alternative with the maximum net value. This relationship exists because, in cost analysis calculations, costs have a postitive sign and any revenues such as salvage value are given a negative sign. This leads to selection of the alternative providing a service at the minimum cost. With net value analysis, the opposite sign convention from cost analysis is used so revenues are positive and costs are negative. This net value sign convention makes us want to select the project with the maximum net value.*

To utilize cost analysis in the evaluation of service producing alternatives, you work with the given or estimated costs for each individual alternative way of providing a service. To utilize net value analysis in service evaluations, you must work with incremental savings that incremental costs will generate. Net value analysis is just a short-cut form of rate of return analysis. For net value or rate of return analyses, you must look at the incremental differences between alternative ways of providing a service. The following example illustrates these techniques.

EXAMPLE 4-7 Cost and Net Value Analysis Compared

A natural gas distribution company is evaluating the economic desirability of replacing or repairing existing gas mains in a small town. At the present time with the existing gas mains it is estimated that 100,000 Mcf (thousand cubic feet) of gas is being lost per year and that this gas could be sold to corporate customers at $1.50 per Mcf. The cost of replacing the gas mains is estimated to be $1,000,000. Replacement of the mains would effectively eliminate all gas loss for the next 10 years. The cost of repairing the gas mains is estimated to be $400,000 which would reduce annual gas loss to 25,000 Mcf in year 1, with gas loss increasing by a constant gradient of 6,000 Mcf per year in years following year 1. Use annual cost analysis for a 10 year evaluation life and $i^* = 15\%$ to determine from an economic viewpoint if the gas mains should be replaced, repaired or left in the present condition. Verify cost analysis results with NAV.

Solution, All Values in Thousands of Dollars:

Cost Analysis

Let costs be positive and look for minimum cost alternative:

```
                -      OC=150    OC=150                   OC=150
Present    ─────────────────────────────────────────────────── L=0
                0       1         2 ....................  10
```

$$AC_{Present} = 150$$

```
           C=1,000      -          -                         -
Replace    ─────────────────────────────────────────────────── L=0
                0       1          2 ....................  10
```

$$AC_{Replace} = 1,000 \overset{.19925}{(A/P_{15,10})} = 199.25$$

```
           C=400    OC=37.5    OC=46.5 ...... gradient ......
Repair     ─────────────────────────────────────────────────── L=0
                0       1          2 ....................  10
```

$$AC_{Repair} = 400 \overset{.19925}{(A/P_{15,10})} + \{37.5 + 9 \overset{3.383}{(A/G_{15,10})}\} = 147.65$$

Very slight economic advantage to repair over present to minimize cost.

Net Annual Value (NAV) Analysis

Let incremental savings and salvage be positive so costs are negative, look for maximum net value alternative.

For net value analysis, we need to evaluate the differences between 1) replace and present and 2) repair and the present, to determine savings generated by the relative incremental costs.

I = incremental savings in cost.

```
Replace    C=1,000      I=150     I=150                    I=150
-Present: ────────────────────────────────────────────────────── L=0
            0            1         2    ...............     10
```

$$NAV = 150 - 1,000(A/P_{15,10}^{.19925}) = -49.25 < 0, \text{ reject since negative}$$

```
           C=400      I=112.5   I=103.5   ..... gradient .....
Repair    ────────────────────────────────────────────────────── L=0
-Present:  0            1         2    .....................  10
```

$$NAV = \{112.5 - 9(A/G_{15,10}^{3.383})\} - 400(A/P_{15,10}^{.19925}) = +2.35$$

The largest and only positive incremental NAV is for repairing so select it. This is the same economic conclusion obtained with annual cost analysis.

4.6 Effect of Evaluation Life on Economic Analysis Results

It was illustrated in Chapter 3 Example 3-21 that project life has little effect on analysis results when you get beyond 10 or 15 years, depending on the profitability of the projects being evaluated. However, for shorter life projects with evaluation lives under 10 years, the evaluation life used can affect the economic choice significantly. For example, sometimes the life over which we choose to evaluate a process improvement is very arbitrarily chosen due to the uncertainty associated with projecting savings in certain process analyses. The following illustration shows how evaluation life can affect economic results in this relatively short evaluation life situation.

EXAMPLE 4-8 Effect of Evaluation Life on Comparison of Two Alternatives.

Evaluate two different levels of improvement being considered for an existing process. The new equipment costs and projected annual savings in labor and materials are as follows:

	Equipment Cost	Projected Annual Savings
Level 1	$200,000	$125,000
Level 2	$350,000	$180,000

For a minimum ROR of 20% evaluate Levels 1 and 2 using NPV analysis assuming zero salvage value for (A) a 3 year evaluation life, and (B) a 5 year evaluation life. (C) For what evaluation life would there be no economic differences between the alternatives?

Solution, All Values in Thousands of Dollars:

A) 3 Year Life

$$NPV_1 = 125(\overset{2.106}{P/A_{20,3}}) - 200 = +63.25 \qquad \text{Select Maximum NPV}$$

$$NPV_2 = 180(\overset{2.106}{P/A_{20,3}}) - 350 = +29.08$$

B) 5 Year Life

$$NPV_1 = 125(\overset{2.991}{P/A_{20,5}}) - 200 = +173.88$$

$$NPV_2 = 180(\overset{2.991}{P/A_{20,5}}) - 350 = +188.38 \qquad \text{Select Maximum NPV}$$

C) Breakeven Life "n"

When there are no economic differences between the alternatives, NPV_1 will equal NPV_2. If we write an equation setting $NPV_1 = NPV_2$ for an unknown life "n", we can solve for the breakeven life "n".

$$125(P/A_{20,n}) - 200 = 180(P/A_{20,n}) - 350$$

$$\text{or,} \quad 150 = 55(P/A_{20,n})$$

$$(P/A_{20,n}) = 150/55 = 2.727$$

By interpolation in the $P/A_{i,n}$ factor column of the 20% tables we get n = 4.34 years. Select Level 2 for an evaluation life greater than 4.34 years. Select Level 1 for an evaluation life less than 4.34 years.

4.7 Investment Analysis When Income or Savings Precedes Costs

When income or savings precedes cost, ROR analysis leads to the calculation of "i" values that have rate of reinvestment requirement meaning instead of rate of return meaning. These results must be used very differently than ROR results since "rate of reinvestment requirement" results greater than the minimum ROR are unsatisfactory (instead of satisfactory with regular ROR). This is illustrated in Example 4-9.

EXAMPLE 4-9 Analysis of Mutually Exclusive Alternatives When Income Precedes Cost

Evaluate the following two mutually exclusive alternatives using ROR, Growth ROR, Future Worth Profit, NPV and PVR. The minimum rate of return $i^* = 10\%$.

```
    C=$100,000        -       -              -
A) ───────────────────────────────────────────   L=$305,200
    0             1    .................  5
```

```
    C=$100,000  I=$41,060        I=$41,060
B) ───────────────────────────────────────   L=$0
    0           1    .................  5
```

Rate of Return Analysis

A)   PW Eq: $100,000 = 305,200(P/F_{i,5})$ $i = ROR_A = 25\%$

B)   PW Eq: $100,000 = 41,060(P/A_{i,5})$ $i = ROR_B = 30\%$

Since the initial costs of projects "A" and "B" are equal, at this point, many people conclude there are no incremental differences in the projects, so "B" is the choice since "B" has the larger ROR on total investment. This is incorrect! Looking at "A-B" so incremental cost is followed by incremental revenue we get the following: (remember negative incremental income is equivalent to cost)

```
       C=0       C=$41,060            C=$41,060
A-B) ─────────────────────────────────────────────  L=$305,200
       0         1    .................  5
```

A-B) AW Eq: $41,060 = 305,200(A/F_{i,5})$

$i = ROR_{A-B} = 20\% > i^* = 10\%$, so Accept A.

Even though project "B" has the largest ROR on total investment, project "A" is the economic choice from incremental analysis. Differences in the distribution of revenues to be realized cause incremental differences in the projects that must be analyzed.

The year 1 through 5 incremental costs of $41,060 per year are referred to as "opportunity costs" by many people since they result from the following rational. Selecting project "A" causes the investor to forgo realizing the project "B" revenues each year. Revenues or savings foregone are lost opportunities or "opportunity costs", so selecting "A" causes opportunity costs of $41,060 in each of years 1-5.

If you look at "B – A", you get incremental income followed by incremental cost so the following rational applies:

```
         C=0        I=$41,060            I=$41,060
B-A)     ─────────────────────────────────────────      C=$305,200
         0              1  ................  5
```

$$B\text{-}A) \quad AW \; Eq: \quad 41,060 = 305,200(A/F_{i,5})$$

$i = 20\%$ (This "i" value does not have ROR meaning. See the following discussion.)

The incremental numbers and trial and error "i" value which are obtained, are the same for A-B. However, note that *on the "B – A" time diagram incremental income is followed by cost. It is physically impossible to calculate rate of return when income is followed by cost. You must have money invested (cost) followed by revenue or savings to calculate rate of return. When income is followed by cost you calculate an "i" value that has "rate of reinvestment requirement" meaning.* The "B – A" incremental "i" value of 20 percent means the investor would be required to reinvest the year one through five incremental incomes at 20 percent to accrue enough money to cover the year 5 cost of $305,200. If the minimum ROR of 10 percent represents investment and reinvestment opportunities thought to exist over the project life, as it should, then a reinvestment requirement of 20 percent is unsatisfactory compared to reinvestment opportunities of 10 percent, so reject "B" and select "A". This is the same conclusion that the "A – B" ROR analysis gave.

Future Worth Profit Analysis from $100,000 Initial Investment

A)   FW Profit = $305,200

$$B) \quad FW \; Profit = \$41,060(F/A_{10,5}^{6.105}) = \$250,671$$

Select Project "A" to maximize future profit.

Since the $100,000 initial investment is the same for both "A" and "B", maximum future profit (value) on total investment is desired.

Growth Rate of Return Analysis

A)   Growth ROR_A is equal to the regular ROR_A, = 25%

B)   Growth ROR_B PW Eq: $100,000 = 250,671(P/F_{i,5})$

$$i = 20.2\%$$

Since the same $100,000 initial investment is involved with both "A" and "B", we want the alternative with the largest Growth ROR, "A". Incremental analysis gives the same conclusion.

A-B)   AW Eq: $0 = 54,529(P/F_{i,5})$ i = Growth ROR_{A-B} = $\infty\%$

Therefore, select "A" since the incremental "A – B" Growth ROR exceeds 10%.

Net Present Value (NPV) Analysis

$$NPV_A = 305,200(P/F_{10,5}^{.6209}) - 100,000 = +\$89,500 \quad \begin{array}{l}\text{Select A}\\ \text{With Max NPV}\end{array}$$

$$NPV_B = 41,060(P/A_{10,5}^{3.791}) - 100,000 = +\$55,700$$

NPV_{A-B} = 89,500 – 55,700 = $33,800 Therefore, Select "A", consistent with selecting the project with the largest NPV.

Present Value Ratio (PVR) Analysis

PVR_A = 89,500 / 100,000 = .895 > 0, acceptable

PVR_B = 55,700 / 100,000 = .557 > 0, acceptable

$$PVR_{A-B} = (89,500 - 55,700) / 41,060(P/A_{10,5}^{3.791})$$

$$= 33,800 / 155,658 = .217 > 0, \text{ so select A.}$$

When each of these evaluation methods is properly applied you consistently come to the same economic conclusion. You only need to utilize one method to make a proper evaluation. Here, as in other examples throughout this text, multiple criteria solutions are presented to illustrate the consistent results obtained with any of the evaluation methods. Proper incremental analysis is the key to the evaluation of mutually exclusive alternatives where only one alternative may be selected.

Summarizing several important considerations about the ROR analysis for this problem, for the incremental ROR analysis of alternatives "A" and "B"

we discussed the need to subtract alternative "B" from alternative "A" so that
we had incremental costs followed by incremental revenues. Then we discussed what happens if you incorrectly subtract alternative "A" from "B".

```
       C=$0        I=$41,060              I=$41,060
B-A)   ─────────────────────────────────────────────   C=$305,200
       0            1    .................   5
```

Incremental "B–A" incomes of $41,060 each year precede the $305,200
incremental "B–A" cost at the end of year 5. When income precedes cost,
the "i" that we calculate is the interest rate that must be obtained through
the reinvestment of the income each period, for the final value of the cumulative incomes and compound interest to equal the cost at that time. A required
reinvestment rate greater than the minimum ROR is unsatisfactory, whereas
an ROR greater than the minimum ROR is satisfactory. Figure 4-1 shows
the cumulative cash position diagram for this situation. Note that the cumulative cash position in this example is positive during the entire project life.
Whenever the cumulative cash position is positive, no investment is involved
and the interest rate "i" means the rate at which money must be reinvested
and not the rate of return on investment.

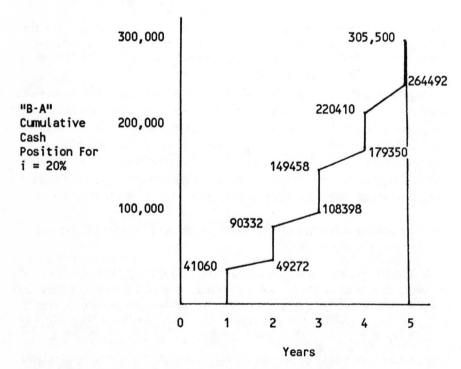

Figure 4-1 Cumulative Cash Position for Income Preceding Cost

Given that the minimum ROR is 10%, do we accept alternative "A" or "B" for the example just discussed? As previously mentioned, if investment preceded income, we would accept alternative "A" because an incremental 20% ROR is better than investing elsewhere at a 10% ROR. However, if "B – A" incremental income precedes cost, we would be rejecting project "B", because the "B – A" rate of reinvestment required at 20% exceeds the other opportunities we have to invest capital which is assumed to be 10%.

EXAMPLE 4-10 ROR Analysis When Income Precedes Costs

Should you borrow $4,000 for a 3 year car loan if your payments will be $1,752 at the end of each year and your alternative choice is to cash in a $4,000 bond investment earning a 12% annual ROR?

Solution:

$$\begin{array}{llll} I=\$4,000 & C=\$1,752 & C=\$1,752 & C=\$1,752 \\ \hline 0 & 1 & 2 & 3 \end{array}$$

PW Eq: $4,000 = 1,752(P/A_{i,3})$, $i = 15\%$

This "i" of 15% is the borrowed money interest rate which represents the required rate of reinvestment. Therefore, cash in the $4,000 bond investment. It would not pay to borrow money at 15% to maintain a 12% investment.

Once again note that the "i" calculated when investment precedes income has completely different meaning than when income precedes investment. Difficulty arises if these two types of projects are mixed in incremental analysis because the interest "i" has two different meanings in the same equation. Techniques for analyzing this type of investment project situation are presented in the following section. It will be shown that the cumulative cash position diagram is a useful tool in the evaluation of this type of problem.

4.8 Alternating Investment, Income, Investment: The Dual Rate of Return Situation

In the last section it was illustrated that when income precedes cost, the "i" value that is calculated if we try to make rate of return analysis is the revenue rate of reinvestment required, not the investment rate of return. When an investment analysis situation yields a time diagram with alternating investment, income, investment, then you have income both following investment and preceding investment. In this situation, the "i" that is calculated from a present worth equation has a combination rate of return, rate of reinvestment meaning at different points in time. This will be shown for several examples using the cumulative cash position diagram. In this investment, income, investment analysis situation it is best to either use analysis methods other than rate of return or to use a modified rate of return analysis.

Alternating investment, income, investment analysis situations occur in a variety of situations. The most common, which is illustrated in the next example, occurs from looking at incremental differences between unequal life alternatives where the bigger investment alternative has bigger period revenues and shorter project life. This is the classical acceleration problem common to mineral and petroleum development type projects where a given mineral or petroleum reserve can be depleted more rapidly by making a bigger initial investment. This evaluation situation also commonly occurs with acceleration type investments in many different types of general industry situations. Other examples of cost, income, cost include 1) An investment in a building or project that generates income for several years after which the building or project must be razed or restored to different condition, 2) Strip mining investments that generate income followed by significant reclamation costs, 3) Forest planting investments followed by clear-cutting which generates income but must be followed by forest replanting costs where environmental laws or company policy require it, 4) Offshore platform development for petroleum production that must be followed by significant platform reclamation costs.

EXAMPLE 4-11 Analysis of Mutually Exclusive Unequal Life Acceleration Type Projects

Investments A and B with costs and revenues shown on the time diagram are mutually exclusive ways of developing a project. Which is best if the minimum ROR, $i^* = 20\%$? Use ROR, NPV, NAV, NFV, Growth ROR and Present Worth Cost Modified ROR analysis.

Solution, All Values in Thousands of Dollars:

I = Revenue, L = Salvage Value, C = Cost

```
     C=182         I=100         I=100         I=100
A)   ─────────────────────────────────────────────        L=0
     0             1             2             3

     C=250         I=184         I=184
B)   ───────────────────────────────────    L=0
     0             1             2
```

Get equal life alternatives by assuming the life of "B" is 3 years with net revenue and cost of zero at year 3.

Rate of Return Analysis, (ROR)

By trial and error the ROR_A = 30% and ROR_B = 30% both of which exceed the 20% minimum rate of return required for the investment of capital. The investments and project lives are unequal so it is difficult to tell intuitively if "A" or "B" is best for i^* = 20%. Projects with equal total investment rates of return are not necessarily economically equivalent. Incremental analysis gives:

```
         C=68          I=84          I=84          C=100
B-A) ─────────────────────────────────────────────────────  L=0
         0             1             2             3
```

ROR PW Eq: $68 + 100(P/F_{i,3}) = 84(P/A_{i,2})$

or, in NPV format: $84(P/A_{i,2}) - 100(P/F_{i,3}) - 68 = 0$

i = 0%   84(2.000) - 100(1.0000) - 68 = 0
i = 10%   84(1.736) - 100(0.7513) - 68 = +2.69
i = 20%   84(1.528) - 100(0.5787) - 68 = +2.48
i = 30%   84(1.361) - 100(0.4552) - 68 = +0.80
i = 40%   84(1.224) - 100(0.3644) - 68 = -1.62

i=0% and i=33.3% are dual rates of return by trial and error.

However, *the term "dual rates of return" is really a misnomer because neither "i" value means rate of return. Both "i" values have a combination rate of return, rate of reinvestment meaning as the following cumulative cash position diagram shows.* Note that a 0% rate of return is bad compared to i^* = 20% whereas a reinvestment rate of 0% is good compared to 20% reinvestment opportunities. Similarly, a 33% rate of return is good but a 33% rate of reinvestment requirement is bad. Both dual ROR values are good part of the time and bad part of the time.

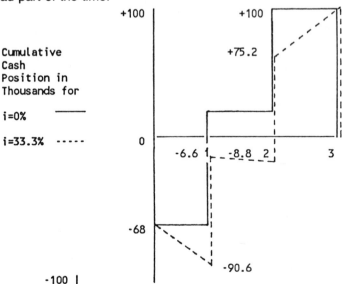

Whenever you are in a negative cumulative cash position, the meaning of "i" is rate of return. Whenever you are in a positive cumulative cash position, the meaning of "i" is rate of reinvestment. It is evident from the cumulative cash position diagram that the dual rates of return have combination rate of return, rate of reinvestment meaning at different points in time which indicates we should use an analysis method other than ROR or use a modified ROR analysis technique that eliminates cost following revenue and the associated rate of reinvestment requirement meaning of "i" values that satisfy a cost, income, cost present worth equation. The net value techniques are valid alternative analysis techniques that avoid the "dual ROR" problem.

Net Present Value Analysis, (NPV)

For $i^* = 20\%$, time zero is a common time for all projects.

$$NPV_A = 100(\overset{2.106}{P/A_{20,3}}) - 182 = +28.6$$

$$NPV_B = 184(\overset{1.528}{P/A_{20,2}}) - 250 = +31.1 \qquad \text{Select B, Largest NPV}$$

Net Annual Value Analysis, (NAV)

Use a common evaluation life of 3 years for NAV and NFV.

$$NAV_A = 100 - 182(\overset{0.47473}{A/P_{20,3}}) = +13.6$$

$$NAV_B = \{184(\overset{1.528}{P/A_{20,2}})-250\}(\overset{0.47473}{A/P_{20,3}}) = +14.8 \qquad \text{Select B}$$

Net Future Value Analysis, (NFV)

$$NFV_A = 100(\overset{3.812}{F/A_{20,3}}) - 182(\overset{1.728}{F/P_{20,3}}) = +49.5$$

$$NFV_B = 184(\overset{2.200}{F/A_{20,2}})(\overset{1.200}{F/P_{20,1}}) - 250(\overset{1.728}{F/P_{20,3}}) = +53.8$$

Select B, Largest NFV

If you want or need to make valid ROR analysis of cost, income, cost situations, the following are two valid modified ROR analysis techniques.

Growth Rate of Return Analysis

There is no need to calculate growth ROR for the "A" and "B" total investments. We already know "A" and "B" are satisfactory from total investment ROR analysis, so we only need to apply growth ROR analysis to the incremental investments. Note that the growth ROR reinvestment step eliminates the alternating investment, income, investment situation and gets us back to incremental investment followed by incremental revenue, the ROR analysis situtation.

```
         C=68          I=84          I=84          C=100
B-A)    ─────────────────────────────────────────────       L=0
         0             1             2             3
```

Reinvesting incremental year 1 and 2 incomes at $i^* = 20\%$:

```
         -             C=84          C=84          -
        ─────────────────────────────────────────────      F = +221.8
         0             1             2             3
```

$$\text{where} \quad F = 84(F/A_{20,2})(F/P_{20,1}) = +221.8$$

with the factors 2.200 and 1.200 shown above.

B-A + Reinvesting incremental income:

```
         C=68          -             -             -
B-A)    ─────────────────────────────────────────────      F = +121.8
         0             1             2             3
```

PW Eq: $68 = 121.8(P/F_{i,3})$, i=Growth ROR_{B-A}=21.4% > 20% Select B

Present Worth Cost Modified Rate of Return Analysis

Another modification for ROR analysis that many individuals and companies use to eliminate the alternating investment, income, investment situation is a present worth modification of the final cost. By present worthing the final cost at the minimum ROR, you convert the problem to a regular cost followed by income type of evaluation. Working with the incremental "B – A" diagram, present worth the final year 3 cost of $100 thousand at i* = 20%, giving the following modified time diagram:

```
                   .5787
         C=68+100(P/F_{20,3})    I=84          I=84          -
B-A)    ─────────────────────────────────────────────
         0                       1             2             3
```

Modified PW Eq: $125.87 = 84(P/A_{i,2})$, i = 21.6% > 20%, Select B

All of the analysis methods utilized for this example, other than regular ROR, have selected alternative "B" consistently. Any of these techniques can and should be used in place of regular rate or return analysis when the investment, income, investment type of analysis is encountered. The combination rate of return, rate of reinvestment meaning associated with cost, income, cost dual rates of return is what makes the dual ROR results useless for valid economic decisions. The existence of dual rates is algebraically caused by the sign changes in cost, income, cost equations. This can be illustrated for incremental "B – A" analysis in this example.

C=68	I=84	I=84	C=100
B-A)			
0	1	2	3

PW Eq: $0 = -68 + 84(P/F_{i,1}) + 84(P/F_{i,2}) - 100(P/F_{i,3})$

Mathematically:

$0 = -68 + 84(1/(1+i)) + 84(1/(1+i))^2 - 100(1/(1+i))^3$

Substitute $X = (1/(1+i))$:

$0 = -68 + 84X + 84X^2 - 100X^3$

This is a third order polynomial equation as a function of X. Algebraic rules indicate that polynomial equations may have as many roots as sign changes, two in this case. Solving for X; X = 1, and X = 3/4 gives i = 0% and i = 33.3%. These are the same dual ROR results obtained earlier by trial and error.

EXAMPLE 4-12 Reclamation Costs Can Cause the Dual ROR Problem

An investment project requires the initial investment of $70,000 to generate a projected stream of positive $40,000 per year cash flows in each of years one through five. However, a reclamation cost of $140,000 is expected to be required at year 6. (The year 6 reclamation cost could relate to restoration of surface land to original contours for an open pit mining operation, reclamation of an offshore platform for an offshore petroleum production project, or reclamation costs for land cleanup from chemical contamination to name several possibilities.) The minimum ROR is 20%. Analyze the economic potential of this project using both NPV and ROR analysis. When cost follows revenue, correct ROR analysis requires use of one of the modified ROR analysis techniques introduced in Example 4-11 (growth ROR, or present worth cost modified ROR analysis).

Solution, All Values in Thousands of Dollars:

C=70	I=40	I=40	I=40	I=40	I=40	C=140
0	1	2	3	4	5	6

ROR Analysis Using an NPV Type of Equation

PW Eq: $40(P/A_{i,5}) - 140(P/F_{i,6}) - 70 = 0$

i =   0%   40(5.000)   - 140(1.0000) - 70 =   -10.0

i =   5%   40(4.329)   - 140(0.7462) - 70 =   -1.3

i =   8%   40(3.993)   - 140(0.6302) - 70 =   +1.5

i = 15%   40(3.352)   - 140(0.4323) - 70 =   +3.6

i = 20%   40(2.991)   - 140(0.3349) - 70 =   +2.7

i = 25%   40(2.689)   - 140(0.2621) - 70 =   +0.9

i = 30%   40(2.436)   - 140(0.2072) - 70 =   -1.6

Note that due to the parabolic variation of the NPV type equation results versus "i", by interpolation, NPV = 0 for the dual rates of return of 6.40% and 26.78%. Each of these rates makes the cumulative cash position zero at the end of project life. Both rates involve a combination meaning of rate of return on investment in early project life and rate of reinvestment rate in the later project years. These dual rates cannot be used directly for decision making purposes as ROR results. However, the dual rates do provide some useful information because they bracket the range of minimum rate of return values for which project net present value is positive. This tells the range of i* for which the project is satisfactory. Whenever dual rates exist, it is easiest to rely on NPV analysis for decision purposes. However, going to growth ROR analysis or present worth cost modified ROR analysis is equally valid but generally more work. NPV calculated at i* always leads to the correct economic decision in this situation, whereas the dual rates problem makes ROR analysis more confusing.

$$\text{NPV @ } i^*_{=20\%} = 40(P/A_{20,5})^{2.991} - 140(P/F_{20,6})^{.3349} - 70 = +2.754 > 0$$

The NPV analysis is quick and simple to make and the positive NPV result tells us the project investment is satisfactory.

Now before getting into the details of the modified ROR analysis, note that NPV at i = 0% is negative for this example, which has dual positive rate values of 6.4% and 26.78%. Whenever the NPV at i = 0% is negative for an investment, income, investment situation, due to the parabolic variation of NPV with changes in "i", dual positive "i" values exist if any real interest rate solutions exist for the NPV equation. If NPV at i = 0% is positive, dual rate values exist with one being negative and the other positive. This test of NPV at i = 0% tells an investor where to look for the dual rates if it is deemed desirable to determine them.

Before presenting the modified ROR analysis calculations, note that in calculating the dual rates at the beginning of this solution, as "i" increased from 0 to 15%, NPV increases rather than decreases. This is a unique result of cost following revenue in the cost, income, cost analysis situation. Whenever you find NPV increasing with increasing interest rates (rather than decreasing as it always does for cost, income analyses, it is the authors experience that this generally is caused by cost following revenue in the analysis.

Two modified ROR analysis techniques exist for making valid ROR analysis of investment, income, investment time diagram situations. Both techniques eliminate cost following income, which is necessary for valid ROR analysis. The techniques are called Present Worth Cost Modified ROR and Growth ROR in this text and are applicable to analysis of this example situation as follows:

Present Worth Cost Modified ROR

To eliminate this investment, income, investment situation, present worth the final cost or costs at the minimum ROR to an equivalent present value, giving the following diagram:

$$C = 70 + 140 \overset{.3349}{(P/F_{20,6})} \qquad I=40 \qquad\qquad I=40 \qquad -$$

$$0 \qquad\qquad\qquad 1 \ldots\ldots\ldots\ldots 5 \qquad 6$$

Modified ROR PW Eq: $116.88 = 40(P/A_{i,5})$

Modified ROR $= i = 21.1\% > 20\%$, so satisfactory. Since this modified ROR result is based solely on income following cost, it is valid for economic decision-making purposes as a rate of return result. Discounting the year 6 cost modifies the magnitude of our ROR result but not its validity for comparison to $i^* = 20\%$ for the economic decision.

Growth ROR

Combine reinvestment of revenue at i^* with the initial project to eliminate cost following revenue as follows:

Initial Project

$$C=70 \qquad I=40 \qquad\qquad\qquad I=40 \qquad C=140$$

$$0 \qquad\quad 1 \ldots\ldots\ldots\ldots\ldots 5 \qquad\quad 6$$

Reinvest Revenues @ $i^* = 20\%$

```
    C=40              C=40           -
_____    F = 357.2
0       1 ................. 5        6
```

$$\text{where, } F = 40(F/A_{20,5})(F/P_{20,1}) = 357.2$$

with 7.442 and 1.200 shown above the factors.

Combine Initial Reinvestment Revenues

```
 C=70              -            -        C=140
_____    F = 357.2
  0      1 ................. 5           6
```

Growth ROR PW Eq: $70 = 217.2(P/F_{i,6})$

Growth ROR = $i = 20.9\% > 20\%$, so satisfactory.

Both the present worth cost modified ROR analysis and growth ROR analysis have given the same economic conclusion, which is in this case and in general, always consistent with NPV analysis economic conclusions. The key to correct ROR analysis of cost, income, cost analysis situations is to modify the analysis to eliminate cost following revenue before making the ROR analysis. The present worth cost and growth ROR modifications are the two basic approaches used to eliminate cost following revenues. However, there are several variations in the way different people apply these modifications. One in particular is worth noting.

In applying the present worth cost modification it is not necessary to bring costs following revenue all the way to year 0. It really is only necessary to present worth costs following revenue year by year until those costs are offset by project revenue. This gives the following modified present worth cost analysis variation for this example.

Present Worth Cost Modified ROR Analysis Variation

Present worth the year 6 cost year by year until offset by project income.

```
 C=18.50          C=62.21            C=116.66
 I=40.00  P/F20,1  I=40.00  P/F20,1  I= 40.00  P/F20,1
NetI=21.50       NetC=22.21        NetC= 74.66        C=140
_____
  3              4                 5                 6
```

New Modified Diagram

```
 C=70   I=40   I=40   I=21.5    -      -      -
_____
  0     1      2      3         4      5      6
```

PW Eq: $0 = -70 + 40(P/A_{i,2}) + 21.5(P/F_{i,3})$

i = Modified ROR = $23.5\% > i^* = 20\%$ so satisfactory

This modified ROR result is several percent bigger than the initial present worth cost modified result. This is because the two modified ROR results relate to very different initial year 0 investments. The results are really equivalent and give the same economic conclusion when compared to the 20% minimum ROR. Remember that you can not and should not look at the magnitude of ROR results and think big is best. A project with a big ROR that relates to a given investment and stream of income may not be as desirable as a project with a smaller ROR that relates to bigger investment and a different stream of income.

EXAMPLE 4-13 A Petroleum Infill Drilling Acceleration Problem Involving Dual Rates of Return

A producing oil field has wells drilled on 160 acre centers. It is proposed to infill drill wells on 80 acre centers to accelerate petroleum production and give more efficient drainage of the petroleum reservoir. Present and proposed costs and net revenues are shown on the following time diagrams with values in thousands of dollars:

```
          C=0   I=900   I=700   I=550   I=410   I=280   I=150
Present   ───────────────────────────────────────────────────  L=0
           0      1       2       3       4       5       6


          C=735  I=1,750 I=1,150 I=600   I=100   I=0     I=0
Accelerate ──────────────────────────────────────────────────  L=0
           0      1       2       3       4       5       6
```

For a minimum ROR of 12%, use rate of return analysis to determine if the acceleration drilling program investment is satisfactory from an economic viewpoint.

Solution:

The "present" producing project is clearly satisfactory since costs for development have already been incurred (so they are sunk). For no additional costs to be incurred, the "present" project revenues are projected to be generated. This relates to an infinite percent return on zero dollars invested in the present project, an economically satisfactory project. The accelerated project total investment ROR is 200%. However, this ROR does not need to be calculated because knowing the present project is satisfactory, we can go to incremental analysis to determine if incremental investment dollars spent on the accelerated production infill drilling program are justified economically by incremental revenues. The incremental diagram involves cost, income, cost as follows because the negative incremental incomes in years 4, 5 and 6 are effectively costs as follows:

Incremental Rate of Return Analysis:

$$
\begin{array}{c}
\text{C=735} \quad \text{I=850} \quad \text{I=450} \quad \text{I=50} \quad \text{C=310} \quad \text{C=280} \quad \text{C=150} \\
\hline
\text{Accelerated} \quad\quad\quad\quad\quad\quad\quad\quad\quad\quad\quad\quad\quad\quad\quad\quad\quad\quad\quad\quad\quad \text{L=0} \\
\text{- Present} \quad 0 \quad\quad 1 \quad\quad 2 \quad\quad 3 \quad\quad 4 \quad\quad 5 \quad\quad 6
\end{array}
$$

If you write a conventional present worth equation for the incremental diagram values, you get dual rates as follows:

PW Eq: $0 = -735 + 850(P/F_{i,1}) + 450(P/F_{i,2}) + 50(P/F_{i,3})$

$\quad\quad\quad - 310(P/F_{i,4}) - 280(P/F_{i,5}) - 150(P/F_{i,6})$

Trial and error, dual "i" values of 17% and 25% result. An investor that treats either of these results as rate of return compared with the minimum ROR of 12% would conclude that the incremental project economics are satisfactory. This turns out to be an incorrect conclusion. Both of the dual rates of 17% and 25% have rate of reinvestment meaning as well as rate of return meaning at different points in time. Required rates of revenue reinvestment of 17% and 25% compared with 12% reinvestment opportunities indicated by the minimum ROR indicate a very unsatisfactory incremental investment whereas rates of return of 17% and 25% compared to the 12% minimum ROR look satisfactory. The unsatisfactory rate of reinvestment meaning is stronger than the rate of return meaning as the following NPV and present worth cost modified ROR analysis results show.

Net Present Value Analysis:

NPV $= -753 + 850(P/F_{12,1}) + 450(P/F_{12,2}) + 50(P/F_{12,3})$

$\quad\quad\quad - 310(P/F_{12,4}) - 280(P/F_{12,5}) - 150(P/F_{12,6})$

$\quad\quad = -13.6 < 0$, so slightly unsatisfactory.

Present Worth Cost Modified ROR Analysis:

Modified Yr 0 Cost $= 735+310(P/F_{12,4})+280(P/F_{12,5})+150(P/F_{12,6})$

$\quad\quad\quad\quad\quad\quad\quad = 1,166.9$

Modified PW Eq: $1,166.9 = 850(P/F_{i,1}) + 450(P/F_{i,2}) + 50(P/F_{i,3})$

Trial and error:

i = Modified ROR = 11% < i^{*} = 12%, so unsatisfactory

Note that any investor who treats either of the positive dual rates of 17% and 25% as rate of return comes to the wrong economic conclusion in this analysis. When cost follows revenue, to make ROR analysis you must modify the analysis to eliminate cost following revenue before you can make ROR analysis.

EXAMPLE 4-14 Cost, Income, Cost from Incremental Service Producing Analysis

It is necessary to evaluate whether an asset should be replaced today for a $20,000 cost or two years from today for a $25,000 cost with operating costs and salvage values as shown on the diagrams for a six year evaluation life. Use incremental ROR analysis for a 15% minimum ROR to reach the economic decision. All values are in thousands of dollars on the diagrams

```
Replace    C=20   OC=1    OC=2    OC=3    OC=4    OC=5    OC=6
Now (A)    _____ L=4
            0      1       2       3       4       5       6

                           C=25
Replace    C=0    OC=5    OC=6    OC=1    OC=2    OC=3    OC=4
Latter (B) _____ L=9
            0      1       2       3       4       5       6
```

Solution:

Analyze "A – B" to get incremental cost followed by incremental savings. However, it is impossible to avoid having incremental costs and negative incremental salvage (effectively cost) in years 3 through 6, giving the dual ROR problem.

R = Incremental Savings which are equivalent to revenue.

```
        C=20   R=4    R=29    C=2     C=2     C=2     C=7
A-B)    _____
         0      1       2      3       4       5       6
```

A modified ROR analysis is needed to eliminate cost following revenue or savings. Present worth cost modified ROR analysis generally is easier to apply than growth ROR so it will be utilized. There is little value obtained from calculating the dual rates of return except to satisfy curiosity, but the dual rates for this analysis are 0% and 4.0%.

Present Worth Cost Modified ROR Analysis:

$$\text{Modified Cost} = 20 + 2\overset{2.283}{(P/A_{15,3})}\overset{0.7561}{(P/F_{15,2})} + 7\overset{0.4323}{(P/F_{15,6})} = 26.48$$

PW Eq: $26.48 = 4(P/F_{i,1}) + 29(P/F_{i,2})$

i = Incremental Investment Modified ROR = 12.5% < $i^* = 15\%$

Reject the incremental investment in "A" and select "B" (replace later). Incremental NPV analysis verifies this modified ROR analysis conclusion.

$$\text{NPV}_{A-B} = 4(P/F_{15,1})^{.8696} + 29(P/F_{15,2})^{.7561} - 2(P/A_{15,3})^{2.283}(P/F_{15,2})^{.7561}$$

$$- 7(P/F_{15,6})^{.4323} - 20 = -1.1 < 0, \text{ so reject A,}$$
$$\text{select B}$$

To complete our discussion of the investment, income, investment situations, it is important to point out and emphasize that *if income follows the second investment, a dual ROR situation may not exist. This means that investment, income, investment, income analysis situations may not give the dual ROR problem but investment, income, investment always does.* Look at the project cumulative cash position diagram for the positive "i" value calculated to test whether combination rate of return, rate of reinvestment meaning is associated with the "i" value at different points in time. Remember, if the cumulative cash position does not go positive at any time, rate of reinvestment meaning does not exist and the meaning of "i" is rate of return for the entire project evaluation life. The following example illustrates this important analysis consideration.

EXAMPLE 4-15 An Investment, Income, Investment, Income Situation Where Conventional ROR Analysis is Valid

Diagram values in thousands of dollars.

C=50	I=30	C=100 I= 30	I=60	I=60	I=60
0	1	2	3	4	5

A development project will require investments of $50,000 at time zero and $100,000 of the end of year two as shown on the time diagram, with incomes of $30,000 at the end of years 1 and 2, and $60,000 at the end of years 3, 4 and 5. For a minimum rate of return of 20%, use ROR analysis to evaluate the economic desirability of this project. Is the "i" value that you calculate meaningful for economic decision making as ROR? Does NPV analysis verify your conclusion?

Solution, All Values in Thousands of Dollars:

NPV Eq: $30(P/A_{i,2}) + 60(P/A_{i,3})(P/F_{i,2})$

$$- 100(P/F_{i,2}) - 50 = 0$$

Since the NPV at i = 0% is positive, only one positive "i" exists that will make NPV = 0. By trial and error, i = 27.46% makes NPV = 0. Is this "i" value of 27.46% a rate of return result or is it one of a pair of "dual rates of return" that have combination rate of return, rate of reinvestment requirement meaning at different points in time? If a companion dual rate of return exists, it would be negative. However, it is possible to avoid the search for the possible companion dual ROR by testing to see if rate of reinvestment meaning is associated with 27.46% "i" value at any point in time. *Dual rates of return always have combined rate of return, rate of reinvestment meaning at different points in time. If rate of reinvestment meaning does not exist at any time, then dual rates of return do not exist for this problem and the 27.46% "i" value can be treated as ROR for decision purposes.*

Evaluation of the cumulative cash position diagram for this project at the project "i" value of 27.46% does show that the cumulative cash position never goes above zero at any time during the project life. Therefore, the "i" of 27.46% means "rate of return" over the entire project life and never means rate of reinvestment. Only when the cumulative cash position goes positive does "i" have the rate of reinvestment meaning.

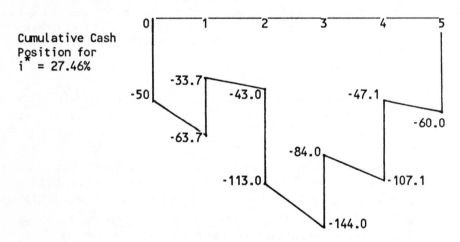

Cumulative Cash
Position for
i* = 27.46%

4.9 Alternating Income, Investment, Income Situations

For the situation when you have alternating income, investment, income on the time diagram, dual rates of return occur for the opposite conditions described in the previous section for the investment, income, investment situation. For income, investment, income situations, dual "i" values that are both positive will exist if NPV at i =0% is positive, and positive dual "i" values will not exist if NPV at i = 0% is negative. Analysis rules are similar to those given in the last section. However, note that for income, investment, income situations that do not give dual positive "i" values, a project is acceptable for an i* greater than the project positive "i" value because this is the region of positive net present value. When dual rates exist, a project is acceptable only for i* values outside the region between the dual rates, because this is the range of i* values that makes NPV positive.

4.10 Evaluation of Non-Mutually Exclusive Investments

Non-mutually exclusive investments are investment alternatives from which more than one choice can be selected depending on available capital or budget restrictions, such as selecting research, development or exploration projects from many alternatives. The ranking of drilling prospects in the petroleum industry is a classic example of non-mutually exclusive alternative analysis. The objective in analyzing non-mutually exclusive projects is to maximize the cumulative profitability that can be generated from the available investment dollars.

To maximize the cumulative profitability that can be generated by investing available investment capital in several non-mutually exclusive alternatives, select the combination of projects that will maximize cumulative net value or cumulative future worth profit. Use of any of these methods requires looking at all the different possible combinations of projects to determine the group of projects that is best for a given budget.

To rank non-mutually exclusive projects in the order that you will want to select them to maximize cumulative net value or future profit for a given budget, two ranking techniques may be used. They are growth rate of return and ratio analysis using either PVR or B/C Ratio as calculated earlier. The following examples will show that often this does not involve selecting the project with the largest individual project net value, and that ranking the projects in the order of decreasing regular ROR on project investments does not properly rank non-mutually exclusive alternatives. Of the basic evaluation techniques discussed earlier in this text, only ratio analysis and growth ROR consistently rank non-mutually exclusive alternatives in the order that you want to select them to maximize cumulative profitability.

To simplify the examples presented for non-mutually exclusive project analysis, net present value (NPV) will be used to illustrate the net value or future worth profit approach rather than presenting the solutions for all methods. If you use NAV, NFV, or FW Profit remember to use a common evaluation life for all alternatives when unequal life projects are involved. The same is true for Growth ROR analysis.

EXAMPLE 4-16 Evaluation of Non-Mutually Exclusive Alternatives Compared to Mutually Exclusive Alternatives With Net Present Value

Consider the following 4 investment alternatives which all have a 5 year life and zero salvage value. Assume that i* = 20% before taxes.

Alternative	Investment, $	Operating Cost Savings Per Year, $
1	10,000	6,000
2	25,000	10,000
3	35,000	15,000
4	50,000	17,000

A) If $50,000 is available to invest and alternatives 1, 2, 3 and 4 are mutually exclusive (only one alternative can be chosen), which alternative should be selected?

B) If $35,000 is available to be invested, and the alternatives are non-mutually exclusive, should we choose alternative 3 or alternative 1 plus 2? We do not have enough money to finance alternative 4 so for financial reasons (rather than economic reasons) it must be left out of this analysis.

Solution:

A) Mutually Exclusive Alternatives.

NPV analysis will be presented here because it is generally the simplest method to use to evaluate mutually exclusive projects.

$$NPV_1 = 6,000(P/A_{20,5}^{2.991}) - 10,000 = +\$7,946$$

$$NPV_2 = 10,000(P/A_{20,5}) - 25,000 = +\$4,910$$

$$NPV_3 = 15,000(P/A_{20,5}) - 35,000 = +\$9,865$$

$$NPV_4 = 17,000(P/A_{20,5}) - 50,000 = +\$ 847$$

Alternative 3 has the largest NPV at $i^* = 20\%$, so for mutually exclusive alternatives, alternative 3 is the economic choice.

B) Non-Mutually Exclusive Alternatives.

If we were to proceed as we did in part (A) and pick the largest NPV, we would select alternative 3 for this analysis also. However, it should be very obvious that if these alternatives are not mutually exclusive, we can make better use of our $35,000 by selecting alternatives 1 plus 2, rather than 3, since this gives us $16,000 in savings each year for the $35,000 investment, rather than the $15,000 savings obtained from alternative 3. Cumulative NPV for alternatives 1 and 2 is $12,856 compared to $NPV_3 = \$9,865$. Therefore, note that the project with biggest NPV is not involved in the economic choice. Only with mutually exclusive alternatives is the biggest NPV project always best.

EXAMPLE 4-17 ROR is Not a Valid Ranking Technique For Non-Mutually Exclusive Alternatives

A research manager must select the best way to allocate $25,000 by investing in one or more of the following five non-mutually exclusive projects. If $i^* = 10\%$, which project or projects should be selected?

```
                              ROR_A=20%
A)   C=$10,000      I=$3,344              I=$3,344
     ─────────────────────────────────────────── L=0
     0             1    ................... 5
```

```
                              ROR_B=18%
B)   C=$10,000          -                    -
     ─────────────────────────────────────────── L=$23,000
     0             1    ................... 5
```

```
                              ROR_C=15%
C)   C=$15,000      I=$2,250              I=$2,250
     ─────────────────────────────────────────── L=$15,000
     0             1    ................... 5
```

```
                              ROR_D=21%
D)   C=$10,000   I=5,100  I=$4,100  declining gradient
     ─────────────────────────────────────────── L=0
     0           1       2    .......... 5
```

```
                              ROR_E=20%
E)   C=$25,000      I=$8,360              I=$8,360
     ─────────────────────────────────────────── L=0
     0             1    ................... 5
```

Solution:

The project rates of return have been calculated to the nearest percent and listed above each time diagram. You should not rank projects by regular ROR, but many people do, and ranking the projects by regular ROR would place "D" first, "E" and "A" second and third, "B" fourth and "C" fifth. This is not the order in which we should select the projects to maximize the profitability of available investment dollars as determined by cumulative NPV analysis.

$$NPV_A = 3,344(P/A_{10,5}^{3.791}) - 10,000 = +\$2,677$$

$$NPV_B = 23,000(P/F_{10,5}^{.6209}) - 10,000 = +4,281$$

$$NPV_C = 2,250(P/A_{10,5}^{3.791}) + 15,000(P/F_{10,5}^{.6209}) - 15,000 = +\$2,843$$

$$NPV_D = (5,100 - 1,000(A/G_{10,5}^{1.810}))(P/A_{10,5}^{3.791}) - 10,000 = +\$2,472$$

$$NPV_E = 8,360(P/A_{10,5}^{3.791}) - 25,000 = +\$6,693$$

The maximum possible cumulative NPV is obtained from projects "B" and "C" giving cumulative NPV of $7,124. Note that this involves selecting the two projects with the lowest ROR values and it does not involve selection of the project with the largest individual project NPV. Also, since money invested elsewhere at the minimum ROR, $i^* = 10\%$ has a zero NPV, note that selecting "A" and "B" and investing $5,000 elsewhere does not give as much cumulative NPV as "B" and "C" give.

Using Growth ROR or Ratio analysis to rank non-mutually exclusive alternatives in the order of decreasing economic desirability instead of using cumulative NPV analysis is advantageous when many alternatives must be analyzed. Consider a major company with 100 research or exploration projects to be evaluated and ranked. Many combinations of projects must be analyzed to determine the group of projects that maximizes cumulative NPV for a given budget, while the use of Growth ROR or Ratios only requires the calculation of these values for each individual project and then ranking the projects in the order of decreasing values. Selecting the projects with the largest Growth ROR or Ratio values first, next largest second, and so forth will give the group of projects that has the maximum possible cumulative NPV. However, the following example illustrates these concepts and that budget constraints sometimes make it necessary to analyze different mutually exclusive groups of non-mutually exclusive alternatives even using growth ROR or Ratio analysis.

EXAMPLE 4-18 Ranking Non-Mutually Exclusive Projects Using Growth ROR Analysis and PVR Analysis

Determine whether an exploration manager should spend $50,000 on project 1 or projects 2 and 3 if the projects are non-mutually exclusive for a minimum ROR 10%.

$$\underset{0 \qquad\qquad 1 \qquad\qquad 2}{\text{1)} \quad \overset{\text{C=\$50,000}}{\underset{}{\underline{\overset{\text{ROR=40\%}}{\text{I=\$20,000} \quad \text{I=\$20,000}}}}} \quad \text{L=\$50,000}}$$

1)
$$\begin{array}{ccc} \text{C=\$50,000} & \overset{\text{ROR=40\%}}{\text{I=\$20,000}} & \text{I=\$20,000} \\ \hline & & \text{L=\$50,000} \\ 0 & 1 & 2 \end{array}$$

2)
$$\begin{array}{ccc} \text{C=\$30,000} & \overset{\text{ROR=33\%}}{\text{I=\$10,000}} & \text{I=\$10,000} \\ \hline & & \text{L=\$30,000} \\ 0 & 1 \quad\cdots\cdots\cdots\cdots & 5 \end{array}$$

3)
$$\begin{array}{ccc} \text{C=\$20,000} & \overset{\text{ROR=25\%}}{\text{I=\$5,000}} & \text{I=5,000} \\ \hline & & \text{L=\$20,000} \\ 0 & 1 \quad\cdots\cdots\cdots\cdots\cdots & 7 \end{array}$$

Solution:

Many people would rank these or any other investment alternatives in the order of decreasing regular compound interest ROR, which in this case ranks project 1 first, project 2 second and project 3 third. However, as was shown in the last example and will be shown for this analysis, ranking by regular ROR often does not give the group of investments that will maximize the profitability that can be generated from available investment dollars.

Maximize Cumulative NPV

$$NPV_1 = 20,000 \overset{1.736}{(P/A_{10,2})} + 50,000 \overset{.8264}{(P/F_{10,2})} - 50,000 = +\$26,033$$

$$NPV_2 = 10,000 \overset{3.791}{(P/A_{10,5})} + 30,000 \overset{.6209}{(P/F_{10,5})} - 30,000 = +\$26,535$$

$$NPV_3 = 5,000 \overset{4.868}{(P/A_{10,7})} + 20,000 \overset{.5132}{(P/F_{10,7})} - 20,000 = +\$14,605$$

Maximum Cumulative NPV = $NPV_2 + NPV_3$ = +$41,605

Projects two and three are selected to maximize cumulative NPV.

Note that ranking by regular ROR does not give the correct answer. However, ranking the alternatives by Growth ROR or PVR does rank the projects correctly as is illustrated in the following calulations. A common evaluation life must be used for all alternatives for Growth ROR ranking.

Growth Rate of Return

Use a common evaluation life of 7 years for each alternative.

1)

$$\begin{array}{l} \text{C=\$50,000 \quad I=\$20,000 \quad I=\$20,000} \\ \overline{\rule{8cm}{0.4pt}} \quad \text{L=\$50,000} \\ \text{0} \qquad\qquad\quad \text{1} \qquad\qquad\quad \text{2} \end{array}$$

Rein-
vest

$$\begin{array}{l} \qquad\qquad\qquad\qquad \text{C=\$50,000} \\ \text{- \quad C=\$20,000 \quad C=\$20,000} \\ \overline{\rule{8cm}{0.4pt}} \quad \text{F = +\$148,210} \\ \text{0} \qquad\quad \text{1} \qquad\qquad \text{2 .... 7} \end{array}$$

$$\text{where, } F = 20,000 \underset{1.772}{(F/P_{10,6})} + 70,000 \underset{1.611}{(F/P_{10,5})} = +\$148,210$$

1+
Rein-
vest

$$\begin{array}{l} \text{C=\$50,000 \quad - \qquad\qquad\qquad -} \\ \overline{\rule{8cm}{0.4pt}} \quad \text{F = +\$148,210} \\ \text{0} \qquad\quad \text{1 .... 7} \end{array}$$

Growth ROR PW Eq: $50,000 = 148,210(P/F_{i,7})$,   i = Growth ROR = 17%

2)

$$\begin{array}{l} \text{C=\$30,000 \quad I=\$10,000 \qquad\qquad I=\$10,000} \\ \overline{\rule{8cm}{0.4pt}} \quad \text{L=\$30,000} \\ \text{0} \qquad\qquad\quad \text{1 .... 5} \end{array}$$

Rein-
vest

$$\begin{array}{l} \qquad\qquad\qquad\qquad \text{C=\$30,000} \\ \text{- \quad C=\$10,000 \qquad C=\$10,000 \qquad -} \\ \overline{\rule{8cm}{0.4pt}} \quad \text{F=+\$110,170} \\ \text{0} \qquad\quad \text{1 .... 5} \qquad\quad \text{7} \end{array}$$

$$\text{where, } F = \{10,000 \underset{6.105}{(F/A10,5)} + 30,000\} \underset{1.21}{(F/P_{10,2})} = +\$110,170$$

2+
Rein-
vest

$$\begin{array}{l} \text{C=\$30,000 \quad - \qquad\qquad\qquad -} \\ \overline{\rule{8cm}{0.4pt}} \quad \text{F=+\$110,170} \\ \text{0} \qquad\quad \text{1 .... 7} \end{array}$$

Growth ROR Eq: $30,000 = 110,170(P/F_{i,7})$,   i = Growth ROR = 20.4%

3)

$$\begin{array}{l} \text{C=\$20,000 \quad I=\$5,000 \qquad\qquad I=\$5,000} \\ \overline{\rule{8cm}{0.4pt}} \quad \text{L=\$20,000} \\ \text{0} \qquad\qquad\quad \text{1 .... 7} \end{array}$$

```
                                          C=$20,000
Rein-            C=$5,000                 C=$ 5,000
Vest     _____  F=$67,430
         0         1 .......................... 7
```

$$\text{where,} \quad F = 5,000(F/A_{10,7})^{9.487} + 20,000 = \$67,430$$

```
3+
Rein-  C=$20,000   -                                       -
Vest   _____  F=$67,430
       0         1 .......................... 7
```

Growth ROR Eq: $20,000 = 67,430(P/F_{i,7})$, $\quad i = \text{Growth ROR} = 19.1\%$

Alternatives 2 and 3 with the largest and next largest Growth ROR values are the economic choices for the available investment budget of $50,000. Ratio analysis verifies these choices as follows:

PVR = NPV a i^* / PW Investment Cost a i^* B/C Ratio = PVR + 1

$$PVR_1 = 26,033/50,000 = 0.52 \qquad \text{B/C Ratio}_1 = 1.52$$
$$PVR_2 = 26,535/30,000 = 0.88 \qquad \text{B/C Ratio}_2 = 1.88$$
$$PVR_3 = 14,605/20,000 = 0.73 \qquad \text{B/C Ratio}_3 = 1.73$$

Both PVR and B/C Ratio results indicate projects 2 and 3 are the economic choices consistent with Growth ROR and cumulative NPV results. Properly calculated ratios and Growth ROR results will always rank non-mutually exclusive alternatives in exactly the same correct order.

It is instructive to note that a higher minimum ROR such as $i^* = 25\%$ causes the choice to switch to alternative 1. When you have good reinvestment opportunities, the short life high ROR project 1 is economically more desirable than when reinvestment opportunities are poor.

NPV for $i^* = 25\%$

$$NPV_1 = 20,000(P/A_{25,2})^{1.440} + 50,000(P/F_{25,2})^{.6400} - 50,000 = +\$10,800$$

$$NPV_2 = 10,000(P/A_{25,5})^{2.689} + 30,000(P/F_{25,5})^{.3277} - 30,000 = +\$6,700$$

$$NPV_3 = 5,000(P/A_{25,7})^{3.161} + 20,000(P/F_{25,7})^{.2097} - 20,000 = +\$0$$

Maximum Cumulative NPV = $NPV_1 = \$10,800$, so select project 1.

Growth ROR for i* = 25%

Growth ROR calculations for i* = 25% verify that project 1 is best based on the following results: Growth ROR_1 = 28.6%, Growth ROR_2 = 28.6%, Growth ROR_3 = 25%. Although the Growth ROR results for projects 1 and 2 are equal, with a $50,000 budget we can either do project 1 with a 28.6% Growth ROR or the combination project 2 and 3 which have Growth ROR results of 28.6% and 25% respectively. Intuitively you know that the Growth ROR of 28.6% on $30,000 invested in projects 2 and the Growth ROR of 25% on $20,000 invested in project 3 has to be less desirable than the Growth ROR of 28.6% on all $50,000 in project 1, so select project 1 as the economic choice.

PVR for i* = 25%

$$PVR_1 = 10,800 / 50,000 = 0.22$$
$$PVR_2 = 6,700 / 30,000 = 0.22$$
$$PVR_3 = 0 / 20,000 = 0.00$$

Since the Growth ROR results for projects 1 and 2 were equal, we expect the ratios to be equal. Once again, as with growth ROR, two mutually exclusive choices exist for spending $50,000 on non-mutually exclusive projects 1, 2 and 3. We can either invest in project 1, or in the combination of projects 2 and 3.

$$PVR_1 = 0.22$$

$$PVR_{2+3} = (6,700 + 0) / (30,000 + 20,000) = 0.13$$

Since the same $50,000 would be invested either way, select the maximum PVR which is project 1. This is consistent with growth ROR results and conclusions. With both PVR and Growth ROR results, the projects were put in the desired selection order but the budget constraint caused us to analyze several mutually exclusive choices before making the final investment decision.

The final two examples in this chapter are designed to illustrate several important considerations about PVR and Growth ROR calculations and applications to non-mutually exclusive alternative analysis situations. The first of these two examples has a primary objective of emphasizing the necessity of netting together all inflows and outflows of money and working with the resultant net costs of incomes in either growth ROR or Ratio calculations.

EXAMPLE 4-19 Ranking Non-Mutually Exclusive Projects Using PVR and Growth ROR

Rank the following non-mutually exclusive alternatives using PVR for $i^* = 15\%$.

```
          I=$110    I=$110              I=$110
  C=$100  C=$200    OC=0                OC=0
A)_____   L=0
  0       1         2 ................. 8
```

```
          I=$150    I=$150              I=$150
  C=$100  C=$90     OC=$40              OC=$40
B)_____   L=0
  0       1         2 ................. 8
```

Solution:

Net Present Value (NPV)

$$NPV_A = 110(P/A_{15,8}) \overset{4.487}{} - 200(P/F_{15,1}) \overset{.8696}{} - 100 = +\$219.6$$

$$NPV_B = \{110(P/A_{15,7}) \overset{4.160}{} - 90\}(P/F_{15,1}) \overset{.8696}{} - 100 = +\$219.6$$

These two projects are identical economically and financially from an out-of-pocket cost viewpoint. To rank them equally with PVR (or Growth ROR) you must first net costs and incomes together that are at the same points in time and work with resultant net costs in the denominator of PVR.

Present Value Ratio (PVR)

$$PVR_A = 219.6 \ / \ \{100 + (200-110)(P/F_{15,1}) \overset{.8696}{}\} = +1.23$$

$$PVR_B = 219.6 \ / \ \{100 + 90(P/F_{15,1}) \overset{.8696}{}\} = +1.23$$

If you incorrectly do not net the project "A" year 1 cost of 200 against the revenue of $110 before calculating the ratio denominator, you calculate

$$PVR_A = 219.6 \ / \ \{100 + 200(P/F_{15,1}) \overset{.8696}{}\} = 0.80 = \text{incorrect } PVR_A$$

This ranks project "A" as economically inferior to project B which is not the case.

Growth Rate of Return

To use Growth ROR as a ranking technique, project net costs must be discounted at the minimum ROR to a common time zero before making the growth ROR calculations for a common evaluation life. This makes the cost basis for Growth ROR calculations identical to the PVR denominator.

```
        C=$100   NetC=$90   I=$110              I=$110
A)      ─────────────────────────────────────────────        L=0
        0          1          2 .............. 8

Reinvest                     C=$110              C=$110
Income  ───────────────────────────────────────────────      F=$1,217.4
ə i*=15%  0        1          2 .............. 8

                                       11.067
                             where,  F = 110(F/A₁₅,₇) = $1,217.4
A+
Reinvest C=$100    C=$90       -                  -
Income  ───────────────────────────────────────────────      F=$1,217.4
ə i*=15%  0        1          2 ................. 8
```

$$\text{where, } F = 110(F/A_{15,7}) = \$1{,}217.4$$

To properly rank projects using Growth ROR, bring the net costs beyond time zero back to time zero by present worthing at the minimum ROR, which is 15% for this analysis. This enables us to calculate rate of growth of a single year 0 sum of money which will always be identical to the denominator of a properly calculated PVR or B/C Ratio. By calculating Growth ROR on year 0 single sums of money, it is clear that projects with the largest Growth ROR are our choices. Those projects must generate the greatest future value possible from available investment dollars.

$$\text{Growth ROR PW Eq:}\quad 100 + 90(P/F_{15,1})^{.8696} = 1{,}217.4(P/F_{i,8})$$

Growth ROR = i = 27.14%

Since the net costs and incomes on the "B" diagram are identical to the "A" diagram, Growth ROR_B = Growth ROR_A = 27.14%

As with PVR analysis, it should be evident that if the year 1 costs and revenues for project "A" are not netted together, a Growth ROR is calculated based on year 0 cost of $100 and year 1 cost of $200 and the 23.79% Growth ROR_A results would rank "A" inferior to "B". This is not a valid result.

Finally, if costs such as major repair or expansion costs occur in project years after positive net income has been realized for one or more years, only the resultant present worth net cost that is not covered by the present worth of net income from the early project years goes into the denominator of PVR calculations or as part of the cost basis for Growth ROR calculations.

The following example concerns ratio analysis ranking of non-mutually exclusive alternatives. It has been shown in numerous earlier examples, that changing the minimum rate of return can and often will change economic choices, which emphasizes the need to use a minimum rate of return in all analysis situations that represents other opportunities thought to exist for the investment of capital. Straying from this requirement causes inconsistent and often incorrect economic decision-making. Similarly, with ratio analysis it is necessary to use breakeven cutoff rates of zero for PVR and one for B/C Ratio. You will not get economic decisions that are consistent with results from other valid techniques if you raise the ratio cutoff rate to say, 0.25 for PVR or 1.25 for B/C Ratio as an alternative to raising the minimum ROR and leaving the cutoff at zero for PVR and one for B/C Ratio. The following example illustrates considerations related to these points.

EXAMPLE 4-20 Ratio Analysis Considerations Related to Net Present Value and Rate Of Return

Alternatives "A" and "B" may be either mutually exclusive or non-mutually exclusive investments. Discuss the analysis of these alternatives for either situation using NPV, PVR, B/C Ratio, ROR and Growth ROR for minimum ROR values of 12%, 15% and 20%. Analyze some of the effects of changing the PVR cutoff value as an alternative to changing minimum ROR.

```
    C=$100      I=$34.67      I=$34.67
A)  ─────────────────────────────────────  L=$0
    0            1 ............ 5
```

```
    C=$100      I=$16.67                    I=$16.67
B)  ─────────────────────────────────────────────────  L=$0
    0            1 ........................... 20
```

Solution:

By Trial and Error, ROR_A = 21.7%, ROR_B = 16.0%

Decision Criteria	i^* = 12%	i^* = 15%	i^* = 20%
NPV_A	+25.00	+16.20	+ 3.70
NPV_B	+25.00	+ 4.80	- 18.50
PVR_A	+ .25	+ .16	+ .04
PVR_B	+ .25	+ .05	- .18
B/C Ratio$_A$	+ 1.25	+ 1.16	+ 1.04
B/C Ratio$_B$	+ 1.25	+ 1.05	+ .82
Growth ROR$_A$	13.1%	15.6%	20.1%
Growth ROR$_B$	13.1%	15.2%	18.4%

For i* = 12%, alternatives "A" and "B" are economically equivalent whether they are mutually exclusive or non-mutually exclusive alternatives. Raising i* to 15% or 20% causes the economic choice to shift to favoring "A" over "B" with all techniques. Note NPV_A is greater than NPV_B for both i* = 15% and i* = 20%; we know "A" is better than "B" if we consider the alternatives to be mutually exclusive. Explicit incremental analysis calculations must be done to verify that conclusion with PVR, B/C Ratio, ROR and Growth ROR, but all techniques give the same economic conclusion.

If "A" and "B" are considered to be non-mutually exclusive alternatives, PVR, B/C Ratio, and Growth ROR, are the valid ranking techniques and all indicate A is better than B for i* = 15% and 20%.

Now let's analyze the effect of using i* = 12% to handle time value of money in ratio calculations, but effectively increase i* by raising the cutoff for acceptable projects from zero to 0.25 with PVR and from 1.0 to 1.25 with B/C Ratio. This is an evaluation approach sometimes used in industry practice. Notice it leads to the conclusion in this case that "A" and "B" are equivalent, whether they are mutually exclusive or non-mutually exclusive. Actually raising i* to 15% or 20% shows clear economic advantage to "A" for the higher i* values with all standard techniques of analysis. Also notice that for i* = 12%, all methods show the alternatives are equivalent. This means incremental ROR analysis ("B – A" to get incremental costs followed by incremental revenues) will give the incremental "B – A" ROR to be 12%. Treating alternatives "A" and "B" as economically equivalent is the conclusion given by ratio calculations at i* = 12% with increased cutoff values of 0.25 for PVR or 1.25 for B/C Ratio. This explicitly means that a 12% incremental ROR on "B – A" is satisfactory. This is a misleading conclusion if other opportunities really exist to invest dollars at an ROR greater than 12%, which raising the cutoff rates on PVR to 0.25 and B/C Ratio to 1.25 implies. Since this approach involves inconsistencies in economic conclusions, it seems undesirable to use it. However, it can be argued that the differences in results from increasing the ratio cutoff instead of increasing i* are small and not significant. Regardless, it is important to be aware that this approach may give economic results and conclusions that are inconsistent with other standard evaluation techniques.

4.11 Summary of Mutually Exclusive and Non-Mutually Exclusive Alternative Analysis

Mutually Exclusive Alternative Analysis

Rate Of Return or Growth Rate of Return. With either regular ROR or Growth ROR analysis of mutually exclusive alternatives you must evaluate both total investment ROR and incremental investment ROR, selecting the largest investment for which both are satisfactory. Use a common evaluation life for ROR or Growth ROR analysis of unequal life alternatives, normally the life of the longest life alternative, assuming net revenues and costs are zero in the later years of shorter life alternatives.

Net Value Analysis. With NPV, NAV or NFV analysis you want the mutually exclusive alternative with the largest net value because this is the alternative with the largest investment that has both a positive total investment net value and a positive incremental net value compared to the last satisfactory smaller investment. When using NAV or NFV to evaluate unequal life alternatives you must use a common evaluation life, normally the life of the longest life alternative, assuming net revenues and costs are zero in the later years of shorter life alternatives as with ROR analysis.

Ratio Analysis. With ratio analysis of mutually exclusive alternatives using either PVR or B/C Ratio, it is necessary to evaluate both total investment ratios and incremental investment ratios. Analogous to ROR analysis, the mutually exclusive alternative with the biggest total investment investment ratio often is not the best economic choice. A bigger investment with a somewhat smaller ratio often is a better mutually exclusive alternative choice.

Future Worth Profit Analysis. Calculate the FW Profit that can be generated by each alternative project if profits and salvage are reinvested at the minimum rate of return, i^*. Select the project that maximizes FW profit for the investment money available to invest. With this method you must compare the FW profit for the same investment dollars in all cases, by assuming the budget money not required in one project will be invested elsewhere at i^*. Always use a common evaluation life for all alternatives.

Non-Mutually Exclusive Alternatives

Rate of Return or Growth Rate of Return. Regular ROR analysis cannot be used to rank non-mutually exclusive alternatives. Use Growth ROR and rank the alternatives in the order of decreasing Growth ROR. This will maximize profit from available investment capital. Use a common evaluation life for Growth ROR analysis of unequal life alternatives, normally the life of the longest alternative.

Net Value Analysis. With NPV, NAV or NFV analysis of non-mutually exclusive projects, select the group of projects that will maximize cumulative net value for the dollars available to invest. This does not necessarily involve selecting the project with largest net value on individual project investment. When using NAV or NFV to evaluate unequal life alternatives you must use a common evaluation life, normally the life of the longest life alternative.

Ratio Analysis. Ranking projects in the order of decreasing present value ratio (PVR) or B/C Ratio is the easiest way of selecting non-mutually exclusive projects to maximize cumulative NPV for available investment dollars.

Future Worth Profit Analysis. Calculate the FW Profit that can be generated by each alternative project if profits and salvage are reinvested at the minimum rate of return, i*. Use a common evaluation life equal to the longest life alternative if unequal life projects are involved. Select the group of investment projects that will maximize the cumulative FW Profit for the money available to invest, analogous to the way NPV and NFV are applied. Assume that any odd dollar amounts can be invested elsewhere at i*, the same as with other techniques of analysis.

Remember, with all of these evaluation methods, the minimum rate of return, i*, is the rate of return that represents the other opportunities which are felt to exist for the use of available investment capital. This term is sometimes called the hurdle rate, discount rate, opportunity cost of capital or just cost of capital.

If you use a valid minimum ROR and apply the discounted cash flow analysis techniques as described in this chapter and summary, you will reach correct economic decisions for your cost, revenue, and timing of cost and revenue project data and assumptions. It is always important to recognize that economic analysis calculation results are just a direct reflection of the input data and analysis assumptions. With any techniques of analysis, economic evaluation conclusions are only as good and valid as the data and assumptions on which they are based.

PROBLEMS

4-1. If a year 0 cost of $300,000 is incurred for equipment replacement, an existing project (A) is expected to maintain the generation of $450,000 before-tax profits each year for year 1 through 10. Two alternatives are being considered for improvement (project B) and improvement combined with expansion (project C) with projected costs and revenues as shown on the time diagrams. All dollar values are expressed in thousands of dollars.

```
A)  C=300        I=450       I=450             I=450
    ───────────────────────────────────────────────      L=0
    0            1           2 ............ 10

B)  C=900        I=550       I=550             I=550
    ───────────────────────────────────────────────      L=0
    0            1           2 ............ 10

C)               I=750
    C=1,200      C=800       I=850             I=850
    ───────────────────────────────────────────────      L=0
    0            1           2 ............ 10
```

For a minimum rate of return of 15% and considering the alternatives to be mutually exclusive, determine whether project "A", "B" or "C" is economically best using ROR, NPV and PVR. Then increase the minimum ROR to 25% from 15% over the entire 10 year evaluation life and re-evaluate the alternative using any valid analysis.

4-2. A company is analyzing the economics of leasing a parcel of land for 6 years for year 0 lease payment of $80,000. The land would be used as a product marketing center requiring construction of a $200,000 building on the land in year 0 and it is estimated that it would generate annual revenues of $290,000 and annual operating costs of $160,000 at the end of years 1 through 6. The lease contract stipulates that at the end of year 6 the building must be torn down and the property restored to its initial conditions and this is estimated to cost $360,000 at the end of year 6. Use rate of return analysis to determine if this project is economically viable for a 20% minimum ROR. Verify your results with NPV. What minimum ROR will make project economics a breakeven with investing elsewhere?

4-3.   A double pipe heat exchanger with steam in the shell is to be insulated
       to reduce heat loss to surroundings. The thickness of insulation, initial
       cost and projected annual cost of heat loss are given in the following
       table. If the minimum ROR is 20% before taxes, determine the op-
       timum thickness of insulation for an insulation life of 6 years with a
       zero salvage value.

Insulation Thickness (Inches)	Initial Cost, $	Annual Heat Loss Cost, $
0	0	1400
1	1200	800
2	1800	600
3	2500	500
4	3500	400

       Base your results on Net Present Value Analysis, then verify them
       using Present Worth Cost Analysis.

4-4.   You have been asked to make rate of return analysis to support or
       reject the economic viability of project development that has the
       estimated potential of generating $450,000 revenue per year and
       operating costs of $310,000 per year for each of the next 10 years
       (assume end-of-year 1 through 10 values). A company has agreed to
       construct and finance the project for deferred payments of $50,000
       per year at the end-of-year 2, 3 and 4 with final lump sum purchase
       cost of $1,400,000 to be made at the end-of-year 5. The year ten
       salvage value is estimated to be $300,000. Make rate of return analysis
       to evaluate project economics for minimum rates of return of (a) 5%,
       (b) 15% and (c) 50%. Do NPV results support your conclusions?

4-5.   It is proposed to achieve labor cost savings on a manufacturing process
       by installing one of two possible equipment automation changes. New
       capital equipment costs and projected savings are as follows:

	Equipment Cost	Projected Annual Savings
Change 1	$150,000	$ 80,000
Change 2	$230,000	$115,000

(A) For a 6 year evaluation life, which change, if any, should be selected if i* = 40% before tax? Use Net Present Value Analysis and assume zero salvage values.

(B) Is there any evaluation life other than 6 years that would switch the economic evaluation result found in (A)? If yes, what is the breakeven life for which there are no economic differences between the alternatives?

4-6.   Rank non-mutually exclusive alternatives A and B using PVR Analysis for i* = 15%.

```
           C=$200              C=$230
  C=$100   I=$110    I=$110    I=$110    I=$110    I=$110
A) ─────────────────────────────────────────────────────         L=0
   0        1         2         3         4 ....... 8


           C=$200              C=$180
  C=$100   I=$110    I=$20     I=$110    I=$110    I=$110
B) ─────────────────────────────────────────────────────         L=0
   0        1         2         3         4 ....... 8
```

4-7.   Two mutually exclusive unequal life investment alternatives, A and B, must be evaluated to determine the best economic choice for i* = 20%. The investments, C, and incomes, I, and salvage values, L, are shown on the time diagrams in thousands of dollars.

```
  C=100    I=40      I=40      I=40      I=40      I=40
A) ─────────────────────────────────────────────────────   L=100
   0        1         2         3         4         5


  C=150    I=60      I=60      I=60
B) ─────────────────────────────────────   L=150
   0        1         2         3
```

A) Determine the dual rates of return that result from a direct incremental ROR Analysis of B-A.

B) Evaluate the projects using NPV Analysis.

C) Evaluate the projects using incremental Growth ROR Analysis.

D) Evaluate the projects using PW cost Modified incremental ROR Analysis.

E) Is the economic choice affected by reducing the minimum ROR to 10% from 20%?

4-8. A friend offers to give you 10 payments of $1000 at annual time periods 0 through 10 except year 3 if you give him $9000 at year 3 as shown on the time diagram. All values are in dollars.

I=1000	I=1000	I=1000	C=9000	I=1000	I=1000
0	1	2	3	4	10

Evaluate this income, investment, income opportunity shown on the time diagram for before-tax minimum rates of return of 10% and 20%.

A) Use Net Present Value Analysis.

B) Analyze the project using Present Worth Cost Modified ROR Analysis.

4-9. A new process can be developed and operated at Levels A or B with capital costs, sales and operating costs as shown. All values are in thousands of dollars.

```
                       Sales=75              Sales=75
        C=100       Op. Costs=35          Op. Costs=35
A)      ─────────────────────────────────────────────────  L=0
        0                   1 .................... 5

                       Sales=100             Sales=100
        C=150       Op. Costs=45          Op. Costs=45
B)      ─────────────────────────────────────────────────  L=0
        0                   1 .................... 5
```

If $i^* = 20\%$, which level of investment should be selected? Use NPV Analysis and verify your results with ROR and PVR Analysis. If the minimum ROR is reduced to 12%, what is the economic choice? If the minimum ROR is 12% for years 1 and 2 and 20% for years 3, 4 and 5, what is the economic choice?

4-10. Mining rights to an ore deposit estimated to contain 60,000 units of ore with an estimated market value of $20 per unit will be purchased for $150,000. The ore can be removed in either 2, 4, 6 or 8 years depending upon the level of mining investment selected. The following table gives the appropriate costs above the purchase cost for production investment and production in thousands:

Recovery Time, yrs.	2	4	6	8
Production Investment ($)	390	330	185	160
Operating Cost/Unit Recovered ($)	10	10	10	10
Units Recovered per year	30	15	10	7.5

If the property value will be neglible after the ore is exhausted, what level of mining production investment should be selected if the before tax minimum ROR is 20%? Use:

A) ROR Analysis

B) Net Present Value Analysis

C) Future Worth Profit Analysis. Compare the future worth profits (at the end of year 8 for i* = 20%) generated by starting with $540,000 and assuming any money not put into a project is invested elsewhere at i* = 20%.

4-11. Evaluate mutually exclusive alternatives A, B and C using NPV Analysis for i* = 15%. Verify your results with PVR Analysis.

```
                                        Rev=$110/yr.
        C=$75          C=$136           OC=$50/yr.
A)      ───────────────────────────────────────────────       L=0
         -1             0                1 ............... 20


                                        Rev=$121/yr.
        C=$82          C=$160           OC=$55/yr.
B)      ───────────────────────────────────────────────       L=0
         -1             0                1 ............... 20


                                        Rev=$135/yr.
        C=$85          C=$170           OC=$60/yr.
C)      ───────────────────────────────────────────────       L=0
         -1             0                1 ............... 20
```

4-12. Use ROR Analysis to compare project A involving the investment of $240,000 to generate a series of equal end-of-year revenues of $50,000 per year for 5 years plus a salvage value of $240,000 at the end of year 5 and project B involving the investment of $240,000 to generate a series of equal end-of-year revenues of $98,500 per year for 5 years with zero salvage value. The projects are mutually exclusive and the minimum ROR is 10%. Verify your results with NPV Analysis.

4-13. Determine the best economic way for a research manager to allocate

$500,000 in the following non-mutually exclusive projects if i* = 20%.

A)
$$\frac{C=\$200,000 \qquad I=\$90,000 \qquad I=\$90,000}{0 \qquad\qquad 1 \ldots\ldots\ldots\ldots\ldots 6}$$
L=0

B)
$$\frac{C=\$500,000 \qquad I=\$300,000 \qquad I=\$300,000}{0 \qquad\qquad 1 \ldots\ldots\ldots\ldots\ldots 3}$$
L=0

C)
$$\frac{C=\$300,000 \qquad I=\$120,000 \qquad I=\$120,000}{0 \qquad\qquad 1 \ldots\ldots\ldots\ldots\ldots 5}$$
L=$100,000

Use NPV Analysis and verify the results with Growth ROR Analysis and PVR Analysis.

4-14. If alternatives A and B are mutually exclusive projects, use ROR Analysis to determine which is economically best if i* = 15%.

A)
$$\frac{C=\$20,000 \qquad I=\$12,000 \qquad\qquad I=\$12,000}{0 \qquad\qquad 1 \ldots\ldots\ldots\ldots\ldots\ldots 12}$$
L=$20,000

B)
$$\frac{C=\$28,000 \qquad I=\$14,000 \qquad\qquad I=\$14,000}{0 \qquad\qquad 1 \ldots\ldots\ldots\ldots\ldots\ldots 12}$$
L=$28,000

Verify your conclusion with NPV and PVR analysis. Then re-analyze the alternatives for i* = 30%.

4-15. Three unequal life investment alternatives with costs, profits and salvage values as shown on the time diagram are being considered.

A)
$$\frac{C=\$160,000 \qquad I=\$150,000 \qquad\qquad I=\$150,000}{0 \qquad\qquad 1 \ldots\ldots\ldots\ldots\ldots\ldots 5}$$
L=$50,000

B)
$$\frac{C=\$320,000 \qquad I=\$275,000 \qquad I=\$275,000}{0 \qquad\qquad 1 \ldots\ldots\ldots\ldots 4}$$
L=$70,000

C)
$$\frac{C=\$480,000 \qquad I=\$500,000 \quad I=\$500,000}{0 \qquad\qquad 1 \ldots\ldots\ldots 3}$$
L=$100,000

Assume $480,000 is available to invest and other opportunities exist to invest all available dollars at a 20% ROR. Use NVP Analysis to determine how the $480,000 should be spent from an economic viewpoint if the alternatives are non-mutually exclusive. The use NPV Analysis to determine which of the alternatives, A, B or C, is best if the alternatives are mutually exclusive. Verify these results with PVR Analysis.

CHAPTER 5

ESCALATED AND CONSTANT DOLLARS

5.1 Inflation and Escalation in Economic Analysis

Many people use the terms inflation and escalation interchangeably but as economists and investment analysts use these terms, they are not interchangeable. Inflation is a term that has different meanings to different people but generally *inflation is defined as a persistent rise in the prices of a Consumer Price Index type basket of goods, services and commodities that is not offset by increased productivity. Deflation refers to a persistent drop in prices. Escalation on the other hand refers to a persistent rise in the price of specific commodities, goods or services due to a combination of inflation, supply/demand and other effects such as environmental and engineering changes.* Note that escalation deals with specific goods and services, while inflation is concerned with a basket of goods and services, so inflation involves average change. Inflation is just one of several factors that contributes to cost or price escalation and it should be evident that escalation is what affects the actual costs and revenues that will be realized for a project. Therefore, escalation of costs and revenues is the consideration that must be accounted for in economic evaluation of investments. Figure 5-1 enumerates these considerations.

Inflation
Supply/Demand
Technological Changes
Market Changes   } Escalated Dollars
Environmental Effects
Political Effects
Miscellaneous Effects

Figure 5-1 Factors Related to "Escalation"

The importance of cost and price escalation and the pyramiding effect it can have on the escalation of investment costs and revenues has been driven home forcefully to investment decision makers around the world in the 1970's and 1980's. Examples are innumerable. To cite one, in 1969 the Alaskan pipeline was estimated to have a cost of $900 million while in 1977 the final cost estimate was close to $8 billion, or about a 900% escalation from the initial estimate. Certainly not all of this cost escalation was due to inflation. Supply/demand effects on labor and materials and other factors such as environmental and engineering changes caused very significant escalation of the project costs. Fortunately, crude oil price escalation prior to the 1986 price decline was sufficient to cover the escalated costs. This example helps emphasize the very significant differences between inflation rates and escalation rates and that in economic evaluation work we are concerned with the effects of escalation of costs and revenues rather than inflation effects alone. However, inflation often has such a significant effect on escalation rates for specific goods and services that we should digress and discuss some of the causes and effects of inflation before later proceeding to present two explicit approaches for handling inflation and escalation properly in economic analyses.

Literally millions of words have been written on the subject of inflation in the past decade. We discussed in Chapter 2 that 6% compound interest will double capital in twelve years but have you thought about the fact that 6% inflation will cut the purchasing power of currency in half in twelve years? The same compound interest factors that work for us with savings apply inversely when accounting for the effect of inflation on purchasing power. Who benefits and who gets hurt most by inflation? There is no firm answer to this question but generally individuals and governments with large amounts of borrowed money benefit to some degree from inflation because they are able to pay off their debt with inflated future dollars that have lower purchasing power than the dollars originally borrowed. On the other hand people on fixed incomes with little or no debt clearly are hurt by inflation because the purchasing power of their income or capital decreases each year approximately proportional to the annual inflation rate. It is necessary to discuss how inflation rates are derived to amplify the meaning of the last statement.

In most countries the quoted inflation rate is derived from the change in an index which is made up of the weighted average of prices of a "basket of goods". In the USA and many other countries this index is called the Consumer Price Index, which in the USA, is made up of about 400 goods and services and commodities purchased by typical consumers. The U.S.

Bureau of Labor Statistics prepares this index on a monthly basis. It is important to note that an increase in the level of one price, or group of prices does not constitute inflation. If the prices of crude oil, iron ore, and uranium rise while the prices of automobiles, wheat and beef fall, we can not be certain whether there has been inflation. In other words, it may not be certain whether the average level of prices has risen or fallen. Lower prices in one set of goods may have offset higher prices of other. An increase in the price of one individual commodity is just that, an individual price increase. It may be due to inflation, excess demand or short supply or a combination of both. This further emphasizes why in economic evaluation work that escalation of costs and revenues for specific goods and services is relevant to the analysis rather than a given inflation rate.

What causes inflation? If the answer to this question were simple and easy to determine, possibly inflation would not be the problem that it is in many countries of the world today. However, there is reasonable general agreement among economists that one of the major contributing factors to inflation in all countries around the world is that governments are spending more money each year than they receive in taxes, royalties or revenues. To cover this deficit budget spending the governments increase the money supply or extend more credit through their central banking systems. Having more money in circulation to compete for goods and services often leads to price increases without a corresponding increase in productivity, which is inflation. If an individual or corporation has deficit spending year after year similar to many governments the result is usually bankruptcy because an individual or corporation cannot increase its money supply like a government can. Numerous authors dating back to Adam Smith have written that inflation is just a disguised form of bankruptcy because inflation enables governments to repay debts with sharply depreciated currencies. From a practical viewpoint if you evaluate the government debt of countries around the world it is very questionable if many of them would be willing to suffer the political, economic and social consequences of developing a balanced budget approach to repay existing debt in today's dollars. In virtually all countries, including the USA, the political and social forces will not tolerate the belt tightening needed to achieve this so the inevitable conclusion is that inflation is here to stay. Note, however, that the rate of inflation that is here to stay has not been specified. It is very likely inflation rates will fluctuate with time. Maybe inflation can be controlled at 6% per year for a few years or maybe 16% per year or maybe 3% per year depending on a particular country's situation and problems. But inflation rates on a long term, multi-decade basis, are not likely to return soon in any country to the 1% to 2% per year inflation rates that prevailed in the USA in the 1950's and early 1960's. Therefore, we must be prepared to account for inflation and escalation properly in the evaluation of the economic merit of future investment alternatives.

There are two basic evaluation techniques that can be used with equal validity to handle inflation and escalation properly in economic analyses. They are escalated dollar analysis and constant dollar analysis. The economic conclusions that are reached are always identical with either approach. *Escalated dollar values refer to actual dollars of revenue or cost that will be realized or incurred at specific future points in time. Elsewhere in the literature you find escalated dollars referred to by the terms current dollars, inflated dollars, nominal dollars, and dollars of the day. Constant dollar values refer to hypothetical constant purchasing power dollars obtained by present worthing escalated dollar values at the inflation rate to some arbitrary point in time, which often is the time that corresponds to the beginning of a project but may be any earlier point in time such as January 1, 1980. Constant dollars are referred to as real dollars or deflated dollars in many places in the literature.* Figure 5-2 relates the definitions of escalated dollars and constant dollars to a variation of Figure 5-1 used earlier to illustrate how inflation and escalation are related.

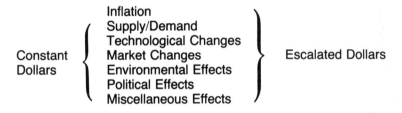

Figure 5-2 "Constant Dollar" Factors as They Relate to "Escalated Dollar" Factors

Constant dollar analysis advocates take the point of view that since escalated dollars have different purchasing power at different points in time it is necessary to convert all dollar values to some hypothetical constant purchasing power value before making an economic analysis. Constant dollar analysis is a valid analysis approach but it is no better than making the analysis directly in terms of escalated dollars and the constant dollar calculations require extra work and chance for error. It must be remembered that the purpose of economic analysis is to compare alternative opportunities for the investment of capital to select the investment alternatives that will maximize the future profit that can be accumulated at some future point in time. If you stop to think about it, the alternatives that will maximize your future profit in escalated dollars must be exactly the same alternatives that will maximize your future profit expressed in terms of constant purchasing power dollars referenced to some earlier date. The key to proper analysis and consistent, correct economic evaluation conclusions lies in recognizing that you cannot mix escalated dollar analyses and constant dollar analyses. To do so is analogous to comparing apples and oranges. You must either compare all alternatives using escalated dollars or you must compare all alternatives using constant dollars; and you must remember that the minimum ROR must be expressed in relation to other escalated dollar investment opportunities for escalated dollars analysis while the minimum rate of return must be expressed in relation to other constant dollar investment opportunities for constant dollar analysis. A very common constant dollar analysis mistake is for an evaluator to calculate constant dollar rate of return for a project and then compare it to other escalated dollar investment opportunities such as a bank interest rate, attainable bond interest rates or another escalated dollar ROR opportunity. These concepts will now be illustrated by a series of examples to clarify the meaning and application of inflation/escalation mechanical calculation considerations in practical evaluation situations.

First, let's consider how both escalated and constant dollar estimates of costs and revenues are obtained for a project. Usually *we start the evaluation of projects by estimating project costs and revenues in today's prices or values. This tells us what the project costs and revenues would be if the project occurred today. Since we know that projects do not occur instantaneously, we must escalate today's prices for both costs and revenues to project the actual or escalated values that will be realized. If we think prices will decline we use negative escalation rates. Then if we want to make constant dollar analysis we deflate our escalated dollars of cost and revenue by multiplying each of them times the single payment present worth factor at the assumed inflation rate, "f", for the number of periods needed to bring each value to the constant purchasing power base.* This present worth calculation washes inflation out of our constant dollar analysis projections and leaves only the supply/demand or other influences reflected in the forecast dollar values as Figure 5-2 illustrated earlier. Note that unless supply/demand and other considerations are nil, which means the escalation rate and inflation rate are equal, the today's dollars value estimates for costs and revenues are not the same as the constant dollars. Thinking that today's dollars are constant dollars because today's dollars are uniformly equal each year is a misconception that many people have. The term "constant dollars" has nothing to do with dollar values being uniform and equal each period.

Constant dollars may increase, decrease, or vary randomly from year to year. It is seldom permissible to make an investment analysis using today's dollar values. Only if today's dollar values happen to represent projected escalated or constant dollar values for an investment do you have reasonable justification for using today's dollar values as the basis for an investment analysis.

Consider the following investment analysis example to illustrate how today's dollar values are the starting basis to get both escalated dollar values and constant dollar values.

EXAMPLE 5-1 Escalated and Constant Dollar ROR Analysis

Today's Dollar Values, C = Cost, I = Income

c_0 = $100 c_1 = $150 I_2 = $400

0   1   2 years

Convert today's dollar values to escalated dollar values assuming cost escalation of 20% per year and income escalation of 10% per year. Calculate the escalated dollar analysis rate of return. Then assume inflation is 15% per year and calculate the constant dollar project ROR.

Solution:

Use single payment compound amount factors ($F/P_{i,n}$ factors) at the appropriate escalation rates to convert today's dollars to escalated dollars as shown on the following diagram.

Escalated Dollar Value Determination

$$c_0 = \$100 \qquad c_1 = \$150(F/P_{20,1}) = \$180 \qquad I_2 = \$400(F/P_{10,2}) = \$484$$

with 1.200 above c_1 term and 1.210 above I_2 term

0   1   2

Escalated Dollar ROR Analysis

When escalated costs and revenues have been obtained, they are the basis for the time value of money calculation to determine the desired evaluation criterion, which in this analysis is ROR.

PW equation: $100 + 180(P/F_{i,1}) = 484(P/F_{i,2})$

i = Escalated Dollar ROR = 47.7% by trial and error

This escalated dollar ROR is compared to the escalated dollar minimum ROR to determine if the project is economically satisfactory.

Constant Dollar Value Determination

Now convert the escalated dollar values to constant dollar values assuming an annual inflation rate of 15%. This is achieved by present worthing the escalated dollars from the previous analysis at the rate of inflation to express all dollar values in terms of time zero purchasing power. Use the single payment present worth factor $(P/F_{i,n})$ factor for the assumed inflation rate as illustrated on the following diagram:

$C_0=\$100 \qquad C_1=\$180(P/F_{15,1})=\$156 \qquad I_2=\$484(P/F_{15,2})=\$366$

0	1	2

The meaning of the constant dollar costs and revenues is as follows: $156 at year 0, would purchase the goods and services that $180 would purchase at year 1, if inflation is 15% per year, and $366 at year 2, if inflation is 15% per year, the goods and services that $484 would purchase at year 2, if inflation is 15% per year. The meaning of these constant purchasing power dollars is only valid when related to purchasing the average goods and services that make up the inflation index that was used to project 15% inflation per year.

Constant Dollar ROR Analysis

PW equation: $100 + 156(P/F_{i',1}) = 366(P/F_{i',2})$

i' = Constant Dollar ROR = 28.5% by trial and error

This constant dollar ROR is compared to the constant dollar minimum ROR to determine if the project is economically satisfactory. Either escalated or constant dollar analysis of this project, or any other, will give the same economic decision. *To reach a decision concerning the economic viability of this project using either the escalated or constant dollar analysis results we must know the other opportunities that exist for the use of our money and whether these other opportunities are expressed in escalated or constant dollars.* For illustration purposes consider that other opportunities exist to have our money invested at an escalated dollar ROR of 35%. Comparing the project's escalated dollar ROR of 47.7% to the minimum rate of return of 35% we conclude that the project is economically satisfactory. If we compared the project's constant dollar ROR of 28.5% to the other escalated dollar opportunities we would be making an invalid comparison. We cannot compare constant dollar results with other escalated dollar project results. All results must be calculated on the same consistent basis before comparison is made. To make a constant dollar analysis result comparison, we must convert the escalated dollar minimum ROR of 35% to the corresponding constant dollar minimum rate of return, which we then compare to the project constant dollar ROR of 28.5%. Mathematically, for escalated dollar ROR analysis, the factor $P/F_{i,n}$ does the job that the product of factors $P/F_{f,n} \times P/F_{i',n}$ does for constant dollar analysis of the same starting escalated dollar values where "i" equals escalated dollar ROR. "i'" equals constant dollar ROR and "f" equals the inflation rate.

$$P/F_{i,n} = P/F_{f,n} \times P/F_{i',n} \quad gives,$$

$$(1/1+i)^n = (1/1+f)^n \times (1/1+i')^n$$

or $\quad 1+i = (1+f)(1+i')$ \hfill 5-1

giving $\quad i' = [(1+i)/(1+f)] - 1$

For our example, escalated dollar ROR, i, of 35% and f = 15% gives:

$i' = [(1+.35)/(1+.15)] - 1 = .174$ or 17.4%

Comparing the project's constant dollar ROR of 28.5% to other constant dollar ROR opportunities of 17.4% leads to the economic conclusion that the project is satisfactory, consistent with the escalated dollar analysis conclusion. Note that if our other opportunities were represented by an escalated dollar bond investment ROR of 10%, the corresponding constant dollar minimum ROR would be negative.

$i^{*'} = [(1+.10)/(1+.15)] - 1 = -.043$ or -4.3%

Money earning a 10% escalated dollar ROR in a 15% inflation climate is losing average purchasing power at a 4.3% rate per year. Yet, if that is the best other opportunity that exists, it is better than doing nothing with the money and losing the average purchasing power at a 15% rate per year.

EXAMPLE 5-2 Escalated and Constant Dollar ROR and NPV Analysis

A proposed investment has the following projected today's dollar costs and revenues:

$C_0=\$20,000$	$C_1=\$40,000$	Rev=\$70,000 OC=\$20,000	Rev=\$70,000 OC=\$20,000	
				L=0
0	1	2	3	

Use ROR and NPV analysis to evaluate the economic potential of this investment project for the following evaluation assumptions. For escalated dollar analysis assume the escalated dollar minimum ROR is 15%. Use Equation 5-1 to calculate the equivalent constant dollar minimum ROR for constant dollar analysis.

A) Assume year 1 development cost will escalate 7% per year. Year 2 and 3 revenues will escalate 8% per year. Operating costs will escalate 9% per year. Make escalated dollar analysis.

B) For the part "A" given escalated dollar minimum ROR and escalation assumptions make constant dollar analysis of the project for assumed inflation of 6% per year over the project life.

C) Use the given today's dollar cost and revenue estimates to evaluate the project and discuss the implicit escalation and inflation rate assumptions involved.

Solution, All Values in Thousands of Dollars:

A) Escalated Dollar Analysis

$$\text{Rev}=70(F/P_{8,2})=81.62 \quad 70(F/P_{8,3})=88.2$$
$$1.166 1.260$$

$$\text{OC}=20(F/P_{9,2})=23.76 \quad 20(F/P_{9,3})=25.9$$
$$1.188 1.295$$

$$C_0=20 \quad C_1=40(F/P_{7,1})=42.8 \quad \text{Net Rev} =57.86 =62.3$$

| 0 | 1 | 2 | 3 |

The today's dollar costs and revenues are converted to escalated dollar values using single payment compound amount factors calculated at the escalation rates. Note that the uniform series compound amount factor, $F/A_{i,n}$, has not been utilized to escalate the uniform revenues and operating costs. The uniform series factor would give cumulative revenue or operating cost at year 3, rather than year by year calculating the desired escalated dollar costs and revenues. Therefore, the uniform series factors are not useful for escalation calculations.

$$\text{Escalated \$ NPV} = -20 - 42.8(P/F_{15,1}) + 57.86(P/F_{15,2})$$
$$.8696 .7561$$

$$+ 62.3(P/F_{15,3}) = +27.49 > 0,$$
$$.6575$$

accept the project

Escalated \$ ROR = 42.5% is the "i" value that makes escalated
                  dollar NPV = 0.

42.5% > i^* = 15%, accept the project

B) Constant Dollar Analysis

The escalated dollar costs and net revenues from part "A" are the basis for the constant dollar calculations.

$$C_0=20 \quad \begin{array}{c} .9434 \\ C_1=42.8(P/F_{6,1}) \\ = 40.38 \end{array} \quad \begin{array}{c} .8900 \\ R_2=57.86(P/F_{6,2}) \\ = 51.49 \end{array} \quad \begin{array}{c} .8396 \\ R_3=62.3(P/F_{6,3}) \\ = 52.30 \end{array}$$

| 0 | 1 | 2 | 3 |

Constant dollar values are obtained by present worthing escalated dollars at the rate of inflation of 6% per year. For constant dollar NPV analysis we must convert the 15% escalated dollar minimum ROR to the equivalent constant dollar minimum ROR for the assumed 6% per year inflation rate. Use Equation 5-1 for this calculation as follows:

$$i^{*\prime} = \{(1+i^*)/(1+f)\}-1 = (1.15/1.06) - 1 = 0.0849 \text{ or } 8.49\%$$

$$\text{Constant \$ NPV} = -20 - 40.38(P/F_{8.49,1})^{.9217} + 51.49(P/F_{8.49,2})^{.8496}$$

$$+ 52.30(P/F_{8.49,3})^{.7831} = +27.48 > 0, \text{ so accept}$$

or

$$\text{Constant \$ NPV} = -20 - 40.38(1/1.0859)^1 + 51.49(1/1.0859)^2$$

$$+ 52.30(1/1.0859)^3 = +27.48 > 0, \text{ so accept}$$

Note that the constant dollar NPV is identical to the escalated dollar NPV within roundoff error calculation accuracy. Constant dollar NPV equations are mathematically equivalent to escalated dollar NPV equations, so of course give the same results. The mathematical equivalency follows:

$$\text{Escalated \$ Calculations} = \text{Constant \$ Calculations}$$

$$(\text{Escalated \$ Value})(P/F_{i^*,n})$$

$$= (\text{Escalated \$ Value})(P/F_{f,n})(P/F_{i^{*\prime},n})$$

since $P/F_{i^*,n} = (P/F_{f,n})(P/F_{i^{*\prime},n})$ as discussed earlier in the development of Equation 5-1. For this analysis in year 2:

$$P/F_{15,2} = 0.7561 = (P/F_{6,2})(P/F_{8.49,2})$$

$$= (0.8900)(0.8496) = 0.7561$$

Constant $ ROR = 34.4% is the "i" value that makes constant dollar net present value equal to zero.

$$34.4\% > i^{*\prime} = 8.49\%, \text{ accept the project}$$

C) Today's Dollar Analysis

Using today's dollars as the basis for evaluation calculations involves one of two different assumptions. Either you assume that today's dollars equal escalated dollar values or you assume that today's dollars equal constant dollar values.

Today's Dollars Equal Escalated Dollars

Assuming that today's dollars equal escalated dollars explicitly assumes that costs and revenues in the future will be the same as they would be today. This implicitly involves the assumption that costs and revenues will escalate at 0% per year over the evaluation life. This is an escalated dollar assumption similar to, but different from the part "A" assumptions, so an escalated dollar minimum ROR must be used in NPV calculations and for ROR analysis decisions. The "today's dollar values equal escalated dollar values" analysis follows:

$$\text{NPV} = -20 - 40(P/F_{15,1}) + 50(P/F_{15,2}) + 50(P/F_{15,3}) = +15.9 > 0 \text{ accept}$$
$$\text{ROR} = 32.2\% > i^* = 15\%, \text{ accept}$$

Note these escalated dollar NPV and ROR results are significantly different from the part "A" escalated dollar analysis results. There are an unlimited number of different ways that escalated costs and revenues can be projected. Assuming today's dollars are equal to escalated dollars is just one specific escalation assumption. It is important to understand specific escalation assumptions used in analyses because they usually significantly affect evaluation results.

A variation of the today's dollar equal escalated dollars assumption is to escalate all capital costs (such as acquisition and development costs) at specified rates and to assume that the escalated dollar net revenues or profits in the income generating years will equal today's dollar net revenues or profits. This is often called "the washout assumption" since it assumes that any escalation of operating costs each year will be offset (washed out) by the same dollar escalation of revenue. Note there are no revenues in the development years, so costs must be escalated in pre-revenue years. The washout assumption only applies to revenues and operating costs in the revenue generating years.

Today's Dollars Equal Constant Dollars

Since constant dollar values are obtained by present worthing escalated dollars at the rate of inflation, the only way today's dollars can equal constant dollars is if all today's dollar values escalate each year at the rate of inflation. Escalating each cost and revenue at the rate of inflation and then present worthing the resulting escalated dollars at the rate of inflation to get constant dollars brings the dollar values back to the starting today's dollar values. This is a constant dollar analysis assumption, so a constant dollar minimum ROR (8.49% for this analysis) must be used in the constant dollar NPV calculations and for the economic decision with constant dollar ROR results. The today's dollars equal constant dollars NPV and ROR results follow:

$$NPV = -20 - 40(P/F_{8.49,1}) + 50(P/F_{8.49,2}) + 50(P/F_{8.49,3})$$

$$= +24.8 > 0, \text{ so accept}$$

$$ROR = 32.2\% > i^{*1} = 8.49\%, \text{ so accept}$$

Note the today's dollars equal escalated dollars NPV result is significantly different from the today's dollars equal constant dollars NPV result. Although the ROR results are 32.2% for both cases, different minimum rates of return are used for the economic decision with ROR in the two cases. These two today's dollar analysis cases are very different and can lead to different investment decisions. Obviously, understanding the escalated dollar or constant dollar inflation and escalation assumptions being made is very important for correct economic decision making.

EXAMPLE 5-3 Escalated and Constant Dollar Cost Analysis of Service Producing Alternatives

Compare two alternatives that provide a service using escalated and constant dollar analysis. Consider alternative "A" to be capital intensive, requiring the expenditure of $100,000 at time zero and no operating costs in years one or two to provide a service for two years while alternative "B" is labor intensive, requiring end of year one and two escalated dollar operating costs of $60,000 and $72,000 respectively. Salvage is zero in both cases. Make present worth cost analysis for escalated dollar minimum rate of return of 30%, then for $i^* = 20\%$, then for $i^* = 10\%$. Assume inflation of 20% per year for all constant dollar calculations. Verify the present worth cost results with incremental NPV analysis.

Solution, All Values in Thousands of Dollars:

Escalated Dollar Diagrams

A) C=100   -   -
    _____
    0   1   2

B)   -   OC=60   OC=72
    _____
    0   1   2

Solution:

Escalated Dollar PW Cost Analysis

1) for i* = 30%, remembering $P/F_{i*,n} = (1/1+i^*)^n$

$PW_A = 100$
$PW_B = 60(1/1.3) + 72(1/1.3)^2 = 88.75$,   Select "B"

2) for i* = 20%

$PW_A = 100$
$PW_B = 60(1/1.2) + 72(1/1.2)^2 = 100$

Results indicate breakeven economics.

3) for i* = 10%

$PW_A = 100$,   Select Smaller Present Worth Cost, "A"
$PW_B = 60(1/1.1) + 72(1/1.1)^2 = 114$

Constant Dollar Diagrams for Inflation Rate, f = 20%

A) C=100   -   -

       0   1   2

$$60(P/F_{20,1})\qquad 72(P/F_{20,2})$$
B)   - $OC=50$ $OC=50$

       0   1   2

Constant Dollar PW Cost Analysis:

1) for an escalated dollar minimum ROR, i* = 30%, the corresponding constant dollar minimum ROR, i*′ is 8.33%

$PW_A = 100$
$PW_B = 50(1/1.0833) + 50(1/1.0833)^2 = 88.75$,   Select Smaller, "B"

2) for i* = 20%, constant dollar i*′ is 0

$PW_A = 100$ Breakeven
$PW_B = 50(1/1.0) + 50(1/1.0)^2 = 100$

Results indicate breakeven economics

3) for i* = 10%, constant dollar i*′ is −8.33%

$PW_A = 100$ Select Smaller, "A"
$PW_B = 50(1/.9166) + 50(1/.9166)^2 = 114$

Note that not only do escalated and constant dollar analysis give the same conclusion, but those conclusions are based upon identical present worth costs.

If we look at the incremental difference between "A" and "B", we can show that incremental NPV analysis gives the same result for escalated or constant dollar analysis.

Incremental Escalated Dollar Diagram

```
                          Savings
A-B)    C=100          60          72
       ─────────────────────────────
        0           1           2
```

Escalated Dollar Incremental NPV Analysis

$i^* = 30\%$, $NPV_{A-B} = 60(1/1.3) + 72(1/1.3)^2 - 100 = -11.25 < 0$, select "B"

$i^* = 20\%$, $NPV_{A-B} = 60(1/1.2) + 72(1/1.2)^2 - 100 = 0$, breakeven

$i^* = 10\%$, $NPV_{A-B} = 60(1/1.1) + 72(1/1.1)^2 - 100 = +14.0 > 0$, select "A"

Incremental Constant Dollar Diagram

```
                          Savings
A-B)    C=100          50          50
       ─────────────────────────────
        0           1           2
```

Constant Dollar Incremental NPV Analysis

For $i^* = 30\%$ and $f=20\%$, equivalent $i^{*'} = 8.33\%$

$NPV_{A-B} = 50(1/1.0833) + 50(1/1.0833)^2 - 100 = -11.25$, select "B"

For $i^* = 20\%$ and $f=20\%$, equivalent $i^{*'} = 0\%$

$NPV_{A-B} = 50(1/1.0) + 50(1/1.0)^2 - 100 = 0$, breakeven

For $i^* = 10\%$ and $f=20\%$, equivalent $i^{*'} = -8.33\%$

$NPV_{A-B} = 50(1/.9166) + 50(1/.9166)^2 - 100 = 14.0$, select "A"

Note the identical incremental NPV results for both escalated and constant dollar analysis, so of course the same economic decision results either way.

Now that we have established that either escalated or constant dollar analysis properly handled gives the same economic analysis conclusions, are there reasons for preferring one method over the other? In general it takes two present worth calculations in constant dollar analysis to achieve the same result that can be obtained with one present worth calculation escalated dollar analysis. Fewer calculations mean fewer chances for math errors, a point in favor of escalated dollar analysis. To make proper after-tax analysis, tax calculations must always be made in escalated dollars as must borrowed money principal and interest payments. For constant dollar analysis, this requires careful diligence to avoid improper mixing of escalated and constant dollars. With escalated dollar analysis all values are in escalated dollars so this is not a problem, another point in favor of escalated dollar analysis. From a practical and ease of calculation viewpoint, there is little to be said for constant dollar analysis that cannot be said more favorably for escalated dollar analysis. However, for those evaluation people who want to make constant dollar analysis rather than escalated dollar analysis, the following steps should be followed for constant dollar analysis:

1) Determine the escalated dollar values for all project costs and revenues.
2) Convert all escalated dollar values to the corresponding constant dollar values for the assumed inflation rates each year.
3) Convert the escalated dollar minimum ROR, i^*, to the corresponding constant dollar value, $i^{*'}$, if the minimum ROR is initially expressed in terms of escalated dollars.
4) Calculate constant dollar NPV using $i^{*'}$, or calculate constant dollar ROR, i', and compare to $i^{*'}$ for the economic decision.

One situation that can give constant dollar analysis a potential intangible advantage over escalated dollar analysis is in evaluation of a project to determine and negotiate the breakeven selling price that a purchaser may be willing to pay for a product. Since in inflationary times a given constant dollar minimum rate of return is always less than the equivalent escalated dollar minimum rate of return, it may be easier to convince a buyer to accept paying the price needed for you to get a 15% constant dollar ROR than a higher but equivalent escalated dollar ROR for a given rate of inflation. This is a potential marketing or negotiation advantage rather than an economic analysis advantage. The following example shows that breakeven analysis economic calculations (such as breakeven selling price) will be exactly the same with either escalated dollar analysis or constant dollar analysis.

EXAMPLE 5-4 Breakeven Revenue Analysis in Escalated and Constant Dollars.

The investment of $30,000 today is estimated to produce 100 product units each year for the next two years when the product is expected to become obsolete. Year 2 salvage value is expected to be zero. Today's dollar operating costs for years 1 and 2 are estimated to be $8,000 per year. Inflation is expected to be 7.0% per year for each of the next two years. If product selling price is projected to escalate 8% per year and operating costs escalate 10% per year, calculate the year 1 and 2 escalated dollar selling price that will give the investor a desired 15% constant dollar ROR on invested dollars.

Solution, All Values in Dollars:

Let X = Today's Dollar Selling Price Per Unit

	Year 1	Year 2
Escalated $ Sales	$X(100)(F/P_{8,1})=108.0X$	$X(100)(F/P_{8,2})=116.6X$
Escalated $ OC	$8000(F/P_{10,1}) = 8,800$	$8000(F/P_{10,2}) = 9,680$
Escalated $ Profit	108.0X - 8,800	116.6X - 9,680
Constant $ Profit	$(108.0X-8,800)(P/F_{7,1})$	$(116.6X-9,680)(P/F_{7,2})$

As shown, today's dollar revenues and operating costs are converted to escalated dollar values using the selling price and operating cost escalation rates of 8% and 10% respectively. If you want to work in escalated dollars you use the resultant escalated dollar profits shown, which are a function of the unknown today's dollar selling price per unit, X. If you prefer to work in constant dollars you present worth escalated dollar profit at the 7% per year rate of inflation to convert escalated dollars to constant dollars.

Escalated Dollar Present Worth Equation Calculations

To write an escalated dollar present worth equation we must use escalated dollar values and handle the time value of money at the escalated dollar minimum ROR that is equivalent to the desired 15% constant dollar minimum ROR for assumed 7% per year inflation. Using Equation 5-1:

$$i^* = (1+f)(1+i^{*'}) -1 = (1.07)(1.15) -1 = .2305 \text{ or } 23.05\%$$

$$30,000 = (108.0X-8,800)(P/F_{23.05,1}) \overset{.81268}{} + (116.6X-9,680)(P/F_{23.05,2}) \overset{.66045}{}$$

Solving for X = $264.26/units = Today's Dollar Selling Price

$246.26(F/P_{8,1}) = $285.40/unit = Year 1 Escalated $ Selling Price

$246.26(F/P_{8,2}) = $308.24/unit = Year 2 Escalated $ Selling Price

Constant Dollar Present Worth Equation Using Constant Dollar Profits

Handle the time value of money using the 15% constant dollar minimum ROR:

$$30,000 = (108.0X-8,800)(P/F_{7,1})(P/F_{15,1})$$

$$+ (116.6X-9,680)(P/F_{7,2})(P/F_{15,2})$$

solving for X = \$264.26/units = Today's Dollar Selling Price

\$246.26(F/P_{8,1}) = \$285.40/unit = Year 1 Escalated \$ Selling Price

\$246.26(F/P_{8,2}) = \$308.24/unit = Year 2 Escalated \$ Selling Price

The same breakeven selling prices result from either escalated or constant dollar analysis.

To conclude the inflation and escalation discussion, a few words should be said about forecasting escalation rates for different commodities or segments of industry. The past often is a good indicator of the future, so analysis of past cost trends for a particular commodity or asset is one way to get an indication of what the future might hold. This approach was very poor in the 1973-1980 period due to the significant increase in energy costs around the world, but no method of analysis is going to predict consistently the effects of that kind of upset to the world economy. The U.S. Bureau of Labor Statistics publishes 70 or more price indices for commodities and materials, 5 or more indices or wage rates and an index of engineering costs which can be obtained to give past trends. "Chemical Engineering" consolidates these Bureau of Labor Statistics into the CE Plant Cost Index published on a bi-monthly basis as a measure of the cost of typical chemical plants. Chemical Engineering also presents the Marshall and Swift equipment cost index bi-monthly. No one has a crystal ball to forecast the future accurately, but the use of available indices can be helpful in determining cost and price trends and rates of change of these trends needed to forecast meaningful escalation rates for costs and revenues needed for investment analyses.

In summary, proper evaluation of investments in various escalated dollar or constant dollar analyses requires understanding how to apply the following three different kinds of rates:

1. **Escalation Rates:** used to convert today's dollar values to escalated dollar values.

2. **Inflation Rates:** used to convert escalated dollar values to constant dollar values.

3. Time Value of Money Rates: used to account for the time value of money using i or i* in escalated dollar analyses, and i′ or i*′ in constant dollar analyses.

These rates are all used in the following example illustrating general escalated and constant dollar analysis calculations involving different escalation rates and inflation rates each year.

EXAMPLE 5-5 ROR and NPV Analysis With Changing Escalation and Inflation Rates Each Year

A cost of $100,000 today is projected to generate today's dollar incomes of $75,000 per year at the end of each of years 1, 2 and 3 with today's dollar operating costs of $25,000 per year at years 1, 2 and 3. Salvage value is zero at year 3. Incomes and operating costs are projected to escalate 10% in year 1, 12% in year 2, and 15% in year 3, so net income minus operating cost escalates at the same given rate each year. Calculate the project escalated dollar ROR and NPV assuming the minimum ROR for each of the 3 years is 15% in escalated dollars. Then assume inflation rates will be 10% in year 1, 8% in year 2 and 6% in year 3, and calculate constant dollar ROR and NPV.

Solution:

Today's Dollar Values (In Thousands of Dollars)

C=100	Net I_1=50	Net I_2=50	Net I_3=50
0	1	2	3

Escalated Dollar Values

C=100	Net I_1=55	Net I_2=61.6	Net I_3=70.84
0	1	2	3

where,

$$\text{Net } I_1 = 50(F/P_{10,1}^{1.100}) = 55.0$$

$$\text{Net } I_2 = 50(F/P_{10,1}^{1.100})(F/P_{12,1}^{1.120}) = 61.60$$

$$\text{Net } I_3 = 50(F/P_{10,1}^{1.100})(F/P_{12,1}^{1.120})(F/P_{15,1}^{1.150}) = 70.84$$

Escalated Dollar Present Worth Equation for ROR Analysis

$$100 = 55(P/F_{i,1}) + 61.6(P/F_{i,2}) + 70.84(P/F_{i,3})$$

i = Escalated Dollar ROR = 37.4% by trial and error

   37.4% > 15%, so satisfactory

Escalated Dollar Net Present Value

$$NPV = -100 + 55(P/F_{15,1})^{.8696} + 61.6(P/F_{15,2})^{.7561} + 70.84(P/F_{15,3})^{.6575}$$

   = +$41.0 > 0, so satisfactory

Constant Dollar Values

C=100   Net I_1=50   Net I_2=51.85   Net I_3=56.25

0   1   2   3

where escalated dollars discounted at the annual inflation rates give the following constant dollar net incomes:

$$Net\ I_1 = 55(P/F_{10,1})^{.9091} = 50.0$$

$$Net\ I_2 = 61.6(P/F_{10,1})^{.9091}(P/F_{8,1})^{.9259} = 51.85$$

$$Net\ I_3 = 70.84(P/F_{10,1})^{.9091}(P/F_{8,1})^{.9259}(P/F_{6,1})^{.9434} = 56.25$$

Constant Dollar Present Worth Equation for ROR Analysis

$$100 = 50(P/F_{i',1}) + 51.85(P/F_{i',2}) + 56.25(P/F_{i',3})$$

i' = Constant Dollar ROR = 26.3% > $i^{*'}$ values shown in next section, so satisfactory.

Constant Dollar Net Present Value Analysis

   For constant dollar NPV analysis we must calculate the constant dollar minimum ROR each year that is equivalent to the 15% escalated dollar minimum ROR for the assumed inflation rates of 10% in year 1, 8% in year 2 and 6% in year 3 using a rearranged version of Equation 5-1.

$$i^*{}_1 = \{(1+i^*)(1+f)\} - 1$$

Year 1, $i^*{}_1 = (1.15/1.10) - 1 = 4.54\%$

Year 2, $i^*{}_1 = (1.15/1.08) - 1 = 6.48\%$

Year 3, $i^*{}_1 = (1.15/1.06) - 1 = 8.49\%$

$$NPV = -100 + 50(P/F^{.9566}_{4.54,1}) + 51.85(P/F^{.9391}_{6.48,1})(P/F^{.9566}_{4.54,1})$$

$$+ 56.25(P/F^{.9566}_{4.54,1})(P/F^{.9391}_{6.48,1})(P/F^{.9217}_{8.49,1})$$

$$= +\$41.0 > 0, \text{ so satisfactory}$$

Note the equivalence of constant dollar NPV and escalated dollar NPV results. Even with different escalation and inflation rates each year, correct analysis gives the same escalated and constant dollar NPV results, so of course the same economic conclusions from either analysis. Similarly, with ROR analysis results in either escalated or constant dollars, as long as you compare project ROR to the minimum ROR expressed in the same kind of dollars (escalated or constant), you get the same economic conclusions from either escalated or constant dollar ROR analysis.

PROBLEMS

5-1 A plant operation is scheduled to be developed for a time zero capital cost of $400 million with year 1 through 10 revenues of $200 million per year less operating costs of $100 million per year with a zero salvage value. Assume a washout of escalation of operating costs and revenue each year. "Washout" means any operating cost escalation is offset by the same dollar escalation of revenue (not the same percent escalation) so profit remains uniform at the today's dollar value profit. A) Evaluate the project ROR and analyze the sensitivity of the result to changing project life to 5 years or 15 years. B) Evaluate the sensitivity of project ROR to increasing the time zero capital cost to $600 million and $800 million for the 10 year project life.

5-2 In 1977 the U.S. gross national product (GNP) increased to $1.7 trillion from $1.5 trillion in terms of actual escalated dollar values. In the same year the Consumer Price Index rose 7%. What was the escalated (current) dollar percent increase in the GNP? What was the constant (real) dollar percent increase in the GNP?

5-3   An investment related to developing a new product is estimated to have the following costs and revenues in "today's" or "time zero" dollars.

		I=$200,000	I=$200,000
C$_0$=$50,000	C$_1$=$150,000	OC=$100,000	OC=$100,000

$$L=0$$

0	1	2 5

A) Evaluate the project escalated dollar ROR if both capital costs and operating costs are estimated to escalate at 15% per year from time zero with income escalating at 10% per year.
B) Use escalated dollar ROR Analysis to analyze the investment assuming a washout of escalation of income and operating costs with a 15% escalation of capital costs per year.
C) Make constant dollar ROR Analysis of Case 'B' assuming the rate of inflation for the next 5 years will be 10% per year.

5-4   A product that sells today for $100 per unit is expected to escalate in price by 6% in year 1, 8% in year 2 and 10% in year 3. Calculate the escalated dollar year 3 product selling price. If inflation is expected to be 5% in year 1, 9% in year 2 and 12% in year 3, determine the year 3 constant dollar product selling price.

5-5   An investor has an opportunity to buy a parcel of land for $100,000. He plans to sell it in 2 years. What will the sale price have to be for the investor to get a 25% constant dollar before-tax ROR with inflation averaging 10% annually? What escalated dollar annual rate of increase in land value will give the needed sale price?

5-6   Determine the breakeven escalated dollar selling price per unit required in each of years 1 and 2 to achieve a 15% constant dollar project ROR, assuming a 12% per year inflation rate. All dollar values are today's dollar values.

	Sales=$X(1000)	Sales=$X(1000)
C=$100,000	OC=$50,000	OC=$50,000

0	1	2

Sales escalation is 10% per year from time 0 when selling price is $X per unit. Operating Cost (OC) escalation is 15% per year from time 0. 1,000 units are to be produced and sold each year.

5-7   What can be paid now (today) to acquire a property that will be developed 2 years from now and which engineers estimate will have today's dollar costs and revenues shown on the following time diagram. All values are in thousands of today's dollars.

```
                              Rev=$150   Rev=$150   Rev=$150
C_Acq=?          -    C=$200   OC=$50     OC=$50     OC=$50
                                                                L=0
   0(now)   1         2        3          4          5
```

Starting from now, it is projected that inflation will be 7% per year. The escalated dollar minimum ROR is 15%. Evaluate the acquisition cost that can be paid now to acquire this property for the following five cases:

Case 1. Make the analysis using today's dollar costs and revenues assuming they are a reasonable projection of escalated dollar capital costs, operating costs and revenues to be incurred (this assumption effectively assumes zero percent escalation of all costs and revenues each year or that escalation of all capital costs and operating costs will be offset by escalation of revenues so that escalation of costs and revenues will have zero effect on economic analysis results).

Case 2. Make the analysis using the today's dollar costs and revenues assuming they represent constant dollar values. (This assumption is valid if you assume that all capital costs, operating costs and revenues will escalate at the 7% rate of inflation each year. Present worthing these escalated dollar values at the same rate of inflation to get constant dollar values gives the original today's dollar values for this assumption.)

Case 3. Use escalated dollar analysis assuming capital cost (C) escalation will be 12% per year, operating cost (OC) escalation will be 10% per year and revenue (Rev) escalation will be 10% per year.

Case 4. Make constant dollar analysis for the Case 3 escalation assumption assuming 7% inflation as given.

Case 5. Use an escalated dollar analysis assuming capital costs escalate at 12% per year and escalation of operating costs is exactly offset by a like-dollar escalation of revenues each year which gives uniform profit margins each year. This commonly is called "the washout assumption".

5-8   An investor has paid $100,000 for a machine that is estimated to produce 5000 product units per year for each of the next 3 years when the machine is estimated to be obsolete with a zero salvage value. The product price is the 'unknown' to be calculated, so it is estimated to be $X per unit in year 1 escalated dollars and to increase 10% per year in year 2 and 6% in year 3. Total operating costs are estimated to be $8,000 in year 1 escalated dollars and to increase 15% in year 2 and 8% in year 3. The annual inflation rate is estimated to be 7%. What must be the year 1, 2 and 3 escalated dollar product selling price if the investor is to receive a 12% annually compounded constant dollar ROR on invested dollars?

CHAPTER 6

UNCERTAINTY AND RISK ANALYSIS

6.1 Introduction

In this age of advancing technology, successful managers must make informed investment decisions that determine the future success of their companies by drawing systematically on the specialized knowledge, accumulated information, experience and skills of many people. In evaluating projects and making choices between investment alternatives, every manager is painfully aware that he cannot and will not always be right. Management pressure is increased by the knowledge that a company's future depends on the ability to choose with a high degree of consistency those investment and market opportunities that have a high probability of success even though the characteristics of future events are seldom precisely known.

In the previous chapters in the text investment analyses all were considered to be made under "no-risk" conditions. That is, the probability of success was considered to be 1.0 for each investment evaluated. This means that by expressing risk and uncertainty quantitatively in terms of numerical probabilities or likelihood of occurrence, where probabilities are decimal fractions in the range of zero to 1.0, we implicitly considered that the probability of achieving projected profits or savings was 1.0 for investment situations evaluated. We are all aware that due to risk and uncertainty from innumerable sources, the probability of success for many investments is significantly different that 1.0. When faced with decision choices under uncertain conditions, a manager can use informal analysis of the risk and uncertainty associated with the investment or he can analyze the elements of risk and uncertainty in a quantitative manner. Informal analysis relies on the decision makers experience, intuition, judgement, hunches and luck to determine whether or not a particular investment should be made. The quantitative analysis approach is based on analyzing the effects that risk and uncertainty can have on an investment situation by using a logical and consistent decision strategy that incorporates the effects of risk and uncertainty into the analysis results. Use of the quantitative analysis approach should not be considered to imply that the informal analysis considerations of experience, intuition and judgement are not needed. On the contrary, the purpose of quantitative analysis of risk and uncertainty is to provide the decision maker with as much quantitative information as possible concerning the risks and uncertainties associated with a particular investment situation, so that the decision maker has the best possible information on which to apply experience, intuition and good judgment in reaching the final decision. The objective of investment decision making from an economic viewpoint under conditions of uncertainty is to invest available capital where we have the highest probability of generating the maximum possible future profit. The use of quantitative approaches to incorporate risk and uncertainty into analysis results may help us be more successful in achieving this objective over the long run.

No matter how comprehensive or sophisticated an investment evaluation may be, uncertainty still remains a factor in the evaluation. Even though rate of return or some other economic evaluation criterion may be calculated for a project with several significant figures of accuracy using the best available cost and income data, the decision maker may still feel uneasy about the economic decision indicated because he or she knows the assumptions on which the calculations are based are uncertain. If the economic evaluation method used does not reflect this uncertainty then every assumption built into an economic analysis is a "best guess" and the final economic result is a consolidation of these "best guesses". Making decisions on the basis of such "best guess" calculations alone can be hazardous. Consider a manager who may select investment alternative "A" with a 20% ROR over investment "B" which has a 15% ROR based on the "best guess" ROR calculation approach. Would this decision be justifiable if the probability of success of alternative "A" was 50% (or one chance in two) compared with a probability of success of alternative "B" of 90%? It is evident that the manager needs some measure of the "risk" involved in each alternative in addition to the "best guess" or most likely rate of return results.

There are several different approaches that can be used to quantitatively incorporate risk and uncertainty into analyses. These include sensitivity analysis or probabilistic sensitivity analysis to account for uncertainty associated with possible variation in project parameters, and expected value or expected net present value or rate of return analysis to account for risk associated with finite probability of failure. The use of sensitivity analysis is advocated for most economic analyses and the use of expected value analysis is advisable if finite probability of project failure exists. Sensitivity analysis is described in the first half of this chapter and expected value analysis is described in the second half.

Sensitivity analysis is a means of evaluating the effects of uncertainty on investment by determining how investment profitability varies as the parameters are varied that affect economic evaluation results. Sensitivity analysis is a means of identifying those critical variables that, if changed, could considerably affect the profitability measure. In carrying out a sensitivity analysis, individual variables are changed and the effect of such a change on the expected rate of return (or some other decision method) is computed. Once all of the strategic variables have been identified, they can be given special attention by the decision maker. Some of the typical investment parameters that often are allowed to vary for sensitivity analysis include initial investment, selling price, operating cost, project life, and salvage value. If probabilities of occurrence are associated with the various levels of each investment parameters, sensitivity analysis becomes probabilistic sensitivity analysis.

It may now be evident to the reader that the term "uncertainty" as used in this text refers to possible variation in parameters that affect investment evaluation. "Risk" refers to the evaluation of an investment using a known mechanism that incorporates the probabilities of occurrence for success and failure and/or of different values of each investment parameter. Both uncertainty and risk influence almost all types of investment decisions, but especially investment involving research and development for any industry and exploration for minerals and oil or gas.

6.2 Sensitivity Analysis to Analyze Effects of Uncertainty

As described in the previous section, sensitivity analysis refers to analysis of how investment profitability is affected by variation in the parameters that affect overall profitability. For a case where rate of return is the economic criterion used to measure profitability, sensitivity analysis involves evaluation of how rate of return varies with parameters such as initial investment, profit per year, project life, and salvage value. It is frequently used to determine how much change in a variable would be necessary to reverse the decision based on average-value or best-guess estimates. It usually does not take into consideration the likelihood of variation. The rate of change in the total outcome relative to the rate of change in the variable being considered will indicate the significance of this variable in the overall evaluation. The laborious nature of sensitivity analysis calculations on a before, or after-tax basis make them particularly suitable for computer analysis. Recently, software developed by the authors (see bibliography) has become available for many microcomputers to enable persons to perform fairly sophisticated after tax cash flow, DCFROR, NPV and PVR sensitivity analysis of mineral, petroleum and non-mineral projects at home or in the office with minimal effort.

EXAMPLE 6-1 Single Variable Sensitivity Analysis

Annual profits of $67,000 are shown on the time diagram for this $240,000 investment case with an expected salvage value of $70,000 after five years. Evaluate the sensitivity of project ROR to plus or minus 20% and 40% variations in initial investment, annual profit, project life and salvage value.

$$\overbrace{\phantom{\text{Profits}}}^{\textstyle \text{Profits}}$$

```
                    Profits
         ┌──────────────────────────────────┐
C=$240,000 $67,000 $67,000 $67,000 $67,000 $67,000
                                              ──────── L=$70,000
    0       1       2       3       4       5
```

Solution:

Using the most expected cost and revenue parameters gives:

PW Eq: $240,000 = 67,000(P/A_{i,5}) + 70,000(P/F_{i,5})$

The "best guess" or "most expected" project ROR is 18%. How will this "most expected" 18% ROR vary as parameters are changed?

A) Initial Investment Sensitivity Analysis

Initial Investment	Change in Prediction	ROR	Percent Change in ROR Prediction
144,000	-40	42.0	133.3
192,000	-20	27.5	52.9
240,000	0	18.0	0
288,000	+20	11.2	-37.9
336,000	+40	5.8	-67.7

The percent variations in the ROR from changes in initial investment costs are very significant. In general, changes in parameters close to time zero (such as initial investment and annual profit) have a much more significant effect on investment ROR than changes in parameters many years in the future from time zero (such as salvage value).

B) Project Life Sensitivity Analysis

Project Life	Change in Prediction	ROR	Percent Change in ROR Prediction
3	-40	5.6	-68.8
4	-20	13.4	-25.5
5	0	18.0	0
6	+20	20.9	16.3
7	+40	22.9	27.1

Note that this sensitivity analysis really involves changes in total cash flow as well as project life. If project life was longer (say 10 years or more), changes in life would have a less sensitive effect on ROR.

C) Annual Profit Sensitivity Analysis

Annual Profit	Change in Prediction	ROR	Percent Change in ROR Prediction
40,200	-40	3.6	-80.2
53,600	-20	11.0	-39.0
67,000	0	18.0	0
80,400	+20	24.8	37.9
93,800	+40	31.5	74.8

Percent variations in ROR due to changes in annual profit are very significant because the changes start occurring close to time zero. Individual parameters such as selling price, production rates and operating costs affect profit.

D) Salvage Value Sensitivity Analysis

Salvage Value	Change in Prediction	ROR	Percent Change in ROR Prediction
42,000	-40	15.9	-11.9
56,000	-20	16.9	- 6.0
70,000	0	18.0	0
84,000	+20	19.0	5.4
98,000	+40	20.0	10.8

Sensitivity analysis shows that accuracy of salvage value is the least important of all the parameters that go into this ROR analysis because salvage value occurs far in the future from time zero. Also, in this case, cumulative salvage dollar value is small compared to cumulative profit. In some evaluations this is not the case and salvage value has a much more sensitive effect.

6.3 The Range Approach to Sensitivity Analysis

The range approach involves estimating the most optimistic and most pessimistic values (or the best and worst) for each factor in addition to estimating most expected values. This approach will make investment decision making easier for the cases where 1) a project appears desirable even when pessimistic values are used and therefore obviously should be adopted from an economic viewpoint, 2) when a project appears to be undesirable even when optimistic values are used and therefore rejection is dictated on economic grounds. When a project looks good with optimistic values but bad with pessimistic values further study of the project and the risk and uncertainty surrounding the project should be made. Application of this method is shown in Example 6-2.

EXAMPLE 6-2 Range Approach Sensitivity Analysis

Use the range approach to evaluate the investment described in Example 6-1 for best and worst case sensitivity analysis using the plus or minus 20% parameter variations with a five year life and a minimum rate of return of 15%.

Solution:

	Best Case	Expected Case	Worst Case
Investment	192,000	240,000	288,000
Annual Profit	80,400	67,000	53,600
Salvage	84,000	70,000	56,000
Project Life in yrs.	5	5	5
ROR, %	36.4	18.0	3.7

The results indicate that the project is satisfactory for the best and most expected conditions but unsatisfactory for the worst conditions. More information is needed on the expected probability of occurrence of the worst case conditions to reach a valid and meaningful decision.

The best, worst and most expected sensitivity analysis results give very useful information that bracket the range of project ROR results that can reasonably be expected. This is the type of information that managers need to reach investment decisions. It is very important to recognize that although a project ROR greater than the minimum rate of return is predicted for the most expected parameters, the result is based on parameters which are subject to variation. This variation should be analyzed over the full range of possible results utilizing the best engineering and management judgments of people involved with a project.

6.4 Probabilistic Sensitivity Analysis

The application of probability distributions to relate sales volume and prices, operating costs and other parameters to probability of occurrence permits "probabilistic analysis" by the Monte Carlo simulation technique. A brief verbal description of the method follows, then the method will be illustrated.

A weakness of traditional techniques for the evaluation of projects is an inability to combine information from a number of sources into a straightforward and reliable profitability indicator. The major factor in this problem is the large number of variables that must be considered. An additional factor is that it is not possible to obtain accurate single-valued estimates of many of the variables.

Probability theory is the study of the uncertainty of events. A basic tool of probability theory is the use of a range of values to describe variables that cannot adequately be quantified by single value estimates. For example, the determination of the least, greatest and most likely values of a variable will more accurately quantify the variable than will the average value.

The distribution and relative possibilities of values assigned to a given variable will remain characteristic of that variable if factors affecting the variable remain constant. Figure 6-1 illustrates three possible distributions of values. The values are plotted on the horizontal axis and the respective probabilities of their occurrence on the vertical axis. Analysis of the three examples indicates that the uncertainty of the parameter described in Example 3 is much greater than that in Example 2. The uncertainty of Example 3 is indicated by the wide range of values.

A majority of the parameters in real evaluations often give an intermediate range of parameter values as illustrated by Example 1. Ideally we would like to have a very small range for all parameters as illustrated by Example 2. In practice we get a combination of small, intermediate and large ranges of parameter value variation for different parameters in actual evaluation situations.

The distributions in Figure 6-1 all have their values symmetrically distributed around the most likely value (the familiar bell-shaped curve is an example of this distribution). A distribution of this type is called the normal distribution. If the most likely value is shifted to either side of the center of the distribution, then it is preferred to as a skewed distribution. *The normal distribution and the skewed distribution are both special types of a general class of curves known as density functions. In the remainder of this discussion normal distributions will be referred to as such and the term*

density function will be used to describe probability distributions that are
not normal. The shape of the distributions will be determined by the nature
of the variables they describe.

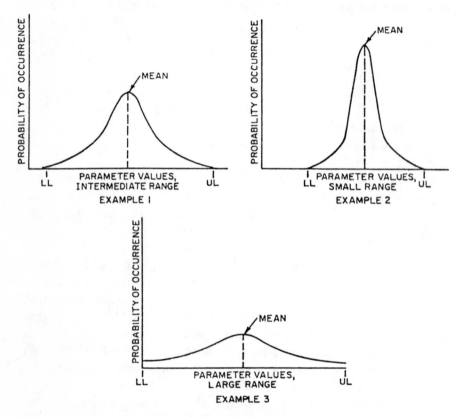

Figure 6-1 Frequency Distribution Graphs Illustrated
(LL = lower limits; UL = upper limits)

In principle, a relative frequency distribution graph is converted to the
equivalent cumulative frequency distribution graph by moving from the left
end of the distribution to the right end and computing the total area that is
less than or equal to corresponding values of the parameter within the range
evaluated. The cumulative area to the left of a given parameter value divided
by the total area under the curve is the cumulative probability that a random
parameter value will be less than or equal to the given parameter value.

Figure 6-2 illustrates typical cumulative frequency distribution graphs that
would result from converting the relative frequency graphs shown in Figure
6-1 to the corresponding plots. Note that Example 3 with a large range of

parameter values has a much flatter cumulative probability curve than Example 2 which has a small range of parameter values. Example 2 has a much higher percentage of the parameter values in a given range of cumulative probability of occurrence compared to Example 3.

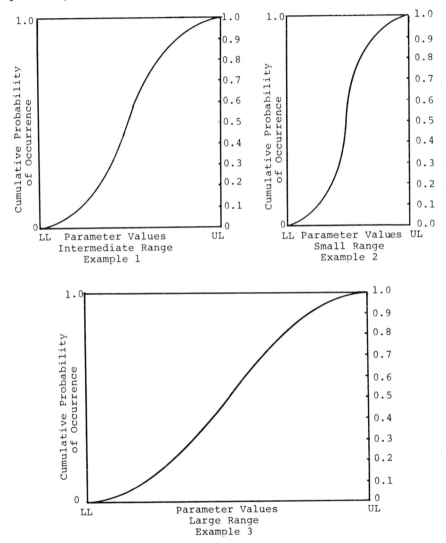

Figure 6-2 Cumulative Frequency Distribution

Now to describe the probabilistic sensitivity analysis approach, consider that we are about to evaluate a new development project. We might be

interested in the effect on our economic evaluation criterion of changes in
project parameters such as initial investment, product selling price per unit,
production rate or sales projections, operating costs, project life and salvage
value. For each of these variables and/or other variables to be investigated,
a frequency distribution plot of probability of occurrence versus parameter
value similar to the examples in Figure 6-1 is prepared by the person or
persons most familiar with and capable of projecting future values of the
parameter involved. These frequency distribution data are then converted
to cumulative probability of occurrence versus parameter value graphs similar
to the examples in Figure 6-2. When these graphs are available for each
parameter that is considered to vary, the use of Monte Carlo simulation is
applied. This generally involves curve fitting a mathematical expression to
describe each cumulative probability of occurrence versus parameter value
so that picking a random number between 0 and 1.0 analogous to the
cumulative probability of occurrence will automatically fix the parameter at
the corresponding value. Different random numbers are selected to fix each
of the different parameters being varied. Then using the randomly selected
parameter values, the economic analysis criterion such as rate of return is
calculated. Then you iterate and do the same thing over again picking a
new set of random numbers to determine a new set of parameters used to
calculate rate of return. This is done over and over again for somewhere
between 100 and 1000 times normally and then a histogram (frequency
distribution plot) of these rate of return results versus probability of occurrence is prepared. The number of iterations (ROR results) that is required is
the number that will give the same shape of final ROR results frequency
distribution graph that would be obtained if many more iterations were made.
To illustrate, consider hypothetical cases 1 and 2 shown in Figure 6-3.

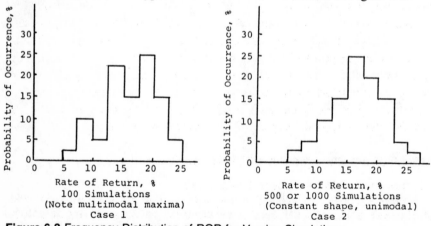

Figure 6-3 Frequency Distribution of ROR for Varying Simulations

The histogram for case 1 has multi-modal (more than one maxima) peaks indicating that statistically we have not made enough simulations to get a rate of return frequency distribution with constant shape. If the input data frequency distribution are unimodal (having one peak as illustrated in Figure 6-1) the output rate of return frequency distribution plot should be unimodal. Case 2 demonstrates for this hypothetical situation that if we go to 500 or 1000 simulations we get a unimodal graph with the same shape indicating that 500 simulations are sufficient for analyzing this hypothetical investment using probabilistic sensitivity analysis.

An important thing to note about probabilistic sensitivity analysis results is that you do not get a single result, but instead you get a range over which the results vary as a function of probability of occurrence and also you get a most expected result. In many investment situations the shape of this curve is more important than the most expected value. For example a project with a most expected ROR of 25% with a range of possible results from negative ROR to positive 40% might be considered less desirable than a project with a most expected ROR of 18% and a range of possible results from 10% to 25% because the certainty associated with the 18% most expected ROR investment is greater than the certainty associated with the other investment. Probabilistic sensitivity analysis enables the decision maker to get a firmer feeling concerning the effects of risk and uncertainty on economic analysis results than any other analysis approach gives.

The weak point of the probabilistic analysis method lies in the subjective assigning of probabilities of occurrence to the levels of parameters that go into the analysis. However, it is generally considered to be best to specifically state the probabilities of occurrence based on the best judgement of people involved with a project and then to base the analysis on these estimates even though they are subjective in nature. In the final analysis any evaluation technique is only as good as the estimates of the input parameters and must be used in conjunction with good engineering logic and managerial judge-ment. Assigning probabilities to parameter estimates is just one more step in quantifying the assumptions that are made. These techniques provide management with additional tools to aid in the decision-making process.

Following is a simplified example that illustrates the principles of applying probabilistic analysis to project ROR sensitivity analysis.

EXAMPLE 6-3 A Simple Probabilistic Sensitivity Analysis

A new product to be produced by one of two different processes. It is felt that there is a 60% probability that the process selected will have initial cost of $50,000, a life of five years and zero salvage value. There is a 40%

probability that an improved process will be selected with initial cost of $40,000, a life of five years and zero salvage value. With either process there is a 50% probability that annual profit will be $20,000 for the five year project life and a 25% probability that the annual profits will be $15,000 or $25,000 per year. Plot project ROR versus probability of occurrence assuming the parameter values are independent of each other.

Solution:

The following table presents the possible combinations of different investment costs, annual profits, probabilities of occurrence and ROR.

Investment	Annual Profit	Probability of Occurrence	$P/A_{i,5}$	ROR (%)
50,000	15,000	(.6)(.25) = .15	3.334	15.2
50,000	20,000	(.6)(.50) = .30	2.500	28.7
50,000	25,000	(.6)(.25) = .15	2.000	41.1
40,000	15,000	(.4)(.25) = .10	2.667	25.4
40,000	20,000	(.4)(.50) = .20	2.000	41.1
40,000	25,000	(.4)(.25) = .10	1.600	56.0
		1.00		

The most probable project ROR is 41.1% with a 35% probability of occurrence. The cumulative probability diagram shows a cumulative probability of 75% that the ROR will be 28.7% or above in Figure 6-5.

Instead of mathematically determining the probability of occurrence of the various ROR results for this problem we could have used the general Monte Carlo simulation technique to get the same results. The general idea of this method as described earlier is to first develop curves for cumulative probability of occurrence versus the economic parameter similar to Figure 6-4. Then random numbers between zero and one are related to cumulative probability of occurrence so that selection of a random number fixes the initial investment for a calculation. Selection of another random number selects the cash flow for that calculation. ROR is then calculated using these values. This procedure is then repeated several hundred or maybe a thousand times until the shape of the ROR versus probability of occurrence curve does not change with additional calculations. For a large number of Monte Carlo simulations the results using this technique for Example 6-3 will be identical to those given in Figure 6-5. The Monte Carlo simulation data are evaluated by forming a histogram from the ROR results. For instance, if one thousand runs are made about three hundred of the ROR results should be 28.7% since we know the mathematical probability of occurrence of this result is .30.

In general, the variations in input data such as selling price, operating cost, production rate, borrowed money interest rate and so forth that are evaluated will be continuous functions of cumulative probability of occurrence rather than the step functions illustrated in Figure 6-4. Continuous input data give a continuous ROR versus probability of occurrence histogram graph for Monte Carlo simulation in general.

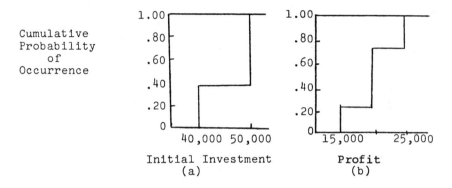

Figure 6-4 Cumulative Probability Diagram

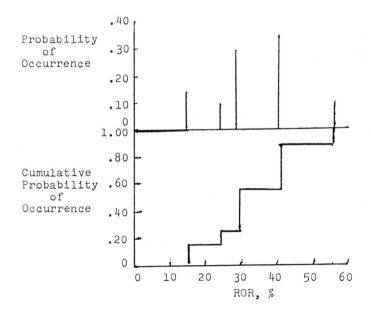

Figure 6-5 Cumulative Probability of Occurrence

6.5 Expected Value Analysis (Economic Risk Analysis)

Expected value is defined as the difference between expected profits and expected costs where expected profit is the probability of receiving a certain profit above all costs times the profit and expected cost is the probability that a certain cost will be incurred times the cost. If you define cost as negative profit and keep the signs straight, you can do as some text authors do and define expected value as the algebraic sum of the expected value of each possible outcome that could occur if the alternative is accepted. Either definition leads to the same expected value result, which sometimes is called a "risk adjusted" result. Several examples of expected value analysis when time value of money considerations are not relevant or significant will be presented first. Then time value of money related examples will be illustrated.

EXAMPLE 6-4 Expected Value Analysis of a Gambling Game

A wheel of fortune in a Las Vegas gambling casino has 54 different slots in which the wheel pointer can stop. Four of the 54 slots contain the number 9. For a $1 bet on hitting a 9, the gambler wins $10 plus return of his $1 bet if he wins. What is the expected value of this gambling game? What is the meaning of the expected value result?

Solution:

```
Probability of Success =  4/54
Probability of Failure = 50/54

Expected Value = Expected Profit - Expected Cost

    = (4/54)($10) - (50/54)($1) = -$0.185
```

The meaning of the $-\$0.185$ expected value result is that it is the average monetary loss per bet of this type that would be realized if the gambler made this bet over and over again for many repeated trials. It is important to recognize that the gambler is not going to lose $0.185 on any given bet. Over a large number of bets, however, the loss per bet would average $.185. This result should make it evident then that a positive expected value is a necessary condition for a satisfactory investment, but not necessarily a sufficient condition as will be discussed later.

EXAMPLE 6-5 Expected Value Analysis of a Simplistic Drilling Venture

If you spend $500,000 drilling a wildcat oil well, geologists estimate the probability of a dry hole is 0.6 with a probability of 0.3 that the well will be a producer that can be sold immediately for $2,000,000 and a probability of 0.1 that the well will produce at a rate that will generate a $1,000,000 immediate sale value. What is the project expected value?

Solution, All Values in Thousands of Dollars:

Expected Value = Expected Profits - Expected Costs

= 0.3(2,000-500) + 0.1(1,000-500) - 0.6(500)

= +200

or rearranging;

Expected Value = 0.3(2,000) + 0.1(1,000) - 1.0(500) = +$200

Over the long run, investments of this type will prove rewarding, but remember that the +$200,000 expected value is a statistical long-term average profit that will be realized over many repeated investments of this type. The expected value of an investment alternative is the average profit or loss that would be realized if many investments of this type were repeated. In terms of Example 6-5 this means if we drilled 100 wells of the type described, we expect statistics to begin to work out and assuming our probabilities of occurrence are correct, we would expect about 60 dry holes out of 100 wells with about 30 wells producing a $2,000,000 income and about 10 wells producing a $1,000,000 income. This makes total income of $70,000,000 from 100 wells drilled costing a total of $50,000,000 leaving total profit of $20,000,000 after the costs, or profit per well of $200,000, which is the expected value result for Example 6-5.

It should now be evident that although expected value has deterministic meaning only if many trials are performed, if we consistently follow a decision-making strategy based on selecting projects with positive expected values, over the long run statistics will work for us and income should be more than sufficient to cover costs. On the other hand, if you consistently take the gambler's ruin approach and invest or bet on investments or gambling games with negative expected values, you can rest assured that over the long run, income will not cover your costs and if you stick with negative expected value investments long enough, you will of course, lose all your capital. This is exactly the situation that exists with all of the gambling games in places such as Las Vegas, Reno and Atlantic City. The odds are always favorable to the house, meaning the gambling house has a positive expected value and therefore the gambler has negative expected value. The gambler has absolutely no realistic hope for success over the long run under these negative expected value conditions. He will lose all the money set aside to gamble with if he sticks with the games long enough.

The reader should notice that in Example 6-5, two different, but equivalent equations were used to calculate expected value as follows:

Let P = Probability of Success, 1 − P = Probability of Failure

Expected Value = (P)(Income-Cost) − (1−P)(Cost)   6-1

or   = (P)(Income) − (1.0)(Cost)   6-2

EXAMPLE 6-6 Expected Value of a Simple General Investment

To illustrate expected value, expected profit, and expected cost, determine them for an investment opportunity where there is a probability of 0.30 that you will receive a $200,000 lump sum profit above your investment if you invest $50,000.

Solution:

Since we assume mutually exclusive events, the probability of failing is 1.0 − 0.30 or 0.70. Expected profit is 0.30($200,000) or $60,000 and the expected cost is 0.70($50,000) = $35,000.

Expected Value = 60,000 − 35,000 = +$25,000

Certainly if you have enough investments of this type in which to invest and enough capital to invest, statistics are very favorable to you, and you would expect to come out ahead over the long run if you made many investments of this type. However, if the loss of $50,000 would break you, you would be foolish to invest in this type of project because there is only a 30% chance of success on any given try. Only if you can stick with this type of investment for many times can you expect statistics to work in your favor so that your probability of success or survival is considerably greater than 30%. This is one important reason why most large companies and individuals carry insurance of various types even though in nearly all cases the expected profit from self-insuring is positive and therefore favorable to the company or individual. If a disaster from fire can break a company or individual financially, that company cannot afford to self-insure. This is why insurance companies spread large policies over many insurance companies. If disaster does strike a large policy holder, the loss will be distributed over several companies, lessening the likelihood of financial disaster for any one company. It is also the reason most individuals carry fire insurance, homeowners or tenant insurance, and car insurance. The direct financial loss or lawsuit loss potential is so great that most of us cannot afford to carry that risk alone even though expected profit is favorable to us if we self insure. The conclusion is that *a positive expected value is a necessary but not a sufficient condition for a satisfactory investment.*

EXAMPLE 6-7 Expected Value Analysis Applied to Insurance

The probability of a chemical plant valued at $1,000,000 being destroyed by fire is estimated to be 0.10% in any given year. The insurance premium for a $1,000,000 policy is $6,000. Calculate the expected cost from fire, compare with the insurance premium, and discuss the ramifications of whether or not the insurance policy should be taken.

Solution:

Expected Annual Cost

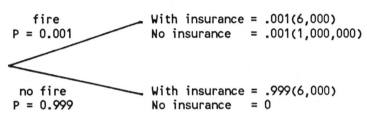

```
fire                With insurance = .001(6,000)
P = 0.001           No insurance   = .001(1,000,000)


no fire             With insurance = .999(6,000)
P = 0.999           No insurance   = 0
```

Expected Annual Cost
With Insurance = .001($6,000) +.999($6,000) = $6,000

Expected Annual Cost
Without Insurance = .001($1,000,000) = $1,000

Annual Savings From Self-Insurance = $6,000 - $1,000 = +$5,000

If this company has many plants around the country so that the $1,000,000 investment in a plant is considered to be a small part of total investment that would not cause the company great financial distress in the event of a major fire or loss, then self-insuring may be worth serious consideration. However, if this plant represents a significant part of total investment, loss of which by fire would seriously impair the company's financial position, then the insurance should be taken even though expected profit is favorable to the company if insurance is not taken.

It is possible that an individual or company may, in some cases, accept investments with a negative expected value based on a "windfall strategy." Examples of this might be playing roulette in Las Vegas or investing in speculative oil well drilling or buying lottery tickets. If the return for success is very large in relation to investment, a person or company may undertake a limited number of these investments with a negative expected value to have a chance at the possibility of a spectacular return. This strategy will ultimately be ruinous because in the long run you will invest more than you receive back in income, unless you restrict your investments to those with positive expected value.

6.6 Expected NPV, Expected PVR, and Expected ROR Analysis

When time value of money considerations are significant, expected NPV, PVR and ROR analysis are methods of including the probabilities of success and failure in analyses when costs and revenues occur at different points in time. If we use appropriate time value of money present worth factors to convert costs and profits at different points in time to lump sum values at time zero or some other chosen time, the expected value analysis approach can be applied to determine if this type of investment would be suitable over the long run for many repeated investments of the same type. With expected NPV and PVR we are of course looking for alternatives with a positive expected value. With expected ROR analysis we calculate the expected ROR value, "i", that will make the expected NPV equation equal to zero. An acceptable expected ROR must be greater than the minimum ROR.

EXAMPLE 6-8 Expected Value Applied to ROR, NPV and PVR Analysis

A research and development project is being considered. The project has an initial investment cost of $90,000 and a probability of .4 that annual profits of $50,000 will be realized during the 5 year life of the project. Salvage value is zero. Assume $i^* = 10\%$.

Should the project be done? Compare expected value, expected net present value, expected rate of return and expected present value ratio analysis.

Solution, in Thousands of Dollars:

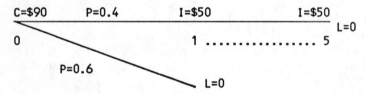

```
C=$90        P=0.4            I=$50                    I=$50
——————————————————————————————————————————————————————————— L=0
0                             1 ................. 5

        P=0.6

                        L=0
```

A) Expected Value Analysis Including Time Value of Money at $i^* = 10\%$

$$EV = 0.4(50,000(P/A_{10,5}) - 90,000) - .6(90,000) = -\$14,180$$

The negative expected value indicates reject investing in the project.

B) Expected Net Present Value

This analysis is identical to the "A" analysis, except we generally use Equation 6-2 to determine Expected NPV. This is just a rearranged form of the Expected Value equation from part "A".

$$\text{ENPV} = 0.4(50,000)(P/A_{10,5}) - 1.0(90,000) = -\$14,180$$

Since the ENPV is negative, we should not invest in the project from an economic viewpoint. Note the expected value analysis in part "A" accounting for the time value of money at 10% per year gave a result identical with the ENPV result.

C) Expected Rate of Return

Expected ROR is the "i" value that makes Expected NPV equal 0.

Expected Present Worth Income @ "i" − Present Worth Cost @ "i" = 0

$$50,000(P/A_{i,5})(.4) - 90,000 = 0$$

"i" = Expected ROR = 3.6% by trial and error, < i* = 10% so reject

As a variation of expected ROR analysis, some people account for risk by increasing the minimum ROR an appropriate amount. The difficulty with this approach is that there is no consistent, rational way to adjust the minimum ROR appropriately to account for risk in different projects. For this example, the risk free ROR is about 47.6% (based on probability of success of 1.0 instead of 0.4) compared to the expected ROR of 3.6%. Expected ROR of 3.6% compared to risk free minimum ROR of 10% indicates the project is economically unsatisfactory. To get the same conclusions based on comparison of risk free ROR and risk adjusted minimum ROR results requires increasing the minimum ROR to about 132% (where 10%/3.6% = X/47.6%, therefore X = 132%). A majority of people who attempt to compensate for risk by adjusting the minimum ROR end up significantly under-compensating for risk. For this example many people will propose increasing the minimum ROR inversely proportional to probability of success (1/0.4) from 10% to 25% when as previously discussed the increase should be from 10% to about 130%. However, there is no way to know this without making an expected ROR type of analysis. Expected value analysis using ROR, NPV or PVR is the preferred approach to incorporate risk into economic analysis calculations.

D) Expected Present Value Ratio Analysis

$$\text{EPVR} = \text{ENPV} / \text{Expected PW Cost} = -14,180/90,000 = -0.16$$

The negative expected PVR indicates the project economics are unsatisfactory for the project parameters built into this analysis.

As Example 6-8 illustrates, expected value analysis in general involves constructing a diagram showing investment costs and all subsequent chance events and dollar values that are anticipated. Standard symbolism uses circles to designate chance nodes from which different degrees of success and failure may be shown to occur. The sum of the probabilities of occurrence on the different branches emanating from a chance node must add up to 1.0. These "expected value diagrams" sometimes are called "decision diagrams" because decision options concerning whether to proceed in one or more different ways or to terminate the project always exist prior to each chance node where different degrees of success or failure may occur. These diagrams often have multiple branches and look very much like a drawing of a tree, which has led to the name "decision tree analysis" being used in industry practice to refer to this type of analysis. In typical decision tree analyses, at different stages of projects, probabilities of success and failure change. As you progress from the research or exploration stage of a project to development and production, risk of failure changes significantly. This is illustrated in the following two examples.

EXAMPLE 6-9 Expected Value Analysis of a Petroleum Project

Use Expected NPV and PVR analysis for a minimum ROR of 20% to evaluate the economic potential of buying and drilling an oil lease with the following estimated costs, revenues and success probabilities. The lease would cost $100,000 at year 0 and it is considered 100% certain that a well would be drilled to the point of completion one year later for a cost of $500,000. There is a 60% probability that well logs will look good enough to complete the well at year 1 for a $400,000 completion cost. If the well logs are unsatisfactory an abandonment cost of $40,000 will be incurred at year 1. If the well is completed it is estimated there will be a 50% probability of generating production that will give $450,000 per year net income for years 2 through 10 (consider uniform revenue is based on assuming declining production is offset by increased selling price) and a 35% probability of generating $300,000 per year net income for years 2 through 10, with a 15% probability of the well completion being unsuccessful, due to water or unforeseen completion difficulties, giving a year 2 salvage value of $250,000 for producing equipment.

Solution, in Thousands of Dollars:

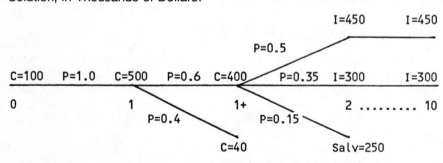

Times 1 and 1+ are effectively the same point in time, the end of year 1. Normally drilling and completion time are separated by weeks or months which puts them at the same point in time with annual periods. Times 1 and 1+ are separated on the diagram to make room for the probabilities of occurrence associated with different events.

Expected Net Present Value (ENPV) at 20%

$$\{ [450 \overset{4.031}{(P/A_{20,9})}(.5) + 300 \overset{4.031}{(P/A_{20,9})}(.35) + 250 \overset{.8333}{(P/F_{20,1})}(.15) - 400] (.6)$$

$$- 40(.4) - 500\} \overset{.8333}{(P/F_{20,1})} - 100 = -49.26$$

This result is only slightly less than zero compared to the total project costs of $1 million, therefore, slightly unsatisfactory or breakeven economics are indicated.

Alternate Form of (ENPV) Equation

$$450 \overset{4.031}{(P/A_{20,9})}(.5) \overset{.8333}{(P/F_{20,1})}(.6) + 300 \overset{4.031}{(P/A_{20,9})}(.35) \overset{.8333}{(P/F_{20,1})}(.6)$$

$$+ 250 \overset{.6944}{(P/F_{20,2})}(.15)(.6) - 400 \overset{.8333}{(P/F_{20,1})}(.6) - 40 \overset{.8333}{(P/F_{20,1})}(.4)$$

$$- 500 \overset{.8333}{(P/F_{20,1})}(1.0) - 100 = -49.26$$

Expected Present Value Ratio (EPVR)

$$EPVR = -49.26 \ / \ 100 + [500 + 400(.6) + 40(.4)](P/F_{20,1}) = -0.07$$

The small negative EPVR result indicates the same slightly unsatisfactory or breakeven economics shown earlier with ENPV analysis.

EXAMPLE 6-10 Expected NPV Applied to Mineral Rights Valuation

A petroleum company wants to determine what can be paid for an oil lease to have an escalated dollar expected ROR of 25% before-tax considerations if the following costs and success probabilities are considered relevant: exploration drilling at time zero will cost $1,000,000 with a 20% probability of success and if the exploration drilling is successful a $10,000,000 development drilling program will be conducted in year 1 with 90% probability of success. Successful drilling will generate profits of $4,000,000 per year for 15 years starting in year 2 assuming that declining production and increasing operating costs are offset by increased selling price for oil. Assume salvage value is zero at the end of year 16.

Solution, in Thousands of Dollars:

The objective is to determine the bid cost, C_{Bid}, that will make ENPV = 0, for $i^* = 25\%$.

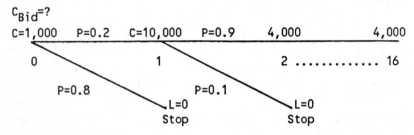

C_{Bid}=?

First determine the expected NPV at year 1 for the year 1 to 16 investments and profits. This calculation is exactly like the Example 6-9 ENPV calculation.

$Year_{1-16}$ ENPV = $4,000(P/A_{25,15})(0.9)$ - $10,000$ = +$3,890

The expected NPV for years 1-16 is the value an investor will get if successful with the time zero investment.

C_{Bid}=?
C=1,000   P=0.2   ENPV$_{1-16}$=+3,890

        0   1

        P=0.8
                          L=0
                          Stop

Now calculate the ENPV at year 0 for the year 0 to 1 costs, values and relative probabilities.

$3,890(P/F_{25,1})(0.2)$ - $1,000$ - C_{Bid} = ENPV Overall = 0

Solve for C_{Bid} giving, C_{Bid} = -380

A negative C_{Bid} indicates we are $380,000 expected present worth profit dollars short of being able to cover the projected drilling costs at a 25% rate of return. Since we cannot justify spending any additional dollars, the decision based on this analysis is "no bid." However, it must be remembered that the expected value results are a direct reflection of the input data to the analysis, and if there is uncertainty associated with the input data, then there is uncertainty associated with the output results.

It was emphasized earlier in this section that expected value represents the average gain or loss per investment that an investor would realize over many repeated investments of the type being analyzed. Whether we work with expected value, expected NPV, expected PVR or expected ROR, the average meaning of results is similar. A common misconception that some people have about expected value analysis is that it often is not valid because investors seldom repeat the same type investments over and over. These people have missed the basic expected value analysis premise that even though each specific investment decision relates to a uniquely different investment, if we consistently select investment alternatives having positive expected value, ENPV or EPVR, (or having expected ROR greater than the minimum ROR), over the long run our average rate of return on invested capital will be greater than the minimum ROR. Similar to material presented earlier in Chapter 4 for risk free analysis, to rank non-mutually exclusive alternatives using risk adjusted results, you must use either expected PVR or expected Growth ROR results. To evaluate mutually exclusive alternatives with risk adjusted results based on any valid analysis technique, incremental analysis is the key to correct economic decision making. These rules hold true even though each investment decision relates to a different investment prospect with different probabilities of success and failure at different stages of each project.

6.7 Probability of Survival (Financial Risk Analysis)

Probability of survival refers to the probability that you will not go bankrupt with a given amount of capital to invest in projects with estimated probabilities of success. This concept is a financial risk analysis consideration rather than specifically relating to economic risk analysis. A project with a large positive expected value and a small probability of success may economically look better than all other investment opportunities under consideration. However, if failure of the project would lead to bankruptcy, the project most likely will be considered financially unacceptable due to the financial risks. The italicized statement preceding Example 6-7 says "a positive expected value is a necessary but not a sufficient condition for a satisfactory investment." This means that a positive expected value indicates an economically satisfactory investment but not necessarily a financially satisfactory investment. Small investors in the oil and gas drilling business usually attempt to reduce their financial risk of total failure (bankruptcy) by taking a small interest in a large number of projects rather than large interests in a few projects. This diversified investment portfolio approach gives the probability of success a better chance to be realized over time as the following example illustrates.

EXAMPLE 6-11 Probability of Survival Applied to Exploration

Consider an exploration manager who is faced with the task of determining whether to invest $1,000,000 of a small company's money in 10 independent exploration projects which will each cost $100,000 with a 10% probability of achieving a $5,000,000 profit above cost. If the company will go bankrupt if not successful on at least 1 exploration project (or if the exploration manager will lose his job), discuss their probability of survival.

Solution:

Expected Value = 5,000,000(.10) − 100,000(.9) = +$410,000

The positive expected value is economically satisfactory and is a necessary but not a sufficient condition for this investment to be satisfactory. The question to be answered now is what is the probability of survival, or stated another way, what is the probability of getting at least 1 success out of 10 tries. This relates to the financial acceptability of the project.

Probability of at Least 1 Success = 1 − Probability of Zero Successes

Probability of Zero Successes = $(.9)^{10}$ = .3485

Therefore, probability of survival = 1 − .3485 = .6515 or 65.15% which is certainly considerably less than a sure thing (100% probability of success). Note that ten projects each having a 10% chance of success do not give a 100% probability of overall success.

Companies often get together in joint ventures on large exploration projects to have more capital available so that enough exploration projects can be made to make the probability of survival higher than it would be if they operated alone. If in Example 6-11 a sum of $2,000,000 is available to invest in 20 projects, the probability of survival increases to 1 − .1214 = .8786 and if $3,000,000 is available the probability of survival is .9577. Joint ventures can increase survival probabilities to very tolerable levels when exploration work is being done in areas where enough geological and geophysical work has been done to predict reasonable probabilities of success on any given try.

The same type of reasoning can be applied to research and development projects in all types of industries, but it is very difficult to come up with truly meaningful probabilities of success. However, if these probabilities are not estimated explicitly, managers will base a decision implicitly on "gut feel" for data, and these authors feel it is better to explicitly state the bases upon which decisions are made.

The statistical basis of the probability of survival calculations just presented is the binomial distribution for mutually exclusive alternatives. The general binomial distribution equation is:

Probability of Exactly "r" successes form "n" tries $= C_r^n P^r (1-P)^{n-r}$

where C_r^n = Combination of "n" things taken "r" at a time.

$$= \frac{n!}{r!(n-r)!} = \frac{\text{n factorial}}{\text{r factorial times } (n-r) \text{ factorial}}$$

$n! = n(n-1)(n-2) ---- (3)(2)(1)$

$0! = 1$ by definition

P = Probability of success on a given try.

$1-P$ = Probability of failure on a given try.

Note that for Example 6-11, the probability of zero success from 10 tries is:

$$C_0^{10} (.1)^0 (.9)^{10} = \frac{10!}{0!10!} (1)(.9)^{10} = (.9)^{10} = .3485$$

6.8 Risk Due to Natural Disaster

Another type of risk to be considered is that due to natural disaster. The following example illustrates the evaluation of data using probabilistic expected value concepts for this type of problem.

EXAMPLE 6-12 Optimum Investment to Minimize Flood Damage Costs

A manufacturing company plans to build a plant on low land near a river that floods occasionally. It is considered necessary to build a levee around its facilities to reduce potential flood damage. Four different sizes of levees that give different levels of protection are being considered and the plant manager wants to know which size levee will minimize total expected annual cost to the company from the sum of 1) amortization of the levee cost over 20 years for a before tax i* of 15%: plus 2) maintenance costs, plus 3) expected damage to the plant and levee if the levee is not high enough or strong enough to hold back flood water. Analyze the following data to determine the optimum levee size.

Levee Size	Levee Cost	Probability of a Flood Exceeding Levee Size During Year	Expected Damage if Flood Exceeds Levee Size	Annual Maintenance
1	$120,000	.20	$ 80,000	$4,000
2	140,000	.10	110,000	5,000
3	160,000	.05	125,000	6,000
4	200,000	.025	150,000	7,000

Solution:

Levee Size	Annual Levee Cost	Expected Damage Per Year	Annual Maint.	Total Expected Annual Cost
1	$120,000(A/P_{15,20})=19,180$ 0.1598	16,000	4,000	$39,180
2	$140,000(0.1598) = 22,370$	11,000	5,000	38,370
3	$160,000(0.1598) = 25,570$	6,250	6,000	37,820
4	$200,000(0.1598) = 31,960$	3,750	7,000	42,710

Levee Size number 3 is the optimum selection to minimize expected equivalent annual cost.

PROBLEMS

6-1   A roulette wheel has 38 different stopping slots numbered from 1 to 36 plus 0 and 00. Eighteen numbers are red, 18 are black. with 0 and 00 green. Calculate the expected value for the following situations where the term "payoff" means in addition to return of the bet or "profit above all costs".
A) The payoff is $35 for a $1 bet on any number.
B) The payoff is $17 for a $1 bet on any line between two numbers (meaning the bettor wins if either number hits).
C) The payoff is $8 for a $1 bet on any corner between four numbers.
D) The payoff is $1 for a $1 bet on red or black or odd or even.

6-2   Due to uncertainty in development costs, the cost of a new manufacturing process is considered to have the following possibilities:

Cost ($)	Probability of Occurrence
5,000	0.10
8,000	0.30
10,000	0.40
14,000	0.20

What is the expected cost of the new process?

6-3   An electronics manufacturer is considering entering into a research
and development venture. The research and development investment
requires $100,000 at time 0 and, if successful, generates $80,000 in
profit each year for 5 years. Salvage value is estimated to be zero.
Experience suggests that such projects have a 40% probability of
success. If the before-tax minimum rate of return is 20%, should the
manufacturer undertake the project? Use expected NPV and expected
ROR Analysis.

6-4   If you bet $5 on the outcome of 3 football games, you can win $25
total (not above the bet cost) if you correctly pick all 3 winners. If
the odds are considered even in each game or if point spreads are
specified that are considered to make each game an even odds bet,
what is the expected value of your bet if you neglect tie game situations?

6-5   An initial investment of $50,000 is projected to generate cash flows
over a 3 year project life as follows:

Year	Cash Flow	Probability of Occurrence
1	$25,000	.40
	18,000	.60
2	30,000	.50
	20,000	.50
3	35,000	.70
	25,000	.30

Evaluate the expected NPV of this investment for a minimum rate of
return of 15%.

6-6   A research and development manager associates a probability of success of 60% (0.6) with a research investment at time zero being
successful and generating the need for an additional $300,000 develop-
ment investment at the end of year 1 which is estimated to have a
probability of 90% (0.9) of successfully generating profits of $200,000
per year for year 2 through 10, assuming a washout of escalation of
operating costs and sales revenue. If failure occurs after the year 0
research investment the salvage value will be a negative $100,000

for reclamation costs at year 1. If failure occurs after the year 1 investment net salvage value will be $250,000 at the end of year 2 for equipment salvage. To achieve a before-tax expected ROR of 25% in this investment, use expected NPV Analysis to determine how much money can be spent on research at time zero assuming the year 10 salvage value is zero? What is the risk free project NPV?

6-7   Calculate the expected net present value of a project which will cost $70,000 at year 0 with a 50% probability of success and success generates a year 1 cost of $120,000 with a 70% probability of success yielding profits of $125,000 per year for years 2 to 7. Failure at year 0 or 1 will result in net salvage and abandonment costs yielding zero cash flow from failure at year 0 and plus $50,000 cash flow at year 2 from failure at year 1. Should this project be considered from an economic viewpoint if the minimum rate of return is 20%?

6-8   A project that would have a year 0 cost of $170,000 is estimated to have a 40% probability of generating net income of $60,000 per year for each of years 1 through 10 with a zero salvage value, a 30% probability of generating net income of $50,000 per year for each of years 1 through 10 with a zero salvage value, a 20% probability of generating net incomes of $40,000 per year for each of years 1 through 10 with a zero salvage value and a 10% probability of failing and generating a $20,000 salvage value at year 1. For a minimum rate of return of 20% calculate the project expected NPV. What is the project expected ROR?

6-9   A petroleum company 2 years ago acquired the mineral rights to a property for which an offer of $1 million cash has been received now at year 0. Development of the property is projected to generate escalated dollar cash flow in millions of dollars of -1.5 in year 0, and $+1.0$, $+1.8$, $+1.2$, $+0.8$ and $+0.4$ in years 1 through 5 respectively. If the minimum DCFROR is 20%, should the company keep and develop the property or sell if there is considered to be a 60% probability of development generating the year 1 through 5 positive cash flow and 40% probability of failure generating zero cash flow in years 1 through 5?

6-10   Two alternatives are being considered for the development of an investment project. Alternative 'A' would start development now with estimated development and equipment costs of $10 million at year 0 and $20 million at year 1 to generate net revenues of $6 million in year 1 and $12 million per year uniformly at years 2 through 10 with a zero salvage value. Alternative 'B' would start development 2 years from now for estimated development and equipment costs of $15 million at year 2 and $30 million at year 3 to generate net revenues of $9 million in year 3 and $18 million per year uniformly at years 4 through 12 with a zero salvage value. Use NPV Analysis for a minimum ROR of 20% to determine the economically better alternative and verify the NPV results with PVR Analysis assuming:

A) 100% probability of success is associated with all investments.

B) Alternative 'A' has a 60% probability of success associated with year 0 cost and 100% probability of success associated with the year 1 cost, with zero net salvage value to be realized if failure occurs at year 0. Alternative 'B' has an 80% probability of success associated with the year 2 cost and a 100% probability of success associated with the year 3 cost, with a zero net salvage value to be realized if failure occurs at year 3.

6-11   An investor has paid $100,000 for a machine that is estimated to have a 70% probability of successfully producing 5000 product units per year for each of the next 3 years when the machine is estimated to be obsolete with a zero salvage value. The product price is the unknown to be calculated, so it is estimated to be $X per unit in year 1 escalated dollars and to increase 10% in year 2 and 6% in year 3. Total operating costs are estimated to be $8,000 in year 1 escalated dollars and to increase 15% in year 2 and 8% in year 3. The annual inflation rate is estimated to be 7%. What must be the year 1, 2 and 3 escalated dollar product selling price if the investor is to receive a 12% annually compounded constant dollar expected DCFROR on invested dollars? Consider zero cash flow to be realized the 30% of the time the project fails. This assumes that equipment dismantlement costs will exactly offset any salvage value benefits.

CHAPTER 7

DEPRECIATION, DEPLETION, AMORTIZATION AND CASH FLOW

7.1 Introduction

Depreciation, depletion and amortization are means of recovering in be-fore-tax dollars, your investment in certain types of property used in your trade or business, or held for the production of income. The basis upon which depreciation, depletion and amortization are calculated is normally the cost of the property, although property acquired as a gift, or in other manners, may have a basis other than cost. The cost of buildings, machinery, equipment and trucks are examples of business property costs that may be recovered by depreciation over the useful life of the asset. Acquisition costs and lease bonus costs paid for mineral rights for natural resources such as oil and gas, minerals, and standing timber, are examples of investment property costs that may be recovered by depletion. Numerous other business costs such as the cost of acquiring a business lease, research and development expenses, trademark expenses, and pollution control equipment costs may be recovered by amortization. Depreciation, depletion, and amortization all achieve essentially the same thing, that is, recovery of the cost or other basis of investments in before-tax dollars through allowable tax deductions over a specified period of time or over the useful life of the investment. If depreciable property is sold, all or a portion of any extra depreciation claimed in prior years may have to be recaptured as taxable income. This concept is addressed in Chapter 8.

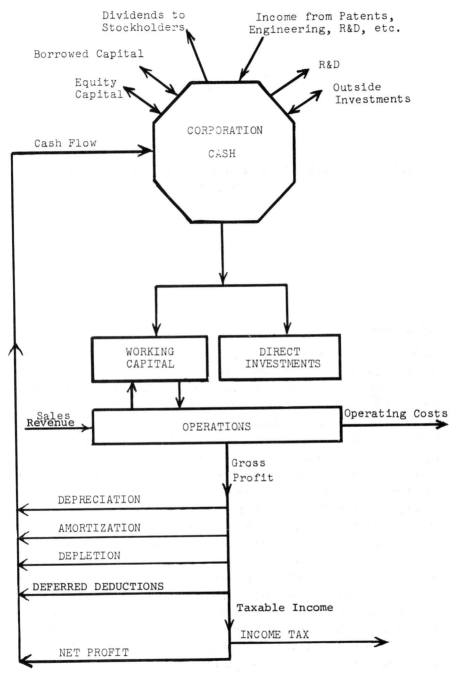

Figure 7-1 Corporate Cash Flow Diagram

Figure 7-1 illustrates how the deductions for depreciation, depletion, and amortization permit recovery of certain capitalized costs in before-tax or tax-free dollars. The word "capitalized" means that the investment cost is not taken as an expense immediately in the year in which it is incurred, but the cost deductions are taken later through depreciation, depletion, or amortization deduction over a period of time greater than one year. Costs that are not "capitalized" are "expensed," which means written off for tax purposes in the year incurred. Note that when a cost is capitalized, depending upon the type of expenditure involved, it is deducted for tax purposes in the following years by either depreciation, depletion, or amortization if it is a tax deductible cost, but never by more than one method. A little thought should make it evident that the government will not permit the same cost to be used more than once as a tax deduction. Depreciation, depletion, and amortization are each applicable to different types of capital expenditures which are broadly described in the remaining sections of this chapter.

The following sections and examples describe and illustrate the methods and many of the qualifying conditions for depreciation, depletion, and amortization calculations. The information in this chapter is based on the "Tax Guide for Small Business," U.S. Department of Treasury, Internal Revenue Service Publication 334, for tax law in effect at the beginning of 1987. The reader is encouraged to obtain this publication for more details concerning specific tax questions. Publication 17 is the companion "Tax Guide for Individuals."

7.2 Cash Flow

Figure 7-1 illustrates the typical flow of a corporation's cash. Annual sales dollars from a satisfactory business venture normally must be sufficient to pay operating expenses and allow for recovery of a prorated portion of investments through depreciation, depletion, amortization, and other deferred tax deductions such as loss carry forward deductions before paying income tax, with the resulting after-tax dollars being the corporation's net profit for the year. Normally, only the operating cost and income tax expenditures are actual corporate disbursements during the tax year. The depreciation, amortization, depletion, and other deferred tax deductions are often called "book" or "non-cash" deductions for tax purposes because they are deductions allowed by the government to permit a business to recover the value of assets with limited useful life in before-tax dollars. Note that assets such as land with unlimited life, or inventories, which normally are used or sold to recover their value are not tax deductible by any method of deduction until they are used and/or sold. A corporation or individual normally does not have to make expenditures equal to depreciation, depletion and amortization tax deductions in the year in which the deductions are taken. For instance, if a corporation paid cash for a depreciable asset, no disbursements are necessary in the following years when the asset is depreciated for tax purposes. On the other hand, if the corporation bought the depreciable asset on time (with borrowed money), money equivalent to the depreciation deduction taken on a year to year basis may in part or whole be needed to make the time payments on the asset. Proper handling of cash flow for this borrowed money situation is discussed in Chapter 11. The point is that depreciation, depletion, amortization and other deferred deductions are non-cash cost deductions for tax purposes and these deductions do not correspond to actual disbursements, except by coincidence. Therefore, this money together with net profit is available to be reinvested elsewhere by the owner of the business. The sum of net profit, depreciation, amortization, depletion and other deferred deduction items is defined as cash flow as shown in Figure 7-1 and summarized in Equations 7-1 and 7-2.

Cash Flow = Net Profit + "Book" or "Non-Cash" Deductions
      − Capital Costs

   = Net Profit + Depreciation + Depletion
      + Amortization + Deferred Deductions
      − Capital Costs   7-1

Alternatively, we can get the same result as follows:

Cash Flow = Sales Revenue − Operating Costs
      − Income Tax − Capital Costs   7-2

Cash flow is the after-tax money that remains available to a company or individual to pay off its debts, invest in new projects, or retain for future investment considerations. Since only rarely does the rate of amortization of investment debt correspond to the rate of recovery of the investment through tax deductions, it is imperative that the cash flow concept be utilized correctly to account for the time value of money in the after-tax analysis of project profitability.

EXAMPLE 7-1 Calculating Cash Flow

An ongoing project is expected to generate revenues of $100,000 next year with operating costs of $30,000 and income taxes totaling $24,000 for the same period. Further, capital costs totaling $20,000 for equipment are also expected to be incurred during the year. Calculate the anticipated project cash flow for next year.

Solution:

Cash Flow = $100,000 − $30,000 − $24,000 − $20,000 = +$26,000

Of these four values (revenues, operating costs, capital costs and income taxes) the only value that is different from determining before-tax cash flow is the income tax. Throughout the remainder of this chapter and into Chapter 8, we will be examining deductions from revenue, both "out-of-pocket" and "non-cash" including depreciation, depletion, amortization, loss carry forwards and writeoffs of book values that allow us to determine our taxable income and the appropriate income tax to be paid or tax savings to be realized. Obviously, failure to recognize the tax component in Example 7-1 would have a very significant impact on the value of the anticipated cash flow and resulting economic analysis calculations.

EXAMPLE 7-2 Before-Tax and After Tax Analysis of a Bank Account

An investor deposits $10,000 in a bank account certificate of deposit and will receive 12% interest at the end of each year for the next 3 years and will receive maturity value of $10,000 at the end of year 3 to recover the initial investment. Assume the investor is in the 40% income tax bracket and calculate before-tax ROR and after-tax ROR on the investment.

Solution:

Before-Tax Time Diagram, C = Cost, I = Income, L = Salvage

```
C=$10,000        I=$1,200      I=$1,200      I=$1,200
                                                      L= $10,000
     0              1             2             3
```

Before-tax ROR is 12.0%

There are no allowable tax deductions on bank account, bond or debenture type investments. Interest income each year is fully taxable whether withdrawn from the account or not. Therefore, 40% of the interest income of $1,200 per year goes to taxes, so $720 = (1200)(1 − .40 tax rate) is the after-tax cash flow from interest each year. The year 3 maturity value of $10,000 just recovers the initial cost so it is cash flow (none of it is paid out in income tax).

```
CF=-$10,000      CF=$720      CF=$720      CF=$720
                                                    CF= $10,000
     0              1             2             3
```

After-tax ROR is 7.2%. Using Equation 3-2, since initial cost (or negative cash flow) equals final salvage (or positive cash flow) the after-tax ROR is 7.2% compared to the before-tax ROR of 12%, a difference most people would consider to be significant. It is important to account for income tax considerations.

If you want to compare the economics of leaving your money in a bank compared to investing in real estate, minerals or petroleum, it makes a difference whether you compare before-tax or after-tax results. Investments in general involve costs that are either depreciable, amortizable, depletable, expensed, or not deductible at all as in the case of land or bank account deposits. This makes the relationship between before-tax and after-tax economic analysis results uniquely different for each investment situation analyzed. This necessitates comparing the economics of investments on an after-tax basis to properly and fairly compare the economic potential of different investments from the viewpoint of tax-paying individuals or organizations.

7.3 Business Costs That May be Expensed

For tax purposes, the fastest method of deducting costs is to "expense" them in the year incurred, which means to deduct them in full amount in the year incurred. Investors would prefer to treat all costs in this manner because the faster you get tax deductions, the faster you get the tax benefits from your deductions, and this improves project economics. However, tax law does not permit "expensing" all costs so we need to enumerate some of the important costs that can be "expensed".

Operating costs may be expensed; including costs for direct labor, indirect labor, materials and supplies used, utilities, freight and containers, borrowed money interest paid, royalties, severance taxes and certain excise taxes such as windfall profits tax on crude oil.

Research and Development costs including labor, supplies, etc., are considered to be the equivalent of operating costs and may be expensed in the year incurred. Alternatively, an investor may elect to amortize these costs straight line over 5 years, but this election is seldom made for reasons illustrated later.

Mineral Exploration costs are expenditures required to delineate the extent and quality of an ore body and may include core drilling, assaying, engineering fees, geological fees, exploratory shafts, pits, drifts, etc. Exploration costs may be expensed in the full amount in the year incurred by individual taxpayers, but corporations (except Subchapter S corporations) may expense only 70% of mineral exploration costs in the year incurred with the remaining 30% deducted by the straight line method over a 60 month period, with the first year deduction proportional to the month such costs are paid or incurred. If exploration expenditures associated with successful ventures are expensed, these deductions are subject to recapture as follows. The taxpayer may elect to forego taking depletion deductions until the cost basis of exploration charges is fully recovered, or, the taxpayer may restore a dollar amount equal to the previously expensed exploration charges as income. If the later option is elected, the taxpayer may add the additional income amount to the cost depletion basis for the property. Recapture may be avoided by not expensing exploration charges but instead, adding such charges to the cost depletion basis of the property.

Mineral Development costs are defined as expenditures incurred after the determination has been made that an ore body is economically viable and the decision has been made to develop the property. Development costs may include exploration type costs after the decision has been made to develop a mine and overburden stripping, underground development shafts, drifts, tunnels, raises, adits, etc. Development costs are not subject to recapture at any point in time and may be expensed in the full amount in the year incurred by individual taxpayers and, analogous to mineral exploration costs, corporations (except Subchapter S corporations) may expense only 70% of mineral development costs in the year incurred with the remaining 30% deducted straight line over a five year, 60 month period, with the first year deduction prorated from the month such costs are paid or incurred. As an alternative to expensing all or 70% of mineral development cost, tax law gives investors the option of deducting these costs by units of production depreciation described later in this chapter.

Petroleum Intangible Drilling Costs, (IDC's) are defined as the cost of drilling oil and gas wells to the point of completion and may include:

Costs of agreements with operators and drilling contractors.
Survey and seismic work related to location of a well.
Road cost to well location to be used during drilling.
Dirt work on location for pits, etc.
Rig transportation and set-up costs.
Drilling costs including fuel, water, drilling mud, etc.
Cost of technical services including engineers, geologists, logging and

drill stem test services.

Cost of swabbing, fracturing and acidizing.

Cementing of surface casing and main casing (not the cost of casing).

Reclamation of well site.

Similar to mineral development costs, IDC's may be expensed in full amount in the year incurred by individuals or corporations that are not "major" or "integrated" producers, (that is they produce less than 1,000 barrels per day of oil, or 6 million cubic feet per day of natural gas, or the combined equivalent). "Major" or "integrated" petroleum producers may only expense 70% of intangible drilling costs in the year incurred and are required to amortize the remaining 30% of their intangible drilling cost's straight line over a five year, (60 month) period beginning in the month the costs are paid or started to be incurred. This provision does not affect the option to expense dry hole intangible drilling costs in the year the dry hole is incurred.

7.4 Depreciation

The term depreciation is used in a number of different contexts. Some of the most common are:

1. Tax allowance
2. Cost of an operation
3. A method of funding financing for a plant replacement
4. Measure of falling value.

In case 1, annual taxable income is reduced by an annual depreciation charge, or allowance, that reduces the annual amount of income tax payable. The annual depreciation charge is merely a paper or "book" transaction and does not involve any expenditure of cash. In the case 2, depreciation is considered to be a manufacturing cost in the same way as labor or raw materials are out of pocket cash costs. In case 3, depreciation is considered as a means of providing for plant replacement, similar to case 2. However, in rapidly changing modern industries, it is doubtful that many plants will ever be replaced because the processes are likely to have become obsolete during operation, so this approach is outdated. In case 4, a plant or a piece of equipment may have a limited useful life, so deducting cumulative depreciation from initial value gives a measure of the asset's falling value, usually called "book value" or adjusted basis.

In this text, the term depreciation is usually used in the context of a tax allowance. Depreciation is a tax deduction comprising, "a reasonable allowance for the exhaustion, wear and tear and obsolescence of property used in a trade or business, or of property held by a tax payer for the production of income." The basis (value) that would be used to find investment gain or loss if property were disposed of is the basis that should be used for determining depreciation. Land may not be depreciated. The first step in computing depreciation is to determine the estimated useful life of the asset or its allowable depreciable life. No average useful life is applicable to all depreciable assets in different types of businesses and the allowable depreciable life is often different from the expected economic life. Frequency of use, age when acquired, your policy regarding repairs, renewals, and replacements, the climate in which used, etc., all can affect the useful life of depreciable assets.

The question of whether certain expenditures are repair expenses (deductible in the year incurred as an operating expense) or a capital expenditure (deductible through annual depreciation deductions) often is important in relation to the tax deduction handling of equipment and facility major repair/rebuild type costs. The distinction between repairs and capital expenditures is not always clear but here is a useful guide: A repair is an expenditure for the purpose of keeping the property in an ordinary efficient operating condition. It does not add to the value or life of the property. It merely keeps the property in an operating condition over its probable useful life for the uses for which it was acquired. Repair costs may be expensed as operating costs for tax deduction purposes. On the other hand, capital expenditures are alterations, additions or improvements that increase the asset useful life or value or make it adaptable for a different use. Capital expenditures must be depreciated rather than expensed.

Depreciable property may be tangible or intangible. Tangible property is any property that can be seen or touched. Intangible property is property, such as a copyright or franchise, that is not tangible. Depreciable property may be personal or real. Personal property is property such as machinery or equipment that is not real estate. Real property is land and generally anything that is erected on, growing on, or attached to land. However, land itself is never depreciable.

Property is depreciable if it meets these requirements:
1) It must be used in business or held for the production of income.
2) It must have a determinable life and that life must be longer than one year.
3) It must be something that wears out, decays, gets used up, becomes obsolete, or loses value from natural causes.

4) It is placed in service or is in a condition or state of readiness and available to be placed in service.

In general, if property does not meet all four of these conditions, it is not depreciable.

Finally, the method of financing the purchase of assets has no effect on depreciation deductions. Whether you pay cash or borrow all the money to acquire an asset, you get the same depreciation deductions. Interest on borrowed money is the only tax deduction that is different with project analyses involving borrowed money instead of cash investments as is discussed in Chapter 11.

7.5 Depreciation Methods

Post-1986 depreciation of tangible property placed in service after 1986 is based on using, 1) the applicable depreciation method, 2) the applicable recovery period (depreciation life), and 3) the applicable first year depreciation convention. Modified ACRS depreciation calculations relate to the following three depreciation methods:

1) Straight Line
2) Declining Balance
3) Declining Balance Switching to Straight Line

A fourth method used to a lesser extent in the past but possibly of greater importance in the future because its use under the new tax law eliminates depreciation as a tax preference item for alternative minimum tax calculation is:

4) Units of Production

The following sections 7.5a through 7.5e illustrate the application of these different methods. The modified ACRS depreciation method is addressed in section 7.5e. Prior to introducing depreciation methods, several timing conventions that affect the first year depreciation deduction need to be addressed.

Under the new tax law, there are three applicable conventions that have an effect on the allowable depreciation deduction in the first year. These conventions apply to the modified ACRS method, the straight line ACRS method (which is straight line depreciation for the recovery period allowed by modified ACRS depreciation) and the alternative ACRS method (which applies longer depreciation lives for straight line depreciation of special categories of assets such as foreign tangible property or tax exempt use or bond financed property). The recovery period begins when an asset is placed in service under the applicable first year deduction convention. The terms recovery period and recovery property are tax terms meaning depreciation period and depreciable property.

Half-Year Convention in First Year

Under the half-year convention, applicable to recovery property other than residential rental and non-residential real property, all property is deemed to be placed in service in the middle of the year. Therefore, one half of the first year's normal depreciation is allowed in the year that the property is placed in service, regardless of when the property is placed in service during the year.

Mid-Quarter Convention in First Year

A mid-quarter convention applies to property, other than nonresidential real property and residential rental property, if more than 40 percent of the aggregate basis of such property is placed in service during the last three months of the tax year. Under the mid-quarter convention, all property placed in service during any quarter of a tax year is treated as placed in service at the midpoint of such quarter. For example, if more than 40% of qualifying class assets were placed in service during the final quarter of a tax year, all assets placed in service in the first quarter would receive the fraction 10.5/12 times the calculated full first year depreciation as the allowed first year depreciation deduction, while assets in the final quarter would receive a first year deduction of 1.5/12 times the calculated first year depreciation. Similarly, assets placed in service during the second and third quarters would receive the fractions 7.5/12 and 4.5/12 times the calculated first year depreciation as the allowed first year depreciation deduction.

Mid-Month Convention

For residential rental property and non-residential real property the mid-month first year convention applies. Under this convention, qualifying property is deemed to be placed in service (or disposed of) during the middle of the month. The allowable deduction is based on the number of months the property was in service. Therefore, for a calender tax year, assets placed in service in January of that year would receive a first year deduction equal to the fraction 11.5/12 times the calculated year 1 depreciation. Thus, one half month's cost recovery (depreciation) is allowed for the month the property is placed in service.

Illustration of these three different first year depreciation conventions is made in the depreciation examples associated with the following sections.

7.5a Straight Line Depreciation

Straight line depreciation is the simplest method for computing depreciation in all countries, but unfortunately, it also is the slowest method of depreciation. The faster you get depreciation tax deductions, the faster you get the tax benefits from the deductions if income exists against which to use the deductions, and the better the economics of any project will be. Therefore, straight line depreciation is generally not desirable for tax deduction purposes if faster methods are allowable.

With the straight line method, depreciation per year is determined by multiplying the cost basis of a property times a straight line depreciation rate which is one divided by the allowable deprecation life, "n", in years. In equation form:

Straight Line Depreciation Per Year = (Cost)(1/n)   7-3

EXAMPLE 7-3 Illustration of Straight Line Depreciation

Assume you purchase a new machine in January of this tax year for $10,000. The estimated life of the machine is 8 years when salvage value is estimated to be $3,000. Determine the annual allowable depreciation deduction by the straight line method assuming the machine is in the 5 year depreciation life category and that the half year convention is applicable in the first year.

Solution:

The actual estimated asset use life and salvage value have no effect on depreciation calculations under current tax law.

			Depreciation
Years 1	:	($10,000)(1/5)(1/2) =	$1,000
Years 2 to 5	:	($10,000)(1/5) =	$2,000
Year 6	:	($10,000)(1/5)(1/2) =	$1,000
		Cumulative Depreciation =	$10,000

Note that because of the half year 1 convention, it takes 6 years to fully depreciate the asset.

7.5b Declining Balance Depreciation

Declining balance depreciation applies a depreciation rate from the straight line rate of 1/n, to 2/n, to a declining balance each year. Many governments specify applicable declining balance rates for different assets, such as .1,

.2 or .3, to be multiplied time the adjusted cost basis. Others specify the depreciation lives and type of declining balance depreciation, such as 150% or 200% declining balance rates now applicable under U.S. tax law, and require the investors to calculate their own rates. For example with 150% declining balance, 1.5/n (where n is the depreciation life), is the depreciation rate. The declining balance rate is applied to a "declining balance" or "adjusted basis" each year as shown in Equation 7-4:

Declining Balance Depreciation Per Year
  = (Declining Balance Rate)(Adjusted Basis)   7-4

where, for any depreciation method:

Adjusted Basis = Cost or Other Basis
                   – Cumulative Depreciation Previously Taken   7-5

The term "book value" or "tax book value" often is used interchangeably with "adjusted basis." The terms "diminishing balance" and "written down value" have interchangeable meaning with "adjusted basis" in Canada and Australia. All these terms represent the remaining undepreciated value of a depreciable asset.

EXAMPLE 7-4 Illustration of Declining Balance Depreciation

Assume the $10,000 cost in Example 7-3 is to be depreciated using 200% declining balance for a 5 year depreciation life and that the cost was incurred in the final quarter of the tax year, so the mid-quarter convention would be appropriate since more than 40% of depreciable cost is incurred in the fourth quarter. Determine the annual depreciation deductions.

Solution:

The 200% declining balance five year life rate is 2/5, or 0.40.

Year	200% D.B. Rate, (2/5)	x	Adjusted Basis	=	200% D.B. Depreciation
1	.40(1.5mo/12mo)		10,000		500
2	.40		9,500		3,800
3	.40		5,700		2,280
4	.40		3,420		1,368
5	.40		2,052		821
6			1,231		
Cumulative Depreciation After 5 Years					8,769

Note that the adjusted basis is not fully depreciated in 5 years. This is a problem with declining balance depreciation. It literally takes infinite years to fully depreciate a given adjusted basis with declining balance depreciation. Switching from declining balance to straight line depreciation enables an investor to fully depreciate an asset in the depreciation life.

7.5c Switching from Declining Balance to Straight Line Depreciation

In the U.S., all depreciation rates for the modified ACRS depreciation of personal property are based on either 150% or 200% declining balance switching to straight line. It is desirable to switch to straight line from declining balance in the year when you will get a bigger deduction by switching. This occurs when the straight line rate exceeds the declining balance rate, because when you switch, the remaining adjusted basis is depreciated straight line over the remaining years of depreciation life.

EXAMPLE 7-5 Declining Balance Switching to Straight Line Depreciation

Assume the $10,000 cost asset described in Example 7-4 is to be depreciated using 200% declining balance switching to straight line for a 5 year depreciation life, use the same mid-quarter convention for the entire $10,000 cost being incurred in the fourth quarter of the first year of depreciation. Calculate the annual depreciation to depreciate the asset as rapidly as possible.

Solution:

In switching to straight line from declining balance depreciation, when you switch methods, the remaining adjusted basis is depreciated straight line over the remaining years of depreciation life. In this analysis it is desirable to switch in year 4 when 2 depreciation years remain. The straight line rate of ½ (or 50%) for switching in year 4 is greater than the declining balance rate of 40%, so switching in year 4 is economically desirable (switching in year 3, the straight line rate would be 1/3 which is less than the 200% DB rate of 40%).

Year	Method	Rate	x	Adjusted Basis	=	200% DB to St Line Depreciation
1	200% D.B.	.40(1.5/12)		10,000		500
2	200% D.B.	.40		9,500		3,800
3	200% D.B.	.40		5,700		2,280
4	St. Line	.50		3,420		1,710
5	St. Line	.50		3,420		1,710
6				0		
Cumulative Depreciation After 5 Years						10,000

Note that the straight line depreciation rate is applied in each of years 4 and 5 to the adjusted basis at the time of switching in year four, and not to the new adjusted basis each year. In general, with 200% declining balance switching to straight line, you always switch methods in the year after the mid-year of the depreciation life. With 150% declining balance switching to straight line, you switch methods in the mid-year of the evaluation life.

7.5d Units of Production Depreciation

Units of production depreciation deducts the asset cost over the estimated producing life of the asset (instead of over a given depreciation life) by taking an annual depreciation deduction equal to the product of the "asset cost" or other basis times the ratio of the "units produced" in a depreciation year, divided by "expected asset lifetime units of production", (such as initial mineral reserves). This method permits the asset to be depreciated for tax purposes in direct proportion to asset use. It is allowed as an alternative depreciation method for tangible depreciable personal property costs and under the 1986 tax reform bill does not result in depreciation being a tax preference item for Alternative Minimum Tax considerations discussed in Chapter 8. Units of production depreciation is also allowed as an alternative to expensing mineral development costs under U.S. tax law.

EXAMPLE 7-6 Units of Production Depreciation

Assume that the $10,000 cost to be depreciated in Example 7-3 is estimated to produce 50,000 product units over its useful life. If 14,000 product units are expected to be produced in year 1, and 12,000 in year 2, calculate the year 1 and 2 units of production depreciation.

Solution:

Year	Depreciation Rate x Cost	Units of Production Depreciation Per Year
1	$10,000 x (14,000/50,000)	$2,800
2	$10,000 x (12,000/50,000)	$2,400

7.5e Modified Accelerated Cost Recovery System (ACRS) Depreciation

The cost of most tangible depreciable property placed in service after December 31, 1986 is recovered using the modified accelerated cost recovery system methods. Cost and recovery methods are the same whether property is new or used. Salvage value is neglected in computing the appropriate depreciation deduction.

Modified ACRS depreciation methods for personal property include 200% declining balance switching to straight line, and 150% declining balance switching to straight line. These rates are sometimes called "accelerated" depreciation rates because they give deductions faster than with straight line depreciation. Alternatively, you may irrevocably elect to use straight line depreciation over the regular depreciable life. The straight line method of depreciation is required for residential rental real property or non-residential real property purchased after 1986. Straight line depreciation often is called "straight line ACRS depreciation".

ACRS depreciable property is often called recovery property. All recovery property is depreciated over one of the following lives; 3 years, 5 years, 7 years, 10 years, 15 years, 20 years, 27.5 years or 31.5 years. Depreciation lives (recovery periods) are determined based on Asset Depreciation Range (ADR) mid-point class lives that were in effect prior to the introduction of ACRS depreciation rates in 1981. Recovery periods follow for some typical depreciable assets:

3 year property includes property with an ADR class life of four years or less. Under the ADR system, property with a midpoint life of four years or less includes: special tools and handling devices for manufacture of products such as food, beverages, rubber products, finished plastic products and fabricated metal products.

5 year property includes property with an ADR class life greater than four years and less than 10 years. Cars and light general vehicles have been added to this class which also includes research and experimentation equipment, qualified technological equipment, bio-mass properties that are small power production facilities, semi-conductor manufacturing equipment, and heavy, general purpose trucks including ore haulage trucks for use over the road.

7 year property includes property with an ADR class life of 10 years but less than 16 years. This class includes office furniture, fixtures, equipment such as mining machinery and oil and gas producing equipment and gathering pipelines, railroad track and equipment used to manufacture chemicals, rubber products, metal products, steel mill and automotive products, food and beverage products, etc. Typical oil and gas equipment that would qualify for this depreciation class include:

Surface and well casing, tubing (including transportation)
Wellhead (christmas tree), pumping system
Downhole equipment including guide shoes, centralizers, etc.

Salt water disposal equipment.
Tank battery and separators including site preparation, and operation
roads.
Installation of flow lines, tank batteries, separators and other equipment.

Typical mining equipment that would qualify for this depreciation class
includes:

Loaders, Dozers, Scrapers, Drills, Large Compressors, Haul Trucks,
Conveyors, and other equipment for quarrying of metallic and non-metal-
lic minerals (including sand, gravel, stone, and clay) and the milling,
benefication and other primary preparation for such material.

10 year property includes property with an ADR class life of 16 years
but less than 20 years. This class includes equipment assets related to petroleum refining, manufacture of tobacco products, grain mill products, sugar
and vegetable oil products, and synthetic natural gas from coal gasification.

15 year property includes property with an ADR class life of 20 years
and more but less than 25 years. This includes waste-water treatment plants,
telephone distribution plants and comparable equipment, liquefied natural
gas plants, gas utility trunk pipelines and related storage facilities, commer-
cial contract petroleum and gas pipelines and conveying systems.

20 year property includes property with an ADR class life of 25 years
and more, other than real property with an ADR midpoint of 27.5 years
and more. Municipal sewers, cable and transmission lines, electric utility
steam power plants and water utility plants are included in this class.

27.5 year residential rental real property includes buildings or structures
with respect to which 80 percent or more of the gross rental income is rental
income from dwelling units. If any portion of the building or structure is
occupied by the taxpayer, the gross rental income from the property includes
the rental value of the unit occupied by the taxpayer.

31.5 year non-residential real property is real property that is not (1)
residential rental property, or (2) property with a class life of less than 27.5
years. The house/senate 1986 tax bill conference committee report indicates

that this class includes property that either has no ADR class life or whose class is 27.5 years or more.

Table 7-1 identifies the depreciation method, ADR class lives and recovery period (depreciation life) for each class of recovery property.

Table 7-1 Personal Property Depreciation Lives and Methods

Recovery Period	Depreciation Method*	Mid-Point ADR Class Lives**
3 Yr	200% DB Depreciation Switching to St. Line	4 yrs or less
5 Yr	200% DB Depreciation Switching to St. Line	4.5 to 9.5 yrs
7 Yr	200% DB Depreciation Switching to St. Line	10 to 15.5 yrs
10 Yr	200% DB Depreciation Switching to St. Line	16 to 19.5 yrs
15 Yr	150% DB Depreciation Switching to St. Line	20 to 24.5 yrs
20 Yr	150% DB Depreciation Switching to St. Line	25 or more yrs

* Depreciation deductions can also be computed using the straight line method over the applicable recovery period.
** Depreciation life (recovery period) is determined by the mid-point life of Asset Depreciation Range (ADR) lives for assets. The ADR lives applicable are for the ADR Class Life Depreciation System in effect before 1981.

Table 7-2 Real Property Depreciation Lives and Methods

Recovery Period	Depreciation Method	ADR Class Life
27.5 Yr	Straight Line Depreciation	—
31.5 Yr	Straight Line Depreciation	—

As an alternative to computing the depreciation deductions each year for each class of depreciable personal property, the following Table 7-3 rates taken times depreciable cost give annual depreciation for three, five, seven and ten year life qualifying depreciable property that would qualify for the half-year convention in the first year only. The rates in Table 7-3 are not valid for personal property subject to the mid-quarter convention or for real property. Under those circumstances, the reader will be required to make his or her own depreciation calculations.

Table 7-3 Modified ACRS Depreciation Rates for Selected Lives*

Year	Depreciation Life			
	3	5	7	10
1	0.3333	0.2000	0.14290	0.1000
2	0.4444	0.3200	0.24490	0.1800
3	0.2222	0.1920	0.17490	0.1440
4	—	0.1440	0.12494	0.1152
5	—	0.1440	0.10412	0.09216
6	—	—	0.10412	0.07372
7	—	—	0.10412	0.07372
8	—	—	—	0.07372
9	—	—	—	0.07372
10	—	—	—	0.07372

* These rates times initial depreciable cost give the annual depreciation deductions for personal property qualifying for 200% declining balance switching to straight line and subject to the half-year convention in the first year. Do not use these rates if the mid-quarter first year depreciation convention applies (see Example 7-7).

EXAMPLE 7-7 Illustration of Modified ACRS Depreciation

Machinery and equipment have been purchased and placed into service prior to the final quarter of the tax year for a cost of $100,000. The modified ACRS depreciation life is 7 years which means the asset is depreciable by 200% declining balance switching to straight line when appropriate for a 7 year life. Determine the annual allowable depreciation deductions. Then look at the effect on depreciation deductions of not getting the asset into service until the final quarter of the year, assuming this is the only depreciable acquisition of the year.

Solution:
When depreciable assets whose cost is 60% or more of total depreciable costs for a tax year are placed in service during the first 3 quarters of a tax year, the half-year convention applies in the first depreciation year.

				200% DB to St Line
Year	Method	Rate x	Adjusted Basis =	Depreciation
1	200% D.B.	(.286)(.5)	100,000	14,290
2	200% D.B.	.286	85,710	24,490
3	200% D.B.	.286	61,220	17,490
4	200% D.B.	.286	43,730	12,494
5	St. Line	.333	31,236	10,412
6	St. Line	.333	31,236	10,412
7	St. Line	.333	31,236	10,412

Cumulative Depreciation	100,000

Using Table 7-3, Modified ACRS Rates

	7 Yr Life		200% DB to St Line
Year	ACRS Rates	x Adjusted Basis	= Depreciation
1	.14290	100,000	14,290
2	.24490	100,000	24,490
3	.17490	100,000	17,490
4	.12494	100,000	12,494
5	.10412	100,000	10,412
6	.10412	100,000	10,412
7	.10412	100,000	10,412
	Cumulative Depreciation		100,000

The mid-quarter convention applies in the first depreciation year when assets whose cost exceeds 40% of total depreciable costs for the tax year are placed in service during the final quarter of the tax year. Costs for each quarter, not just the final quarter, are affected by this convention. A half quarter deduction is allowed in the quarter assets are placed in service.

				200% DB to StLine
Year	Method	Rate x	Adjusted Basis =	Depreciation
1	200% D.B.	(.286)(1.5/12)	100,000	3,575
2	200% D.B.	.286	96,425	27,578
3	200% D.B.	.286	68,847	19,690
4	200% D.B.	.286	49,157	14,059
5	St. Line	.333	35,098	11,699
6	St. Line	.333	35,098	11,699
7	St. Line	.333	35,098	11,699
	Cumulative Depreciation (Within Roundoff)			100,000

7.6 Election to Expense Limited Depreciable Costs

U.S. tax law permits limited expensing of depreciable personal property that would otherwise be treated as a depreciable capital cost. Up to $10,000 ($5,000 for married persons filing separate returns) of depreciable personal property costs can be expensed in the year the property is placed in service. Should the cost of qualified depreciable property placed in service during the year exceed $200,000, the expense amount of $10,000 is reduced by the excess. Further, the total cost of the property that may be expensed is limited to the taxable income of the taxpayer as derived from the active business.

7.7 Depletion Methods

The owner of an economic interest in mineral deposits, oil and gas wells, or standing timber may recover his cost through federal tax deductions for depletion over the economic life of the property. You have an economic interest if through investment you have: (1) acquired any interest in minerals in place or standing timber, (2) received income by any form of legal relationship from extraction of the minerals or severance of the timber, to which you must look for a return of capital.

Oil, gas, and mineral depletion is computed by two methods: (1) cost depletion, and (2) percentage depletion. You must compute your depletion each year by both methods and use the one that gives you the greater tax deduction. You can switch methods from year to year with the exception that major oil and gas producers may only take cost depletion on oil and gas properties. The line of demarcation between small independent producers and integrated (or major) oil and gas producers is 1000 barrels per day of crude oil production or 6 million cubic feet of natural gas production, or the combined equivalent of both oil and gas production using 6000 cubic feet of gas as equivalent to one barrel of crude oil. Only cost depletion is applicable to timber.

7.7a Cost Depletion

The capitalized costs that generally go into the cost depletion basis for petroleum and mineral projects are for mineral right acquisition and or lease bonuses or their equivalent ascertained costs. Cost depletion is computed by dividing the total number of recoverable units in the deposit at the beginning of a year (tons, barrels, etc., determined in accordance with prevailing industry methods) into the adjusted basis of the mineral property for that year, and multiplying the resulting rate per unit (1) by the number of units for which payment is received during the tax year, if you use the cash receipts and disbursements method, or (2) by the number of units sold if you use an accrual method of accounting. The "adjusted basis" is the original mineral rights acquisition or lease cost plus any additional capital costs for the mineral property, less the total of all depletion allowed or allowable over the life of the property, from the larger of allowed cost or percent depletion. The depletion allowed or allowable each year is the greater of percentage depletion or cost depletion. The adjusted basis for cost depletion calculations can never be less than zero. In equation form cost depletion equals:

$$(\text{Adjusted Basis}) \frac{\text{Mineral Units Removed \& Sold During the Year}}{\text{Mineral Units Recoverable at Beginning of the Year}}$$

where Adjusted Basis = Cost Basis ± Adjustments − Cumulative Depletion

Mineral rights acquisition, lease bonuses, and other equivalent ascertained costs including geological and geophysical survey costs and recording, legal and assessment costs normally are the primary expenditures that go into the cost depletion adjusted basis. The IRS permits most other capital costs to be depreciated or amortized, and companies generally do not put any costs in the cost depletion basis that are not required to be put there. The examples and discussion illustrate the reason for this; percent depletion can be taken even if the cost depletion basis is zero. This means that you normally want to deduct every capital cost possible by a means other than cost depletion, because you still get percent depletion which is usually larger than cost depletion anyway. The major oil and gas producers have lost this benefit since they are no longer eligible for percent depletion.

EXAMPLE 7-8 Cost Depletion Calculations Illustrated

You own an oil property for which you paid $150,000 in mineral rights acquisition costs last year. Recoverable oil reserves are estimated at 1,000,000 barrels. 50,000 barrels of oil are produced this year and are sold for $29.00 per barrel. Your operating and overhead expenses are $180,000 this year and allowable depreciation is $120,000. You also expect the same production rate, operating costs, and selling price next year. Calculate the cost depletion for this year and also next year assuming we do not use percent depletion this year (percent depletion is calculated later for this example). This is an integrated petroleum company analysis viewpoint.

Solution:

$$\text{Year 1: Cost Depletion} = (150,000)\left(\frac{50,000 \text{ barrels}}{1,000,000 \text{ barrels}}\right) = \$7,500$$

$$\text{Year 2: Cost Depletion} = (150,000 - 7,500)\left(\frac{50,000 \text{ barrels}}{950,000 \text{ barrels}}\right)$$

$$= \$7,500$$

If percentage depletion had been taken in year 1, rather than cost depletion, the cost depletion basis for year 2 is the year 1 basis minus year 1 percentage depletion. This is illustrated in the next section in Example 7-10.

7.7b Percentage Depletion

Percentage depletion is a specified percentage of gross income after royalties from the sale of minerals removed from the mineral property during the tax year, but the deduction for depletion under this method, cannot exceed 50% of taxable income from the property after all deductions except depletion and loss carry forward deductions. If percent depletion exceeds 50% of taxable income, you are allowed to take 50% of the taxable income before depletion as your percentage depletion deduction. (There is no limitation on the maximum annual cost depletion that can be taken, except that the accrued cost depletion cannot exceed the cost basis of the property.) However, unlike depreciation and cost depletion, percentage depletion accruals are not limited to the cost basis of the property; that is, percent depletion may be taken after the cost basis in the property has been recovered. Investors generally do not put any costs in the cost depletion basis that do not have to be there since percentage depletion can be taken on mineral properties by any investor, or by independent oil and gas producers.

In applying the 50% limit on percentage depletion when operating loss carry forwards from previous years are available, the depletion calculations and the 50% limit test are applied before loss carry forwards.

Table 7-4 Procedure to Determine Allowable Depletion

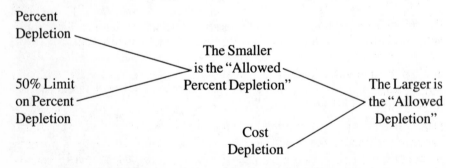

A 15 percent depletion rate for oil and gas is used by independent producers (and royalty owners) by taking gross income from well-head price sale revenue after royalties (or royalty revenue by royalty owners) times the 15 percent depletion rate given in Table 7-5. For other minerals the percent of gross income allowable as a deduction is based upon the type of deposit being mined. Some of the percentages for the more common ores and minerals are shown below:

Table 7-5 Applicable Percentage Depletion Rates

Deposits	Percentage Depletion Rates, %
Oil and Gas*	15
Sulphur and uranium; and if from deposits in the U.S.; asbestos, mica, lead, zinc, nickel, molybdenum, tin, tungsten, mercury, vanadium, and certain other ores and minerals including bauxite	22
If from deposits in the U.S., gold silver, copper, iron ore**, and oil shale	15
Coal**, lignite and sodium chloride	10
Clay and shale used in making sewer pipe, bricks, or used as sintered or burned lightweight aggregates	7½
Gravel, sand, stone	5
Most other minerals and metallic ores	14

* Integrated (or major) petroleum producers defined in the next paragraph are not eligible for percent depletion. Also, the fixed contract pre 2/1/75 natural gas percent depletion rate is 22%.

** The percent depletion rates for coal and iron ore drop to 8% and 12% respectively after the cost depletion adjusted basis has been recovered by either percent or cost depletion deductions.

The percentage depletion rates from Table 7-5 are applied to the "gross income from the property," which is the gross income from "mining" or well head price for oil and gas. "Mining" includes, in addition to the extraction of minerals from the ground, treatment processes considered as mining applied by the mine owner or operator to the minerals or the ore, and transportation that is not over 50 miles from the point of extraction to the plant or mill in which allowable treatment processes are applied. Treatment processes considered as mining depend upon the ore or mineral mined, and generally include those processes necessary to bring the mineral or ore to the stage at which it first becomes commercially marketable; this usually means to a shipping grade and form. However, in certain cases, additional processes are specified in the Internal Revenue Service regulations, and are considered as mining. Net smelter return or its equivalent is the gross income on which mining percentage depletion commonly is based. Royalty owners get percentage depletion on royalty income so companies get percentage depletion on gross income after royalties. Small "independent" oil and gas producers are eligible to take percent depletion while "integrated" oil and gas producers are not eligible to take percent depletion. For all tax deduction eligibility purposes, the line of demarcation between "integrated" and "independent" oil and gas producers is defined as individuals or corporations with 1,000 barrels per day of domestic crude oil production or 6 million cubic feet per day of natural gas production or the combined equivalent production of oil and gas based on one barrel of oil being equivalent to 6,000 cubic feet of natural gas.

7.8 Windfall Profits Tax

The same 1,000 bbl/day oil production limit that determines producer eligibility for percentage depletion separates independents and major oil companies for windfall profits (excise) tax calculation purposes. The windfall tax law is very complicated, but the following is a brief simplified summary to give the reader a general idea of the windfall tax calculations. See your tax accountants for specific windfall tax details.

Table 7-6 Windfall Profits Tax Percentages

	Tier 1 Old Oil	Tier 2* Stripper Oil* or Natl Pet Reserve	Heavy, and Incremental Tertiary Oil	Tier 3 New Oil by a Major or Independent
Major	70.0%	60.0%	30.0%	22.5% in 1987
Indepndnt	50.0%	30.0%	30.0%	20.0% in 1988
				15% in 1989
				and after
Approx Base Oil Price 5/1/79	$12.81/bbl + inflation/yr	$15.20/bbl + inflation per yr	$16.55/bbl + inflation/yr + 2%/yr	

* Stripper oil (10 bbl or less crude oil production per day) windfall tax applies only to major producers.

The windfall profit tax is based on sales price reduced by adjusted base price and severance taxes related to the excess of the sales price over the adjusted base price.

Sales Price
– Adjusted Base Price
– Severance Tax Adjustment
_____
Windfall Profit   7-6

Windfall Profit x Windfall Tax Rate = Windfall Profit Tax   7-7

Windfall profit tax is limited to the lesser of the windfall tax just calculated or 90% of net income calculated by a specified format. The 90% net income limitation can reduce or eliminate windfall tax on marginal production. The reader is referred to a windfall profits tax manual for details. Finally, windfall profits tax is scheduled to be phased out between 1991 and 1993, if Congress does not extend it.

EXAMPLE 7-9 Percentage Depletion, Windfall Tax and Cash Flow

For the case study described in Example 7-8, with 50,000 bbl of oil production this year, selling price of $29.00/bbl (assume to be after royalties), operating costs of $180,000 and depreciation of $120,000, compare percentage and cost depletion for this year and next year (years 1 and 2) assuming the analysis is for a small producer eligible for either percentage or cost depletion. The 15 percent depletion rate is applicable. Assume the base oil price is $25.00/bbl for windfall profit tax calculation purposes and use a 15% windfall tax rate. Assume severance taxes are negligible. Use a 40% income tax rate and calculate cash flow for this year.

Solution:
Royalty owners pay windfall tax and get percent depletion on royalty revenues so we can base the analysis on net revenues after royalties.

	Year 1
Net Revenue, (50,000 bbl @ $29.00/bbl)	$1,450,000
- Operating costs	-180,000
- Windfall Tax, (50,000*($29-$25/bbl)(.15)	-30,000
- Depreciation	-120,000
Taxable Income Before Depletion	1,120,000
- 50% Limit for % Depletion (.5)(1,120,000)	560,000
- Percentage Depletion (.15)(1,450,000)	-217,500*
- Cost Depletion (From Example 7-9)	7,500
Taxable Income	902,500
- Tax @ 40%	-361,000
Net Income (Profit)	541,500
+ Depreciation	120,000
+ Depletion Taken	217,500
Cash Flow From Sales This Year	879,000

*Since the $217,500 percentage depletion is less than the 50% limit for percentage depletion, $217,500 is the allowable percentage depletion. This is greater than the $7,500 cost depletion so $217,500 is the largest allowable depletion deduction.

In year 2, if the revenues and deductions are assumed to be the same as year 1, percentage depletion is the same. However, the cost depletion deduction differs in the second year because the cost basis must be adjusted for the actual depletion deduction taken. In this example the year 1 depletion deduction was for percentage depletion.

Remembering from Example 7-8 that the property was acquired for a cost of $150,000 the year 2 cost depletion would be calculated as follows:

Year 2 Cost Depletion = (150,000 − 217,500)(50,000/950,000) < 0

No cost depletion is allowable when the cost basis is negative. There is no cumulative limit on percentage depletion so it again would be selected in year 2.

EXAMPLE 7-10 Illustration of Depletion Calculations for Co-Product Ores

A mining operation yields annual sales revenue of $1,500,000 from an ore containing the co-products lead, zinc and silver. $1,000,000 of the revenue is from lead and zinc, and $500,000 from silver. Operating costs are $700,000 and allowable depreciation is $100,000. Determine the taxable income assuming the cost depletion basis is zero and that operating costs and depreciation are proportional to revenue from different ores.

Solution:

Since silver is a 15% depletion rate mineral while lead and zinc are 22% depletion rate minerals, sales revenues must be prorated for percent depletion calculation purposes.

Sales Revenue	$1,500,000
- Operating Costs	-700,000
- Depreciation	-100,000
Taxable Before Depletion	700,000
50% Limit on % Depletion	350,000
Lead, Zinc % Depletion (.22)(1,000,000)	-220,000 ⎫ select
Silver % Depletion (.15)(500,000)	- 75,000 ⎭ 295,000
Taxable Income	$ 405,000

7.9 Amortization

It is permissible for a business to deduct each year as amortization, a proportionate part of certain capital expenditures. Amortization permits the recovery of these expenditures in a manner similar to straight line depreciation over five years or a different specified life. Only certain specified expenditures may be amortized for Federal income tax purposes. Some of these expenditures are summarized as follows:

(1) 30% of the cost associated with intangible drilling costs must be amortized over a 60 month period by all integrated oil and gas producers and 30% of the cost of mineral development costs incurred by corporate taxpayers must be amortized over a 60 month period. (2) A corporations organization expenses under certain conditions may be amortized. (3) The cost of acquiring a lease for business purposes (other than a mineral lease) may be recovered by amortization deductions over the term of the lease. (4) Research and experimental expenses may be amortized over a 60 month period or longer, or deducted currently as a business expense if connected with your trade or business. (5) The cost of certified pollution control facilities may be amortized over a period of 60 months for installations in plants that were in existence prior to 1976.

The annual allowable amortization for qualifying expenditures is calculated in the same way that straight line depreciation is calculated for depreciable assets, with first year amortization proportioned to months of service.

EXAMPLE 7-11 Illustration of Amortization

A total of $30,000 was spent on air pollution control facilities on January 1, 1987. Determine the allowable annual amortization deduction for this equipment for years 1987-91, assuming the investor tax year is the calendar year.

Solution:

The annual amortization deduction for 5 years equals:

(1/5)(30,000) = $6,000 per year.

7.10 Four Financial Situations That Affect Cash Flow Calculations

All investors whether individual, corporate or government, fall into one of four financial situations for cash flow calculation purposes. The four financial situations are:

Expense   An investor has other taxable income from existing salary, business or investment sources against which to use negative taxable income in any year from a new project being analyzed so the project is credited with tax savings from these deduction in the year incurred.

Stand Alone An investor does not have other taxable income against which to use negative taxable income in any year so it must be carried forward to be used against project revenues when they are realized. This approach is often referred to as making a project "stand alone".

Carry Forward An investor has sufficient loss carry forwards from negative taxable incomes on other projects so that it is anticipated no tax will be payable for a specific period of time into the future. This requires accumulating all tax payments, tax savings and any tax credits to the point in time in the future when it is anticipated that the investor may again begin paying taxes.

Before-Tax An investor is a tax-free entity such as a government, or charitable organization that is not required to pay any federal or state income taxes on revenues associated with investments.

If other income exists against which to use deductions from new projects, the investor realizes the tax benefits more quickly than when other income does not exist and negative taxable income must be carried forward. The economics of projects will always look better for investors who have other income against which to use deductions when incurred, compared to an investor that does not have other income. Tax savings are inflows of money, and the faster they are realized, the better project economics look. Therefore, it is very important to analyze the economic potential of projects from the viewpoint of the financial situation of the investor. This is true in all industries and countries. It is incorrect to carry negative taxable income forward in an analysis if other taxable income exists, and it also is incorrect to credit a project with tax savings from negative taxable income in any year if the investor is in a financial situation that requires carrying negative taxable income forward.

The Tax Reform Act of 1986 placed severe limitations on the ability of investors to utilize tax deduction losses from passive income investments against non-passive investment income. In the past these deductions could be used against any income but this is restricted by the 1986 tax bill. A passive activity is defined as one that involves the conduct of any trade or business in which the taxpayer does not materially participate. Also, any rental activity or limited partnership is a passive activity regardless of whether the taxpayer materially participates. An exception to this rule does exist for investors with annual taxable income less than $100,000. These taxpayers may use up to $25,000 of passive loss deductions and the deduction equivalent of passive tax credits attributable to rental real estate each tax year against income from non-passive sources such as salary and compensation for personal services.

As with any investment, before considering a tax shelter investment plan investor's should consult a tax accountant to determine if the investment is appropriate for the investors tax and financial position and to consider all tax ramifications of investments such as possible applicability of the alternative minimum tax (discussed in Chapter 8).

In this text, examples and problems in Chapter 7 are presented primarily from the viewpoint of investors who must carry negative taxable income forward. Chapter 8 illustrates analyses from both viewpoints of carrying losses forward and crediting projects with tax savings in the year negative taxable income is incurred. Chapters 9 and 10 emphasize analyses primarily from the viewpoint of investors that have other income against which to used deductions. The four financial situations enumerated at the beginning of this section are related to DCFROR and NPV analysis in Examples 8-6 and 8-8. The next example illustrates carrying negative taxable income forward.

EXAMPLE 7-12 Illustration of Loss Carry Forward Cash Flow Analysis

An individual investor is considering acquiring and developing a mineral property believed to contain 1,000,000 units of mineral reserves (mineral units could be ounces of silver, barrels of oil, etc.). The mineral rights acquisition cost for the property would be $2,000,000 at year 0. Mineral development (or petroleum drilling) cost of $800,000 and tangible equipment costs (mining equipment or oil/gas producing equipment and pipelines) of $1,000,000 also are projected to be incurred at year 0. Modified ACRS depreciation will be based on the 7 year depreciation life assets, starting in year 1, assuming the half year 1 convention is applicable. Production is projected to be uniform for each of years 1 and 2 at 200,000 units per year. Product selling price is estimated to be $30.00 per unit in year 1 and $34.00 per unit in year 2. Operating expenses are estimated to be $700,000 in year 1, and $800,000 in year 2. Royalty owners will receive 20% of revenues each year. Assume the mineral is a 15% depletion rate mineral and that the investor is an "independent" producer if the mineral is oil. Use an effective income tax rate of 40%. Determine project cash flow for years 0, 1, and 2 assuming the investor does not have other income against which to use negative taxable income in year 0, so it must be carried forward to make project economics stand alone. Then calculate the cash flows using Equation 7-2.

Solution:

Depreciation (200% DB Switching to St.Line, DB Rate is 2/7 = .286):

Year 1   (1,000,000)(.286)(.5) = 143,000
Year 2   (1,000,000-143,000)(.286) = 245,102

Year 1 Cost Depletion:

$$\frac{200,000 \text{ units produced}}{1,000,000 \text{ units in reserve}} \times \$2,000,000 \text{ Acq. Cost} = \$400,000$$

Year 2 Cost Depletion:

$$\frac{200,000}{800,000} \times (\$2,000,000 - \$720,000) = \$320,000$$

Cash Flow Calculations

	Year 0	Year 1	Year 2
Sales Revenue	-	6,000,000	6,800,000
- Royalties @ 20%	-	-1,200,000	-1,360,000
Net Revenue	-	4,800,000	5,440,000
- Operating Costs	-	-700,000	-800,000
- Development	-800,000	-	-
- Depreciation	-	-143,000	-245,102
Taxable Before Depletion	-800,000	3,957,000	4,394,898
- 50% Limit on % Depletion	-	1,978,500*	2,197,449*
- Percentage Depletion	-	-720,000*	-816,000*
- Cost Depletion	-	400,000	320,000
- Loss Forward	-	-800,000	-
Taxable Income	-800,000	2,437,000	3,578,898
- Tax @ 40%	-	-974,800	-1,431,559
Net Income	-800,000	1,462,200	2,147,339
+ Depreciation	-	143,000	245,102
+ Depletion	-	720,000	816,000
+ Loss Forward	-	800,000	-
- Capital Costs	-3,000,000	-	-
Cash Flow	-3,800,000	3,125,200	3,208,441

*   Largest Allowable Depletion Deduction Using Table 7-4.

Cash Flow Calculations Using Equation 7-2

Yr 0, CF = -800,000 - 3,000,000 = -3,800,000

Yr 1, CF = 6,000,000 - 1,200,000 - 700,000 - 974,800 = 3,125,200

Yr 2, CF = 6,800,000 - 1,360,000 - 800,000 - 1,431,559 = 3,208,441

PROBLEMS

7-1 Equipment (such as oil and gas producing equipment, mining machinery, or certain general industry equipment) has been purchased and put into service for a $2,000,000 cost. Calculate the modified ACRS depreciation (200% declining balance switching to straight line), and straight line ACRS depreciation per year, for a 7 year depreciation life, with the half year 1 convention applicable for both methods, assuming the equipment is put in service in year 1.

7.2 An owner may calculate depreciation using the "units of production" methods of depreciation. Consider a depreciable asset costing $100,000 that is expected to have a useful life of 120,000 units of production. Salvage value is estimated to be negligible. Estimated annual production for the next 7 years is 30,000, 30,000, 20,000 and 10,000 per year over the remaining 4 years. Use the "units of production" depreciation method and determine the depreciation each year.

7-3 A company has acquired a vehicle and light trucks costing $100,000 in the first quarter of the tax year and research equipment costing $500,000 in the fourth quarter of the tax year, so the mid-quarter convention is appropriate for depreciation calculations (more than 40% of depreciable cost is in the last quarter). The assets qualify as 5 year life depreciable property. Compute the modified ACRS depreciation and straight line depreciation for each year.

7-4 Depreciable residential rental real property has been purchased for $800,000 during the fourth month of the taxpayer's tax year. For the applicable 27.5 year depreciation life, determine the annual allowable straight line depreciation deductions. Remember that for real property, the first year depreciation is proportional to months of service and subject to the mid-month convention.

7-5   Mineral rights to a petroleum property have been leased by a small independent petroleum company for a $500,000 lease bonus fee at year 0. Following year 0 development, it is estimated that production will start in year 1 with 200,000 barrels of oil production from initial reserves estimated to be 1,000,000 barrels, and a selling price estimated to be $18 per barrel. Royalties are 16% of gross income. Operating costs in year 1 are estimated to be $200,000 with allowable depreciation estimated to be $150,000. Assume a 40% effective income tax rate and that there is no tax loss carry forward from year 0 to year 1:

A) Determine the year 1 cash flow assuming the property is acquired and developed at year 0 by a small independent petroleum company.

B) Determine the year 1 cash flow assuming the property is acquired and developed at year 0 by a major integrated petroleum company and the year 1 amortization deduction from 30% of drilling cost in year 0 is $80,000.

7-6   Mineral rights to a gold/silver mineral property can be leased by a company for a $500,000 bonus cost at year 0. Following year 0 development, it is estimated that the year 1 production will be 200,000 tons of ore from initial reserves estimated to be 1,000,000 tons of ore, with net smelter return value of the ore estimated to be $18 dollars per ton. Royalties are 16% of gross income. Operating costs in year 1 are estimated to be $200,000 with allowable year 1 depreciation estimated to be $150,000. Assume a 40% effective income tax rate, and determine the estimated year 1 cash flow for an individual investor, assuming that there is no tax loss carry forward from year 0 to year 1.

7-7   A mineral reserve containing 100,000 tons of gold ore is to be developed and produced uniformly (20,000 tons per year) over years 1 through 5 by an individual investor. The estimated net smelter return value of the ore is $120 per ton in year 1, and the net smelter return is expected to increase $15 per ton in each following year. Annual operating costs are estimated to be $900,000 in year 1, escalating $100,000 per year in the following years. A one-time mineral development start-up cost of $500,000 is to be incurred in year 0 and deducted as an expense at year 0. A mineral rights acquisition cost of $600,000 also will be incurred in year 0 (the basis for cost depletion calculations), along with equipment cost of $1,000,000 to be depreciated using modified ACRS depreciation beginning at year 1, for a 7 year life with the half year 1 convention. Write off the remaining book value from the depreciable asset at year 5. Other income and tax obligations do not exist against which to use negative taxable income, so losses must be carried forward to make the project economics stand alone. Determine the project cash flows for years 0 through 5, assuming a 40% effective income tax rate.

7-8   A mineral project involves production of ore from a 5,000,000 ton ore reserve. Year 0 acquisition cost of $2,000,000 is the basis for cost depletion. Development expenses of $1,500,000 will be incurred during year 1 and deducted at year 1 in the maximum amount allowable. No other income exists against which to use deductions, so all negative taxable income will be carried forward until used against project income (stand alone analysis). Producing equipment costing $3,000,000 at year 0, will go into service in year 1 and be depreciated using the 7 year life modified ACRS depreciation using the half year 1 convention. Production is estimated to be 500,000 tons of ore per year, starting in year 1. Net smelter return ore value is estimated to be $10 per ton in year 1, $11 per ton in year 2, and $12 per ton in year 3. Royalties are 10% of revenues (net smelter return) each year. Operating costs are expected to be $3,000,000 in year 1, $3,300,000 in year 2, and $3,600,000 in year 3. The allowable percentage depletion rate is 15%. The effective income tax rate is 40%. Determine the cash flows for years 0, 1, 2 and 3, without taking writeoffs on remaining tax book values at year 3, assuming:

A) The investor is an individual. Expense 100% of mineral development cost in year 1.

B) The investor is a corporation. Expense 70% of mineral development in year 1, and capitalize the other 30% and deduct straight line over 60 months assuming the cost is incurred in month 7 of year 1 so take six months of deduction (6/12 of a full year) in year 1.

7-9   Petroleum mineral rights have been acquired at year 0 for $200,000 and an oil well is projected to be drilled and completed at year 0 for intangible drilling costs (IDC's) of $500,000 and depreciable producing equipment and tangible completion costs of $400,000 which are depreciable over 7 years using modified ACRS depreciation starting in year 1 with the half year convention. Gross oil income is expected to be $700,000 in year 1, $600,000 in year 2, and $500,000 in year 3, with royalties of 15% of gross income each year. Operating costs are estimated to be $50,000 per year in each of years 1, 2 and 3 with no windfall profits tax. Producible oil reserves are estimated to be 200,000 barrels with 30,000 barrels produced in year 1, 27,000 barrels in year 2, and 24,000 barrels in year 3. Assume no other income exists so all negative taxable income will be carried forward and used against project taxable income (stand alone analysis economics). Use a 40% tax rate and calculate the cash flows for each of years 0, 1, 2, and 3 without taking writeoffs on remaining tax book values at year 3 for:

A) A small independent petroleum producer eligible for either percent or cost depletion and who may expense 100% of IDC's in year 0.

B) A major "integrated" petroleum producer eligible only for cost depletion and required to deduct 30% of IDC's straight line over 60 months, beginning in the month the cost is incurred (assume the IDC cost is incurred in month 7 of tax year 0 so the year 0 deduction is 6/12 of a full first year deduction).

CHAPTER 8

INCOME TAX, CASH FLOW, WORKING CAPITAL AND DISCOUNTED CASH FLOW ANALYSIS

8.1 Introduction

The objective of this chapter is to relate income tax effects, working capital, and the concept of cash flow to discounted cash flow analysis as it relates to rate of return, net value analysis and ratio decision criteria, applied after tax considerations. After-tax rate of return analysis commonly is referred to as Discounted Cash Flow Rate of Return, or DCFROR analysis. Other names given to this method in the literature and textbooks are Profitability Index, or P.I., Investor's Rate of Return, True Rate of Return, and Internal Rate of Return. All of these names refer to the same method which easily is the most widely used economic analysis decision method in practice, even though Net Present Value and Ratios have advantages over DCFROR in certain analysis situations described in earlier chapters of the text.

The effects of income tax considerations often vary widely from one investment alternative to another, so it generally is imperative to compare the relative economics of investment alternatives on an after-tax basis to have a valid economic analysis. Income taxes, both federal and state if applicable, are project costs, just as labor, materials, utilities, property taxes, borrowed money interest, insurance and so forth are project operating costs.

It doesn't make sense to leave income taxes out of analysis any more than it would make sense to omit labor or materials or any other operating cost from an analysis.

As described in Chapter 7, cash flow is what is left from sales revenue each year after paying all the out-of-pocket expenses for operating costs, capital costs and income taxes. All tax deductible expenses, except income taxes, are put into the operating cost category. Capital costs include costs such as building and equipment costs, that are deductible over a period of time greater than a year, or non-deductible costs such as the cost of acquiring land.

In making proper after-tax analyses of investment alternatives you must be careful to recognize that for economic analysis work, the tax considerations that are relevant are what a company or individual does for tax purposes, and not what a company does for "book" purposes, which means for financial accounting or shareholder reporting purposes. There sometimes is a tendency for evaluation personnel and accountants to get confused on this point. What a company does for annual report book purposes has no relevance to economic analysis of projects except for a possible effect on alternative minimum tax for corporations discussed later in this chapter. What a company actually does in the way of taking tax deductions and credits on various capital and operating costs is what effects the amount of cash flow that new investments will generate at different points in time. To determine valid cash flow each evaluation period for economic analysis requires accounting for the proper costs, revenues and tax deductions at the points in time they will be incurred. It should be evident that this requires using actual tax considerations rather "book" tax considerations which are different from actual tax considerations for literally all publicly owned companies.

8.2 Forms of Business Organizations and Tax Considerations

This section briefly discusses, from the Federal income tax viewpoint, the three most important types of business organizations in the U.S. which are: the sole proprietorship, the partnership and the corporation. Since tax considerations often are extremely important in choosing a particular form of business organization, persons planning to go into business should become familiar with the tax consequences of the different types of business organizations.

Different income tax rates apply to corporations and to individuals. Individual income tax rates apply to sole proprietors, individual members of partnerships, and Subchapter S corporations. An individual engaging in business alone is a sole proprietor. A partnership must file a partnership income return, which is merely an information return. Each partner is taxed on his or her share of the partnership earnings whether or not those earnings are distributed.

Regular corporate income is taxed to the corporation at corporation rates. Corporation earnings, when distributed to the shareholders as dividends, are taxed as ordinary income at the appropriate individual tax rate. However, earnings of a corporation structured under Subchapter S of the Internal Revenue Service code are taxed only once at individual income tax rates, so double taxation of taxable income is avoided with Subchapter S corporations.

You may be liable for several types of Federal taxes in addition to income tax, depending upon the type of business in which you are engaged. For example, federal excise and employment taxes apply equally whether you conduct your business as a sole proprietorship, partnership, or corporation.

Regardless of the form of your business organization, you must keep records to determine your correct tax liability. These records must be permanent, accurate, complete and must clearly establish income, deductions, credits, employee information, etc. The law does not specify any particular kind of records.

Every taxpayer must compute his or her taxable income and file an income tax return on the basis of a period of time called a tax year. Beginning in 1987, for all taxpayer's except regular "C" corporations, a tax year is the 12 consecutive months in the calender year ending December 31. A fiscal year for "C" corporations is 12 consecutive months ending on the last day of any month, as specified by corporation by-laws.

8.3 Corporate and Individual Federal Income Tax Rates

Both corporate and individual Federal income tax rates vary with the incremental level of taxable income after all allowable deductions have been taken as shown below for married, single and corporate taxpayers under the Tax Reform Act of 1986. Since the new individual tax rates go into effect April 1, 1987, effective tax rates for 1987 are in between the 1986 and new 1988 rates as Tables 8-1 and 8-2 show.

Married Couples Filing Joint Returns

Taxable Income Over:	But Not Over:	Pay	+ % On Excess	Of The Amount Over
$ 0	3,000	0	11%	0
3,000	28,000	330	15%	3,000
28,000	45,000	4,080	28%	28,000
45,000	90,000	8,840	35%	45,000
Over	90,000	24,590	38.5%	90,000

To illustrate use of this table, a married couple with $50,000 of taxable income in 1987 would pay tax as follows: Tax on $45,000 is $8,840. Tax on $50,000 – $45,000 is $5,000 (.35) = $1,750. Total tax on $50,000 taxable income is $8,840 plus $1,750 or $10,590.

Single Individuals

Taxable Income Over:	But Not Over:	Pay	+ % On Excess	Of The Amount Over
$ 0	1,800	0	11%	0
1,800	16,800	198	15%	1,800
16,800	27,000	2,448	28%	16,800
27,000	54,000	5,304	35%	27,000
Over	54,000	14,754	38.5%	54,000

Table 8-1 Income Tax Rates for Individuals in 1987

Note that the 1987 (and 1988 and later years) rate schedules do not contain a zero bracket (i.e., zero tax rate) as existed for 1986 and earlier years. The zero bracket has been replaced by a new standard deduction taken in arriving at taxable income.

In 1988 and beyond, the law stipulates a five percent surtax that applies to taxpayers whose income exceeds certain levels which depend on the tax filing status of an individual. The purpose of this tax surcharge is to phase out the tax benefits realized by high income tax payers from the 15 percent rate on the lowest increment of taxable income and from a taxpayer's personal and dependency exemptions. Table 8-2 illustrates the effect of this surtax for married couples filing a joint return and for single individuals for 1988 and beyond.

Married Couples Filing Joint Returns (Claiming 2 Exemptions)		Single Individuals (Claiming 1 Exemption)	
If taxable income is:	Tax Rate	If taxable income is:	Tax Rate
Not over $29,750	15%	Not Over $17,850	15%
Over $29,750 up to $71,900 .	28%	Over $17,850 up to $43,150 .	28%
Over $71,900 up to $171,090 .	33%	Over $43,150 up to $100,480 .	33%
Over $171,090	28%	Over $100,480	28%

Table 8-2 Income Tax Rates for Individuals for 1988

The five percent surcharge for married couples claiming two exemptions and filing joint returns can be explained in the following manner. Income above $71,900 is subject to the five percent surtax until the surtax is applied to sufficient incremental taxable income to phase out two benefits generated by higher income earners as follows: 1) benefit of the reduced 15% tax rate, versus 28%, on the first increment of $29,750 in taxable income and, 2) benefit of the two personal exemptions that would be claimed by a married couple with no other dependents. The tax saving from $29,750 taxed at 15% versus 28% is $(.28 - .15)(29,750) = \$3,867.50$. A five percent surcharge on $77,350 incremental taxable income dollars recaptures this tax benefit, effectively giving a 33 percent tax rate on taxable income from $71,900 to $149,250. To eliminate the 1988 personal exemption tax benefit for wealthy taxpayers, each exemption adds $10,920 to taxable income at the 33 percent rate (28% plus 5% surcharge). In 1988 each personal exemption reduces taxable income by $1,950, saving tax of 28 percent times $1,950 amounting to $546. Paying a 5 percent surcharge tax on an extra $10,920 of taxable income recaptures this exemption tax savings. With two exemptions, taxable income taxed at 33 percent increases from $149,250 by two times $10,920 to $171,090. Taxable income above $171,090 is taxed at 28%. Obviously changing the number of exemptions claimed changes the range of incremental taxable income taxed at 33 percent. In 1989 the personal exemption is scheduled to increase to $2,000 which would change the range of taxable income taxed at 33 percent from the 1988 range.

After 1988, the income brackets, not the tax rates, are scheduled to be adjusted for inflation each year and rounded down to the next lowest multiple of $50.00.

Corporate tax rates have also been revised and become effective for taxable years beginning after July 1, 1987. Corporations with a tax year that includes this date are required to pro-rate taxes based on a weighted average of the 1986 and 1987 rates for the number of months each rate is applicable for a corporate fiscal year that includes July 1, 1987.

Taxable Income	Effective July 1, 1987	Prior Law
Not Over $25,000	15%	15%
Over $25,000 but not over $50,000	15%	18%
Over $50,000 but not over $75,000	25%	30%
Over $75,000 but not over $100,000	34%	40%
Over $100,000	34%	46%

Table 8-3 Corporate Income Tax Rates

5% Additional tax on corporate income over $100,000. A corporation with taxable income over $100,000 must pay an additional tax equal to five percent of the amount in excess of $100,000, up to a maximum additional tax of $11,750. This extra tax operates to phase out the benefits of graduated rates for corporations with taxable incomes between $100,000 and $335,000. A corporation having taxable income of $335,000 or more gets no benefit from the graduated rates and pays, in effect, a flat tax at a 34-percent rate.

Since both corporate and individual income tax rates vary at different levels of taxable income, it is necessary to use incremental analysis concepts to determine the proper tax for new project income. However, for many corporate evaluations, any new project income will be incremental income above the first $75,000 of corporate income from other sources. In this situation, which is very common, the 34 percent Federal corporate tax rate is relevant for all new project income for taxable years beginning after July 1, 1987, and therefore is the rate that should be used in evaluating new investment projects. Remember that corporations and individuals also pay state tax in most states, so the overall effective federal plus state tax rate will be greater than the 34 percent for corporations or 28 percent for individuals. Usually the effective rate will be in the range of 36 percent to 40 percent for corporations, or 30 to 34 percent for individuals, as will be developed in Section 8.7.

8.4 Corporate and Individual Capital Gains Tax Treatment

The tax reform act continues to make a distinction between capital and ordinary gains and losses. However, all capital gain is now treated as ordinary income subject to either the appropriate corporate income tax rates (effective July 1, 1987), or the appropriate individual tax rates. Even though the individual income tax rate could exceed 28 percent with the surtax (33 percent) the maximum capital gains rate for individuals is the 28 percent rate. Further, the new tax law requires taxpayers to continue computing capital gains by the previous methods as is discussed in the following paragraphs.

If a gain or loss is from the disposition of a capital asset, individuals or corporations have a capital gain or loss. If a capital asset is held six months or less, the gain or loss from its sale or exchange is considered to be a short term gain or loss. If the asset is held longer than six months, the gain or loss is considered long term.

Short term capital gains and losses are merged by adding the gains and losses separately and subtracting one total from the other to determine the net short term capital gain or loss. Similarly, long term capital gains and losses are merged to determine the net long term capital gain or loss. The total net short or long term capital gain or loss is then determined by merging the net short term capital gain or loss with the net long term capital gain or loss.

Net short term capital gains are taxed as ordinary income for both individuals and corporations. Under the 1986 Tax Reform Act, long term capital gains are also taxed as ordinary income for both individuals and corporations. Corporations may deduct capital losses only to the extent of capital gains. An individual may deduct capital losses in full amount against capital gains plus up to a maximum of $3,000 in combined short term and long term capital losses may be deducted against ordinary income per year.

Although preferential tax rate treatment for capital gains has been eliminated for both individuals and corporations, Tax Code provisions still require characterizing income as ordinary or capital gain income and losses as ordinary or short term or long term capital losses. The capital gains tax structure has been retained to facilitate reinstatement of a preferential capital gains tax structure if it becomes desirable in the future.

EXAMPLE 8-1 Illustration of Corporate and Individual Capital Gains Tax Treatment

An investor with about $500,000 of annual taxable income purchased a parcel of land 3 months ago for $50,000 and now has an offer to sell it for $60,000. Neglecting the time value of money, what selling price after owning the land 7 months, will give the investor the same after-tax profit as the $60,000 selling price now? Evaluate this problem from the standpoint of an individual whose ordinary income tax rate on the incremental income would be 28%.

Solution:

If the property is sold now, short term capital gain tax is:

10,000(.28) = $2,800, Therefore a $7,200 profit is realized if the land is sold now. Holding the asset for 7 months will give exactly the same profit since long term and short term gains are both taxed at the 28 percent ordinary income tax rate.

Profit = Gain − Income Tax

$7,200 = (X − 50,000) − (X − 50,000)(.28)

where "X" is the before-tax breakeven selling price

.72X = 7,200 + 36,000, Therefore, X = $60,000, same selling price.

If the tax rate now is different from the future tax rate, then current and future selling prices would differ for the same profit.

Ordinary net operating losses for individual and corporate businesses may be carried back for 3 years or forward for up to 15 years. Capital losses cannot be carried back but can be carried forward without time limit.

8.5 Tax Treatment of Investment Terminal (Salvage) Value

Whenever an asset such as land, common stock, buildings, or equipment is sold by individuals or corporations, the sale value (terminal value) is compared to original cost, or remaining tax book value of depreciable, depletable, amortizable or non-deductible asset costs to determine gain or loss. If the sale results in a gain, tax must be paid on the gain. If the sale results in a loss, the loss is deductible under the tax rules governing the handling of ordinary deductions and capital loss deductions. As we showed earlier, under the new 1986 tax law, all gain is taxed at the ordinary income tax rates for both corporations and individuals but it is still necessary to compute whether ordinary gain or loss, or long term capital gain or loss is realized. If a loss results from the sale, the investor is eligible for either an ordinary income deduction write-off or a long or short term capital loss deduction write-off, once again depending on the type of asset involved, the tax position of the investor, and length of time the asset has been owned.

When either depreciable or non-depreciable property has been held for more than six months and sale value exceeds original cost, the increase in the value of property (difference in sale value and original cost) usually is treated as a long term capital gain. Any gain due to depreciation (difference in original cost and remaining tax book value) is treated as ordinary income.

These tax considerations are the same for individuals or corporations as illustrated in the following example.

EXAMPLE 8-2 Illustration of Terminal Value Tax Treatment

Assume an asset will be purchased in July of 1987 for a cost of $100,000 and sold two years from that date for $180,000. The asset is being acquired by a corporation or individual with a 40% effective Federal plus state income tax rate. Calculate the tax owed on the sale for the following scenarios:

A) the asset is land, common stock, or other non-depreciable property
B) the asset is equipment depreciable over 5 years by ACRS (200% DB)
C) the asset is a residential rental property

Solution:

A) Land & common stock are not depreciable, long term capital gain is:

```
$180,000 - $100,000 = $80,000 long term capital gain taxed as
                              ordinary income.

Long Term Gain Tax = $80,000(.40) = $32,000 = ordinary income tax.
```

B) Depreciable equipment (personal property)

```
Year 1 Depreciation = $100,000(2/5)(.5) = $20,000
Year 2 Depreciation =  $80,000(2/5)     = $32,000
Cumulative Depreciation to Date           $52,000

Final Tax Book Value = $100,000-$52,000  = $48,000
```

Gain due to equipment depreciation is taxed as ordinary income. ($100,000 − $48,000)(.40) = $20,800 ordinary income tax to be paid on gain due to depreciation.

Gain due to increase in asset value is taxed as a long term gain at ordinary income tax rates ($180,000 − $100,000)(.40) = $32,000.

Note; under current tax law we get the identical tax due subtracting the final tax book value from the sale value and multiplying that result times the ordinary income rate of 40 percent. This occurs because long term capital gains are taxed at the same rate as short term gains.

($180,000 − $48,000)(.40) = $52,800 = ($20,800 + $32,000)

C) Depreciable Residential Rental Property

Real residential rental property is depreciated straight line over 27.5 years with the first year deduction proportional to the months of service using the mid-month convention. Remember the asset was placed in service in July so we have 5.5 months prorated depreciation in year 1 assuming the corporate fiscal year is the same as a calender year.

```
Year 1 Depreciation = ($100,000/27.5)(5.5/12) = $1,666.67
Year 2 Depreciation = ($100,000/27.5)        = $3,636.36
                      Cumulative Depreciation = $5,303.03

Final Tax Book Value = $100,000-$5,303 = $94,697

Total Sale Gain =      $180,000-$94,697 = $85,303

Tax on Gain =          0.40($85,303) = $34,121
```

Instead of paying normal Federal income tax, if it is higher, individuals or corporations have to pay an alternative minimum tax on regular taxable income adjusted upward for a variety of tax preference items and deduction adjustments. Section 8.6 introduces the reader to the fundamental concept of Alternative Minimum Tax for both individuals and corporations.

8.6 Minimum Tax and Alternative Minimum Tax

The alternative minimum tax (AMT) is a flat tax at a rate of 21 percent for individuals or 20 percent for corporations imposed on a taxpayer's alternative minimum taxable income. To obtain alternative minimum taxable income (AMTI) take regular taxable income and make "adjustments" to certain deductions to reflect AMTI treatment of certain items, then add the amount of tax preference items. The principal difference between "adjustments" and "preference items" is an adjustment can be either positive or negative while tax preference items are always positive. All individual or corporate taxpayers must compute taxable income under both regular tax and AMT methods in order to determine the appropriate tax to pay in a given year. The largest of these two tax calculation results is the tax liability for that year. It is possible to have negative taxable income and therefore zero regular tax liability, and still be subject to paying alternative minimum tax in the same period.

Alternative minimum tax is figured on benefits received in the form of certain deductions, lower tax rates, and exclusions from tax. These benefits are referred to as "tax preferences" or "tax preference items" or "preference adjustments" because they result from the preferential treatment provided by the tax law. Preference items vary somewhat between individual and corporate taxpayers. A partial listing of tax preference items that in general, are applicable to both individuals and corporations follows:

Depreciation. For property placed in service after 1986, the tax payer must recompute depreciation of real property over a 40 year straight line life. Personal property must be depreciated over the applicable depreciation life using 150 percent declining balance.

Mining Exploration and Development Costs. Mining exploration or development costs incurred prior to production that are expensed for tax purposes, must be amortized, straight line, over 10 years for AMT purposes.

Intangible Drilling Costs. The pre-1987 tax preference for intangible drilling costs is retained, except that the amount of the intangible drilling costs for the year that exceeds 65 percent, (rather than 100 percent as under pre-1987 law) of the taxpayers net income for the tax year from oil, gas and geothermal properties is treated as a tax preference item.

Percentage Depletion. This tax preference is applied to all percentage depletion taken in excess of the applicable adjusted cost basis (which is the cost depletion basis figured before reduction of the basis by the percentage depletion deduction) of the property. This preference is computed separately for each property being depleted.

Many other preference items exist and are discussed in detail in any good tax manual. The tax preference items (or calculation adjustments) are added or integrated with taxable income to get "alternative minimum taxable income" which for individuals is taxed at 21 percent and for corporations at 20 percent. The greater of calculated regular tax and alternative minimum tax is the tax obligation for the year. Individual taxpayers with less than $150,000 of alternative minimum taxable income get to reduce alternative minimum taxable income by 1) $40,000 for joint returns, 2) $30,000 for single individuals and 3) $20,000 for married individuals filing separately. However, such exemption amounts are reduced at a rate of $0.25 for each $1.00 that alternative minimum taxable income exceeds $150,000 for joint return filers, $112,500 for single taxpayers, and $75,000 for married taxpayers filing separate returns. The above mentioned preferences give the reader a feeling for calculations involved in computing alternative minimum tax as illustrated in Example 8-3.

Note that income and tax deductions related to alternative minimum tax (AMT) calculations relate to income and deductions for all investments and income sources relevant to a taxpayer in a tax year. It is very difficult to assess potential AMT liability on a project by project basis because the AMT analysis relates to cumulative tax year income and deductions for an investor, rather than individual project income and deductions.

EXAMPLE 8-3 Alternative Minimum Tax Calculation

A single individual has regular taxable income of $250,000 from professional service work and mining and chemical plant investment income reduced by deductible expenses and itemized deductions that include tax preference item deductions of $200,000 for mineral development, a $60,000 first year 200% declining balance depreciation deduction for 7 year life assets costing $420,000, and a $50,000 percentage depletion deduction on mineral revenue from a property with a zero cost depletion basis. Use the 28% regular federal individual tax rate to calculate the regular tax obligation and use the 21% alternative minimum tax (AMT) rate for individuals to calculate the alternative minimum tax.

Solution:

Regular Federal Tax = $250,000(.28) = $70,000

Alternative Minimum Taxable Income (AMTI) =

Regular Taxable Income + Development Deduction Preference + Percentage Depletion Preference + Depreciation Preference

Development Preference = $200,000 − $200,000/10 = $180,000
Percentage Depletion Preference = $50,000 − 0 = $ 50,000
Depreciation Preference = $60,000 − $45,000 = $ 15,000

where the AMT depreciation of $45,000 is is calculated as follows by 150% declining balance:

$45,000 depreciation = (1.5/7)(420,000)(.5)

AMTI = $250,000 + $180,000 + $50,000 + $15,000 = $495,000
AMT = $495,000(.21) = $103,950 > 70,000 regular tax

The tax obligation is the greater of AMT and regular tax which in this case is the $103,950 AMT.

Whether you adjust regular taxable income for tax preference item amounts to get AMTI as calculated here, or whether you start with regular taxable income and recalculate AMTI by substituting the adjusted AMTI allowed deductions for regular tax deductions gives the same AMTI. This relates to the difference in using "adjustments in deductions" and "tax preference items" to get AMTI.

Note that if the taxpayer's regular taxable income was zero, yielding a zero regular tax, the AMT would be $245,000(.21) = $51,450 since the tax preference items are still the same. The $30,000 exemption for single individuals is not applicable since it is fully phased out for AMTI above $232,500.

If the $200,000 mineral development cost was instead a petroleum intangible drilling cost, the tax preference amount would be determined by subtracting 65% of investor oil and gas and geothermal property income from the $200,000 drilling cost. For example, if the investor has $100,000 of oil and gas income, then $200,000 minus ($100,000)(.65), or $135,000 would be the intangible drilling cost tax preference item. If no oil and gas income exists, then the full $200,000 drilling cost is a tax preference item.

A corporate tax preference item that is new in 1987 and potentially significant is one-half of the amount by which corporate net before-tax shareholder reporting "financial" book income exceeds the AMTI. Some accountants feel this will prove to be the most significant tax preference item for many corporations in future years. In 1990 and later years this preference item increases from 50 percent to 75 percent of the amount by which corporate net before-tax shareholder report "financial" book income exceeds AMTI. Shareholder report financial book income is discussed in comparison to taxable income in the later part of Chapter 9.

If a taxpayer incurs a net operating loss from AMTI calculations, the loss may be carried forward. However, only 90 percent of the AMTI in any year can be offset by AMTI loss carry forward deductions from earlier years. Other regulations exist regarding the limited use of various tax credits against alternative minimum tax obligations. Readers should consult a good tax manual or tax accountant for specific information regarding the many complicated aspects of this tax legislation.

8.7 Effective Tax Rates for Combined State and Federal Income Tax

Often it is convenient for evaluation purposes to combine the tax rates of two agencies such as a state and federal government to determine the effective tax rate that accounts for both with one calculation. For the typical corporate analysis where state corporate tax is deductible for purposes of calculating federal corporate tax, but federal corporate tax is not an allowable deduction when calculating state corporate tax, the following effective tax rate results for U.S. corporations:

Effective Corporate Tax Rate $= s + f(1-s)$ $\qquad$ 8-1

where: "s" is the incremental state tax rate in decimal form

"f" is the incremental federal tax rate in decimal form

In states where federal tax for individuals is not allowed as a state tax deduction, Equation 8-1 is valid for individuals as well as for corporations.

For an individual taxpayer living in a state where state tax is deductible for federal tax and federal tax is deductible for state tax the following effective tax rate would result:

Effective Individual Tax Rate $= s(1-f) + f(1-s)$ 8-2

where: "s" is the incremental state tax rate in decimal form
      "f" is the incremental federal tax rate in decimal form

Equations 8-1 and 8-2 are illustrated in the following examples.

EXAMPLE 8-4 Calculation of Corporate Effective Tax Rates

Consider a $120,000 increment of corporate income subject to the incremental federal corporate tax rate of 34% and a 6% state corporate tax rate. Calculate the effective federal plus state tax rate and the tax to be paid on the income for this corporation.

Solution:

Using Equation 8-1;

Effective Corporate Tax Rate $= .06 + .34(1-.06) = .3796$ or 37.96%

Total Tax Due $= \$120,000(.3796) = \$45,552$

The same result could be obtained without the use of the effective tax rate as follows:

State Tax $= \$120,000(.06)$ $= \$\ 7,200$
Federal Tax $= (\$120,000 - 7,200)(.34) = \underline{\ 38,352}$
Total Tax $\$45,552$

EXAMPLE 8-5 Calculation of Individual Effective Tax Rates

Consider a $120,000 increment of individual income subject to the incremental federal individual tax rate of 28% and an 8% state individual tax. Calculate the effective federal plus state tax rate and the tax to be paid on the income for this individual assuming:

A) The individual lives in a state that allows federal tax as a deduction in calculating state taxable income.
B) The individual lives in a state that does not allow federal tax as a deduction in calculating state taxable income.

Solution:

A) Using Equation 8-2, the individual effective tax rate is;
   $.08(1-.28) + .28(1-.08) = .3152$ or 31.52%

   Total Tax Due $= \$120,000(.3152) = \$37,824$

B) Using Equation 8-1, the individual effective tax rate is;
.08 + .28(1 − .08) = .3376 or 33.76%
Total Tax Due = $120,000(.3376) = $40,512

8.8 Tax Credits and Investment Tax Credits

The Tax Reform Act of 1986 repealed the 10 percent investment tax credit (ITC) for property placed in service after December 31, 1985. However, the tax rules that applied to property placed in service prior to 1986 will continue. The only exceptions to the repeal of ITC apply to certain transition property and qualified progress expenditures. These exceptions generally relate to investment situations where investment decisions were made prior to 1986 but investment costs were to be incurred in 1986 and later years.

Many energy credits were eliminated by the new tax bill. However, certain business energy property is eligible for the business energy investment credit, and it may also qualify for the regular investment tax credit under transition rules.

Solar Energy Property. Qualifying solar energy systems receive a 12% credit in 1987 and a 10% credit in 1988. This credit is scheduled to expire in 1989.

Geothermal Property. A 10% credit is available in 1987 and 1988 and is scheduled to expire in 1989.

Ocean Thermal. A 15% credit is available through 1988 for equipment to convert ocean thermal energy to usable energy. The credit expires in 1989.

Biomass Property. A 10% credit is available in 1987 and 1988 and expires in 1989. The residential energy credit, wind property and small scale hydro-electric project credits were allowed to expire at the end of 1985.

Research and Experimentation Credit. Incremental Research Expenditures that exceed the average research expenditures for the preceding 3 years may also qualify for a 20% research tax credit in 1987 and 1988. The new tax bill describes and modifies the definition of "qualified research expenditures" to exclude product development type expenses. Research and development costs in the experimental or laboratory sense are generally allowed research costs. See a tax manual for details.

Rehabilitation Expenditure Credits. Certain expenditures related to the rehabilitation of qualified old buildings entitle taxpayers to the following rehabilitation cost tax credits.

1) Certified Historic Structures – 20% of qualified rehabilitation costs. Historic structures are either residential or non-residential buildings listed in the National Register or located in a registered historic district and certified as being of historic significance to the district.
2) Qualified Rehabilitated Buildings – 10% of qualified rehabilitation costs for buildings placed in service before 1936.

The depreciation basis of a rehabilitation property must be reduced by the full rehabilitation credit. Refer to a tax manual for specific tax rules that describe qualified rehabilitation costs.

Tax credits from all sources are credits against your tax bill and not deductions from taxable income, such as depreciation. A dollar of tax credit saves a dollar of tax cost, while a dollar of depreciation saves only the tax rate times a dollar in tax cost.

Tax credits of all types are limited in any tax year to the lesser of the income tax liability or $25,000 plus 75% of tax liability in excess of $25,000.

Recapture of investment tax credit relates to the following. If you dispose of a depreciable asset on which you took investment tax credit in an earlier year, in the year of disposal you have to pay back to the government (recapture as extra tax paid), any investment tax credit taken earlier that is in excess of what you should have taken for the actual full years of asset use. Recapture is proportional to years of equipment use not realized, compared to depreciation life on which investment tax credit was based. Although investment tax credit has been eliminated for most new investment costs incurred after December 31, 1985, investment tax recapture related to the disposal of certain depreciable assets will be relevant for the 1986-1990 period.

8.9 Discounted Cash Flow Rate of Return (DCFROR), Net Present Value (NPV) and Ratio Analysis

DCFROR is defined commonly as the rate of return that makes the present worth of positive and negative after-tax cash flow for an investment equal to zero. This is another way of saying DCFROR is the rate of return that makes after-tax NPV equal to zero. Discounting means "present worthing" and the name "discounted cash flow rate of return" comes from the fact that classically, present worth or discounting equations most often have been used to obtain the DCFROR. It already has been shown many times earlier in this text that the same rate of return results from writing an annual or future worth equation or in general by comparing costs and incomes (or negative and positive cash flow) at any point in time, as long as all cash flows are brought to the same point in time. It was mentioned earlier in this chapter that other names commonly used for DCFROR are Profitability Index, P.I., Investor's ROR, True ROR, and Internal ROR or IRR. Polls of industry presently indicate that DCFROR is the number one economic evaluation decision method used by about two thirds of industrial companies that use a formal economic evaluation procedure to evaluate the economic potential of investments. In this regard it is relevant to note that most major industrial companies use formal discounted cash flow investment evaluation procedures of the type described, discussed, and illustrated in this text.

Net present value (NPV) on an after-tax basis equals the present worth of positive and negative cash flow calculated at the after-tax minimum rate of return. NPV greater than zero indicates a satisfactory investment. Project DCFROR is compared to the after-tax minimum rate of return, "i*", to determine if a particular project is satisfactory compared to other alternative uses that exist for the investment capital. *For after-tax analysis using any valid analysis technique, the minimum rate of return, "i*", must be expressed on an after-tax basis. Comparing an after-tax DCFROR for a project with other investment opportunities expressed on a before-tax basis would be meaningless.* With proper handling of inflation and escalation in analyses it was emphasized earlier that all alternatives must be compared on the same basis, either using escalated dollar analysis or constant dollar analysis. Similarly, with after-tax analysis, all alternatives must be on an after-tax basis including other opportunities represented by the minimum rate of return, i*.

After-tax present value ratio, (PVR), or benefit/cost ratio, (B/C Ratio), are calculated using after-tax positive and negative cash flow similar to the NPV and DCFROR calculations. Correct ratio denominators are the present worth of project negative cash flow not covered by positive cash flow in the year negative cash flow is incurred or in earlier years. PVR greater than zero is satisfactory while B/C Ratio greater than one is satisfactory.

To calculate DCFROR, NPV or Ratios, the first thing that must be done is to calculate after-tax cash flow for each year of the evaluation life. This includes converting all capital costs and salvage values to after-tax values by accounting properly for all appropriate tax considerations. It is desirable to place the after-tax negative and positive cash flows on a time diagram to insure that the subsequent evaluation handles them at the correct point in time.

After-tax evaluation calculation procedures are illustrated in Examples 8-6, 8-7 and 8-8 for relatively straightforward evaluation cases. In Chapters 9, 10, 11 and 12, DCFROR, NPV and Ratios are applied to a wide variety of evaluation situations that will familiarize the reader with the handling of these and other evaluation methods in a diversity of investment situations. The DCFROR, NPV, and Ratio calculations are very straightforward once the after-tax cash flows are determined. The key to correct, successful economic evaluation work rests heavily on experience with proper methods for the following evaluation points: 1) correct handling of all allowable income tax deductions, especially depreciation, amortization, depletion and deferred deductions to determine correct taxable income, 2) adding back to net profit the proper non-cash deductions to obtain cash flow (deferred deductions, amortized research and development expenses, and special tax writeoffs are add-back items frequently mishandled), 3) proper handling of tax considerations for costs that may be written off for tax purposes in the year in which they are incurred against other income rather than being capitalized and deducted over a period of time greater than one year, 4) correct accounting for tax effects on salvage value, either tax to be paid or tax writeoffs to be taken (in some investment situations such as land investment, salvage value may be the major project income so it is imperative that salvage tax considerations be handled correctly to get valid analysis results), 5) proper handling of incremental investment tax considerations when looking at differences between alternatives, such as in equipment replacement analysis or mutually exclusive income alternative analysis.

The next example illustrates the sensitivity of DCFROR analysis for different methods of handling the tax deductions for a given cost. Some costs such as equipment and buildings are depreciable by either the modified ACRS rates or by straight line depreciation. Other costs such as operating expenses, research, development, intangible drilling costs and mineral exploration or development may, at least in part, be expensed in the year incurred. Expensing is the fastest method of deducting costs for tax purposes and depending on the investor financial situation, may require either, 1) carrying losses forward, if other taxable income does not exist against which to use negative taxable income in any year, (making the project "stand alone"), 2) crediting the project with tax savings in the year negative taxable income is incurred by assuming other taxable income will exist against which to use deductions, or 3) because the company or individual may have sufficient loss carry forwards so that it does not anticipate paying taxes for a number of years all tax effects may be carried forward to a specific point in time. Economic results are affected significantly by the method that costs may be deducted for tax purposes and by the financial assumption concerning whether income will or will not exist against which to use negative taxable income in the year incurred.

EXAMPLE 8-6 The Effect of Tax Deduction Timing and the Investor Financial Situation on DCFROR Results

A $100,000 investment cost has been incurred by an individual to generate a project with a 5 year life and estimated zero salvage value. Project escalated dollar income is estimated to be $80,000 in year 1, $84,000 in year 2, $88,000 in year 3, $92,000 in year 4, and $96,000 in year 5. Operating expenses are estimated to be $30,000 in year 1, $32,000 in year 2, $34,000 in year 3, $36,000 in year 4, and $38,000 in year 5. The effective income tax rate is 32%. Determine project DCFROR if the initial $100,000 investment goes into service in year 1 and is:

A) Depreciable straight line for a 5 year life, (half year convention applicable in year 1).
B) Depreciable by modified ACRS (200% DB) for a 5 year life, (half year convention applicable in year 1).
C) Expensed as a development cost in year 0 with negative taxable income carried forward to be used against project income. (Stand alone economics).
D) Expensed as development cost in year 0 with losses carried forward for the situation where the investor has sufficient loss carry forward deductions to eliminate all tax until year 4.
E) Expensed as development cost in year 0 assuming other taxable income exists against which to use the deduction.

Solution

Note that the cumulative amount of tax deduction is $100,000 by all five methods of analysis. Only the timing of the tax deductions differs between methods. Since all methods of analysis involve the same cumulative revenues and tax deductions, they also involve the same cumulative tax and cash flow. However, as you go from A) straight line depreciation, to, B) modified ACRS depreciation, to, C) expensing and carrying forward, to, D) expensing and carrying losses forward to year 4, to E) expensing against other income, the timing of tax deductions and therefore tax savings is affected significantly, causing relatively important differences to occur in the DCFROR results.

A) Straight Line Depreciation

The half year 1 deduction causes book value amounting to a half year depreciation deduction to exist at the end of year 5. This book value is deducted (written off) as additional year 5 depreciation.

Year	0	1	2	3	4	5	Cumulative
Revenue		80.0	84.0	88.0	92.0	96.0	440.0
-Oper Costs		-30.0	-32.0	-34.0	-36.0	-38.0	-170.0
-Depreciation		-10.0	-20.0	-20.0	-20.0	-30.0	-100.0
Taxable		40.0	32.0	34.0	36.0	28.0	170.0
-Tax @ 32%		-12.8	-10.2	-10.9	-11.5	-9.0	-54.4
Net Income		27.2	21.8	23.1	24.5	19.0	115.6
+Depreciation		10.0	20.0	20.0	20.0	30.0	100.0
-Capital Costs	-100.0						-100.0
Cash Flow	-100.0	37.2	41.8	43.1	44.5	49.0	115.6

PW Eq: $0 = -100 + 37.2(P/F_{i,1}) + 41.8(P/F_{i,2}) + 43.1(P/F_{i,3})$

$$+ 44.5(P/F_{i,4}) + 49(P/F_{i,5})$$

$$i = DCFROR = 30.86\%$$

B) Modified ACRS Depreciation

Year	0	1	2	3	4	5	Cumulative
Revenue		80.0	84.0	88.0	92.0	96.0	440.0
-Oper Costs		-30.0	-32.0	-34.0	-36.0	-38.0	-170.0
-Depreciation		-20.0	-32.0	-19.2	-14.4	-14.4	-100.0
Taxable		30.0	20.0	34.8	41.6	43.6	170.0
-Tax @ 32%		-9.6	-6.4	-11.1	-13.3	-14.0	-54.4
Net Income		20.4	13.6	23.7	28.3	29.6	115.6
+Depreciation		20.0	32.0	19.2	14.4	14.4	100.0
-Capital Costs	-100.0						-100.0
Cash Flow	-100.0	40.4	45.6	42.9	42.7	44.0	115.6

PW Eq: $0 = -100 + 40.4(P/F_{i,1}) + 45.6(P/F_{i,2}) + 42.9(P/F_{i,3})$

$$+ 42.7(P/F_{i,4}) + 44.0(P/F_{i,5})$$

$$i = DCFROR = 32.24\%$$

C) Expensed as Development and Carried Forward (Stand Alone)

Year	0	1	2	3	4	5	Cumulative
Revenue		80.0	84.0	88.0	92.0	96.0	440.0
-Oper Costs		-30.0	-32.0	-34.0	-36.0	-38.0	-170.0
-Development	-100.0						-100.0
-Loss forward		-100.0	-50.0				-150.0
Taxable	-100.0	-50.0	2.0	54.0	56.0	58.0	20.0
-Tax @ 32%			-0.6	-17.3	-17.9	-18.6	-54.4
Net Income	-100.0	-50.0	1.4	36.7	38.1	39.4	-34.4
+Loss forward		100.0	50.0				150.0
-Capital Costs							
Cash Flow	-100.0	50.0	51.4	36.7	38.1	39.4	115.6

PW Eq: $0 = -100 + 50(P/F_{i,1}) + 51.4(P/F_{i,2}) + 36.7(P/F_{i,3})$

$$+ 38.1(P/F_{i,4}) + 39.4(P/F_{i,5})$$

i = DCFROR = 35.24%

D) Carry Losses Forward to Year 4

Year	0	1	2	3	4	5	Cumulative
Revenue		80.0	84.0	88.0	92.0	96.0	440.0
-Oper Costs		-30.0	-32.0	-34.0	-36.0	-38.0	-170.0
-Development	-100.0						-100.0
Taxable	-100.0	50.0	52.0	54.0	56.0	58.0	170.0
-Tax @ 32%					-35.8	-18.6	-54.4
Net Income	-100.0	50.0	52.0	54.0	20.2	39.4	115.6
-Capital Costs							
Cash Flow	-100.0	50.0	52.0	54.0	20.2	39.4	115.6

PW Eq: $0 = -100 + 50(P/F_{i,1}) + 52(P/F_{i,2}) + 54(P/F_{i,3})$

$$+ 20.2(P/F_{i,4}) + 39.4(P/F_{i,5})$$

i = DCFROR = 36.44%

E) Expense as Development Against Other Income

Year	0	1	2	3	4	5	Cumulative
Revenue		80.0	84.0	88.0	92.0	96.0	440.0
-Oper Costs		-30.0	-32.0	-34.0	-36.0	-38.0	-170.0
-Development	-100.0						-100.0
Taxable	-100.0	50.0	52.0	54.0	56.0	58.0	170.0
-Tax @ 32%	32.0	-16.0	-16.6	-17.3	-17.9	-18.6	-54.4
Net Income	-68.0	34.0	35.4	36.7	38.1	39.4	115.6
-Capital Costs							
Cash Flow	-68.0	34.0	35.4	36.7	38.1	39.4	115.6

PW Eq: $0 = -68 + 34(P/F_{i,1}) + 35.4(P/F_{i,2}) + 36.7(P/F_{i,3})$

$$+ 38.1(P/F_{i,4}) + 39.4(P/F_{i,5})$$

i = DCFROR = 44.16%

The reader should observe from these analysis results that the faster an investor realizes tax deductions and the tax benefits from the tax deductions, the better the economics of projects become. Expensing the $100,000 cost against other income gives almost a 50 percent increase in the DCFROR that is obtained by straight line depreciation of the cost. If you have to carry negative taxable income forward, "to make the project economics stand alone" as in part "C", the project economics do not look as good as when other income is assumed to exist against which to use deductions in the year incurred, as in part "E". *Higher tax rates accentuate these effects.*

An Alternative to E)	Year 0 Develop as an Expensable Cost	Year 0 Develop as a Depreciable Cost
Revenue		
-Oper Costs		
-Development	-100.0	
-Development as Depreciation		-100.0
Taxable	-100.0	-100.0
-Tax payment	32.0	32.0
Net Income	-68.0	-68.0
+Depreciation		100.0
-Capital Costs		-100.0
Cash Flow	-68.0	-68.0

An alternative to treating the development cost in part "E" as a tax expense item is to consider it to be depreciable with a rate of 1.0 in year 0. This is an approach sometimes used in industry practice, so the reader should be aware of the equivalence of either approach as the year 0 cash flow calculations for part "E" on the previous page illustrate.

Example 8-6 involved a single investment cost that was depreciable for tax deduction purposes. Most businesses also require inventory and start-up costs commonly called working capital, which are not depreciable as discussed in the following section.

8.10 Working Capital

Working capital is the money necessary to operate a business on a day-to-day basis. It normally is comprised primarily of money required for raw material inventory, in-process materials inventory, product inventory, accounts receivable, and ready cash. For evaluation purposes, working capital generally is considered to be put into a project at the start of a business or production operation and to be fully recovered at the end of the project's expected life.

Working capital is not allowable as a tax deduction in the year it is incurred so it often has a very negative effect on project economics. Working capital cost may not be expensed, depreciated, amortized or depleted until it is actually used. One way to explain working capital and why it is not deductible for tax purposes in the year it is incurred, is to consider the determination of the "Cost of Goods Sold" as it is handled on corporate or individual business tax returns. Table 8-4 illustrates the steps necessary to calculate the annual cost of goods sold for a business operated either by an individual, partnership, or corporation. In this cost of goods sold calculation, value of inventories at the year end is working capital and note it is not tax deductible.

Beginning of Year Inventory
+ Raw Material Costs from Purchases During the Year
+ Labor Costs to Convert Raw Material or Parts Into Products
+ Materials & Supply Costs Incurred During the Year
+ Other Costs Related to Production of Products
_____

= Cost of Materials, Supplies and Goods Available for Sale
− Inventory Value at End of Year Based on Cost
  (This is money tied up in Working Capital)
_____

= Cost of Goods Sold (Deductible as Annual Operating Cost)

Table 8-4 Calculation of Cost of Goods Sold Related to Working Capital

Working capital represents the capital cost required to generate raw material inventories, in-process inventories, product inventories and spare parts inventories. As inventories are used and product sold, working capital cost items become allowable tax deductions as operating costs through the cost of goods sold calculation. However, as inventory items are used they typically are replaced so inventories are maintained at a similar level over the project life. If significant increases or decreases in working capital are projected to occur from year to year, positive or negative working capital costs can be accounted for from year to year in project analyses.

Now it should occur to you that raw material and parts in inventory often are acquired at different costs during a year. How do you determine the value of items left in inventory at the end of a tax year when items were acquired for different costs during the year with some used and some left in inventory? FIFO and LIFO are the two basic inventory accounting systems that determine the costs of items used during a tax year to be deducted as operating expenses and the costs of items left in inventory and treated as working capital. FIFO is the acronym that stands for "First-In-First-Out". Using FIFO inventory accounting, the first items to go into inventory are considered to be the first items to come out and be used and deducted as operating expenses. Therefore, under FIFO inventory accounting, the last items purchased during a tax year are the cost basis for inventory assets tied up in working capital. LIFO is the acronym for "Last-In-First-Out". Using LIFO inventory accounting, the last items to go into inventory are considered to be the first items to come out and be used and deducted as operating expenses. Therefore, under LIFO inventory accounting, the first items purchased during a tax year or in inventory from earlier years are the cost basis for inventory assets tied up in working capital. In an inflationary climate the cost of items purchased during a year generally increases, and LIFO gives tax deductions for the bigger cost items purchased later in the tax year than are realized with FIFO. In a deflationary climate the opposite is true. A majority of companies use LIFO inventory accounting and LIFO is the implicit inventory accounting assumption built into the handling of working capital in this text. Under LIFO, money tied up in working capital is constant each year with changes in item costs accounted for as operating cost changes.

In accounting terminology working capital is defined as the difference between current assets and current liabilities. This definition is consistent with our "Cost of Goods Sold" calculation explanation of working capital. When a new business or production facility is started-up, it often generates and produces product for three or four months before product is sold and income is received for product sold. Assuming the business pays cash for raw materials, labor, parts and supplies during the start-up period, the cost of these items increases the "current assets" of the business. If all items have been paid for with cash (no time payments), no current liabilities are accrued, so current assets minus zero current liabilities equals the working capital which is the value of items in inventory including product inventory. The term "start-up cost" often is used in reference to the development of product inventory. It typically is necessary to have the money (working capital) to operate a business for 2, 3, or 4 months during the time between commencement of production and when sales revenue starts coming in at a rate sufficient to cover operating costs on an on-going basis. The operating costs during this start-up period are really going into the generation of product inventory, which is one component of working capital.

EXAMPLE 8-7 A General Project Analysis Involving Working Capital, Cash Flow, DCFROR and NPV Analysis

A company wants to evaluate the economic feasibility of introducing a new product that will require the development and construction of a new plant with the following estimated costs and revenues expressed in dollars.

Year	0	1	2-4	5
Revenue	-	6,000,000	8,000,000	10,000,000
Operating Costs	-	1,500,000	2,000,000	2,500,000
Development	2,000,000			
Equipment	10,000,000			
Buildings	2,000,000			
Working Capital	1,000,000			
Land	1,500,000			

The $1,000,000 working capital requirement could be from $400,000 to be invested in inventories for raw materials, spare parts and supplies, plus $600,000 to be invested in product inventory for the operating cost value of product that has been produced but not sold.

The development cost will be expensed in year 0. Assume other income exists against which to use deductions in the year incurred. Equipment goes into service in year 1 so start depreciation in year 1, using modified ACRS 7 year life depreciation with the half year 1 convention. Buildings are depreciated over 31.5 years and assumed to go into service in the first month of year 1. Write off the remaining book value on all equipment, buildings, land and working capital investments at the end of year 5. Assume a washout of escalation of revenues and operating costs over years 1 through 5. Assume the project could be sold at the end of year 5 for $15,000,000. For an effective tax rate of 40%, and for a minimum DCFROR of 15%, calculate the project NPV and the DCFROR. Then re-calculate DCFROR and NPV assuming there is a one year delay in the start of production with zero net cash flow in year 1 and the year 1 through year 5 cash flow realized in years 2 through

6, neglecting any changes in cash flow due to revenue and operating cost escalation changes.

Solution, All Values in Thousands of Dollars:

Year	0	1	2	3	4	5
Revenue		6,000	8,000	8,000	8,000	25,000*
-Oper Costs		-1,500	-2,000	-2,000	-2,000	-2,500
-Development	-2,000					
-Depreciation***		-1,489	-2,512	-1,813	-1,313	-1,104***
- Writeoffs						-6,270
Taxable	-2,000	3,011	3,488	4,187	4,687	15,126
-Tax @ 40%	800	-1,204	-1,395	-1,675	-1,875	-6,050
Net Income	-1,200	1,807	2,093	2,512	2,812	9,076
+Depreciation		1,489	2,512	1,813	1,313	1,104
+Writeoffs						6,270
-Capitl Costs	-14,500**					
Cash Flow	-15,700	3,296	4,605	4,325	4,125	16,450

*The year 5 revenue includes the $15,000 salvage value.

**The capital cost of $14,500 includes $10,000 in equipment, $2,000 in buildings, $1,000 in working capital and $1,500 for land.

***The year 5 writeoff includes remaining book values for land, working capital, and depreciable assets which is equal to:
$1,500 + $1,000 + $2,082 + $1,688 = $6,270

Depreciation, Equipment

Yr 1 $(10,000)(2/7)(.5)$ = 1,429
Yr 2 $(10,000-1,429)(2/7)$ = 2,449
Yr 3 $(8,571-2,449)(2/7)$ = 1,749
Yr 4 $(6,122-1,749)(2/7)$ = 1,249
Yr 5 $(4,373-1,249) / 3$ = 1,041
Year 5 Writeoff on
Remaining Book Value   = 2,082
Total Depreciation   = 10,000

Note that use of the Modified ACRS Rates in Table 7-3 back in Chapter 7 gives the same depreciation.

Depreciation, Building

Yr 1 $(2,000/31.5)(11.5/12)$ =   60
Yr 2-5 $(2,000/31.5)$ =   63
Year 5 Writeoff on
Remaining Book Value   = 1,688
Total Depreciation   = 2,000

DCFROR Analysis

$$0 = 3,296(P/F_{i,1}) + 4,605(P/F_{i,2}) + 4,325(P/F_{i,3}) + 4,125(P/F_{i,4})$$

$$+ 16,450(P/F_{i,5}) - 15,700$$

$i = DCFROR = 22.98\%, > i^* = 15\%,$ so acceptable

NPV Analysis

$$0 = 3,296\overset{.8696}{(P/F_{15,1})} + 4,605\overset{.7561}{(P/F_{15,2})} + 4,325\overset{.6575}{(P/F_{15,3})} + 4,125\overset{.5718}{(P/F_{15,4})}$$

$$+ 16,450\overset{.4972}{(P/F_{15,5})} - 15,700 = +4,028, > 0,$$ so acceptable

Case 2) One Year Delay in the Start of Production

CF = -15,700	0	3,296	4,605	4,325	4,125	16,450
0	1	2	3	4	5	6

DCFROR = 17.31%,   NPV = +1,456

The analysis results are very sensitive to the timing of the start of production. A one year delay typically reduces DCFROR results by one-fourth or more and reduces NPV results by one half or more, as illustrated for this analysis.

8.11 Mineral and Petroleum Project After-Tax Analysis

Mineral and petroleum project analyses are similar to non-mineral analyses in terms of general procedure. In any discounted cash flow type analysis you first convert all project revenues and costs to positive and negative cash flows. You do this by accounting for the tax deductibility of costs and the tax to be paid, or tax savings to be realized, on resulting positive or negative taxable income each year.

The unique feature about discounted cash flow analysis of mineral or petroleum projects, compared to non-mineral projects, is the handling of certain tax deductions. Chapter 7 addressed the tax handling of mineral exploration and development costs and petroleum intangible drilling costs and pointed out that 100% of these costs may be expensed for "individual" mineral project operators, or "independent" petroleum producers. "Corporate mineral operators, or "major", integrated petroleum producers, may only expense 70% of these costs. The other 30% of the intangible drilling or mining development costs are amortized over 60 months, with the first year deduction proportional to the months the cost was incurred. Mineral rights acquisition, or lease bonus costs, are unique to mineral and petroleum operations, and represent the basis for cost depletion deduction calculations, as described and illustrated in Chapter 7. Percentage depletion deductions also are unique to mineral and petroleum projects. All mineral producers and independent petroleum producers get to take the greater of allowed percentage depletion and cost depletion, while major integrated petroleum producers are only allowed to take cost depletion. There are some unique severance and excise tax considerations related to mineral and petroleum projects. Most non-mineral, petroleum and mineral projects alike involve depreciable costs, so there is nothing unique to mineral and petroleum project evaluations in this regard. A typical mineral/petroleum project discounted cash flow analysis is illustrated in the following example.

EXAMPLE 8-8 A Mineral (or Petroleum) Project Evaluation Using DCFROR, NPV and PVR.

An individual investor is considering acquiring and developing a mineral property believed to contain 500,000 units of mineral reserves (mineral units could be barrels of oil, tons of coal, ounces of gold, etc.). The mineral rights acquisition cost for the property would be $900,000 at year zero. A mineral development cost (or intangible drilling cost) of $1,200,000 is anticipated at time zero along with tangible equipment costs (mining equipment or oil and gas producing equipment, pipelines, and tangible well completion costs) of $1,000,000 and working capital costs of $300,000, all projected to be incurred at year 0. Modified ACRS depreciation (200% DB, half year 1 convention applied) will be based on a 7 year depreciation life starting in year 1 when assets are placed into service. Write off the remaining undepreciated book value at year 5. Mineral production is projected to be uniform each year of the 5 year project life at 100,000 mineral units per year with mineral reserves depleted at the end of year 5. Product selling price is estimated to be $30.00 per unit produced in year 1, escalating 10% per year in succeeding years. Operating expenses are estimated to be $1,000,000 in year 1, escalating 8% per year in succeeding years. Royalties are 15% of revenues each year. The property and equipment are expected to have no net salvage value although recovery of the $300,000 working capital investment is expected from inventory liquidation at the end of year 5. When applicable, assume the mineral produced is a 15% depletion rate mineral, (for all mineral or independent petroleum producer evaluations only). Use an effective income tax rate of 32% for individuals and 38% for corporations. Calculate the project DCFROR, NPV and PVR for a minimum after-tax rate of return of 20%, assuming:

A) The project is being evaluated by an individual mineral producer or small independent petroleum producer for the following financial positions:

1) Assume other income exists against which to use all deductions in the year deductions are incurred.
2) Make the project "stand alone"; this requires carrying negative taxable income forward until it can be utilized against project income.
3) The investors have sufficient loss carry forwards from other projects so that it is anticipated that no tax will be paid until evaluation year 3, then assume any negative taxable income will be expensed against other income.

B) The project is a mineral venture being evaluated by a corporation. Expense all deductions against other income as in A1, and begin amortizing the 30% of development costs with a full 12 month deduction in year 0.

C) The project is a petroleum venture being evaluated by a major integrated producer. Expense all deductions against other income as in A1, and begin amortizing the 30% of development costs with a full 12 month deduction in year 0.

D) A government is considering investing in the project so taxes are not relevant.

Solution, All Values in Thousands of Dollars:

A_1) Individual or Independent, Expense Against Other Income.

Year	0	1	2	3	4	5
Revenue		3,000	3,300	3,630	3,993	4,392
-Royalties		-450	-495	-545	-599	-659
Net Revenue		2,550	2,805	3,085	3,394	3,733
-Oper Costs		-1,000	-1,080	-1,166	-1,260	-1,360
-Development	-1,200					
-Depreciation		-143	-245	-175	-125	-104
-Deprec Writeoff						-208
Before Depltn	-1,200	1,407	1,480	1,744	2,009	2,061
-50% Limit		704	740	872	1,005	1,030
-Percent Depl		-382	-421	-463	-509	-560
-Cost Depltn		180	129	32		
Taxable	-1,200	1,025	1,059	1,281	1,500	1,501
-Tax @ 32%	384	-328	-339	-410	-480	-480
Net Income	-816	697	720	871	1,020	1,021
+Depreciation		143	245	175	125	312
+Depletion		382	421	463	509	560
+Work Cap Ret.						300**
-Capitl Costs	-2,200*					
Cash Flow	-3,016	1,222	1,386	1,509	1,654	2,193

*The capital cost is $300 working capital, $900 mineral rights acquisition cost, and $1,000 depreciable equipment.
**Working capital return of $300 is after-tax cash flow since it just recovers the intial working capital cost and no taxable gain or loss exists.
The largest allowable depletion deduction has a minus (−) sign in front of it.

Depreciation Calculations

Period ACRS Rate X Cost = Depreciation

Year 1   .1429   X 1,000 =   142.9
Year 2   .2449   X 1,000 =   244.9
Year 3   .1749   X 1,000 =   174.9
Year 4   .1249   X 1,000 =   124.9
Year 5   .1041   X 1,000 =   104.1
Year 5 Remaining Book Value =   208.3

Depletion Calculations

Cost Depletion

(100/500)(900) = 180
(100/400)(900-382) = 129
(100/300)(518-421) = 32
(100/200)(97-463) <   0

DCFROR Calculation

$$0 = -3,016 + 1,222(P/F_{i,1}) + 1,386(P/F_{i,2}) + 1,509(P/F_{i,3})$$

$$+ 1,654(P/F_{i,4}) + 2,193(P/F_{i,5})$$

$$i = DCFROR = 39.15\%$$

NPV Calculation for i* = 20%

$$NPV = 1,222(P/F_{20,1}) + 1,386(P/F_{20,2}) + 1,509(P/F_{20,3})$$

$$+ 1,654(P/F_{20,4}) + 2,193(P/F_{20,5}) - 3,016 = +1,517$$

PVR Calculation

1,517 / 3,016 = .5031

A₂) Individual Mineral or Independent Petroleum Producer, Carry Losses Forward, (Stand Alone)

Year	0	1	2	3	4	5
Revenue		3,000	3,300	3,630	3,993	4,392
-Royalties		-450	-495	-545	-599	-659
Net Revenue		2,550	2,805	3,085	3,394	3,733
-Oper Costs		-1,000	-1,080	-1,166	-1,260	-1,360
-Development	-1,200					
-Depreciation		-143	-245	-175	-125	-104
-Deprec Writeoff						-208
Before Depltn	-1,200	1,407	1,480	1,744	2,009	2,061
-50% Limit		704	740	872	1,005	1,030
-Percent Depl		-382	-421	-463	-509	-560
-Cost Depltn		180	129	32		
-Loss Forward		-1,200	-175			
Taxable	-1,200	-175	884	1,281	1,500	1,501
-Tax @ 32%			-283	-410	-480	-480
Net Income	-1,200	-175	601	871	1,020	1,021
+Depreciation		143	245	175	125	312
+Depletion		382	421	463	509	560
+Loss forward		1,200	175			
+Work Cap Ret.						300**
-Capitl Costs	-2,200*					
Cash Flow	-3,400	1,550	1,442	1,509	1,654	2,193

*The capital cost is $300 working capital, $900 mineral rights acquisition cost, and $1,000 depreciable equipment.

**Working capital return of $300 is after-tax cash flow since it just recovers the initial working capital cost and no taxable gain or loss exists.

The largest allowable depletion deduction has a minus (−) sign in front of it.

DCFROR Calculation

$$0 = -3,400 + 1,550(P/F_{i,1}) + 1,442(P/F_{i,2}) + 1,509(P/F_{i,3})$$

$$+ 1,654(P/F_{i,4}) + 2,193(P/F_{i,5})$$

$$i = DCFROR = 37.17\%$$

NPV Calculation for $i^* = 20\%$

$$NPV = 1,550(P/F_{20,1}) + 1,442(P/F_{20,2}) + 1,509(P/F_{20,3})$$

$$+ 1,654(P/F_{20,4}) + 2,193(P/F_{20,5}) - 3,400 = +1,445$$

PVR Calculation

$$1,445 / 3,400 = .4251$$

The "stand alone" loss carry forward economic results are less desirable than the part A_1 expense against other income economic results for all techniques of analysis. Receiving income tax benefits more slowly in the A_2 analysis gave less desirable economic results in comparison with A_1 results. In the next analysis (A_3) tax cost is deferred further into the future than in the A_2 analysis so economic results for A_3 are slightly better than A_2 analysis results.

A_3) Individual or Independent, Carry all Tax Effects to Year 3.

Year	0	1	2	3	4	5
Revenue		3,000	3,300	3,630	3,993	4,392
-Royalties		-450	-495	-545	-599	-659
Net Revenue		2,550	2,805	3,085	3,394	3,733
-Oper Costs		-1,000	-1,080	-1,166	-1,260	-1,360
-Development	-1,200					
-Depreciation		-143	-245	-175	-125	-104
-Deprec Writeoff						-208
Before Depltn	-1,200	1,407	1,480	1,744	2,009	2,061
-50% Limit		704	740	872	1,005	1,030
-Percent Depl		-382	-421	-463	-509	-560
-Cost Depltn		180	129	32		
Taxable	-1,200	1,025	1,059	1,281[*]	1,500	1,501
-Tax @ 32%				-693	-480	-480
Net Income	-1,200	1,025	1,059	588	1,020	1,021
+Depreciation		143	245	175	125	312
+Depletion		382	421	463	509	560
+Loss forward						
+Work Cap Ret.						300[***]
-Capitl Costs	-2,200[**]					
Cash Flow	-3,400	1,550	1,725	1,226	1,654	2,193

*The year 3 tax of $693 includes regular tax of .32(1,281) = 410 plus delayed tax of 283 = .32(884) due to using 884 of loss forward deductions from outside sources in year 2 (in addition to the 1,200 year 0 development deduction) to eliminate year 2 taxable income. Using the 884 loss forward deduction in year 2 precludes our being able to use it in year 3 against other income, causing the extra 283 tax in year 3.

**The capital cost is $300 working capital, $900 mineral rights acquisition cost, and $1,000 depreciable equipment.

***Working capital return of $300 is after-tax cash flow since it just recovers the intital working captial cost and no taxable gain or loss exists.

The largest allowable depletion deduction has a minus ($-$) sign in front of it.

Companies such as U.S. Steel (now called USX) that generated large multi-billion dollar loss carry forward deductions in the 1970's and early 1980's should analyze the economics of projects using the part A_3 analysis approach. In the analysis of this project, because we assumed for the A_3 analysis that loss carry forward deductions would be used up by year 3, the economics for part A_3 results are not as good as the part A_1 expense against other income results. Sometimes part A_3 type results will be better than part A_1 type results. For example, if you assume that losses will be carried forward until year 10 instead of year 3, that pushes ultimate tax cost far enough into the future to make the analysis similar to the before-tax analysis in part D which yields a 45% DCFROR which is bigger than the A_1 DCFROR of 34%. Because of the time value of money if you push tax costs 10 years into the future they have fairly insignificant effect on analysis results.

DCFROR Calculation

$$0 = -3,400 + 1,550(P/F_{i,1}) + 1,725(P/F_{i,2}) + 1,226(P/F_{i,3})$$

$$+ 1,654(P/F_{i,4}) + 2,193(P/F_{i,5})$$

$$i = DCFROR = 37.83\%$$

NPV Calculation for i* = 20%

$$NPV = 1,550(P/F_{20,1}) + 1,725(P/F_{20,2}) + 1,226(P/F_{20,3})$$

$$+ 1,654(P/F_{20,4}) + 2,193(P/F_{20,5}) - 3,400 = +1,478$$

PVR Calculation

$$1,478 / 3,400 = .4348$$

B) Corporate, Mineral Evaluation

Year	0	1	2	3	4	5
Revenue		3,000	3,300	3,630	3,993	4,392
-Royalties		-450	-495	-545	-599	-659
Net Revenue		2,550	2,805	3,085	3,394	3,733
-Oper Costs		-1,000	-1,080	-1,166	-1,260	-1,360
-Development	-840					
-Depreciation		-143	-245	-175	-125	-104
-Amortization	-72	-72	-72	-72	-72	
-Deprec Writeoff						-208
Before Depltn	-912	1,335	1,408	1,672	1,937	2,061
-50% Limit		668	704	836	969	1,030
-Percent Depl		-382	-421	-463	-509	-560
-Cost Depltn		180	129	32		
Taxable	-912	953	987	1,209	1,428	1,501
-Tax @ 38%	347	-362	-375	-460	-543	-570
Net Income	-565	591	612	750	886	931
+Depreciation		143	245	175	125	312
+Depletion		382	421	463	509	560
+Amortization	72	72	72	72	72	
+Work Cap Ret.						300**
-Capitl Costs	-2,560*					
Cash Flow	-3,053	1,188	1,350	1,460	1,592	2,103

*The capital cost is $300 working capital, $900 mineral rights acquisition cost, $1,000 depreciable equipment, and 30% of the $1,200 development cost.
**Working capital return of $300 is after-tax cash flow since it just recovers the initial working capital cost and no taxable gain or loss exists.

The largest allowable depletion deduction has a minus ($-$) sign in front of it. The $72 amortization deduction in years 0 through 4 is (1/5)(.3)($1,200 Mineral Development).

DCFROR Calculation

$$0 = -3,053 + 1,188(P/F_{i,1}) + 1,350(P/F_{i,2}) + 1,460(P/F_{i,3})$$

$$+ 1,592(P/F_{i,4}) + 2,103(P/F_{i,5})$$

$$i = DCFROR = 36.79\%$$

NPV Calculation for i* = 20%

$$NPV = 1,188(P/F_{20,1}) + 1,350(P/F_{20,2}) + 1,460(P/F_{20,3})$$

$$+ 1,592(P/F_{20,4}) + 2,103(P/F_{20,5}) - 3,053 = +1,331$$

PVR Calculation

$$1,331 / 3,053 = .4360$$

The only difference in a corporate mineral project analysis and a major petroleum analysis is in the handling of depletion. Whereas all mineral producers get to take the greater of percentage or cost depletion, major petroleum producers only get to take cost depletion on oil and gas production.

C) Major Integrated Company, Petroleum Evaluation

Year	0	1	2	3	4	5
Revenue		3,000	3,300	3,630	3,993	4,392
-Royalties		-450	-495	-545	-599	-659
Net Revenue		2,550	2,805	3,085	3,394	3,733
-Oper Costs		-1,000	-1,080	-1,166	-1,260	-1,360
-Intangible	-840					
-Depreciation		-143	-245	-175	-125	-104
-Amortization	-72	-72	-72	-72	-72	
-Cost Depltn		-180	-180	-180	-180	-180
-Deprec Writeoff						-208
Taxable	-912	1,155	1,228	1,492	1,757	1,881
-Tax @ 38%	347	-439	-467	-567	-668	-715
Net Income	-565	716	761	925	1,090	1,166
+Depreciation		143	245	175	125	312
+Depletion		180	180	180	180	180
+Amortization	72	72	72	72	72	
+Work Cap Ret.						300**
-Capitl Costs	-2,560					
Cash Flow	-3,053	1,111	1,258	1,352	1,467	1,958

*The capital cost is $300 working capital, $900 mineral rights acquisition cost, $1,000 tangible depreciable equipment and 30% of the $1,200 intangible drilling cost (IDC).

**Working capital return of $300 is after-tax cash flow since it just recovers the initial working capital cost and no taxable gain or loss exists.

The $72 amortization deduction in years 0 through 4 is (1/5)(.3)($1,200 IDC).

DCFROR Calculation

$$0 = -3,053 + 1,111(P/F_{i,1}) + 1,258(P/F_{i,2}) + 1,352(P/F_{i,3})$$

$$+ 1,467(P/F_{i,4}) + 1,958(P/F_{i,5})$$

$i = DCFROR = 33.12\%$

NPV Calculation for i* = 20%

$$NPV = 1,111(P/F_{20,1}) + 1,258(P/F_{20,2}) + 1,352(P/F_{20,3})$$

$$+ 1,467(P/F_{20,4}) + 1,958(P/F_{20,5}) - 3,053 = +1,023$$

PVR Calculation

$1,023 / 3,053 = .3350$

Note that part C results with only cost depletion are less desirable than part B results with a percentage depletion and all other factors the same. This shows the sensitivity and importance of percentage depletion to mineral project and independent petroleum producer project economic results.

D) Before Tax Analysis

Year	0	1	2	3	4	5
Revenue		3,000	3,300	3,630	3,993	4,392
-Royalties		-450	-495	-545	-599	-659
Net Revenue		2,550	2,805	3,085	3,394	3,733
-Oper Costs		-1,000	-1,080	-1,166	-1,260	-1,360
Net Income		1,550	1,725	1,919	2,134	2,373
+Work Cap Ret.						300
-Capitl Costs	-3,400					
Cash Flow	-3,400	1,550	1,725	1,919	2,134	2,673

* The capital cost is $300 working capital, $900 mineral rights acquisition cost, $1,000 tangible equipment the $1,200 development or intangible drilling cost (IDC).

DCFROR Calculation

$$0 = -3,400 + 1,550(P/F_{i,1}) + 1,725(P/F_{i,2}) + 1,919(P/F_{i,3})$$

$$+ 2,134(P/F_{i,4}) + 2,673(P/F_{i,5})$$

$i = DCFROR = 45.32\%$

NPV Calculation for i* = 20%

$$NPV = 1,550(P/F_{20,1}) + 1,725(P/F_{20,2}) + 1,919(P/F_{20,3})$$
$$+ 2,134(P/F_{20,4}) + 2,673(P/F_{20,5}) - 3,400 = +2,303$$

PVR Calculation

$$2,303 / 3,400 = .6775$$

The variations in economic decision criteria can be significant for different types of investors who may have one of the several different tax positions presented in Example 8-8. Each evaluation must approximate as closely as possible the actual tax position for a given investor. Evaluation results reflect input cost, revenue, and timing of input cost and revenue assumptions as well as tax effect assumptions. It is important to project inflows and outflows of money from either revenues, costs, or tax savings and tax costs to fit the investor situation and physical project timing as closely as possible. Only if this is done will evaluation results be valid for economic decision making.

PROBLEMS

8-1   A man invests $22,000 at year 0 in a repair business including $2,000 for working capital for spare parts. He estimates that he can sell the business in 3 years for $14,000 including the $2,000 working capital return. The man plans to depreciate the $20,000 non-working capital investment using a 5 year depreciation life starting in year 1. Expected annual income is $35,000 and operating costs are expected to be $25,000 per year, assuming a washout of escalation of income and operating costs each year. Taxable income from the business will be taxed at an effective rate of 40%. Calculate DCFROR for a 3 year evaluation life, assuming:

A) Straight line ACRS depreciation using the half year convention in the first year.

B) Modified ACRS depreciation with the half year convention in the first year.

8-2

```
Working Capital                                    Working Capital
Cost = $50,000                                     Return = $50,000
Res & Development          Sales = $500,000               $500,000
Cost = $100,000           OC = $400,000                   $400,000
```
```
      0                        1 ................. 5
```

As shown on the time diagram, research and development expenses of $100,000 on a project are expected to generate increased sales of $500,000 per year from existing process equipment for increased annual operating costs of $400,000. A washout of annual escalation of operating costs and revenues is assumed. The effective income tax rate is 40%. Determine the DCFROR on investment capital if:

A) Research and development costs are deducted for tax purposes as operating expenses at year 0. Other income is assumed to exist against which to use the year 0 negative taxable income.

B) Research and development costs are expensed at time zero with negative taxable income carried forward to be used against project revenues (stand alone analysis).

C) Research and development costs are capitalized and deducted for tax purposes by amortization over years 1 to 5.

8-3   Development of a coal property which a corporation may purchase for a mineral rights acquisition cost of $10 million is being considered. Mineral development capital of $10 million will be needed in evaluation year 0 for overburden stripping with the cost considered to be incurred in the first month of year 0. Mine equipment costs of $15 million also will be incurred in year 0 along with $2 million cost for working capital. The mine life is estimated to be 5 years. Mine equipment will be depreciated over 7 years using modified ACRS rates, starting in year 0 with the half year convention. Salvage value and working capital return will be $5 million at the end of year 5 with any taxable gain taxed as ordinary income. The effective tax rate is 40%. Coal reserves are estimated to be 5 million tons and production for years 1 through 5 is projected to be 1 million tons per year. Coal selling price is estimated to be $30 per ton in year 1, escalating 10% per year in years 2 through 5. Royalties are 8% of revenue. Mining operating costs are estimated to be $12 per ton in year 1, also escalating by 10% per year in following years. Calculate the project DCFROR and NPV for a minimum DCFROR of 20% to determine if the mine development economics are satisfactory for:

A) No other income exists against which to use tax deductions, so carry negative taxable income forward and use against project income. This makes the project economics "stand alone".

B) Other taxable income does exist so realize tax benefits from negative taxable income in the year incurred.

8-4   Annual cash flow from a new investment is projected to be:

Cash Flow	-$150,000	$60,000	$70,000	$80,000	$90,000
Year	0	1	2	3	4

As the year 1 through 4 positive cash flows are realized it is anticipated that they will be invested in treasury bonds paying 12% annual interest. Calculate the DCFROR on the investment and calculate the Growth DCFROR on the investment assuming a 40% income tax rate is relevant and that after-tax treasury bond interest will be reinvested each year in identical bonds.

8-5   A manufacturing plant can be purchased for $180,000. An additional $20,000 must be invested in working capital for raw material and spare parts inventory and accounts receivable money tied up in operating costs. The $180,000 plant cost will be depreciated straight line over 7 years using the half year depreciation convention in year 1. Actual salvage value is estimated to be $150,000 for used machinery and equipment and working capital return at year 15. Annual sales revenue is estimated to be $100,000 in year 1 with operating costs of $40,000. In years 2 to 15, escalation of operating costs and sales revenue are projected to be a washout. The effective income tax rate is 40%. The minimum ROR is 15% after taxes. Calculate the project DCFROR and NPV.

8-6   A mining investor operating as a corporation is considering buying the mineral rights to a small mineral property. The mineral rights acquisition cost will be $1,000,000 at year 0 and depreciable mining equipment costs will be $1,000,000 at year 1 in escalated dollars. Modified ACRS depreciation will be used for a 7 year depreciation life starting in year 2 with the half year convention. Mineral development cost of $500,000 will be incurred in month 7 of year 1. Production rates will be 100,000 units per year in years 2 and 3 and 150,000 units per year in years 4 and 5 which will deplete the reserves. Salvage value of all assets at year 5 is considered to be nil. The mineral product will be sold for $20 per unit while production operating costs are estimated to be $8 per unit. Assume a washout of escalation of operating costs and sales revenue each year and neglect the effect of escalating sales revenue on percent depletion. The mineral produced is in the 22% percentage depletion category. The effective income tax rate is 40%. Assume other income does not exist so carry negative taxable income forward to make project economics stand alone. Determine the project cash flow for each year and calculate DCFROR and NPV for a minimum DCFROR of 15%.

8-7   XYZ Corp. is evaluating the purchase and development of a petroleum property that can be acquired for $100,000 now (evaluation year 0). The purchase would be followed immediately by intangible drilling costs of $750,000 at year 0 and $250,000 at year 1. Tangible well completion and producing equipment costs of $1,000,000 would be required at year 1. Anticipated production is 200 barrels of oil per day (BPD) in year 2, decreasing each year by 40BPD in years 3 through 6. Assume oil will sell for $22 per barrel (before royalties of 14% of sales) in the first producing year, with oil price escalating by 8% annually thereafter. Assume 350 operating days per year. Operating costs are estimated to be $175,000 in the first producing year and escalating 10% annually until production is suspended at the beginning of year 7. XYZ Corp. has an effective tax rate of 38%. The company has other oil income against which to expense pre-tax losses, however all oil production by the company is less than 1000 BPD now and in the foreseeable future. The well completion and producing equipment costs will be depreciated by modified ACRS depreciation for a 7 year depreciation life starting in evaluation year 2 with the half year convention. Use DCFROR and NPV (for $i^* = 15\%$) to evaluate this investment for the 6 year project life if:

A) Risk of failure is neglected, i.e. the probability of successful well completion and production through evaluation year 6 is 100%.

B) The probability of success between year 0 and year 1 is 40% and after year 1 is 100%. If drilling at year 0 results in failure, the company will take a writeoff of the acquisition cost at the end of year 1 when the property will be abandoned for a $50,000 cost.

C) The part "A" and "B" analyses are for a major petroleum producer and drilling costs are incurred in the 7th month of years 0 and 1.

8-8   Consideration is being given to the investment of $420,000 at time zero for machinery and equipment to be depreciated using 7 year straight line ACRS depreciation starting in year 1 with the half year convention. Annual sales are projected to be $400,000 less annual operating costs of $200,000. Escalation of operating costs and sales revenue is expected to be a washout from year to year. $100,000 for working capital investment is also needed at time zero and working capital return is expected to equal the initial working capital investment at the end of the project. Salvage value of the machinery and equipment is expected to be zero. The minimum DCFROR is 15% and the effective income tax rate is 35%. Calculate DCFROR and NPV for:

A) A 9 year evaluation life.
B) An 18 year evaluation life.

CHAPTER 9

AFTER-TAX INVESTMENT DECISION METHODS AND APPLICATIONS

9.1 Introduction

DCFROR is used more widely as an after-tax investment economic decision method than all other economic decision methods combined, with two out of three companies emphasizing DCFROR analysis over other techniques. NPV is the second most used economic decision method and ratios are the third most used evaluation technique. These discounted cash flow investment analysis techniques are the best approaches known today for evaluating the economic potential of alternative investments. It is important to remember that all of the discounted cash flow techniques are systematic, quantitative approaches to evaluating investments based on given sets of assumptions and input data. If you put garbage in, you will get garbage out of any analysis calculation using any technique of analysis. There is nothing magical about discounted cash flow results. They are based on the evaluation assumptions concerning; 1) tax considerations, 2) handling inflation and escalation, 3) risk adjusting or not risk adjusting results when finite probability of failure exists, 4) the financial situation of the individual or organization for which the analysis is being made, 5) significance of terminal value magnitude, timing and tax considerations, 6) cash investment analysis versus leveraged analysis with borrowed money, 7) correct handling of the discounted cash flow analysis calculations whether it involves DCFROR, NPV, PVR or another technique, and finally, 8) correct application of the discounted cash flow analysis results to analyze mutually exclusive or non-mutually exclusive income or service producing alternatives.

Proper use of the discounted cash flow analysis techniques gives investors a better chance of correctly analyzing the potential of alternative investments than can be achieved using any other evaluation technique. The key to successful application of the discounted cash flow techniques is consistency. If you analyze a project in escalated dollars you must compare it with results of other projects analyzed in escalated dollars. As discussed in Chapter 11, if you leverage a project with borrowed money, you should compare it to other projects analyzed with similar borrowed money leverage.

Broad acceptance and utilization of discounted cash flow analysis occurred in most industries around the world in the decades of the 1960's and 1970's. Prior to that time, techniques of analysis such as payback period, which is described in the next section, and several different average and/or accounting rate of return calculations which are defined and illustrated in Section 9.8 of this chapter were utilized by investors to evaluate the economic potential of investments. It will be shown that the older techniques do not properly account for the timing and tax effects related to project costs and revenues. Therefore, the older techniques are inconsistent in their usefulness for evaluating economic differences in project investments. This is the primary reason investors have shifted in recent decades from using these older analysis techniques to using the discounted cash flow analysis techniques.

9.2 Payback Period Analysis

Payback period (or payout period) is the time required for positive project cash flow to recover negative project cash flow from the acquisition and/or development years. Payback can be calculated either from the start of a project or from the start of production. For the calculation of payback period, positive cash flow is generally considered to flow uniformly during a year rather than at end, middle or beginning of a year. Sometimes payback period calculations are based on discounted cash flow at a specified discount rate such as 10%, 12% or some other rate that often represents the minimum DCFROR.

The basic economic analysis philosophy behind the use of payback period as an evaluation technique is that the faster you get investment dollars back from project cash flow, the better the economics of an investment. However, this often is not the case. Payback can be very misleading as an indicator of economic differences in investment projects.

As a measure of risk, or financial analysis rather than economic analysis reasons, payback period calculations can be useful. If an investor is considering a foreign investment in an underdeveloped country associated with high political instability, if the investor cannot recover initial investments within a year or two, he may elect to forego investing even though long-term investment calculation results look very good. Similarly, a company in a tight financial situation and needing money to meet current obligations such as for operating expenses and debt repayment may elect to invest in projects with short payback periods to help meet short-term cash flow needs, even though these projects have much poorer economic potential than other potential investments with longer payback periods.

EXAMPLE 9-1 Payback Period Calculations

If projects A and B are mutually exclusive investments, which is indicated to be preferable using non-discounted payback period, discounted payback period, NPV, PVR and DCFROR. The minimum rate of return is 12%.

```
Cash Flow = -100          -          -          -        285.6
Project A) _____

            0          1          2          3        4 years


Cash Flow = -100        46.2       46.2       46.2      46.2
Project B) _____

            0          1          2          3        4 years
```

Solution:

Assuming cash flow is realized uniformly over year 4, Project "A" Non-Discounting Payback = 3 + (100/285.6) = 3.35 years. If project "A" cash flow is assumed to be lump sum cash flow such as from the sale of real estate or common stock, then the Project "A", Non-Discounted Payback is 4 years.

Project "B", Non-discounted Payback = 2 + (100 − 92.4)/46.2 = 2.16 years

Non-discounted Payback Indicates Select Project "B", with the smaller payback.

Diagrams for Discounted Cash Flow at 12%

```
Discounted Cash Flow = -100     -        -        -      285.6(P/F12,4)=181.5
A) _____

                        0        1        2        3          4 year
```

Project "A" Discounted Payback = 3 + (100/181.5) = 3.55 years

If the project "A" cash flow is assumed to be a lump sum cash flow, then Discounted Payback = 4 years.

```
Discounted Cash Flow = -100    41.25    36.83    32.88     29.36
B) _____

                        0        1        2        3          4 years
```

Project "B" Discounted Payback = 2 + (100 − 78.08)/32.88 = 2.67 years

Discounted Payback Indicates Select Project "B", the smaller payback.

Net Present Value

$NPV_A = 285.6(P/F_{12,4}) - 100 = +81.5$ Select Largest NPV, "A"

$NPV_B = 46.2(P/A_{12,4}) - 100 = +40.3$

Present Value Ratio

$PVR_A = 81.5 / 100 = +0.815$

$PVR_B = 40.3 / 100 = +0.403$

Since both ratios relate to the same investment dollars, select "A", whether the alternatives are mutually exclusive or non-mutually exclusive.

Discounted Cash Flow Rate of Return

Trial and error analysis gives $DCFROR_A = 30\%$ and $DCFROR_B = 30\%$. Because of differences in the distribution of positive cash flow on the project "A" and "B" diagrams, these 30% DCFROR results have very different meaning after the first year. Incremental analysis must be made for a valid economic decision with DCFROR. Make the incremental analysis so that incremental cost (negative cash flow) is followed by revenue (positive cash flow).

```
Incremental Cash Flow    0    -46.2    -46.2    -46.2    +239.4
For Project A-B)        _____
                         0     1        2        3        4 years
```

PW Eq: $0 = -46.2(P/A_{i,3}) + 239.4(P/F_{i,4})$

Trial and Error, i = incremental "A − B" DCFROR = 29.9% > i* = 12%

Select Project A

All discounted cash flow analysis techniques indicate "Select A". Payback period indicates "Select B", showing the inconsistency in this technique as a method for selecting investments that will maximize profitability from available investment dollars.

9.3 Savings are Analogous to Income

In economic evaluation work we very frequently find ourselves confronted with analysis of determining the most economic way to provide a service. This is the most common type of evaluation problem of all and in Chapter 3 we discussed the five basic economic analysis approaches to analyze this type of problem. The five basic approaches are 1) comparison of present worth costs, 2) comparison of annual worth costs, 3) comparison of future worth costs, 4) incremental ROR or Net Value Analysis or 5) breakeven analysis such as service life breakeven analysis. Of these five methods incremental ROR and Net Value analysis are very popular because of the large number of companies and individuals that use ROR and Net Value analysis as the primary decision making criterion for all types of project analyses. Incremental analysis of alternatives that provide a service always generates incremental costs and savings, and dollars saved are just like dollars earned!

For after-tax DCFROR, Net Value, or Ratio analysis of alternatives involving savings you must convert savings to after-tax cash flow exactly the same as incremental income must be converted to cash flow. If an incremental investment generates savings by reducing operating costs below a former level, the lower operating costs will result in lower tax deductions for operating costs which means you have more taxable income in the same amount as if the savings were incremental revenue.

The following example illustrates DCFROR and NPV analysis of an investment that generates savings.

EXAMPLE 9-2 DCFROR and NPV Analysis Involving Savings

A natural gas distribution company is evaluating the economic potential of installing a new compressor that costs $420,000 to satisfy gas compression requirements and save 80,000 MCF per year of natural gas (where MCF equals thousand cubic feet) compared to the present operating costs. The gas saved could be sold to industrial customers for $3.00 per MCF and compressor life is estimated to be 10 years with zero salvage value. The new compressor would be depreciated straight line over a 7 year life starting at year 0 with the half year convention. Assume compressor maintenance costs will be exactly offset by increased sales revenues due to increased gas selling prices. The effective income tax rate is 40% and the minimum DCFROR is 12%. Use DCFROR and NPV analysis to determine if it is economical to buy the new compressor. Assume other income exists against which to use deductions in any year.

Solution:

To illustrate the concept of incremental analysis that is required to make a proper economic evaluation of the example problem, consider the following. Let X equal the "new" compressor natural gas usage in thousands of MCF per year so X + 80,000 MCF per year represents "present" compressor natural gas use (MCF per year). The savings of $240,000 (80,000 MCF times

$3.00) per year from going to the new compressor must be converted to cash flow the same as incremental income would be converted to cash flow.

All Values in Thousands, Except Selling Price

Service Costs, C = Capital Cost, OC = Operating Costs, S = Savings:

```
          -     OC = (X+80)MCF($3.00/MCF)    OC = (X+80)MCF($3.00/MCF)
Old      ─────────────────────────────────────────────────────────────
          0              1      .........................  10


      C=$420    OC = X MCF($3.00/MCF)        OC = X MCF($3.00/MCF)
New      ─────────────────────────────────────────────────────────────
          0              1      .........................  10


New  C=$420           S = $240                      S = $240
-Old     ─────────────────────────────────────────────────────────────
          0              1      .........................  10
```

Incremental Cash Flow Calculations

Year	0	1-6	7	8-10
Savings		240	240	240
-Depreciation	-30	-60	-30	
Taxable Inc.	-30	180	210	240
-Tax ā 40%	12	-72	-84	-96
Net Income	-18	108	126	144
+Depreciation	30	60	30	
-Capital Costs	-420			
Cash Flow	-408	168	156	144

PW Eq: $0 = -408 + 168(P/A_{i,6}) + 156(P/F_{i,7}) + 144(P/A_{i,3})(P/F_{i,7})$

i = DCFROR = 39.2% > i^* = 12%, new compressor is satisfactory

$$\text{NPV ā } i^* \text{ 12\%} = -408 + 168(\overset{4.111}{(P/A_{12,6})} + \overset{.4523}{156(P/F_{12,7})}$$

$$+ \ 144\overset{2.402}{(P/A_{12,3})}\overset{.4523}{(P/F_{12,7})} = +510 > 0, \text{ satisfactory}$$

The DCFROR of 39.2%, which is more than three times the minimum DCFROR of 12%, indicates very satisfactory economics for the new compressor, consistent with positive NPV of $510,000 that is greater than the cost of $420,000 that generated the NPV. Whenever NPV is positive and similar in magnitude to the cost that generated it, project economics are very good.

9.4 Sunk Costs and Opportunity Costs in Evaluations

Sunk costs are costs that have already been incurred in the past and that nothing we do now or in the future can effect. Economic analysis studies for investment decision making purposes deal with project costs and revenues and tax effects yet to be incurred now or in the future. *Sunk costs are not relevant to the analysis of either income or service producing investment alternatives except for remaining sale value and tax effects, which are opportunity cost considerations* discussed in the next paragraph. Past commitments to expend money as well as past expenditures are sunk revenues and costs. Revenues realized in the past from a project are sunk revenues the same as past costs are sunk costs. Classic examples of sunk costs include the costs of equipment acquired several years ago and now being considered for replacement, the costs for research or exploration work incurred in earlier years, or the cost of common stock or land several years ago for a personal investment. In all of these situations the cost is in the past and, except for remaining sale value and tax effects, is not relevant to our analysis of whether to develop, keep or replace the asset or investment.

Opportunity cost is hidden or implied cost that is incurred when a person or organization forgoes the opportunity to realize positive cash flow from an investment in order to take a different investment course of action. For example, if you elect not to sell your personal automobile for its second-hand value of $8,000 in order to keep it and use it, you are incurring an opportunity cost of $8,000. In analyzing whether to replace the vehicle (or any other existing asset) with a new vehicle or asset the opportunity cost of $8,000 must be accounted for as illustrated in Chapter 10 Examples 10-2 and 10-3 related to replacement analysis.

Another opportunity cost situation involves analysis of whether to sell a project or property or whether to keep and develop the project or property. If an investor forgoes realizing a sale value positive cash flow in order to keep and develop a property, an opportunity cost equal to the positive cash flow that could be realized from selling must be included in the analysis of development economics. Proper incremental analysis of mutually exclusive develop versus sell alternatives automatically accounts for the proper opportunity cost in that analysis situation as illustrated in Example 9-3.

A personal investment situation involving important opportunity cost considerations concerns analysis of whether to keep or sell common stock purchased in the past. Assume you purchased stock three months ago for

$20 per share and the price has dropped to $8 per share. The original $20 per share cost is sunk but the tax effects are not. If you sell for $8 per share you also get a $20 per share tax deduction which is $12 per share in excess of what is needed to eliminate any gain from the sale. The $12 per share excess tax deduction would be short term capital loss that could be used against other short term capital gains (assume other gains exist). For a 30% effective income tax rate, the $12 per share deduction would save $3.60 per share in taxes from using the deduction against other short term capital gain income, giving total cash flow from selling of $11.60 per share ($8 sale value plus $3.60 tax savings). An investor who forgoes selling for $8 per share is actually incurring an opportunity cost of $11.60 per share to keep the stock. This rationale relates to common stock sales that stock brokers often refer to as "tax selling".

Finally, the minimum rate of return (or opportunity cost of capital or hurdle rate) is the classic example of the most widely used opportunity cost in economic analysis. As discussed in several places earlier in the text, the minimum rate of return is not the cost of borrowed funds, (an investor may not even be using borrowed funds), but minimum rate of return represents other opportunities thought to exist for the investment of capital both now and in the future over the life of a project. An investor incurs an opportunity cost equal to the rate of return that could be realized by investing elsewhere in other projects if he elects to invest in a new project being analyzed. Thus the term minimum rate of return is interchangeable with opportunity cost of capital.

Example 9-3 illustrates sunk cost and opportunity cost handling in a develop versus sell income-producing analysis situation while Example 9-5 illustrates sunk costs and opportunity costs in a breakeven analysis related to service-producing assets. In Chapter 10 sunk cost and opportunity cost considerations are applied to the evaluation of service-producing alternatives in Examples 10-2 and 10-3.

EXAMPLE 9-3 Sunk Costs and Opportunity Costs in The Analysis of Develop versus Sell

The time diagram shows costs and revenues in thousands of dollars for a six year project life with research costs in years −1 and 0 (year 0 represents the start of production with negative numbering of pre-production years). To simplify cash flow analysis consider the project to be non-mineral or petroleum, so depletion is not applicable. Assume the year 0 equipment cost is placed into service at year 0 with straight line, 5 year life depreciation starting at year 0 with the half year convention. Escalation of year 1 through 5 sales and operating costs is projected to be a washout. Project salvage value is zero. Other taxable income and tax obligations are assumed to exist against which to use tax deductions in any year. The effective tax rate is 40%.

```
                   Research or
Research or        Exploration
Exploration        Cost = 100    Annual Sales = 250      250
Cost = 150         Eq.Cost = 200 Annual OC    = 90        90
                                                                  L = 0
     -1                 0                         1 ....... 5
```

Assume the escalated minimum DCFROR is 15% and make the following three analyses.

A) Calculate project DCFROR assuming the evaluation is being made prior to year −1, so none of the project dollar values shown on the diagram are sunk.

B) Make DCFROR analysis to determine if project development should continue, assuming the evaluation is being made after the year −1 costs have already been incurred (so they are sunk) but prior to incurring the year 0 costs. Assume the year −1 research or exploration costs have generated no assets of value for sale to outside interests (so no opportunity cost will be incurred from keeping the property for continued development).

C) Make the "B" analysis assuming the year −1 research costs have generated patents for which a $200,000 cash sale value offer at year 0 has been received.

Solution, All Values in Thousands of Dollars:

Case A) Year −1 Cost Is Not Sunk

Year	-1	0	1-4	5
Revenue			250	250
-Oper. Costs			-90	-90
-Development	-150	-100		
-Depreciation		-20	-40	-20
Taxable Inc.	-150	-120	120	140
-Tax â 40%	60	48	-48	-56
Net Income	-90	-72	72	84
+Depreciation		20	40	20
-Capital Costs		-200		
Cash Flow	-90	-252	112	104

PW Eq @ Yr -1:

$$0 = -90 -252(P/F_{i,1}) + 112(P/A_{i,4})(P/F_{i,1}) + 104(P/F_{i,6})$$

i = DCFROR = 16.7% > i^* = 15%, so satisfactory

Case B) Year −1 Cost Is Sunk

The year −1 costs and tax effects are sunk and not relevant to the analysis. No opportunity cost exists from not selling the property because no year 0 sale value exists. Year 0 through 5 cash flows are the same as for part "A".

Year	-1	0	1-4	5
Develop Cash Flow	-90(Sunk)	-252	112	104
Abandon Cash Flow	-90(Sunk)	0	0	0
Develop - Abandon	0	-252	112	104

PW Eq @ Yr 0:

$$0 = -252 + 112(P/A_{i,4}) + 104(P/F_{i,5})$$

i = DCFROR = 33.85% > i^* = 15%, so satisfactory

Case C) Year −1 Cost Is Sunk and an Opportunity Cost Exists

The year −1 cost and tax effects are still sunk. However, the year 0 sale value of $200,000 minus tax of .40($200,000) or $80,000 would yield sale cash flow of $120,000. An investor who passes up the opportunity to realize positive cash flow from selling in order to retain or develop, incurs an opportunity cost equal to the positive cash flow. This opportunity cost occurs naturally from proper incremental analysis of the mutually exclusive develop versus sell alternatives as follows:

Year	-1	0	1-4	5
Develop Cash Flow	-90(Sunk)	-252	112	104
Sell Cash Flow	-90(Sunk)	+120	0	0
Develop - Sell	0	-372	112	104

PW Eq @ Yr 0:

$$0 = -372 + 112(P/A_{i,4}) + 104(P/F_{i,5})$$

i = DCFROR = 14.94% < i^* = 15%, so slightly unsatisfactory

From an economic viewpoint, development is slightly less desirable than selling. Note that the Develop minus Sell incremental analysis converts the sale positive cash flow of $120,000 to a negative incremental $120,000 cash flow. This is effectively a $120,000 opportunity cost that the investor incurs in addition to the year 0 development cost if development is accepted. Even though development alone looks satisfactory as shown in the "B" analysis, proper accounting for the opportunity cost from keeping the property instead of selling makes selling a slightly better or breakeven alternative compared to developing.

9.5 Breakeven Analysis After-Tax

Breakeven analysis involves specifying all project parameters except one and calculating what that parameter needs to be to give a project a specified DCFROR. Breakeven analysis involves a wide variety of evaluation calculations such as determination of breakeven selling price or revenue, breakeven acquisition cost, or breakeven number of units to be produced to give an investor a specified DCFROR on invested dollars. Breakeven analysis is very common and important in all types of industries. The following four examples illustrate different types of breakeven calculations and applications.

EXAMPLE 9-4 Escalated Dollar and Constant Dollar Breakeven Revenue Analysis

If an investor spends $100,000 on equipment and $50,000 on development at time 0 to generate revenues for a 5 year period and zero salvage value, what uniform and equal annual net revenues after operating costs for years 1 through 5 are required to give:

A) 20% before-tax escalated dollar ROR.

B) 20% before-tax constant dollar ROR assuming 10% inflation per year.

C) 20% after-tax escalated dollar DCFROR for expensing the $50,000 development cost against other income at year 0 and depreciating the $100,000 equipment cost straight line over years 1 through 5 starting in year 1 with a full year deduction to simplify the analysis. Use a 40% effective tax rate.

D) 20% after-tax constant dollar DCFROR assuming 10% per year inflation for the tax considerations of part "C".

Solution:

A) Before-Tax, Escalated Dollar Breakeven Analysis

$$\text{Net Revenue Per Year} = \$150,000(A/P_{20,5}) = \$50,157$$
$$\overset{.33438}{}$$

B) Before-Tax, Constant Dollar Breakeven Analysis

$1 + i = (1 + f)(1 + i')$ where $f = 0.10$ and $i' = 0.20$, so the equivalent escalated dollar ROR, $i = 0.320$ or 32.0%

$$\text{Net Revenue Per Year} = \$150,0000(A/P_{32,5}) \overset{.4264}{} = \$63,960$$

Alternate Solution to Case "B".

Convert all escalated dollar breakeven revenues, "X", to equivalent constant dollar results by present worthing "X" at the 10% inflation rate to express all revenue in terms of year 0 purchasing power. Then handle the time value of money by present worthing again at the constant dollar minimum ROR of 20%.

$$150,000 = X(P/F_{10,1})(P/F_{20,1}) + X(P/F_{10,2})(P/F_{20,2})$$

$$+ X(P/F_{10,3})(P/F_{20,3}) + X(P/F_{10,4})(P/F_{20,4})$$

$$+ X(P/F_{10,5})(P/F_{20,5})$$

$$X = \text{Net Revenue Per Year} = \$63,960$$

C) After-Tax, Escalated Dollar Breakeven Analysis

For after-tax analysis, first convert costs and revenues to cash flows expressed in terms of the unknown parameter, "X". All Values are in Dollars:

```
Year                  0             1-5
======================================
Revenue                             X
-Development       -50,000
-Depreciation                    -20,000
-----------------------------------------
Taxable Inc.       -50,000       X-20,000
-Tax @ 40%          20,000      -.4X+ 8,000
-----------------------------------------
Net Income         -30,000       .6X-12,000
+Depreciation                     20,000
-Capital Costs    -100,000
-----------------------------------------
Cash Flow         -130,000       .6X+ 8,000
```

$$\text{PW Eq:} \quad 0 = -130,000 + (.6X + 8,000)(P/A_{20,5})^{2.991}$$

$$0 = -130,000 + 1.7946X + 23,928$$

X = \$59,106 net revenue per year to give a 20% escalated dollar DCFROR.

D) After-Tax Constant Dollar Breakeven Analysis

The easiest analysis is to work in escalated dollars and use the escalated dollar minimum DCFROR of 32% that is equivalent to the 20% constant dollar DCFROR, as calculated in part "B".

$$PW \ Eq: \quad 0 = -130,000 + (.6X + 8,000)(P/A_{32,5}^{2.3452})$$

$$0 = -130,000 + 1.4071X + 18,762$$

X = $79,055 net revenue per year to give a 20% constant dollar DCFROR.

Note the four breakeven results are all different. *It is very important to explicitly understand the assumptions related to all economic analysis calculations to properly interpret and apply the results for investment decision making. Breakeven calculations are no exception. Whether results relate to before-tax or after-tax calculations, done in escalated or constant dollars, with or without risk adjustment, and on a cash investment or leveraged basis are some key assumptions that have significant effect on any proper economic analysis.* There is no substitute for understanding the calculation mechanics and the meaning of relevant discounted cash flow analysis assumptions in order to be able to apply evaluation results properly for economic decision making.

EXAMPLE 9-5 Opportunity Cost in Breakeven Analysis

A decision must be made to either overhaul an existing machine to meet new tighter product standards or to replace it. Breakeven revenue analysis is desired for a 3 year evaluation life. Your task is to determine the 3 equal annual end of year before-tax breakeven revenues that would cover appropriate costs and give a 20% escalated dollar DCFROR for the existing machine based on the following cost, value and tax data. The existing machine has a present secondhand market value of $7,000 now at year 0 and a tax book value of zero. If the existing machine is kept, a $10,000 overhaul cost must be incurred now at year 0 to retrofit the machine to handle new product quality standards. The overhaul cost would be depreciable starting in year 0 using modified ACRS 7 year life depreciation with the half year convention. Annual escalated dollar operating costs are projected to be $3,000 at year 0, $6,000 in year 1, $7,000 in year 2 and $4,000 in year 3 with a $2,000 escalated dollar salvage value at the end of year 3. (The $3,000 year 0 operating costs represents month zero through six costs which are closer to time zero than year 1. The $6,000 year 1 operating costs are month 7 through 18 costs and so forth.) Assume any taxable gain on salvage is taxed as ordinary income. Other taxable income does exist against which to use tax deductions in the year they are realized. The effective income tax rate is 40%.

Solution:

If the investor forgoes selling the equipment for $7,000 to keep and retrofit it for use, the $7,000 must be accounted for as opportunity cost reduced by 40% tax to be paid ($2,800) on the $7,000 sale gain. This gives after-tax opportunity cost of $4,200, which equals the after-tax cash flow that could be realized from selling.

```
Opportunity Cost = $4,200
Retrofit Cost   = $10,000    Rev=$X      Rev=$X      Rev=$X
Operating Costs = $ 3,000    OC=$6,000   OC=$7,000   OC=$4,000
                          _____
                                                         Salvage
         0           1           2           3      = $2,000
```

Modified ACRS Depreciation
(Using Table 7-3 Rates for a 7 Year Life Asset)

```
Year 0  (.1429)($10,000) = $1,429
Year 1  (.2449)($10,000) = $2,449
Year 2  (.1749)($10,000) = $1,749
Year 3  (.1249)($10,000) = $1,249
                           _____
Cumulative Depreciation = $6,876

Year 3 Book Value = $10,000 - 6,876 = $3,124
```

Breakeven Cash Flow Calculations

Let X equal the before-tax uniform and equal revenue in each of years 1, 2 and 3 that will give the investor a 20% escalated dollar DCFROR. Note that there are three different costs that are handled differently for tax purposes.

Year	0	1	2	3
Revenue		X	X	X+2,000
-Oper. Costs	-3,000	-6,000	-7,000	-4,000
-Depreciation	-1,429	-2,449	-1,749	-1,249
-Deprec Writeoff				-3,124
Taxable	-4,429	X-8,449	X-8,749	X-6,373
-Tax a 40%	+1,771	-.4X+3,380	-.4X+3,500	-.4X+2,549
Net Income	-2,657	.6X-5,069	.6X-5,250	.6X-3,824
+Depreciation	1,429	2,449	1,749	1,249
+Deprec Writeoff				3,124
-Capital Costs	-14,200			
Cash Flow	-15,429	.6X-2,620	.6X-3,500	.6X+549

Find breakeven revenue per year, "X", to make NPV = 0 for i* = 20%

$$0 = -15,429 + (.6X-2,620)(P/F_{20,1})^{.8333} + (.6X-3,500)(P/F_{20,2})^{.6944}$$

$$+ (.6X+549)(P/F_{20,3})^{.5787}$$

$$0 = 1.2638X - 19724.94$$

Breakeven Annual Revenue, X = $15,608

It is of interest to observe that if the investor desired to achieve a 12.2% constant dollar DCFROR for assumed annual inflation of 7% per year over the project life, the breakeven analysis would give the same result. A 12.2% constant dollar DCFROR is equivalent to a 20% escalated dollar DCFROR for 7% inflation per year using Equation 6-1:

$$1 + i = (1 + f)(1 + i')$$

Constant dollar breakeven calculations and escalated dollar breakeven calculations are equivalent if the appropriate equivalent escalated dollar and constant dollar minimum DCFROR rates are used. Getting the same economic conclusions with either escalated or constant dollar analysis means getting the same breakeven parameter results with either type breakeven analysis. You get the same breakeven results with either correct escalated or constant dollar calculations.

EXAMPLE 9-6 Expected Value Breakeven Analysis

An investor has paid $100,000 to develop a facility that is estimated to have a 70 percent probability of successfully producing 5,000 product units per year for each of the next two years, after which the facility is expected to be obsolete with a zero salvage value. The 30 percent probability of failure is associated with an escalated dollar facility salvage value of $50,000 at year 1. Today's dollar operating costs are $40,000 per year and they are estimated to escalate 15 percent in year 1 and 10 percent in year 2. Product selling price is estimated to escalate 25 percent in year 1 and 15 percent in year 2. Determine the required escalated dollar selling price per unit in each of years 1 and 2 to give the investor a 12 percent constant dollar expected DCFROR assuming inflation will be 6 percent in year 1 and 10 percent in year 2. The $100,000 cost will be depreciated using 200% declining balance depreciation for a 5 year life starting in year 1 with a half year deduction. Other income exists against which to use deductions in any year. The effective income tax rate is 40% and all salvage considerations are treated as ordinary income.

Solution:

Let X = Today's Dollar Selling Price Per Unit

Escalated Dollar Values:

Revenue $5,000X(F/P_{25,1})$ $5,000X(F/P_{25,1})(F/P_{15,1})$

Operating Costs $40,000(F/P_{15,1})$ $40,000(F/P_{15,1})(F/P_{10,1})$

Cost = 100,000   p=0.7

```
Cost = 100,000   p=0.7
                                                    Salvage = 0
       0                1                2
         p=0.3
                    Salvage = 50,000
```

To work in escalated dollars, which are the dollars shown on the diagram, we must calculate the escalated dollar minimum DCFROR for year 1 and 2 that is equivalent at the 12% constant dollar DCFROR for the inflation rates of 6% in year 1 and 10% in year 2.

$1 + i^* = (1 + f)(1 + i^*)$

Year 1: $f = 0.06$, $i^{*'} = 0.12$, so $i^* = 0.187$ or 18.7%

Year 2: $f = 0.10$, $i^{*'} = 0.12$, so $i^* = 0.232$ or 23.2%

Cash Flow Calculations

Year	0	1(Failure)	1(Success)	2(Success)
Revenue		50,000	6,250X	7,187X
-Oper Costs			-46,000	-50,600
-Depreciation			-20,000	-32,000
-Writeoff		-100,000		-48,000
Taxable		-50,000	6,250X-66,000	7,187X-130,600
-Tax @ 40%		20,000	-2,500X+26,400	-3,306X+ 52,240
Net Income		-30,000	3,750X-39,600	3,881X- 78,360
+Depreciation			20,000	32,000
+Writeoff		100,000		48,000
-Capital Costs	-100,000			
Cash Flow	-100,000	70,000	3,750X-19,600	3,881X+1,640

Expected PW Eq:

$$0 = -100,000 + 70,000(P/F_{18.7,1})\overset{0.8425}{}(.3) + (3,750X-19,600)(P/F_{18.7,1})\overset{0.8425}{}(.7)$$

$$+ (3,881X+1,640)(P/F_{23.2,1})\overset{0.8117}{}(P/F_{18.7,1})\overset{0.8425}{}(.7)$$

X = $18.55 per unit is the today's dollar selling price.

Year 1 Escalated Dollar Price is $18.55(1.25) = $23.19

Year 2 Escalated Dollar Price is $23.19(1.15) = $26.67

These breakeven selling price results are "risk adjusted" or "expected" selling prices. If seven out of every ten projects of this type are successes and three out of ten are failures with costs and revenues as projected, the calculated breakeven selling prices will give the investor an average 12% constant dollar DCFROR.

EXAMPLE 9-7 Breakeven Acquisition Cost Valuation of a Petroleum Joint Venture Project

An independent petroleum producer (investor) has the opportunity to participate in the joint venture development of an oil well. The well has several potentially productive zones and the operator feels the well has a 100% probability of successfully generating crude oil production of 36,000 barrels in year 1, 24,000 barrels in year 2, 12,000 barrels in year 3, with the well expected to be shut in at the end of year 3. However, the potential production zones differ significantly in depth so drilling, fracturing and well completion costs could vary over a wide range, depending on the zone(s) completed. You have been asked to calculate the maximum breakeven tangible and intangible well costs that the independent producer could incur and realize a 15% escalated dollar DCFROR on invested capital for the following assumptions. Well development costs will be incurred at year 0 and 70% of well costs are expected to be intangible with 30% tangible. The investor will have no mineral rights acquisition cost basis. The investor will have a 50% working interest and a 36% net revenue interest over the well life. Crude oil prices are estimated to be $25 per barrel uniformly over the 3 year well producing life with total well escalated dollar operating costs of $80,000 each year. Other income is considered to exist against which to use deductions in any year and if the well is unsuccessful a writeoff will be taken on all remaining book values at year 1. The investor effective tax rate is expected to be 40%. Neglect tangible asset salvage values.

Determine the total well cost for tangible (30%) and intangible (70%) costs that will give the 50% working interest investor a 15% escalated dollar DCFROR on invested dollars.

Solution:

Let the total well drilling and completion cost equal "X" in thousands of dollars, so investor cost is 0.5X with a 50% working interest.

Tangible Well Cost = (0.3)(0.5X) = 0.15X

Intangible Well Cost = (0.7)(0.5X) = 0.35X

Use Table 7-3, Modified ACRS depreciation rates times .15X to get annual depreciation assuming the well goes into service in year 1.

Cash Flow Calculations in Thousands of Dollars

Year	0	1	2	3
Total Revenue		900	600	400
Work Int Revenue (36%)		324	216	144
-Work Int Op Costs		-40	-40	-40
-Depreciation		-.02144X	-.03674X	-.02624X
-Writeoff				-.06559X
-IDC's	-.35X			
Inc. Before Depl	-.35X	284-.02144X	176-.03674X	104-.09183X
Percent Depletion		-48.6	-32.4	-21.6
50% Limit Test - Make Later				
Taxable Income	-.35X	235.4-.02144X	143.6-.03674X	82.4-.09183X
Tax a 40%	.14X	-94.1+.00858X	-57.4+.01470X	-33.0+.03673X
Net Income	-.21X	141.3-.01286X	86.2-.02204X	49.4-.05510X
+Depreciation		+.02144X	+.03674X	+.02624X
+Writeoff				+.06559X
+Depletion		+48.6	+32.4	+21.6
-Tangible Cost	-.15X			
Cash Flow	-.36X	189.9+.00858X	118.6+.01470X	71.0+.03673X

$$\text{PW Eq:} \quad 0 = -.36X + (189.9+.00858X)\underset{.8696}{(P/F_{15,1})} + (118.6+.01470X)\underset{.7561}{(P/F_{15,2})}$$

$$+ (71.0+.03673X)\underset{.6575}{(P/F_{15,3})}$$

$X = 950.273$ or $\$950,273$ = Total Well Cost

Checking the 50% limit on percentage depletion by inserting the breakeven cost (intangible and tangible) "X" back into the cash flow calculations to compute taxable income before depletion for calculation of the 50% limit shows that it is not a limit in years 1 and 2, but it does limit the depletion deduction in year 3. Assume that neglecting tangible asset salvage offsets the relatively small effect of the year 3 limit on percentage depletion to save the effort of iterating the calculations.

If the investor feels that total well costs will be less than $950,273, this investment appears satisfactory from an economic viewpoint for the assumptions made. The investor's 50% working interest would require incurring half of the $950,273 total cost, which is $475,136.

9.6 Comparison of Tax Deferred, Tax Free and Taxable Investments

For investors in all tax brackets *the tax deferral aspects of investments in individual retirement accounts (IRA's), tax deferred annuities and pension plans make these investments very competitive with most other taxable interest or profit generating investment opportunities. The greater the tax rate, the greater the economic advantage associated with tax deferred type of investments.* There is a 10% penalty for withdrawing funds from an IRA prior to age 59 1/2, but even with that penalty an IRA investment is very competitive with other similar non-tax deferred investments. With self-directed IRA's you can put IRA investments into common stock, real estate, or other general investments as well as bonds, debentures, and certificates of deposit. The new tax law limits eligibility for full IRA benefits to married couples with taxable income less than $40,000 per year or single persons with taxable income of $25,000 per year. IRA eligibility is phased out for the $10,000 incremental taxable income above these base salary amounts. However, if you do not participate in a qualified company pension plan, these limits do not apply. The following example demonstrates comparison of tax deferred (IRA type) investments with currently taxable investments and tax-free municipal bond investments.

EXAMPLE 9-8 Comparison of Different Types of Personal Investments

Consider the investment by an individual of $2,000 of before-tax salary income at the end of each year for the next 20 years. Assume the investor is in the 30% effective federal plus state tax bracket and compare the year 20 future after-tax cash flow generated by investing this money five different ways.

A) Put $2,000 per year into an individual retirement account (IRA) at an assumed annual interest rate of 8% in bonds or certificates of deposit. The investments are tax deductible from ordinary income each year by individuals who qualify as described preceding this example. Tax on accrued interest is deferred until the account is liquidated (assumed to be at year 20) when account value is taxed as ordinary income.

B) Put $2,000 per year into an IRA as in part "A", but the IRA investments are in common stock or mutual funds assumed to have a 12% rate of growth per year.

C) Take $2,000 of salary each year and pay the normal 30% tax which leaves $1,400 per year after-tax to invest in long term certificates of deposit or bonds like the part "A" investment earning interest at 8% per year. Tax must be paid each year on accrued interest so money grows at a 5.6% after-tax interest rate. (8%)(1 – .3 tax rate) equals 5.6% after-tax interest.

D) Take the $1,400 after-tax salary each year and invest in common stock that pays no dividends and is assumed to grow in value at 12% per year.

E) Take the $1,400 after-tax salary each year and invest in municipal bonds (interest each year is tax free). Assume a AAA municipal bond interest rate of 7% per year.

Solution:

A) Individual Retirement Account (IRA) in Bonds or C.D.'s

The advantage of IRA investments is that they keep tax dollars as well as normal after-tax investment dollars working for the investor over the 20 years. All tax on qualified investment dollars and accrued interest is deferred until liquidation date (year 20).

$$\text{IRA} \quad \underset{0 \qquad 1 \qquad 2 \;\ldots\ldots\ldots\; 20}{\overline{\begin{array}{cccc} \text{-} & \$2,000 & \$2,000 & \$2,000 \end{array}}} \quad \begin{array}{l} 45.762 \\ F = \$2,000(F/A_{8,20}) \\ = \$91,524 \end{array}$$

Year 20 Cash Flow $= \$91,524(1 - .3 \text{ tax rate}) = \$64,067$

B) Individual Retirement Account (IRA) in Stock or Mutual Funds

$$\text{IRA} \quad \underset{0 \qquad 1 \qquad 2 \;\ldots\ldots\ldots\; 20}{\overline{\begin{array}{cccc} \text{-} & \$2,000 & \$2,000 & \$2,000 \end{array}}} \quad \begin{array}{l} 72.052 \\ F = \$2,000(F/A_{12,20}) \\ = \$144,104 \end{array}$$

Year 20 Cash Flow $= \$144,104(1 - .3 \text{ tax rate}) = \$100,873$

C) Certificates of Deposit (C.D.)

$$\text{C.D.} \quad \underset{0 \qquad 1 \qquad 2 \;\ldots\ldots\ldots\; 20}{\overline{\begin{array}{cccc} \text{-} & \$1,400 & \$1,400 & \$1,400 \end{array}}} \quad \begin{array}{l} 35.298 \\ F = \$1,400(F/A_{5.6,20}) \\ = \$49,417 \end{array}$$

5.6% is the after-tax accrued interest rate.

Year 20 Cash Flow $= \$49,417$ since tax is paid yearly on both accrued interest and salary before investment.

D) Common Stock

Initial investments are in after-tax dollars so there is no tax deferral on salary. However, the increase in the value of common stock each year is not taxed until the stock is sold, when gain is taxed as ordinary income.

$$\underset{\text{Stock} \;\; 0 \qquad 1 \qquad 2 \;\ldots\ldots\ldots\; 20}{\overset{\text{Common}}{\overline{\begin{array}{cccc} \text{-} & \$1,400 & \$1,400 & \$1,400 \end{array}}}} \quad \begin{array}{l} 72.052 \\ F = \$1,400(F/A_{12,20}) \\ = \$100,873 \end{array}$$

Year 20 Cash Flow $= 100,873(1 - .3 \text{ tax rate}) = \$70,611$

E) Municipal Bond (Muni Bond)

Although initial investments are in after-tax dollars, interest is tax free (not just deferred as with an IRA). Assume interest (dividend) is reinvested each year in identical municipal bonds.

IRA

$$
\begin{array}{c|ccccc}
& \$1,400 & \$1,400 & & \$1,400 & 40.995 \\
\hline
0 & 1 & 2 & \ldots\ldots\ldots\ldots & 20 &
\end{array}
$$

$F = \$1,400(F/A_{7,20})$
$= \$57,393$

Year 20 Cash Flow = \$57,393

For the assumptions made for this comparison, the greatest year 20 cash flow is generated by the IRA investment in common stock with the non-tax deferred common stock investments second best. Note that for either common stock or bond and C.D. type investments, tax deferred IRA type investments generate greater future value than the non-tax deferred investments. Many people would feel that there is greater risk associated with common stock investments compared to bonds and certificates of deposit, but as interest rates have dropped precipitously in the mid 1980's more and more investors have been willing to accept the higher risk of common stock investments in an effort to get the potentially higher return on invested capital.

9.7 International Project Evaluation Considerations

Companies, individuals and governments invest and sell products outside their own countries for many different reasons. Reduction of operating costs, penetration of international markets, hedging against currency exchange rate variations, and improvement of technical service to international customers are some of the reasons. Whether you are evaluating international investments from the viewpoint of a domestic U.S. company considering investing or selling product in another country or from the viewpoint of a foreign company considering investing or selling product in another country, *two international evaluation considerations that are not present in domestic evaluations must be given serious attention. First, projecting currency exchange rates for each year of the life of projects to be evaluated is a major uncertainty in international investment or sales agreement evaluations.* Whether you are investing or selling in a foreign market, you must project currency exchange rates over the life of projects to make a valid economic analysis of these investments. Projecting exchange rates involves significant uncertainty and probably is at least as difficult as projecting selling prices for crude oil, gold and other minerals and commodities. *Second, foreign investment projects must be evaluated after-tax using the tax law of the country in which the investment is located.* The following example illustrates these considerations for a hypothetical Australia mining project analysis with mineral product being sold internationally in U.S. dollar denominated contracts.

EXAMPLE 9-9 An International Project Analysis

An Australian company is considering acquisition and development of a small coal property in Queensland, Australia. All project costs will be incurred in Australian dollars but revenues will be realized in U.S. dollars based on contracts with companies in Japan. (Many international contracts are based in U.S. dollars even when U.S. companies are not involved.) The mineral rights acquisition cost for the property will be $10 million Australian (A) at year 0. Mine equipment cost of $30 million A will be incurred at year 0, along with overburden stripping mineral development costs of $6 million A at year 0 and $4 million A at year 1. Working capital cost requirements are estimated to be $2 million A at year 0. Coal reserves are estimated to be 4 million tons to be produced uniformly over years 1 through 4. Coal will be sold under long-term contract at $40.00 U.S. per ton in year 1 with escalation of operating costs and severance type state taxes each year assumed to be offset by escalation of coal revenues. Mining operating costs and transportation costs are estimated to be $15 A per ton of coal produced. A state severance tax of 8% of coal revenues will apply to all production. Final year 4 working capital return and salvage value of equipment is estimated to be $5 million A. The Australia corporate income tax rate is 49% and other income is assumed to exist against which to use deductions in any year. Mining equipment is depreciable straight line over 5 years starting in year 0 with a half year deduction. Assume a writeoff on remaining book value at the end of year 4. Mineral rights acquisition and mineral development costs are deductible starting with production in year 1 by straight line over 10 years or the shortest estimate of producing mine life, whichever is lesser. As in the U.S., working capital is deductible only against working capital return. Assume an exchange rate of $0.70 U.S. per $1.00 A over the 4 year project life for the base analysis and evaluate DCFROR and NPV for a minimum DCFROR of 15%, working in Australian dollars. Then look at the sensitivity of the Australian dollar strengthening to $0.85 U.S. per $1.00 A over the project life, and weakening to $0.55 U.S. per $1.00 A over the project life.

Solution, All Values in Millions of Australian Dollars:

It is common, but not necessary, to make investment analyses using the currency of the country in which the project occurs. Most costs are generally expressed in terms of that currently (and therefore most tax deductions) so only revenue from foreign sales needs to be converted to the home country currency. This analysis is done in Australian dollars.

Equipment Depreciation:

```
(1/5)(30)(1/2) = 3.0 in year 0
(1/5)(30)      = 6.0 in years 1, 2, 3 & 4
Book Value Writeoff = 3.0 taken in year 4.
```

Acquisition Cost/Mineral Development Deduction:

(1/4)(20) = 5.0 in years 1, 2, 3 & 4.

Revenue Per Year:

(1 million tons)($40.00 U.S.)($1.00 A/$0.70 US) = $57.1 A

Year	0	1	2	3	4
Revenue		57.1	57.1	57.1	62.1*
-State Severance Tax		-4.6	-4.6	-4.6	-4.6
-Operating Expenses		-20.0	-20.0	-20.0	-20.0
-Depreciation	-3.0	-6.0	-6.0	-6.0	-9.0
-Working Cap Bk Value					-2.0
-Acq/Development		-5.0	-5.0	-5.0	-5.0
Taxable Income	-3.0	21.5	21.5	21.5	21.5
-Tax @ 49%	1.5	-10.5	-10.5	-10.5	-10.5
Net Income	-1.5	11.0	11.0	11.0	11.0
+Depreciation	3.0	6.0	6.0	6.0	9.0
+Working Cap Bk Value					2.0
+Acq/Development		5.0	5.0	5.0	5.0
-Capital Costs	-48.0**	-4.0			
Cash Flow	-46.5	18.0	22.0	22.0	27.0

*Includes salvage and working capital return.

**Capital costs are $30 equipment, $10 mineral rights, $6 development and $2 working capital

DCFROR = 29.8% and NPV @ 15% = +15.7 A, for $0.70 U.S. per $1.00 A.

Now change the exchange rate to $0.85 U.S. per $1.00 A over the project life (based on significant strengthening of the Australian dollar against the U.S. dollar).

New Revenue Per Year: (1 million tons)($40.00 U.S.)($1.00 A/$0.85 US) = $47.1 A which is a reduction of $10 A revenue each year from $57.1 A. Severance tax each year reduces to $3.8 A from $4.6 A, giving a net reduction in before-tax cash flow of $9.2A per year (in millions of dollars). This reduces income tax each year by (.49)(9.2) = 4.5 which results in annual net reduction in after-tax cash flow of 9.2 − 4.5 = $4.7 A. The new cash flow stream is:

Year	0	1	2	3	4
Cash Flow	-46.5	13.3	17.3	17.3	22.3

DCFROR = 17.2% and NPV @ 15% = +2.3 A, for $0.85 U.S. per $1.00 A.

Now change the exchange rate to $0.55 U.S. per $1.00 A over the project life (based on significant weakening of the Australian dollar against the U.S. dollar).

New Revenue Per Year: (1 million tons)($40.00 U.S.)($1.00 A/$0.55 US) = $72.7 A which is an increase of $15.6 A from base case revenue of $57.1 A. Severance tax each year increases to $5.8 A from $4.6 A, giving a net increase in before-tax cash flow of $14.4 A per year. This increases income tax each year by (.49)(14.4) = 7.1 which results in annual net increase in after-tax cash flow of 14.4 − 7.1 = $7.3 A. The new cash flow stream is:

Year	0	1	2	3	4
Cash Flow	-46.5	25.3	29.3	29.3	34.3

DCFROR = 48.2% and NPV @ 15% = +36.5 A, for $0.55 U.S. per $1.00 A.

You can see by comparison of results that changes in the exchange rate cause a very significant impact on the results of this international investment analysis. Note that weakening of the domestic (Australia) currency has enhanced investment economics for the domestic company selling in a foreign country and vice versa. Investors must be aware of these currency fluctuation impacts to survive in the international investment arena today.

9.8 Net Income Analysis Compared to Cash Flow Analysis

Before discounted cash flow analysis received industry acceptance around the world as the standard basis for economic analysis of investments, net income rather than cash flow was the basis for rate of return analysis of investments. There are several old rate of return analysis techniques and all are based on looking at various ratios of annual or average net income divided by either cumulative initial investment cost, average investment cost, or remaining book value of investment costs. Using net income as the basis for investment analysis implicitly treats depreciation, amortization and depletion like all other tax deductions, that is as out of pocket costs. Of course depreciation, amortization and depletion are not out of pocket annual costs and it can be very misleading to treat them as such for evaluation purposes. The following simple example introduces and illustrates two net income based rate of return definitions and calculations in comparison with DCFROR. More than twenty years ago these two net income based ROR techniques were the most widely used economic evaluation techniques.

EXAMPLE 9-10 Net Income Based ROR Analysis Compared to DCFROR

A depreciable investment expected to cost $10,000 is projected to generate revenues of $9,400, $8,400, $7,400, $6,400 and $5,400 at each of years 1 through 5 respectively with zero salvage value at year 5. Operating costs are expected to be $3,500 each year. The $10,000 investment will be depreciated straight line over a 5 year life starting in year 0 with the half year convention utilized. Make two analyses for:

A) The $10,000 investment is a single year 0 cost.

B) The $10,000 investment is incurred uniformly, $2,500 per year, over years −3, −2, −1 and 0.

The income tax rate is 40%. Assume other income exists against which to use deductions in the year incurred. Calculate DCFROR, Accounting ROR, and Average ROR on Initial Investment. The Accounting and Average ROR techniques are defined in the solution to this example.

Solution, All Values are Expressed in Thousands of Dollars:

The first thing that must be done for either net income or cash flow based economic analysis is to calculate after-tax net income and cash flow.

Year	0	1	2	3	4	5
Revenue		9.4	8.4	7.4	6.4	5.4
-Oper Costs		-3.5	-3.5	-3.5	-3.5	-3.5
-Depreciation	-1.0	-2.0	-2.0	-2.0	-2.0	-1.0
Taxable	-1.0	3.9	2.9	1.9	0.9	0.9
-Tax payment	0.4	-1.6	-1.2	-0.8	-0.4	-0.4
Net Income	-0.6	2.3	1.7	1.1	0.5	0.5
+Depreciation	1.0	2.0	2.0	2.0	2.0	1.0
-Capital Costs	-10.0					
Cash Flow	-9.6	4.3	3.7	3.1	2.5	1.5

DCFROR Analysis

PW Eq: $0 = -9.6 + 4.3(P/F_{i,1}) + 3.7(P/F_{i,2}) + 3.1(P/F_{i,3})$

$$+ 2.5(P/F_{i,4}) + 1.5(P/F_{i,5})$$

By trial and error, i = DCFROR = 21.6%

Accounting ROR Analysis

Accounting ROR is also called "Return on Capital Employed (ROCE), Return on Assets (ROA), and Return on Equity (ROE). Accounting ROR equals net income each year divided by the remaining investment value that has not been deducted for tax purposes (book value) each year. Using net income as the bottom line number rather than cash flow as the basis for the analysis of projects implicitly treats depreciation, amortization and depletion tax deductions as costs each year rather than as non-cash cost deductions.

The book value used in the denominator of the accounting ROR calculations is usually an arithmetic average annual book value.

Year	0	1	2	3	4	5
Net Income		2.3	1.7	1.1	0.5	0.5
Book Value	10	9.0	7.0	5.0	3.0	1.0
Average Year Book Value		9.5	8.0	6.0	4.0	2.0
Accounting ROR %	-	24.2	21.2	18.3	12.5	25.0

Accounting ROR results in this analysis and in general are different each year. This obviously makes it physically impossible to use this evaluation technique to fairly and consistently compare the economic potential of investment alternatives. Sometimes people compare accounting ROR results for a particular project year like year 3, but that is a very arbitrary choice. *A primary use of this technique is to calculate allowed return on regulated investments. Around the world regulated utility investment return is based on the accounting ROR type calculation.*

Average ROR on Initial Investment Analysis

This technique is called the "operator method", "engineers method" and "DuPont method" in older literature. *Average ROR on Initial Investment equals arithmetic average net income over the project earning life divided by cumulative investment costs in the development years.* This technique probably was developed because investors recognized the futility of trying to use year by year accounting ROR results for economic decision-making.

$$\text{Average ROR on Initial Investment} = \frac{[(2.3 + 1.7 + 1.1 + .5 + .5)/5](100)}{10} = 12.2\%$$

This 12.2% average ROR is a "simple interest" ROR rather than a compound interest ROR because it is based on the initial investment each year rather than the remaining unamortized investment values that compound interest ROR results are based upon. Note that the 12.2% average ROR result is significantly different from the 21.5% project DCFROR.

Now if we assume the $10,000 investment cost is incurred uniformly over years -3, -2, -1 and 0 and the investment goes into service in year 0, so depreciation still starts in year 0, the net income and cash flow calculations for years 1 to 5 are the same as in the first analysis.

DCFROR Analysis for Investment Costs Over Years -3, -2, -1, 0

PW Eq: $2.5(F/A_{i,3})(F/P_{i,1}) + 2.1 = 4.3(P/F_{i,1}) + 3.7(P/F_{i,2})$

$$+ 3.1(P/F_{i,3}) + 2.5(P/F_{i,4}) + 1.5(P/F_{i,5})$$

i = DCFROR = 11.7%

Incurring the investment cost earlier to receive the same annual cash flows has lowered the DCFROR significantly to 11.7% from 21.6%. However, the Accounting ROR and Average ROR on Initial Investment results are unchanged because they do not account for the time value of money. Whether costs are incurred over several years or as a lump sum has no effect on the old analysis technique results. This is indicative of the primary reason investors in all industries have shifted from the old techniques to discounted cash flow analysis for evaluation of investment alternatives. However, *public companies still emphasize net income earnings rather than cash flow earnings in reporting company economic results to shareholders on a quarterly and annual basis. Earnings per share of common stock are net income earnings. Further, the net income reported to shareholders is calculated using different deductions than the deductions used for tax reporting purposes.* The next section discusses the rational for these differences in tax and shareholder reporting procedures.

9.9 Tax Deductions Versus Shareholder Reporting Deductions

Much has been written in recent years about the so called "growing credibility gap" business faces because of the many differences between what is permissible and done for tax accounting (tax deduction) purposes versus what is permissible and done for book accounting (shareholder reporting) purposes. It is acceptable U.S. and worldwide accounting procedure to do things differently for tax purposes and book purposes in the accounting for various types of costs. There are innumerable legitimate reasons for doing this but it can make the meaning of reported earnings (book earnings) for a given company very questionable since there are practically an unlimited number of differences between what a company can do for tax purposes and what it can show for book purposes.

The reasons for doing things differently for tax and book purposes differ from company to company, but most often the basic motivation is to show better earnings for a given accounting period with acceptable book accounting deductions than could be shown using actual tax deductions. The justification often given for using book accounting instead of actual tax deductions is that acceptable book accounting procedures smooth out deductions by spreading cost deductions more uniformly over project life. For example, this eliminates deduction perturbations caused by accelerated depreciated or expensing exploration, development or intangible drilling costs. As the following examples show, bigger deductions for tax purposes are good in that they shelter more income from taxation, reducing taxes and giving bigger cash flow. However, this also results in smaller net income and that is the problem. Investment brokers and people all over the world have traditionally evaluated companies on a basis of net income earnings rather that cash flow. Therefore, even though corporate management knows that maximizing cash flow is what is important to the economic and financial health of a company, the same corporate management must be concerned with the public's opinion of its company and this forces management to use acceptable Financial Accounting Standards Board procedures to make net income earnings look as good as legitimately possible today. However, always keep in mind that you cannot get something for nothing. Using shareholder book accounting procedures, earnings are made to look better today at the potential expense of making them look poorer in the future.

Using past, present or future acceptable accounting procedures, no matter what they permit, there is no substitute for an analyst looking at present and future cash flow projections in addition to or instead of net income to analyze the growth potential of a given investment or company. The present worth of future cash flow at a specified minimum ROR for a given investment is a strong indication of the investment's value now for an investor. Net income is merely an intermediate step in obtaining cash flow and its use possibly is over-emphasized as an investment analysis tool. Keep in mind that cash flow as the basis for valid economic evaluation methods has just gained universal acceptance in the past two decades. A similar change in accounting procedures to place more emphasis on cash flow rather than, or as well as net income possibly will occur in the next decade.

Current U.S. tax law and Financial Accounting Standards Board procedures specify that for shareholder earnings calculation purposes, straight line depreciation is to be used based on lives of five years to thirty five years for personal property while asset ACRS tax depreciation lives range from 3 years to 20 years. Similarly, general development costs, mineral development costs and petroleum intangible drilling costs that are expensed for tax deduction purposes are deducted straight line or by units of production depreciation over the estimated production life of a property for shareholder earnings calculation purposes. The following example illustrates these considerations.

EXAMPLE 9-11 Public Company Tax and Shareholder Income Statements

A new company invested $440,000 last year in 5 year life depreciable assets. The assets were put into service this year and $100,000 was spent on the development of software products estimated to be saleable for the next 10 years. Sales revenue of $500,000 and operating expenses of $300,000 were realized this year. Assume the effective company income tax rate is 40% and determine the tax and shareholder report net income and cash flow for this year.

Solution, All Values in Thousands of Dollars:

	Actual Tax Base on Accelerated Deductions	Hypothetical Tax Based on St. Line 10 Yr Deprec. & Development	Shareholder Income Statement, St. Line Deductions
Revenue	500	500	500
-Oper Expenses	-300	-300	-300
-ACRS 5 Yr Deprec. on $440 ə 20%	-88		
-St. Line Deprec. on $440, 10 years		-44	-44
-Development	-100		
-Develop St Line, 10 Yr		-10	-10
Taxable Income	12	146	146
-Corp. Tax ə 40%	-5	-58	-5
-Deferred Tax			-53
Net Income	7	88	88
+Depreciation	88	44	44
+Develop, St Line		10	10
+Deferred Tax			53
-Develop. Cap. Cost		-100	-100
Cash Flow	95	42	95

Note that although cash flow is identically the same $95,000 from both tax and shareholder report calculations, the net income results are very different. Investors looking at net income earnings as a measure of economic success are likely to be more impressed with the $88,000 shareholder report net income than the $7,000 tax report net income. A caveat in the 1986 tax law change related to public company reporting now requires half of the difference between shareholder report taxable income and alternative minimum taxable income to be treated as tax preference item for corporate alternative minimum tax calculations. Many accountants feel this will significantly affect the alternative minimum tax obligations for many public companies.

Petroleum companies have two different basic book accounting approaches called "successful efforts" and "full cost" accounting that are used for handling intangible drilling cost deductions for shareholder net income earnings calculation purposes. All intangible drilling costs for both dry holes and successful wells generally are expensed for tax purposes in the year incurred (major producers expense only 70% of successful well drilling costs and amortize the other 30% over 60 months). *For shareholder earnings reporting purposes under successful-efforts accounting (used by all of the major integrated international petroleum companies), dry hole intangible drilling costs are expensed for shareholder earnings calculation purposes but successful well drilling costs are capitalized and depreciated by straight line or units of production depreciation over the life of the field or producing unit for shareholder reporting purposes. Under full-cost accounting (used by a majority of small or medium sized independent petroleum companies), for shareholder earnings calculation purposes all intangible drilling costs for both successful and unsuccessful wells are capitalized and depreciated by straight line or units of production depreciation over the life of the field or producing unit.* Full-cost accounting advocates argue that many wells, dry or not, are drilled to determine the boundaries of a particular field and should be part of the overall cost of finding oil and gas. They also assert that the full-cost method is better than the successful-efforts method in matching cost deductions and revenues.

Given the same level of exploration activity, successes, and production a company using successful-efforts accounting will report lower earnings to shareholders in the early years of projects than a full-cost company will report since a larger portion of drilling cost is written off earlier. But the same company will report higher earnings to shareholders in later years from using successful-efforts accounting in comparison to full-cost accounting which smooths the earnings more uniformly over the production life. Full-cost accounting is attractive to young exploration companies because earnings look better in the early years than they would with successful efforts accounting which helps in raising drilling venture capital. The following example illustrates these tax deductions versus shareholder book deduction concepts. Although the example relates to a petroleum company the concepts illustrated are generally applicable to public company shareholder earnings calculations in all types of industries. Think of general industry development costs or mineral development costs as equivalent to petroleum intangible drilling costs to generalize this example.

EXAMPLE 9-12 Petroleum Company Shareholder Earnings Versus Tax Earnings

A new petroleum exploration corporation has raised $2 million with a 1 million share common stock equity offering at a net $2 per share. The company has acquired the mineral rights to a property for $100,000 from a major petroleum company (so percentage depletion may not be taken on either oil or gas production) and has drilled two wells in its first year of operation. One well was a dry hole costing $100,000, the other was a producing oil well with intangible drilling costs of $120,000, tangible well and pipeline costs of $70,000, crude oil revenues of $700,000 and operating expenses of $70,000 including severance taxes. 14,000 barrels of crude oil were produced in the first year with initial producible reserves estimated to be 70,000 barrels over

7 years. Royalty owners get 15% of all crude oil revenues. Assume a 40% income tax rate and calculate the net income and cash flow this year (total and per common stock share) for: A) Normal accelerated tax deductions for an independent petroleum producer. B) Capitalize all intangible drilling costs and deduct them straight line over the 10 year estimated producing well life. Depreciate tangible costs straight line over the estimated 10 year producing well life. Use full first year straight line deductions. C) Use accelerated deductions from part "A" for tax purposes and straight line deductions from part "B" for shareholder reporting purposes. This is full-cost accounting (all drilling costs are capitalized for shareholder earnings reporting purposes) in accordance with Financial Accounting Standards Board procedures. D) Use accelerated deductions for tax purposes and straight line deductions based on successful- efforts accounting for shareholder earnings reporting purposes (expense dry hole cost but capitalize successful well drilling cost).

Solution, All Values in Thousands of Dollars:

	Tax (Accel.)	Tax (St.Line)	Shareholder (Full-Cost)	Shareholder (Success-Ef.)
Revenue	700	700	700	700
-Royalties	-105	-105	-105	-105
-Op. Costs	- 70	- 70	- 70	- 70
-IDC	-220	- 22	- 22	-112
-Depreciation	- 10	- 7	- 7	- 7
-Cost Deplet.	- 20	- 20	- 20	- 20
Taxable Income	275	476	476	386
-Tax @ 40%	-110	-190	-110	-110
-Deferred Tax			- 80	- 44
Net Income	165	286	286	232
+Depreciation	10	7	7	7
+Cost Deplet.	20	20	20	20
+Deferred Tax			80	44
+IDC	220	22	22	112
-IDC	-220	-220	-220	-220
-Tangible Costs	- 70	- 70	- 70	- 70
-Mineral Rts Cost	-100	-100	-100	-100
Net Cash Flow	25	- 55	25	25
Net Income/Share	$0.165	$0.286	$0.286	$0.232
Cash Flow/Share	$0.025	-$0.055	$0.025	$0.025

The accelerated tax deductions give smaller taxable income than straight line deductions and this yields a smaller tax obligation and bigger cash flow. Cash flow represents the net inflow or outflow of money each year so cash flow is what management wants to maximize, which is why accelerated deductions are taken for tax purposes. However, when brokers and common stock shareholders around the world talk about earnings per share of common stock they usually refer to net income earnings per share of common stock rather than cash flow earnings. When you look at net income earnings to evaluate a company you are treating deductions for depreciation, depletion and amortization as out of pocket costs in the amount deducted each year. This makes the method chosen to deduct various costs critically important to the net income earnings results that will be obtained. Taking the straight line deductions shown in the second column of the previous cash flow calculation table and using them for shareholder report earnings calculation purposes with full-cost accounting of drilling costs gives bigger net income earnings than with successful efforts accounting. The single difference between full cost and successful efforts net income calculation is in the handling of dry hole drilling cost. It must be expensed for shareholder reporting under successful efforts accounting while it is capitalized and deducted straight line under full cost accounting. Comparing the full-cost accounting net income earnings of $286,000 with the successful-efforts accounting net income earnings of $232,000 illustrates the difference for this example. Note that the net cash flow is identically $25,000 for both approaches and this is the same net cash flow obtained with accelerated deductions for tax purposes. Most companies now evaluate projects (or other companies for acquisition purposes) using annual cash flow projections over the life of projects. Unless general investors adopt this cash flow analysis approach instead of looking at point value net income earnings, it will continue to be necessary to deal with shareholder reporting calculation procedures that are different from normal tax deduction procedures. However, remember that it is what is done for tax purposes that really determines when companies or individuals realize tax savings or incur tax costs, so proper project analysis must be based on tax deduction considerations and not shareholder earnings report deduction considerations.

PROBLEMS

9-1   At the present time a company is purchasing a raw material required
       for its production operation for $0.259 per pound. Projected annual
       usage for the next 3 years is 525,000 pounds, 470,000 pounds and
       460,000 pounds respectively at years 1, 2 and 3. The company is
       considering the economic desirability of installing equipment now,
       at year 0, for a cost of $39,000 that will enable them to use a cheaper
       raw material costing $0.143 per pound. However, using the cheaper
       raw material will increase operating costs by an estimated $0.04 per
       pound. Development costs to change over to the new process are
       estimated to be $8,000 during the first year (to be expensed for tax
       purposes at the end of year 1). Equipment will be placed into service
       at the beginning of year 1 and depreciated straight line over 5 years
       with a half year deduction starting in year 1. The effective federal
       plus state tax rate is 40%.

   A) What DCFROR can be expected on the equipment and develop-
       ment cost investments to change to the cheaper raw material if a
       3 year evaluation life is used with a zero salvage value, and a
       tax writeoff is taken on the book value of the equipment at the
       end of year 3 due to scrapping it at that time.?
   B) What is the payback period?
   C) What is the constant dollar DCFROR assuming 10% inflation per
       year?

9-2   An independent petroleum company with existing petroleum produc-
       tion in excess of 1000 barrels per day acquired the mineral rights to
       a property 2 years ago for $400,000. A well was drilled in the fifth
       month of year 0 for intangible drilling costs of $600,000. Geolog-
       ical evaluation of well logs indicates that completion of the well is
       associated with a 60% probability of producing 40 barrels of crude
       per day with a price of $30 per barrel during the first year (350
       producing days) of production (assume to be year 1) with a 40%
       probability of producing nothing and realizing a net abandonment
       cost and producing equipment salvage of $100,000 income at year
       1. The new well producing equipment and tangible completion cost
       would be $200,000 at year 0 with a $100,000 intangible completion
       cost for fracturing in month 7 of year 0 if the well is completed.
       This $100,000 cost is treated as an intangible drilling cost for tax
       deduction purposes. If the well produces the revenue of 40 barrels

per day during the first year (which is estimated to be 25% of reserves) the royalty owners have offered to sign a contract giving the company the option to sell the well to the royalty owners for $350,000 cash at year 1 including all producing equipment and mineral rights. Modified ACRS depreciation over 7 years will start in year 1 with the half year convention on tangible costs. Other income and tax obligations exist against which to use the year 0 intangible drilling cost (IDC) deductions. The effective tax rate is 40% and any gain or loss on the sale is taxed or deducted as ordinary gain or loss. Royalties are 18% of crude oil revenue and production operating costs are estimated to be $60,000 in year 1. Neglect any windfall tax. For a minimum escalated dollar DCFROR of 20%, use Expected NPV Analysis to evaluate if the well should be completed or abandoned at year 0, assuming the well will be sold at year 1 if completed.

9-3   A petroleum company wants you to evaluate the economics of abandoning a stripper oil well versus selling the well to an interested investor. If the well is abandoned, a $20,000 abandonment cost must be incurred now (year 0) and a salvage value of $30,000 will be realized on the used producing equipment. $5,000 of book value remains on the producing equipment and it will be written off against the salvage value or other income at year 0 if the well is sold or abandoned. Assume other income exists against which to use deductions. The effective ordinary income tax rate is assumed to be 40%. Calculate the stripper well selling price that will make the economics of selling at year 0 a breakeven with abandonment at year 0.

9-4   A real estate broker who makes his living by buying and selling properties is evaluating the purchase of 10 acres of land for $60,000 cash now to be sold in the future for a profit. What escalated dollar sale value must the land have in 2 years to give a constant dollar investment DCFROR of 20% per year if annual inflation is projected to be 10%? Assume that the capital gain from the land sale will be taxed as ordinary income at an effective tax rate of 30%.

9-5   A company incurred a cost of $500,000 2 years ago to acquire the development rights to a property for which an offer of $1 million cash has been received now at time 0. Any gain from the sale would be taxed as ordinary income at the effective tax rate of 40%. Development of the property would generate escalated dollar after-tax cash flow in millions of dollars of -1.5 in year 0 and $+1.0$, $+1.8$, $+1.2$, $+0.8$ and $+0.4$ in years 1 through 5 respectively. If the minimum escalated dollar DCFROR is 20%, should the company keep and develop the property or sell if there is considered to be a 60% probability of development generating the year 1 through 5 positive cash flow and 40% probability of failure generating zero cash flow in years 1 through 5? What development probability of success will make the economics of development a breakeven with selling?

9-6   A corporation has an investment opportunity that will involve a time zero $100,000 depreciable cost for machinery and equipment. It will be depreciated starting in year 1 with an additional machinery and equipment expenditure of $50,000 incurred in year 1. Use 7 year life modified ACRS depreciation for all equipment with the half year convention in the first year. Working capital investment of $25,000 is required at time zero. Income attributed to these investment is $200,000 in year 1 and $280,000 per year in years 2 and 3. Operating costs are estimated to be $140,000 the first year and $190,000 per year in years 2 and 3. The effective tax rate is 40%. It is estimated that the business developed by this investment can be sold at the end of year 3 for $250,000 (including equipment and working capital). What discounted cash flow rate of return would be earned by this investment opportunity? What additional development cost could be incurred and expensed for tax purposes against other income at year 0 and still obtain a 15% DCFROR on invested dollars?

9-7   An individual investor is evaluating the purchase of 100 acres of land today for $100,000. The investor expects to be able to sell the land 3 years from now for $250,000. The investor wants to know the escalated dollar DCFROR on invested dollars that she can expect to receive on this investment. Gain from the sale should be assumed to be individual long term capital gain, taxed at the effective ordinary income tax rate assumed to be 30%. Property tax costs of $2,500 in each of years 1, 2 and 3 are assumed to be expensed against other ordinary income each year including year 3. After determining the escalated dollar DCFROR on invested dollars, determine the equivalent constant dollar DCFROR if inflation is assumed to be 8% per year over the 3 year investment life.

9-8   An individual has $100,000 to invest and is considering two ways of investing it. Using a 10 year economic evaluation life you are asked to analyze the investments to select the best investment alternative using after-tax year 10 future value analysis. Assume the individual has a 30% effective federal plus state tax rate. The investment alternatives are as follows: 1) buy common stock projected to grow at an average before-tax rate of 10% per year over the next 10 years. Ordinary income tax applies to the sale value 10 years from now. The stock is assumed to pay no annual dividends, 2) buy a new 10 year life corporate bond with a 10% annual dividend rate and reinvest dividends as received in a bond fund account projected to pay an average annual before-tax interest rate of 10% per year. Account for the payment of tax on bond dividend income annually. After making the analysis requested determine the common stock before-tax rate of growth that would make the two investments economically equivalent.

9-9   The investment of $500,000 at time zero for depreciable machinery and equipment will generate sales revenues for 5 years that increase by a constant arithmetic gradient of $10,000 each year to exactly offset escalation of operating costs each year which start at $50,000 per year in year 1 and increase $10,000 per year. The initial investment will be depreciated over 7 years using modified ACRS depreciation starting in year zero with the half year convention. Assume a zero salvage value. The effective income tax rate is 40%. What breakeven sales revenue is needed each year to yield a 25% DCFROR on investment dollars?

9-10   Project costs, sales and salvage value for a 6 year life processing plant are shown on the diagram in thousands of dollars. Assume costs and revenues are in escalated dollars and assume a washout of escalation of operating costs and sales revenue in each of revenue-producing years 2 through 6.

```
                      C_Work Cap =$200
                          C_Equip =$500      Sales/Year=$900 ..... $900
  C_Res=$100           C_Develop =$300       O.C./Year=$200 ..... $200  Salvage
  ───────────────────────────────────────────────────────────────────     = $400
  0                          1                2 ............ 6
```

The salvage value is for working capital return and depreciable asset salvage. Expense research and development costs at year 0 and 1.

Assume other income exists against which to use negative taxable income in any year. Depreciate capital equipment straight line over 5 years starting in year 1 with a half year deduction. The effective income tax rate is 40%. Use an escalated dollar minimum DCFROR of 15% and:

A) Determine whether project economics are favorable using NPV analysis.

B) Determine the additional research cost in year 0 on a before-tax basis that would cause the project to have a 15% DCFROR.

C) Determine if it is economically desirable to accept an offer of 900,000 at year 1 to sell the patent rights from the year 0 research. In other words, analyze if it would be better to keep the patent rights and continue with the year 1 development or to sell at year 1. Assume sale gain would be taxed as ordinary income.

D) What patent selling price at year 1 makes selling a breakeven with development?

9-11 How are the method of analysis and NPV economic results for problem 9-10 affected if you make constant dollar analysis using 10% inflation per year and the 15% escalated dollar minimum ROR?

9-12 Evaluate the economic potential of the project described in problem 9-10 if the research at time zero has a 40% probability of success and if successful leads to the end of year 1 development, equipment and working capital costs which yield a process with a 70% probability of success that results in the year 2 through 6 sales and salvage value given. Assume that, if the year 1 investment is a failure, at the end of year 2 the working capital return of $200,000 will be realized and a writeoff of the $500,000 depreciable cost will be taken against other income. Assume that if the time zero research fails no salvage is realized.

9-13 Work problem 9-10A for the situation where sales per year are unknown instead of $900,000 per year and determine the selling price per unit for sales of 10,000 units per year to give a 15% project DCFROR. Assume that escalation of the selling price per unit after year 2 will be sufficient for sales revenue increases to washout any operating cost increases, that is, you will be calculating the year 2 breakeven selling price per unit and it will escalate in following years to cover cost increases.

9-14   It is proposed to invest $200,000 now at year zero in a facility depreciable by 7 year life modified ACRS depreciation starting in year zero with the half year convention. An additional $100,000 will be spent on research and development at year zero (expensed for tax purposes at year zero) to produce a new product. It is estimated that this facility and research work have a 60% probability of successfully producing 1000 product units per year in each of years 1, 2 and 3. At year 3 the facility is projected to become outdated and to be sold for an escalated $50,000 salvage value. The product units would sell for $280 per unit today and selling price is projected to escalate 12% in year 1, 10% in year 2 and 8% in year 3. Operating costs are to be incurred in years 1, 2 and 3 and are estimated to be $40 per unit today in year 0 and to escalate 10% per year. If the project fails, assume the facility will be sold at year 1 for an escalated $100,000 salvage value with a writeoff taken on the remaining book value at year 1. Assume that other income and tax obligations do not exist against which to use tax deductions and tax credits in year 0, but that other income will exist in year 1 against which to use possible failure writeoff deductions. Assume the effective tax rate is 40%. For a constant dollar minimum DCFROR of 10% and inflation rates of 6% in year 1, 8% in year 2 and 10% in year 3, calculate the constant dollar expected NPV for the project. Verify that escalated dollar expected NPV equals constant dollar expected NPV by calculating the escalated dollar expected NPV.

9-15   A natural gas pipeline to transport gas from a new gas well would cost our company $220,000 with operating costs of $5,000 per year projected over the 6 year project life. The XYZ Pipeline Company has a gathering line nearby and has offered to transport our gas for $0.10 per MCF (thousand cubic feet of gas) by spending $50,000 to build a gathering line to connect our well to their existing line. To determine whether $0.10 per MCF is a reasonable transport charge, calculate the breakeven price per MCF transported that would give our company a 12% DCFROR on the $220,000 pipeline investment for the following production schedule and modified ACRS depreciation for a 7 year life starting in year 1 with the half year convention

on the pipeline cost. Use mid-year average production and time value
of money factors. Assume a 40% income tax rate.

Year	0	1	2	3	4	5	6
Point Prod. MMCF/Day	10.0	6.0	4.5	3.0	2.0	1.0	0.0
Average Annual Prod.	< 8 >	<5.25 >	<3.75 >	<2.50 >	<1.50 >	< .5 >	MMCF/ Day
Annual Line Load Factor		65%	75%	75%	80%	80%	80%
Annual Prod. MMCF		1900	1440	1030	730	440	150

9-16 Development of a coal property which our corporation purchased two
years ago for a mineral rights acquisition cost of $10 million is being
reconsidered. Our company has other income and tax obligations
against which to use tax deductions in any year. Mineral development
capital of $10 million will be needed in evaluation year 0 for overbur-
den stripping with the cost considered to be incurred in the first month
of year 0. Mine equipment costs of $15 million also will be incurred
in year 0 along with $2 million cost for working capital. The mine
life is estimated to be 5 years. Mine equipment will be depreciated
over 7 years using modified ACRS rates, starting in year 0 with the
half year convention. Salvage value and working capital return will
be $5 million at the end of year 5 with any taxable gain taxed as
ordinary income. The effective tax rate is 40%. Coal reserves are
estimated to be 5 million tons and production for years 1 through 5
is projected to be 1 million tons per year. Coal selling price is estimated
to be $30 per ton in year 1, escalating 10% per year in years 2 through
5. Royalties are 8% of revenues. Mining operating costs are estimated
to be $12 per ton in year 1, also escalating by 10% per year in
following years. Calculate the project DCFROR and NPV for a
minimum DCFROR of 20% to determine if the mine development
economics are preferable to selling assuming that we have an offer
to sell the coal property at year 0 for $20 million cash with any gain
taxed as ordinary income. Calculate the sale price that will make
selling a breakeven with development.

CHAPTER 10

REPLACEMENT ANALYSIS

10.1 General Replacement Philosophy

Replacement of physical assets usually is considered for one of three general reasons: 1) the present asset is inadequate for the job, for instance, more capacity may be needed, 2) the present asset is worn out or physically impaired causing excessive maintenance or declining efficiency and, 3) the present asset is obsolete, that is, improved assets are available that do the job more efficiently.

In engineering economy literature related to replacement, the present asset sometimes is described as the "defender" and the proposed new asset is called the "challenger". This appropriately describes the alternatives in replacement studies, but whatever the alternatives are called the most important aspect concerning replacement is that it should be based on asset performance economy and not on physical deterioration. There frequently is a reluctance on the part of managers to replace physically satisfactory equipment even though economic savings will result from the replacement. Financial and intangible considerations often get entangled with the economics of the replacement of equipment. Sometimes managers state that it is not economical to replace equipment at this time when they mean that from an economic viewpoint the replacement should be made now, but because of financial and intangible considerations the replacement will be deferred. It is quite important to separate economic, financial, and intangible considerations to get the final replacement decision in proper perspective. This generally will result in more decisions based on the economic viewpoint.

Intangible replacement considerations may include the relative risks and uncertainties involved between alternatives. Economic analysis of replacement alternatives usually is based upon the assumption that risk and uncertainty are similar for the different alternatives under consideration. This may not be the case. Old assets when compared to new assets have relatively lower capital cost, shorter life and higher operating cost and, therefore, relatively lower projection risk and uncertainty. If the projected annual costs for an old and new machine that will perform the same service are equal the intangible difference in the risk between the two alternatives may sway the decision to the old asset, although that is a relative judgement on the part of the evaluator and managers involved with the decision.

Replacement analysis does not require any new engineering economy decision method techniques. The techniques of ROR, annual worth, present worth, future worth and breakeven analysis and minor variations of these methods applied after tax considerations are the decision methods used for a large majority of industrial replacement analyses. *From a practical viewpoint, you can think of all investment decisions as being replacement decisions concerning whether to replace a present asset or investment opportunity yielding some minimum rate of return with another investment that promises to give a higher return on investment* (or lower annual cost, present cost or future cost if the same service is performed). In most replacement situations such as comparing an old and a new asset the tax deduction advantages differ greatly between alternatives. In almost all cases replacement analyses should be made after tax to obtain valid decision-making results. Before-tax analysis can lead to incorrect economic decisions because tax considerations often are very different between replacement alternatives being evaluated.

10.2 Sunk Costs and Opportunity Costs Related to Replacement

As discussed earlier in Section 9.4 sunk costs are not relevant to analyses since such costs occurred in the past and cannot be altered by present or future action. The concept that past costs are not relevant to investment evaluation studies is called the "sunk cost" concept. If you buy equipment for $3,000 and use it two or three weeks before deciding you don't like it and want to sell it you may find that $2,000 is the best used equipment sales price that you can get. The $1,000 loss is a sunk cost that resulted from a poor past decision that cannot be altered by present or future action. Economic decisions related to future action should not be permitted to be affected adversely by sunk costs except for the remaining values and tax effects from the sunk costs. Example 10-2 and 10-3 illustrate these considerations, but the following paragraphs present discussion related to the concepts.

Two considerations often confusing to replacement analysts are 1) proper handling of sunk costs and 2) proper handling of opportunity costs (trade-in or second-hand sale values). Correct handling of these items is necessary for correct replacement analysis.

Sunk costs must not be considered in evaluating expected future costs of one alternative versus another. Only tax considerations that remain to be realized from sunk costs should have an effect on economic analyses involving sunk costs. This means that actual value should be used in economic analyses rather than book value whenever actual values can be obtained. Also, actual tax considerations such as tax depreciation should always be used. If a machine originally costing $5,000 has been depreciated to a book value of $3,000 and has a current salvage value of $2,000 replacement analysis of this machine must be based on the current value of $2,000 because the difference of $1,000 between book value of $3,000 and actual value of $2,000 is a sunk cost that future action will not retrieve. However, depreciation for the analysis should be based on the $3,000 book value. A tax writeoff benefit is the only potential value of a sunk cost other than salvage value. The owner has the choice of keeping the machine or holding $2,000 cash plus the potential tax writeoff benefit, not $3,000 cash equal to book value.

Trade-in value involves two sources of confusion. These occur primarily because it is possible to make valid replacement analysis either working with costs and revenues handled from the accounting "receipts and disbursements" viewpoint or from the actual valid viewpoint. It will be discussed and illustrated that either approach is valid as long as they are not mixed for different assets. First, from the accounting viewpoint, since no receipts or disbursements are necessary if an old asset is kept, nothing is paid out and analysts value the old asset at zero value for evaluation purposes. From the standpoint of calculating actual cost of service with the old asset, the asset has an actual cash value (true trade-in value or second hand market value) and that value should be used in a cost analysis, rather than zero. An example further illustrating the accountant's viewpoint using zero present value for trade-in assets will be discussed later in this chapter. Second, the trade-in value used must be the actual value of the used asset and not an artificially inflated trade-in price. If the true present value of a used asset is not used in the economic evaluation of that asset, then the economic evaluation criterion used will not reflect correctly the actual cost of using the asset for some projected future period of time.

To handle sunk costs and trade-in values correctly in replacement analyses it has been found that taking the "outsider viewpoint" helps clear the confusion regarding sunk costs and trade-in values. If you own an asset originally worth $5,000, but now depreciated to $3,000 with a present trade-in salvage value of $2,000, an outsider can see that analysis of the old asset should be based on its actual $2,000 value because that is what it is now worth regardless of whether you paid more or less for it and regardless of the amount of depreciation you may have already taken on it. After-tax analysis, however, should account for the tax deduction benefit from the full $3,000 book value as a writeoff if the old equipment is sold or traded, or as depreciation deductions if the old equipment is kept. It is also easy for the outsider to see that from an actual value analysis viewpoint the actual $2,000 value should not be considered to be zero in the analysis just because no accounting transactions are made if the old asset is kept. The outsider can see that the new asset analysis should be based on actual cash value and not a fictitious trade-in value if you want to evaluate the true cost of operating the new asset for some future period of time. You may find it helpful to think in terms of selling the old asset for $2,000 with an option to cancel the sale within 24 hours and then considering the following two alternatives: 1) apply the $2,000 to repurchase the old asset; 2) apply the $2,000 to the purchase price of a new asset. From an outsiders viewpoint you can see that the $2,000 value of the present asset (net salvage value) is really available for use by either alternative. In other words you incur an "opportunity cost" of $2,000 if you keep the old equipment instead of selling it and having $2,000 cash.

10.3 Evaluation of Alternatives That Provide The Same Service

The following examples illustrate several of the important types of service producing asset evaluation problems that confront economic evaluation analysts. The use of actual value analysis is emphasized in these examples but the accounting viewpoint or "receipts and disbursements" type of analysis is also illustrated. It is shown in Examples 10-2 and 10-3 that the same relative differences between replacement analysis alternatives exist using either actual value or accounting viewpoint analysis, so the same economic conclusion will be reached with either method.

The Example 10-1 illustrates the after-tax application of the four primary analysis methods utilized in industry practice for comparing alternatives that provide a common service. Following this example which introduces service producing after-tax analysis, examples related to replacement analysis are presented.

EXAMPLE 10-1 Service Producing Analysis Using Annual Cost, Present Worth Cost, Incremental DCFROR and NPV Methods

The installation of automated equipment costing $60,000 is proposed to reduce labor and material costs for an operation over the next four years. The equipment would be scrapped at the end of four years. Labor and maintenance operating costs with the new equipment are expected to be $10,000 in year one, $12,000 in year two, $14,000 in year three and $16,000 in year four in escalated dollars. The operating costs per year under the existing labor intensive mode of operation are projected to be $40,000 in year one, $42,000 in year two, $44,000 in year three and $46,000 in year four in escalated dollars. New equipment depreciation will be based on the modified ACRS seven year rates beginning in year 0 with the half year convention. Write off the remaining book value at the end of year 4. The effective income tax rate is 40% and minimum DCFROR is 20%. It is assumed that other income exists against which to use all deductions in the year incurred and that the alternatives will provide the same service. Evaluate the alternatives using a four year evaluation life with:

A) Incremental DCFROR Analysis
B) Incremental NPV Analysis
C) Equivalent Annual Cost Analysis
D) Present Worth Cost Analysis

Solution:

A and B) For incremental DCFROR and NPV analysis, the easiest solution approach is to examine the incremental differences between the alternatives before-tax, then account for the tax considerations on the incremental costs and savings to get after-tax costs and cash flow. This analysis approach follows:

Before-Tax Diagrams, $=$ Cost, OC $=$ Operating Cost, S $=$ Savings

	C=$60,000	OC=$10,000	OC=$12,000	OC=$14,000	OC=$16,000
New					
	0	1	2	3	4

		OC=$40,000	OC=$42,000	OC=$44,000	OC=$46,000
Old					
	0	1	2	3	4

	C=$60,000	S=$30,000	S=$30,000	S=$30,000	S=$30,000
New -Old	0	1	2	3	4

It was shown in Chapter 3 that negative incremental operating costs are the same as positive savings. The savings of $30,000 yearly are converted to cash flow, accounting for depreciation of the $60,000 investment with a writeoff of remaining book value at year 4 included in year 4 depreciation.

Incremental Cash Flow's

Year	0	1	2	3	4
Revenue		30,000	30,000	30,000	30,000
-Depreciation	-8,571	-14,694	-10,496	-7,497	-6,247
-Deprec Writeoff					-12,495
Taxable	-8,571	15,306	19,504	22,503	11,258
-Tax @ 40%	3,429	-6,122	-7,802	-9,001	-4,503
Net Income	-5,143	9,184	11,703	13,502	6,755
+Depreciation	8,571	14,694	10,496	7,497	18,742
-Capital Cost	-60,000				
Cash Flow	-56,571	23,878	22,198	20,999	25,497

PW Eq: $0 = -56,571 + 23,878(P/F_{i,1}) + 22,198(P/F_{i,2})$

$$+ 20,999(P/F_{i,3}) + 25,497(P/F_{i,4})$$

i = Incremental Investment DCFROR = 22.9%

Compared to i^* = 20% in escalated dollars, this is a slightly satisfactory incremental investment, indicating accept the new equipment. Getting 22.9% DCFROR is slightly better than getting a 20% DCFROR in other projects. (Note that if you make a before-tax analysis, the $30,000 savings per year give a 34.9% before-tax ROR on the $60,000 initial investment which possibly could lead to a different economic conclusion, depending on the before-tax minimum ROR used. Analyses must always be done after-tax to be valid.) NPV analysis verifies the DCFROR results:

NPV @ i^* = 20%:

$$-56,571 + 23,878(P/F_{20,1}) \overset{.8333}{} + 22,198(P/F_{20,2}) \overset{.6944}{}$$

$$+ 20,999(P/F_{20,3}) \overset{.5787}{} + 25,497(P/F_{20,4}) \overset{.4823}{} = +3,190$$

An NPV result of $+3,190$ is greater than zero and satisfactory, again indicating slight economic advantage to accepting the new equipment.

C and D) For cost analysis on a present, annual or future basis, we must convert the operating costs and depreciation deductions to after-tax cash flow, which accounts for the tax savings from using these items as tax deductions. Then we can calculate the after-tax present worth and annual worth costs for each alternative. Remember, it is assumed other income exists against which to use all deductions.

New Machine Cash Flows and Cost Analysis

Year	0	1	2	3	4
Revenue					
-Oper Costs		-10,000	-12,000	-14,000	-16,000
-Depreciation	-8,571	-14,694	-10,496	-7,497	-6,247
-Deprec Writeoff					-12,495
Taxable	-8,571	-24,694	-22,496	-21,497	-34,742
-Tax @ 40%	3,429	9,878	8,998	8,599	13,897
Net Income	-5,143	-14,816	-13,497	-12,898	-20,845
+Depreciation	8,571	14,694	10,496	7,497	18,742
-Capital Cost	-60,000				
Cash Flow	-56,571	-122	-3,002	-5,401	-2,103

$$\text{PW Cost}_{NEW} = 56,571 + 122\overset{.8333}{(P/F_{20,1})} + 3,002\overset{.6944}{(P/F_{20,2})}$$

$$+ 5,401\overset{.5787}{(P/F_{20,3})} + 2,103\overset{.4823}{(P/F_{20,4})}$$

$$= \$62,898$$

$$AC_{NEW} = 62,898\overset{.3863}{(A/P_{20,4})} = \$24,297$$

The sign convention used in both the present worth cost and annual cost calculations is that negative cash flow is equivalent to a positive cost and positive cash flow is equivalent to a negative cost.

Old Machine Cash Flows and Cost Analysis

Year	0	1	2	3	4
Revenue
-Oper Costs		-40,000	-42,000	-44,000	-46,000
Taxable		-40,000	-42,000	-44,000	-46,000
-Tax @ 40%		16,000	16,800	17,600	18,400
Net Income		-24,000	-25,200	-26,400	-27,600
-Capital Costs
Cash Flow		-24,000	-25,200	-26,400	-27,600

$$\overset{.8333}{} \qquad \overset{.6944}{} \qquad \overset{.5787}{}$$
$$PWCost_{OLD} = 24,000(P/F_{20,1}) + 25,200(P/F_{20,2}) + 26,400(P/F_{20,3})$$

$$\overset{.4823}{} $$
$$+27,600(P/F_{20,4}) = \$66,088$$

$$\overset{.3863}{} $$
$$AC_{OLD} = 66,088(A/P_{20,4}) = \$25,530$$

Since annual cost results are obtained by taking present worth cost results for both alternatives times the same capital recovery factor, clearly the results of either cost analysis must give the same economic conclusion. Comparison of the new and old equivalent annual costs or present worth costs gives the same economic decision reached with incremental DCFROR and NPV analysis. The results for all four methods show slight economic advantage to the new alternative. Notice that the difference between the present worth cost results gives the identical $3,190 incremental difference that we got with incremental NPV analysis, giving further indication and proof of the relationship between the different methods of analysis and why they all consistently give the same economic conclusion.

EXAMPLE 10-2 Replacement Involving Sunk Cost and Opportunity Cost

Equipment that cost $7,000 two years ago has been depreciated to its present book value of $4,900 using straight line depreciation for a 5 year life with a half year 1 deduction. The present net salvage value of equipment is $3,500 (sale value minus removal costs) and operating costs for the next four years for which the equipment is needed are expected to be $3,000, $3,300, $3,600 and $3,900 respectively. The old equipment would have zero salvage value in four years. Consideration is being given to selling the existing old equipment and replacing it with new equipment that costs $9,000 and would be depreciated over seven years using the modified ACRS depreciation starting in year 1 with the half year convention. A writeoff on remaining book value would be taken at the end of year four when the asset is scrapped for a $0 salvage value. Operating costs with the new equipment are estimated to be $1,000, $1,100, $1,200 and $1,300 per year respectively over the next four years. Assume a 40% effective income tax rate and that other income exists against which to use tax deductions in any year. Also assume that the alternatives provide the same service. Use present worth cost analysis to compare the alternatives for a minimum escalated dollar DCFROR of 15%.

Solution:

When sunk costs and trade-in values are involved in economic analyses, as they usually are in replacement analyses, there are three different, equivalent, equally valid ways of handling the year 0 dollar values for correct economic analysis results. These three ways will be called Cases 1, 2 and 3.

	Actual Value Viewpoints		Accounting Viewpoint
	CASE 1	CASE 2	CASE 3
OLD	C=3500+560 tax saving	C=3500	C=0
	0 Book Value = 4900	0 Book Value = 4900	0 Book Value = 4900
NEW	C=9000	C=9000-560 tax saving	C=9000-560-3500=4940
	0 Book Value = 9000	0 Book Value = 9000	0 Book Value = 9000

The $7,000 cost of the old asset 2 years ago is a sunk cost that does not affect the analysis except for the tax effects of remaining tax book value of $4,900 yet to be deducted by depreciation. The $560 year 0 tax saving if the old asset is sold results because the sale value is proposed to be $1,400 less than the remaining tax book value ($3,500 sale value − $4,900 book value). This $1,400 loss would be written off against other income saving $560 in tax for the stated 40% effective income tax rate.

In Case 1, which represents "actual values", the $3,500 sale value and $560 tax savings from the writeoff if the old asset is sold are treated as opportunity costs incurred by the owner if the old asset is kept instead of being sold. If the owner passes up the opportunity to sell the old asset in order to keep and use it he forgoes receiving the $4,060 cumulative sale and tax benefits, so this is a real cost, commonly called an opportunity cost" for keeping and using the old equipment.

Case 2 is a variation of Case 1 based on handling the $560 tax saving as a reduction in the net cost of the new alternative instead of an additional opportunity cost associated with the old asset. Subtracting $560 from both Case 1 alternatives at year 0 gives Case 2.

Case 3 commonly is called the "accounting viewpoint" and it represents the net inflows and outflows of money (receipts and disbursements) if the old or new assets are utilized.

Notice the incremental New-Old year 0 cost is $4,940 for all cases, so incremental DCFROR, NPV or PVR analysis results would be identical for Cases 1, 2 and 3. With cost analysis, since both alternatives differ by the same values at year 0 as you go from Case 1,to Case 2,to Case 3, the alternatives are ranked the same with present, annual or future cost results for any of the 3 cases, since the year 1 through 4 operating cost, depreciation and salvage values are exactly the same for all cases. For example in the following cash flow analysis for the "OLD" machine the year 1 through 4 operating cost and depreciation deducations are the same whether year 0 values are handled using the Case 1, 2 or 3 dollar values. The same is true for the "NEW" analysis.

Old Machine Cash Flows

Year	0	0	0	1	2	3	4
Revenue							
-Oper Costs				-3.0	-3.3	-3.6	-3.9
-Depreciation				-1.4	-1.4	-1.4	-0.7
Taxable				-4.4	-4.7	-5.0	-4.6
-Tax @ 40%				1.8	1.9	2.0	1.8
Net Income				-2.6	-2.8	-3.0	-2.8
+Depreciation				1.4	1.4	1.4	0.7
-Capital Costs	-4.1	-3.5					
Cash Flow	-4.1	-3.5	0.0	-1.2	-1.4	-1.6	-2.1

$$\text{PW Cost, Case 1} = 4.1 + 1.2\overset{.8696}{(P/F_{15,1})} + 1.4\overset{.7561}{(P/F_{15,2})}$$

$$+ 1.6\overset{.6575}{(P/F_{15,3})} + 2.1\overset{.5718}{(P/F_{15,4})} = 8.45$$

PW Cost, Case 2 = 7.85

PW Cost, Case 3 = 4.35

Note that going from Case 1 to Case 2 reduces the present worth cost by the $600 difference in the year 0 Case 1 capital cost of $4,100 and the year 0 Case 2 capital cost of $3,500. A similar reduction of $3,500 occurs in going from Case 2 to Case 3. The same differences occur in present worth cost results for the New Machine Case 1, 2 and 3 analyses shown on the next page.

New Machine Cash Flows

Year	0	0	0	1	2	3	4
Revenue							
-Oper Costs				-1.0	-1.1	-1.2	-1.3
-Depreciation				-1.3	-2.2	-1.6	-1.1
-Deprec Writeoff							-2.8
Taxable				-2.3	-3.3	-2.8	-5.2
-Tax @ 40%				0.9	1.3	1.1	2.1
Net Income				-1.4	-2.0	-1.7	-3.1
+Depreciation				1.3	2.2	1.6	3.9
-Capital Costs	-9.0	-8.4	-4.9				
Cash Flow	-9.0	-8.4	-4.9	-0.1	0.2	-0.1	0.8

$$\text{PW Cost, Case 1} = 9.0 + 0.1\overset{.8696}{(P/F_{15,1})} - 0.2\overset{.7561}{(P/F_{15,2})} + 0.1\overset{.6575}{(P/F_{15,3})}$$

$$- 0.8\overset{.5718}{(P/F_{15,4})} = 8.54$$

PW Cost, Case 2 = 7.94

PW Cost, Case 3 = 4.44

The very slight present worth cost advantage of $90 is favorable to the "Old" alternative for all three cases although it is apparent that these results are really a breakeven.

If you increase the minimum DCFROR in this analysis or any other comparison of either service producing or income producing alternatives, the more capital intensive alternative (New in this analysis) is always hurt more relative to the less capital intensive alternative with the smaller year 0 cost. To illustrate, change i* to 25% from 15% for this analysis and note how the present worth costs change for Case 1 results.

$$\text{PW Cost}_{OLD}, \text{Case 1} = 4.1 + 1.2\overset{.8000}{(P/F_{25,1})} + 1.4\overset{.6400}{(P/F_{25,2})} + 1.6\overset{.5120}{(P/F_{25,3})}$$

$$+ 2.1\overset{.4096}{(P/F_{25,4})} = 7.63$$

$$\text{PW Cost}_{NEW}, \text{Case 1} = 9.0 + 0.1\overset{.8000}{(P/F_{25,1})} - 0.2\overset{.6400}{(P/F_{25,2})} + 0.1\overset{.5120}{(P/F_{25,3})}$$

$$- 0.8\overset{.4096}{(P/F_{25,4})} = 8.67$$

Notice now that the present worth cost advantage of the old equipment compared to the new has spread from $90 to $1,040.

10.4 Evaluation of Alternatives that Provide Different Service

When different service producing alternatives are projected to give different service per day, week or year (or other periods), it is necessary to get the alternatives on a common service-producing basis per period (as well as for a common evaluation life) before comparing the economics of the alternatives. The need to do this is tied to the assumption that extra service produced by an alternative (or alternatives) can be utilized. If the extra service cannot be utilized, the alternatives must be compared economically using the project costs as they are stated without adjustment, which has been the basis for most service-producing analyses done previously in the text.

However, if the extra service can be utilized, get alternatives that provide different service on a common service producing basis using one of the following approaches:

1. Add additional costs to the less productive alternative or alternatives to get service produced equivalent to the most productive alternative. Adjust all values including capital costs, operating costs, major repairs and salvage values.

2. Compare the less productive alternative or alternatives costs with the appropriate fraction of the more productive alternative costs. Adjust all values including capital costs, operating costs, major repairs and salvage values.

3. Charge the less productive alternative with a lost productivity opportunity cost from lower production or lower quality product that will be incurred if the less productive alternative is used. This opportunity cost represents projected lost or deferred profits.

While few people would neglect to account for different capacities of different sized assets such as haul trucks, compressors, or heat exchangers in economic analyses, the same people will often forget to account for differences in operating hours of service or number of units to be produced per period with the old assets compared to new. The following example relates to comparison of service producing assets with the potential to provide different service.

EXAMPLE 10-3 Analysis of Alternatives That Provide Different Service

Three existing two year old machines have an open market sale or trade-in value of $65,000 each and remaining tax book value of $25,000 each. Replacement of the three existing machines with two new machines that each give 150% of the productivity per machine being realized with each old machine is being considered. The new machines would cost $120,000 each. The service of either the old or new machines is needed for the next four years so a four year evaluation life should be used. If the old machines are kept, remaining book value will be depreciated straight line at years 1 and 2. Salvage value of the old machines in four years from now is estimated to be zero but the machines are considered to be operable for four more years. Escalated dollar operating costs per machine for the old machines are projected to be $30,000 in year one, $35,000 in year two, $40,000 in year three and $45,000 in year four. Operating cost per machine for new machines is to be $25,000 in year one, $30,000 in year two, $35,000 in year three and $40,000 in year four.

The new machines would be depreciated using modified ACRS 7 year life depreciation starting in year 1 with the half year convention. Salvage value is estimated to be $30,000 per machine in year four and taxable gain is taxed as ordinary income. The effective federal plus state tax rate is 40%. Other income exists against which to use all tax deductions in the year incurred. The minimum DCFROR is 15%. Evaluate whether the old machines should be replaced using present worth cost analysis.

Solution, All Values in Thousands of Dollars:

	Actual Value Viewpoints		Accounting Viewpoint
	CASE 1	CASE 2	CASE 3
"3" OLD	C=195-48 tax if sold	C=195	C=0
	0 Book Value = 75	0 Book Value = 75	0 Book Value = 75
"2" NEW	C=240	C=240+48 tax if sold	C=240+48-195=93
	0 Book Value = 240	0 Book Value = 240	0 Book Value = 240

The $48 tax if the 3 old assets are sold is based on taxing the $120 capital gain ($195 sale value − $75 book value) as ordinary income (taxed at the effective income tax rate of 40%).

The year 1 to 4 cash flow calculations for the OLD and NEW alternative are the same for each case. Only the year 0 costs differ from case to case. Also, notice the incremental NEW-OLD cost of $93 is identical for each case.

3 Old Machine Cash Flows

Year	(Case 1) 0	1	2	3	4
Revenue					
-Oper Costs		-90	-105	-120	-135
-Depreciation		-37.5	-37.5		
Taxable		-127.5	-142.5	-120	-135
-Tax @ 40%		51	57	48	54
Net Income		-76.5	-85.5	-72	-81
+Depreciation		37.5	37.5		
-Capital Costs	-147				
Cash Flow	-147	-39	-48	-72	-81

$$\text{Case 1 PW Cost}_{OLD} = 147 + 39\overset{.8696}{(P/F_{15,1})} + 48\overset{.7561}{(P/F_{15,2})} + 72\overset{.6575}{(P/F_{15,3})}$$

$$+ 81\overset{.5718}{(P/F_{15,4})} = \$310.8$$

$$\text{Case 2 PW Cost}_{OLD} = \text{Case 1 PW Cost}_{OLD} + 48 = \$358.8$$

$$\text{Case 3 PW Cost}_{OLD} = \text{Case 1 PW Cost}_{OLD} - 147 = \$163.8$$

2 New Machine Cash Flow

Year	(Case 1) 0	1	2	3	4
Revenue					60
-Oper Costs		-50	-60	-70	-80
-Depreciation		-34	-59	-42	-30
-Deprec Writeoff					-75
Taxable		-84	-119	-112	-125
-Tax @ 40%		34	48	45	50
Net Income		-50	-71	-67	-75
+Depreciation		34	59	42	105
-Capital Costs	-240				
Cash Flow	-240	-16	-12	-25	30

$$\text{Case 1 PW Cost}_{NEW} = 240 + \overset{.8696}{16(P/F_{15,1})} + \overset{.7561}{12(P/F_{15,2})} + \overset{.6575}{25(P/F_{15,3})}$$

$$\overset{.5718}{- 30(P/F_{15,4})} = \$262.3$$

$$\text{Case 2 PW Cost}_{NEW} = \text{Case 1 PW Cost}_{NEW} + 48 = \$310.3$$

$$\text{Case 3 PW Cost}_{NEW} = \text{Case 1 PW Cost}_{NEW} - 147 = \$115.3$$

Providing the service with the NEW machines has a $48,500 present worth cost advantage for all cases, so select NEW. Notice that if you compared 1.5 old assets to 1 new asset, the advantage is similarly favorable to the new, but by $24,250 (a factor of two difference). Similar results occur for comparison of 1 old asset with 2/3 of a new asset.

If investment tax credit (applicable to assets placed in service prior to January 1, 1986) must be recaptured at time zero upon sale of the OLD assets, this enhances the economics of keeping the OLD assets relative to the NEW assets because the extra tax reduces the opportunity cost of keeping the OLD assets relative to the NEW assets.

Note that while the accounting approach leads to correct economic decisions it does not give true equivalent annual cost. The accounting approach should not be used if you really want to know what it costs to operate equipment in addition to obtaining valid economic replacement decisions because it combines trade-in financing with cost economics.

EXAMPLE 10-4 Exchange of Old Asset Versus Separate Sale

The solutions of Example 10-3 just presented (and all other replacement analysis solutions presented in this chapter) are all based on separate sale of the old machines and separate purchase of the new machines. *If old assets actually are traded in on new assets rather than being sold separately, existing tax law permits the investor to choose either the separate sale/separate purchase handling of tax considerations or adjustment of the book value of new assets to account for the gain or loss from trade-in of the old assets* as follows for the Example 10-3 assets.

There are only two different cases for laying out the old and new alternative time diagrams for a valid trade-in exchange analysis as shown in the solution. The Case 1 situation does not exist for exchange economics of the "Old" assets because there is no tax to be paid from selling the "Old". The Case 2 and 3 analysis of the "Old" assets is the same for exchange as in separate sale, separate purchase in Example 10-3.

Solution:

    CASE 2 (Actual Value Viewpoint)   CASE 3 (Accounting Viewpoint)

"3" C=195   C=0

OLD ───────────────────────   ───────────────────────

    0 Book Value = 75   0 Book Value = 75

"2" C=240   C=240-195=45

NEW ───────────────────────   ───────────────────────

    0 Book Value = 240-195+75=120   0 Book Value = 240-195+75=120

The "OLD" present worth costs for Case 2 and 3 are identical to Case 2 and 3 present worth cost "OLD" for Example 10-3. The "NEW" cash flows for Cases 2 and 3 are based on depreciating the initial new cost reduced by trade-in gain from "OLD".

"Exchange" Analysis of 3 Old for 2 New Machines

Year	0	1	2	3	4
Revenue					60
-Oper Costs		-50	-60	-70	-80
-Depreciation		-17	-29	-21	-15
-Deprec Writeoff					-37
Taxable		-67	-89	-91	-72
-Tax @ 40%		27	36	36	29
Net Income		-40	-53	-55	-43
+Depreciation		17	29	21	52
-Capital Costs	-240				
Cash Flow	-240	-23	-24	-34	9

$$\text{Case 2 PWCost}_{NEW} = 240 + 23\overset{.8696}{(P/F_{15,1})} + 24\overset{.7561}{(P/F_{15,2})}$$

$$+ 34\overset{.6575}{(P/F_{15,3})} - 9\overset{.5718}{(P/F_{15,4})} = \$295.4$$

$$\text{Case 3 PWCost}_{NEW} = \text{Case 2 PWCost}_{NEW} - 195 = \$100.4$$

Comparison of Case 2 present worth cost "NEW" of $295.4 to equivalent present worth cost "OLD" Case 2 of $358.8 gives a $63.4 present worth cost advantage to selecting "NEW". The same result is obtained comparing Case 3 present worth cost "NEW" of $100.4 to $163.8 present worth cost of "OLD".

Exchange of assets has made the "NEW" assets relatively more desirable than the "OLD" in comparison with separate sale/separate purchase. This is because exchanging eliminates immediate tax on gain from sale of the "OLD" which increases the opportunity cost of keeping the "OLD" asset rather than disposing of it by an exchange for "NEW".

10.5 Replacement Analysis Using Breakeven Revenues Required and Breakeven Standard Costs per Unit of Service

There are two alternatives to comparing after-tax cost of service using present worth, future worth, annual worth, incremental DCFROR or incremental NPV to evaluate the economics of different ways of providing service. One alternative approach often used is to compare the breakeven revenues required each year or other period for each alternative to yield a specified minimum DCFROR. Assuming all alternatives give the same service the alternative with the minimum revenue requirement is the economic choice. Utilities commonly use this cost of service analysis approach and sometimes it is referred to by the acronym "UAERR" which stands for "Uniform Annual Equivalent Revenue Required". A second alternative approach is to compare the standard cost per unit of service for different alternative ways of providing service, calculated easiest by dividing after-tax present-worth cost of service by present-worth after-tax units of service, handling the time value of money at a specified minimum DCFROR. This technique enables evaluators to make proper analysis of different service producing alternatives that have different and changing productivity each year or other period. Example 10-5 illustrates both of these analysis approaches. However, before looking at the details of Example 10-5 one note of caution needs to be mentioned about revenue requirement calculations and the use of breakeven revenue results. *If you want to know the revenues required to cover the costs that you will have invested if you provide service in different ways, you must use actual values rather than accounting viewpoint values in your analysis calculations.* The relative differences between results will be the same using either actual values or accounting values, but only the breakeven revenues that are based on actual value analysis costs represent rental or lease values that cover your investment costs at the minimum DCFROR. *If you always use actual after-tax value analysis (which is the case one approach illustrated in Examples 10-2 and 10-3 and Case two in Example 10-4) the results will always be valid for use in determining appropriate lease or rental values as well as for comparing economic differences in alternative ways of providing a service.*

EXAMPLE 10-5 "Breakeven Revenues Required" Analysis and Breakeven Standard Costs per Unit of Service

Evaluate the old and new alternatives described in Example 10-3 using "breakeven revenue required" analysis and breakeven standard cost per unit (operating hours) of service. The problem is restated here for convenience of the reader and to add operating hours of service for each alternative in the analysis.

An existing machine has a present trade-in value of $65,000 and a remaining book value of $25,000. Replacement of the existing unit with a new machine that will provide 150% of the productivity provided by the existing machine is being considered. The service of either the old or new machine is needed for the next four years so a four year evaluation life will be used. Consider that the old machine is expected to run 2,000 hours per years and the new machine will run 3,000 hour per year which gives 150% of the old machine productivity. If the old machine is kept, the remaining book value of $25,000 will be depreciated straight line over the years 1 and 2. Salvage on the old machine is assumed to be zero four years from now. The existing machine operating costs are projected to be $30,000 in year one, $35,000 in year two, $40,000 in year three and $45,000 in year four.

The new machine, which costs $120,000, will be depreciated over a seven year modified ACRS depreciation life starting in year 1 with the half year convention. Write off the remaining book value at the end of year four. Salvage is estimated to be $30,000 at the end of year four. Operating expenses for the new machine will be $25,000 in year one, $30,000 in year two, $35,000 in year three and $40,000 in year four. The effective state and federal income tax rate is 40%. It is assumed that other income exists against which to use deductions in the year incurred and that all values are in escalated dollars. For an escalated dollar minimum DCFROR of 15%, determine whether the old machine should be replaced by the new machine. Then look at the sensitivity of the breakeven hourly cost for each machine given the following accelerated production schedule. The old machine production schedule will be 3,000 hours in year one, 2,500 hours in year two, 1,500 hours in year three and 1,000 hours in year four. The new machine production schedule will be 4,000 hours in year one, 3,500 hours in year two, 2,500 in year three and 2,000 hours in year four.

Solution, All Calculation Values in Thousands of Dollars:

Three old machines are required to provide the service equivalent to two new machines. If we calculate the breakeven uniform annual equivalent revenues required (UAERR) for one old machine and multiply the result by three, we will have a result that can be compared with two times the UAERR for one new machine for equivalent service comparison. UAERR is sometimes called the annual "standard cost of service" in service contract situations.

In terms of units of service produced by each alternative, note that 3 old machines produce 6,000 units (operating hours) of service per year and 2 new machines produce 6,000 units (operating hours) of service per year. In other analyses, units produced may represent annual product units produced, miles driven, tons hauled and so forth, instead of operating hours of service used in this example. The breakeven before-tax revenue required to cover the costs of owning and operating equipment over its useful life is presented. Time diagrams are in thousands of dollars as follows:

Year	0	1	2	3	4
OLD	C=65-16	OC=30	OC=35	OC=40	OC=45
NEW	C=120	OC=25	OC=30	OC=35	OC=40

The (-16) component of the capital cost of the old machine at year zero accounts for the tax that would have been paid had the old asset been sold. The tax cost is determined by multiplying the tax rate times sale taxable gain which is the difference between old machine opportunity sale price and its tax book value (treated here as ordinary income). Reducing the sale value by the tax on the gain yields the after-tax opportunity cost of $65 - (65 - 25)(.4) = 49$

Old Machine Breakeven Cost Per Hour Cash Flows

Year	0	1	2	3	4
Revenue		2X	2X	2X	2X
-Oper Costs		-30.0	-35.0	-40.0	-45.0
-Depreciation		-12.5	-12.5		
Taxable		2X-42.5	2X-47.5	2X-40.0	2X-45.0
-Tax @ 40%		-.8X+17.0	-.8X+19.0	-.8X+16.0	-.8X+18.0
Net Income		1.2X-25.5	1.2X-28.5	1.2X-24.0	1.2X-27.0
+Depreciation		12.5	12.5		
-Capital Costs	-49.0				
Cash Flow	-49.0	1.2X-13.0	1.2X-16.0	1.2X-24.0	1.2X-27.0

"X" is the before-tax breakeven standard cost per hour of service or breakeven revenue required per hour of service. "X" times operating hours per year is the "uniform annual equivalent revenue required".

$$\text{PW Eq: } 0 = -49 + (1.2X-13.0)\underset{.8696}{(P/F_{15,1})} + (1.2X-16.0)\underset{.7561}{(P/F_{15,2})}$$

$$+ (1.2X-24.0)\underset{.6575}{(P/F_{15,3})} + (1.2X-27.0)\underset{.5718}{(P/F_{15,4})}$$

$$103.6 = 3.426X$$

Therefore, "X" is $30.24 per hour for an old machine providing 2,000 hours of service per year for four years. Similarly, the breakeven cost per hour for the new machine is determined as follows:

New Machine Breakeven Cost Per Hour Cash Flows

Year	0	1	2	3	4
Revenue		3X	3X	3X	3X+30.0
-Oper Costs		-25.0	-30.0	-35.0	-40.0
-Depreciation		-17.1	-29.4	-21.0	-15.0
-Deprec Writeoff					-37.5
Taxable		3X-42.1	3X-59.4	3X-56.0	3X-62.5
-Tax @ 40%		-1.2X+16.9	-1.2X+23.8	-1.2X+22.4	-1.2X+25.0
Net Income		1.8X-25.3	1.8X-35.6	1.8X-33.6	1.8X-37.5
+Depreciation		17.1	29.4	21.0	52.5
-Capital Costs	-120.0				
Cash Flow	-120.0	1.8X- 8.1	1.8X- 6.2	1.8X-12.6	1.8X+15.0

$$\text{PW Eq: } 0 = -120.0 + (1.8X-8.1)(P/F_{15,1}) + (1.8X-6.2)(P/F_{15,2})$$

with factors $.8696$ and $.7561$ over the first two terms respectively

$$+ (1.8X-12.6)(P/F_{15,3}) + (1.8X+15.0)(P/F_{15,4})$$

with factors $.6575$ and $.5718$ over these two terms respectively

$$131.439 = 5.139X$$

Therefore "X" is $25.58 per hour for the new machine providing 3,000 hours of service per year for 4 years.

If it is feasible for the owner to utilize the total production capabilities of the new machine, there is a $4.66 per hour advantage to acquiring the new machine. However, if three old machines were presently performing the task, the acquisition of two new machines would result in before-tax annual savings of 6,000 hours per year times $4.66 saved per hour which is equal to $27,960 for each of four years which is equivalent to before-tax present worth savings of $79,825 (or $47,895 present worth savings after-tax).

Since the cost per operating hour of service is less with the new compared to the old, $25.58 per hour compared to $30.24 per hour, it is clear that for the same 6,000 hours of service per year, the new alternative is the economic choice. The "New UAERR" for 6,000 hours of service is $153,480 (6,000 x $25.58) and the "Old UAERR" is $181,440 (6,000 x $30.24).

It is instructive to note that after-tax annual cost of service divided by one minus the tax rate gives the same UAERR results within roundoff error accuracy, where annual cost equals present worth cost per machine times A/P$_{15,4}$, and present worth cost per machine comes from the left side of equations in this example.

$$\text{UAERR}_{OLD} = \frac{\overset{103.600 \quad .35027}{\overbrace{(\text{PW Cost})(A/P_{15,4})(3 \text{ Machines})}}}{(1 - 0.40 \text{ tax rate})} = 181.440$$

$$\text{UAERR}_{NEW} = \frac{\overset{131.440 \quad .35027}{\overbrace{(\text{PW Cost})(A/P_{15,4})(2 \text{ Machines})}}}{(1 - 0.40 \text{ tax rate})} = 153.464$$

Being able to mathematically convert cost analysis results to breakeven revenue results and vice versa proves that you must get the same economic conclusions with either method of analysis.

Breakeven standard costs per hour can be calculated a different way by dividing the present worth cost of owning and operating a machine by the present worth after-tax hours discounted at the same minimum rate of return. This implies that the hours are multiplied by one minus the tax rate, or 2,000 hours multiplied by $(1 - .4$ tax rate) for the old machine, and 3,000 hours multiplied by $(1 - .4$ tax rate) for the new machine, as follows:

Old Machine

$$103.6 \ / \ 1.2 \overset{2.855}{\overbrace{(P/A_{15,4})}} = \$30.24 \text{ per hour}$$

New Machine

$$131.44 \ / \ 1.8 \overset{2.855}{\overbrace{(P/A_{15,4})}} = \$25.58 \text{ per hour}$$

This simplified method illustrates that breakeven standard cost per hour calculations are really present worth costs divided by the present worth after-tax hours. Present worthing any series of cash flows which are derived from hourly rental or unit sales implicitly involves discounting after-tax hours or units.

This gives us a straight forward approach for comparing economic differences between service producing alternatives that have different production rates every year (or period). This cost per unit of service approach makes it much easier to evaluate the sensitivity of alternatives to variations in the hours of production per annum as illustrated in the following production schedules for this example.

Year	0	1	2	3	4
OLD, Hours		3,000	2,500	1,500	1,000
NEW, Hours		4,000	3,500	2,500	2,000

Old Machine

$103.6 / 1.8(P/F_{15,1}) + 1.5(P/F_{15,2}) + .9(P/F_{15,3}) + .6(P/F_{15,4})$

$103.6 / 3.634 = \$28.51$ per hour

New Machine

$131.44 / 2.4(P/F_{15,1}) + 2.1(P/F_{15,2}) + 1.5(P/F_{15,3}) + 1.2(P/F_{15,4})$

$131.44 / 5.347 = \$24.58$

For decreasing operating hours of service schedule, the difference in cost per hour of service between the alternatives is $28.51 − $24.58 or $3.93 per hour of service. For the uniform hours of service the difference was $30.24 − $25.58 or $4.66 per hour of service. Handling the variations in operating hours of service correctly makes the differences in cost per hour of service smaller, reducing the economic advantage of the "new" compared to the "old". This is due to the fact that the cumulative operating hours of service from the old asset (8,000 hours per machine) are being realized more rapidly (3,000 of 8,000 hours in year 1 for example) than for the new machine.

10.6 Unequal Life Service-Producing Alternatives

In Chapter 3, it was emphasized that to compare the economic differences between service-producing alternatives with unequal lives you must determine a common study period for all alternatives before you can made the analysis. This is true after-tax as well as before-tax and is illustrated in Example 10-6, which is the after-tax analysis of the same alternatives analyzed on a before-tax basis in Example 3-27 in Chapter 3.

EXAMPLE 10-6 Comparison of Unequal Life Alternatives that Provide the Same Service

Three alternative processing methods A, B and C with costs, salvage values and lives given on the time diagrams are being considered to carry out a processing operation for the next three years. It is expected that the process will not be needed after three years. A major repair costing $3,000 at the end of year two would extend life of alternative "A" through year three with a third year operating cost of $2,500 and the salvage equal to $1,000 at the end of year three instead of year two. The salvage of alternative "B" is estimated to be $3,000 at the end of year three and the salvage of alternative "C" is estimated to be $7,000 at the end of year three. For a minimum DCFROR of 15%, which alternative is economically best? Use after-tax equivalent annual cost analysis. Assume modified ACRS depreciation for a seven year life for all alternatives starting in year 0 with the half year convention. Remaining book value is deducted against other income at the end of the evaluation lives. Assume sufficient income exists against which to use all deductions in the year incurred. The effective tax rate is 40%. Assume the $3,000 major repair at the end of year two for alternative "A" is expensed at the end of year two as an operating cost. Compare the alternatives for a three year evaluation life.

```
   C=$6,000       OC=$1,500       OC=$2,000
A) ─────────────────────────────────────────   L=$1,000
   0               1               2

   C=$10,000  OC=$1,000  OC=$1,400  OC=$1,800  OC=$2,200
B) ──────────────────────────────────────────────────────  L=$2,000
   0          1          2          3          4

   C=$14,000   OC=$500   OC=$600   OC=$700   OC=$800   OC=$900
C) ──────────────────────────────────────────────────────────  L=$5,000
   0           1         2         3         4         5
```

Solution, Diagrams For a 3 Year Evaluation Life:

```
                        C=$3,000
   C=$6,000    OC=$1,500  OC=$2,000  OC=$2,500
A) ─────────────────────────────────────────   L=$1,000
   0            1          2          3

   C=$10,000  OC=$1,000  OC=$1,400  OC=$1,800
B) ─────────────────────────────────────────   L=$3,000
   0          1          2          3

   C=$14,000   OC=$500    OC=$600    OC=$700
C) ─────────────────────────────────────────   L=$7,000
   0           1          2          3
```

Case "A" Cash Flows

Year	0	1	2	3
Revenue				1,000
-Oper Costs		-1,500	-5,000	-2,500
-Depreciation	-857	-1,469	-1,050	-750
-Deprec Writeoff				-1,874
Taxable	-857	-2,969	-6,050	-4,124
-Tax @ 40%	343	1,188	2,420	1,650
Net Income	-514	-1,782	-3,630	-2,474
+Depreciation	857	1,469	1,050	2,624
-Capital Costs	-6,000			
Cash Flow	-5,657	-312	-2,580	150

$$AC_A = \{5,657 + 312(P/F_{15,1}) + 2,580(P/F_{15,2})$$
$$- 150(P/F_{15,3})\}(A/P_{15,3}) = \$3,408$$

Case "B" Cash Flows

Year	0	1	2	3
Revenue				3,000
-Oper Costs		-1,000	-1,400	-1,800
-Depreciation	-1,429	-2,449	-1,749	-1,249
-Deprec Writeoff				-3,124
Taxable	-1,429	-3,449	-3,149	-3,173
-Tax @ 40%	571	1,380	1,260	1,269
Net Income	-857	-2,069	-1,890	-1,904
+Depreciation	1,429	2,449	1,749	4,373
-Capital Costs	-10,000			
Cash Flow	-9,429	380	-140	2,469

$$AC_B = \{9,429 - 380(P/F_{15,1}) + 140(P/F_{15,2})$$
$$- 2,469(P/F_{15,3})\}(A/P_{15,3}) = \$3,320$$

Case "C" Cash Flows

Year	0	1	2	3
Revenue				7,000
-Oper Costs		-500	-600	-700
-Depreciation	-2,000	-3,429	-2,449	-1,749
-Deprec Writeoff				-4,373
Taxable	-2,000	-3,929	-3,049	178
-Tax ⌐ 40%	800	1,571	1,220	-71
Net Income	-1,200	-2,357	-1,829	107
+Depreciation	2,000	3,429	2,449	6,122
-Capital Costs	-14,000			
Cash Flow	-13,200	1,071	620	6,229

$$AC_C = \{13,200 - 1,071(P/F_{15,1}) - 620(P/F_{15,2})$$
$$- 6,229(P/F_{15,3})\}(A/P_{15,3}) = \$3,374$$

Select Case "B" with the smallest equivalent annual cost although results are effectively breakeven.

10.7 Leasing Compared to Purchasing

Leasing assets is an alternative way of providing a service compared to purchasing assets. *Economically, leasing compared to purchasing is analogous to replacement analysis. Continuing to provide service with old equipment that has high annual operating and maintenance costs is an alternative to purchasing new equipment just like leasing is an alternative to purchasing.* Lease/purchase and replacement analysis evaluations are classical time value of money analysis situations that are handled with identical evaluation procedures illustrated earlier in this chapter in Examples 10-1 through 10-6. However, sometimes there is legal uncertainty concerning whether asset property payments are to be treated as lease payment expenses for tax deduction purposes and deducted as operating expenses in the year incurred or as mortgage payments (interest and principal) to pay for purchase of a property to be depreciated. Under general income tax rules where equipment or other depreciable property is leased with an option to buy, under "operating lease" conditions the lessor (owner) is allowed depreciation and the lessee deducts lease payments as rental expense. If the lease is in substance a sale of the property, then the lease is called a "capital lease" and the lessee is required to capitalize all payments and to depreciate the leased property in lieu of deducting the payments as rental expense. For lease or rental payments to be expensed in the year incurred, a lease (operating lease) or rental must have economic substance other than tax benefits. In the absence of evidence of a true lease or rental situation agreements for the lease of property with an option to buy will be treated as purchases (capital leases) and sales if one or more of the following conditions are present:

1) portions of payments are specifically applicable to the purchase price,
2) the lessee will acquire title upon payment of a stated amount of rentals,
3) the lessee is required to pay a substantial part of the purchase price in the early years of asset life,
4) the rental payments exceed fair rental value,
5) the option purchase price is nominal compared to the expected value of the asset when the option is exercised,
6) some part of the "rent" payment is designated as interest,
7) total rental payments plus option price approximates value for which property could have been bought plus interest and carrying charges, and
8) the lease may be renewed at nominal rentals over the life of the property.

Following is an example illustrating a typical cash investment purchase of an asset compared to leasing under a qualified operating lease agreement. Leveraged lease/purchase analyses are discussed and illustrated in Chapter 11 in Example 11-5.

EXAMPLE 10-7 Leasing Versus Purchase of a Vehicle

At present a company is leasing an executive vehicle. Analysis is being made of whether to provide the service of a new vehicle for the next three years by leasing or purchasing based on the following costs and salvage values:

```
            C=$10,000      OC=$1,000    OC=$1,500    OC=$2,000
Purchase   ─────────────────────────────────────────────────        L=$2,000
                0              1            2            3


       Lease OC=$1,750     OC=$3,500    OC=$3,500    OC=$1,750
                  -        OC=$1,000    OC=$1,500    OC=$2,000
Lease      ─────────────────────────────────────────────────        L=0
                0              1            2            3
```

Lease costs in the first 6 months of year 1 are treated as year 0 lease costs and lease costs in the last 6 months of year 3 are treated as year 3 costs to best account for the correct timing. Operating costs are expensed for tax deduction purposes and include gas, oil, license fees, insurance and maintenance in both cases plus the lease cost in the leasing case. Assume the vehicle purchase cost will be depreciated starting in year zero using ACRS rates for a five year life with the half year convention. Assume other income exists against which to expense all operating costs in the years incurred. Use an effective tax rate of 40%. Which alternative is more economical for a minimum DCFROR of 15%?

A) Use incremental DCFROR analysis
B) Use incremental NPV analysis
C) Use present worth cost analysis
D) Use annual cost analysis
E) Use uniform annual equivalent revenue required analysis
F) Discuss the comment the "since leasing is an alternative method of financing to borrowing and buying, the appropriate minimum DCFROR should be the after-tax cost of borrowed money rather than opportunity cost of capital".

Solution, All values in Thousands of Dollars:

```
C = Capital Costs,  S = Savings,  L = Salvage

                   C=10
Incremental        S=1.75      S=3.5        S=3.5        S=1.75
Purchase           ─────────────────────────────────────         L=2.0
- Lease            0           1            2            3
```

Negative incremental operating costs are the same as positive savings and must be converted to cash flow each year. Do not net incremental operating costs and capital costs together in year 0 since the incremental capital cost of 10 is depreciable while the incremental savings of 1.75 is equivalent to revenue that must be converted to cash flow. Only costs and revenues handled in the same manner for tax purposes may be netted together in after-tax analyses.

Incremental Cash Flows

Year	0	1	2	3
Revenue	1.75	3.50	3.50	3.75
-Depreciation	-2.00	-3.20	-1.92	-1.44
-Deprec Writeoff				-1.44
Taxable	-0.25	0.30	1.58	0.87
-Tax @ 40%	0.10	-0.12	-0.63	-0.35
Net Income	-0.15	0.18	0.95	0.52
+Depreciation	2.00	3.20	1.92	2.88
-Capital Costs	-10.00			
Cash Flow	-8.15	3.38	2.87	3.40

A) Incremental DCFROR Analysis

PW Eq: $0 = -8.15 + 3.38(P/F_{i,1}) + 2.87(P/F_{i,2}) + 3.40(P/F_{i,3})$

i = Incremental DCFROR = 8.95% by trial and error which is less than the minimum rate of return of 15%, so accept the lease alternative.

B) Incremental NPV Analysis

$$\text{Incremental NPV} = -8.15 + 3.38(\overset{.8696}{P/F_{15,1}}) + 2.87(\overset{.7561}{P/F_{15,2}}) + 3.40(\overset{.6575}{P/F_{15,3}})$$

= -.80 which is less than 0 so reject purchase and accept the leasing alternative

C and D) Present Worth and Annual Worth Cost Analysis

Purchase Cash Flows

Year	0	1	2	3
Revenue				2.00
-Oper Costs		-1.00	-1.50	-2.00
-Depreciation	-2.00	-3.20	-1.92	-1.44
-Deprec Writeoff				-1.44
Taxable	-2.00	-4.20	-3.42	-2.88
-Tax @ 40%	0.80	1.68	1.37	1.15
Net Income	-1.20	-2.52	-2.05	-1.73
+Depreciation	2.00	3.20	1.92	2.88
-Capital Costs	-10.00			
Cash Flow	-9.20	0.68	-0.13	1.15

Lease Cash Flows

Year	0	1	2	3
Revenue				
-Oper Costs	-1.75	-4.50	-5.00	-3.75
Taxable	-1.75	-4.50	-5.00	-3.75
-Tax @ 40%	0.70	1.80	2.00	1.50
Net Income	-1.05	-2.70	-3.00	-2.25
-Capital Costs				
Cash Flow	-1.05	-2.70	-3.00	-2.25

$$\text{PW Purchase} = 9.20 - 0.68(P/F_{15,1}) \overset{.8696}{} + 0.13(P/F_{15,2}) \overset{.7561}{} - 1.15(P/F_{15,3}) \overset{.6575}{}$$

$$= 7.95$$

$$\text{PW Lease} = 1.05 + 2.70(P/F_{15,1}) \overset{.8696}{} + 3.00(P/F_{15,2}) \overset{.7561}{} + 2.25(P/F_{15,3}) \overset{.6575}{}$$

$$= 7.15$$

Select Lease to minimize cost of service. Notice that present worth purchase minus present worth lease equals the magnitude of incremental NPV of 0.80. Remember the NPV sign convention is opposite the present worth cost sign convention so incremental purchase minus lease NPV is -0.80.

AC Purchase $= 7.95(A/P_{15,3}) = 3.48$

AC Lease $= 7.15(A/P_{15,3}) = 3.13$

Select Lease to minimize cost of service per period.

E) Uniform Annual Equivalent Revenue Required

UAERR $=$ Annual Cost $/ (1 - \text{tax rate})$

UAERR Purchase $= 3.48/(1-.4) = 5.80$

UAERR Lease $= 3.13/(1-.4) = 5.21$

Select leasing to minimize required breakeven revenue.

F) Discussion Regarding "The Cost of Borrowed Money" as the Appropriate Discount Rate for Lease Versus Purchase Analysis

The fact that lease obligations financially affect corporate balance sheets similar to borrowed money is a financial consideration that seems to confuse some people into thinking that leasing compared to purchasing is a unique type of service-producing economic analysis. Financial analysis concerns where money to finance investment opportunity comes from. The objective of economic analysis is to determine the best of alternative investment opportunities to maximize the future value of available investment dollars. It does not make any difference whether available investment capital comes from borrowing or cash flow from existing projects: we must compare new project or incremental project economic results with equivalent results for other investment opportunities thought to exist. The minimum DCFROR of 15% represents the after-tax rate of return thought to be attainable by investing elsewhere in this example. If we put money into purchasing instead of investing elsewhere at a 15% DCFROR, we incur a 15% DCFROR opportunity cost. The cost of borrowed money is not relevant to our analysis. In fact we are not even using any borrowed money in this cash purchase vs lease analysis. Leveraged lease analysis is discussed in Chapter 11.

Consider that borrowed money interest is 10% per year, the tax rate is 40%, so the after-tax cost of money is 6.0%. Comparing the incremental purchase-lease DCFROR of 8.95% to the 6.0% after-tax cost of money, the economic choice is to select purchase. This is the opposite choice that we get using an after-tax minimum rate of return of 15%. To show that the use of a cost of borrowed money minimum rate of return of 6% is incorrect, look at the future worth of incremental cash flow available if we lease or if we purchase and discuss the meaning of assumptions involved in the calculations.

```
Purchase     Cash Flow = -8.15       3.38       2.87       3.40
- Lease                  _____

                           0          1          2          3
```

If we lease we have an extra $8.15 cash flow available to invest elsewhere in year 0 at the minimum rate of return.

Lease Future Value

$$\text{If } i^* = 15\%, \text{ Year 3 Value} = 8.15(F/P_{15,3}) = \$12.40$$

with 1.521 above $(F/P_{15,3})$

$$\text{If } i^* = 6.0\%, \text{ Year 3 Value} = 8.15(F/P_{6.0,3}) = \$9.70$$

with 1.191 above $(F/P_{6.0,3})$

If we purchase we have the year 1, 2 and 3 cash flows to reinvest elsewhere.

Purchase Future Value

$$\text{If } i^* = 15\%, \text{ Year 3 Value} = 3.38(F/P_{15,2}) + 2.87(F/P_{15,1})$$

with 1.322 above $(F/P_{15,2})$ and 1.150 above $(F/P_{15,1})$

$$+ 3.40 = \$11.19$$

$$\text{If } i^* = 6.0\%, \text{ Year 3 Value} = 3.38(F/P_{6.0,2}) + 2.87(F/P_{6.0,1})$$

with 1.124 above $(F/P_{6.0,2})$ and 1.060 above $(F/P_{6.0,1})$

$$+ 3.40 = \$10.24$$

If other investment opportunities really exist to invest cash flow elsewhere at a 15% DCFROR, the greatest future worth (12.4 vs 11.19) is generated by leasing and investing the incremental 8.15 purchasing cost elsewhere at 15%.

If other opportunities really exist to invest money elsewhere at a 6.0% DCFROR, the greatest future worth (9.70 vs 10.24) is generated by purchasing and investing the savings cash flow elsewhere at 6.0%. However, it is appropriate to mention at this time that the after-tax cost of borrowed money has no relation to cash flow reinvestment opportunities unless mortgage lending investments represent other investment opportunities used to determine the minimum DCFROR. That is not the case in this analysis since it is stated that the minimum DCFROR is 15%, not 6.0%.

There are no analysis situations related to the correct evaluation of either income or service-producing alternatives where the after-tax cost of borrowed money is the relevant discount rate (minimum DCFROR) to use unless borrowed money is unlimited so the minimum DCFROR becomes the same as the after-tax cost of money. Few, if any, individuals or companies are in the unlimited borrowed money situation.

10.8 Optimum Replacement Life for Equipment

It frequently is necessary to replace equipment, vehicles, piping systems and other assets on a periodic basis. Determination of the optimum replacement life for these replacement situations is a very important type of evaluation problem. In general, it can be shown to be economically desirable to replace assets when the after-tax operating, maintenance and repair costs for the old assets are greater than the equivalent annual cost projected for the new assets. However, in many real situations the analysis becomes more complicated because new assets often have different productivity than old assets, requiring the prorating of costs in some manner to get all the alternatives on the basis of providing the same productivity or service. Also, if existing assets have a positive fair market value the incremental opportunity cost of using existing assets one more period must be accounted for in addition to operating type costs in a correct optimum replacement study. In other words, optimum replacement time calculations are dynamic by nature. Using yearly evaluation periods, every year you must estimate: 1) the second hand market value of existing assets (which determines the opportunity cost related to keeping the asset another year), 2) salvage a year later for the existing assets, 3) operating, maintenance and repair costs to operate the existing asset one more year, and 4) any major repair or rebuild costs to operate one more year. Using these values calculate the annual cost of operating one more year with the existing asset. Compare the existing asset annual cost for one more year of operation with the equivalent annual cost of operating with a new (replacement) asset for the expected optimum useful life of the new asset. Replace when the after-tax annual cost of operating one more year with existing assets is projected to be greater than the equivalent cost of a new alternative for its optimum expected life. This criteria assumes that the annual cost of operating with existing assets will get bigger in future years due to asset age and obsolescence.

PROBLEMS

10-1   A machine produces 1000 units of product per day in an existing manufacturing operation. The machine has become obsolete due to tightened product quality standards. Two new replacement machines are being evaluated from an economic viewpoint. Replacement machine A will cost $15,000 and will produce the needed 1000 units of product per day for the next 3 years with annual escalated dollar operating costs projected to be $6,000 in year 1, $7,000 in year 2 and $8,000 in year 3 with a $2,000 escalated dollar salvage value at the end of year 3. Replacement machine B will cost $21,000 and can produce up to 1500 units of product per day for the next 3 years with annual escalated dollar operating costs of $5,000 in each of years 1, 2 and 3 for either 1000 or 1500 units per day, with a $3,000 escalated dollar salvage value at the end of year 3. Depreciate both machines using 5 year life modified ACRS depreciation starting in year 0 with the half year convention. Assume that other taxable income exists that will permit using all tax deductions in the year incurred. For an effective income tax rate of 40%, use present worth cost analysis for a minimum escalated dollar DCFROR of 20% to determine if machine A or B is economically best assuming:

A)   no use exists for the extra 500 units of product per day that machine B can produce,

B)   another division of the company can utilize the extra 500 units of product capacity per day of machine B and that division will pick up one third of machine B capital cost, operating costs, depreciation, salvage value and related tax effects.

10-2   An existing machine A has a $2,000 sale value at year 0 and an estimated 2 more years of useful life with end-of-year operating costs of $3,000 at year 1 and $4,000 at year 2 when the salvage value is expected to be zero. At year 2 a replacement machine A that would provide the same service is estimated to have a cost of $23,000 with annual operating costs of $2,000 in year 3, $2,500 in year 4 and $3,000 in year 5 when the salvage value is estimated to be $8,000. An alternative new machine B would cost $20,000 now and would provide the same service as the original replacement machine A and could be operated for an annual cost of $1,500 in year 1 escalating $500 per year in following years. Machine B is estimated to have a salvage value of $3,000 5 years from now. Use present worth cost analysis to compare these alternatives for a 5 year evaluation life and a minimum DCFROR of 15% for the following situations.

A) The service to be received from each machine is assumed to be the same. The existing machine A is fully depreciated and has a zero tax book value. Replacement machines A or B will be depreciated using the modified ACRS depreciation for a 7 year life with depreciation starting in the year the costs are incurred with the half year convention. Other income exists against which to use deductions in the years incurred and the effective income tax rate is 40%.

B) If machine B provides the capability of giving 40% more productivity than machine A over each of the 5 years and we assume the additional productivity can be utilized, compare the economics of machines A and B if operating costs will be the same as in part 'A' for both machines.

10-3 A 4 year old machine has a remaining book value of $21,000 and a second- hand salvage value of $30,000. You need to analyze the cost of keeping this asset to lease to another party for the next 3 years. A major repair of $25,000 at year 0 that can be expensed for tax deduction purposes will extend the life of the old asset another 3 years. Operating costs in years 1, 2 and 3 are projected to be $15,000, $18,000 and $21,000 respectively. The salvage value at year 3 is estimated to be 0. The income tax rate is 40% and the minimum escalated dollar DCFROR is 20%. Other income exists against which to use deductions in any year.

A) Determine the after-tax actual value end-of-year equivalent annual cost of operating with the old machine for years 1, 2 and 3. Assume that the remaining book value of $21,000 will be deducted as depreciation at year 0 if the asset is kept.

B) Determine the three uniform and equal beginning-of-year lease payments (at years 0, 1 and 2) that will give the owner of the old machine a 20% DCFROR on invested dollars.

10-4   All values are in thousands of dollars.

A)

C=$50	OC=$12	OC=$15	OC=$18	OC=$21	OC=$24
					L=$3
0	1	2	3	4	5

B)

C=$15	C=$32 OC=$20	C=$50 OC=$16	OC=$3	OC=$4	OC=$5
					L=$25
0	1	2	3	4	5

The time diagrams show the capital costs (C), operating costs (OC) and salvage values (L) for two alternatives under consideration for providing needed processing operation service for the next 5 years. Alternative A involves acquisition of new equipment now with annual labor intensive operating costs and salvage values as shown. Alternative B involves buying used equipment now and replacing it with new labor saving equipment currently in the development stage, but expected to be available for installation in two stages at years 1 and 2 for costs and salvage values as shown. All new and used capital costs are to be depreciated using 7 year life modified ACRS depreciation starting in the years costs are incurred with the half year convention, with the exception that the year 1 and 2 alternative B replacement costs go into service at year 2, so start depreciating the total $82,000 cost at year 2. Take writeoffs on the remaining book values in the year assets are replaced or sold. Assume other income exists against which to use deductions in the year incurred. The effective income tax rate is 40%. For a minimum DCFROR of 15% use DCFROR analysis to determine the economically better alternative.

10-5   Evaluate the economics of replacing a D9 caterpillar using the following data. Compare the old D9 with a new D9L by the "equivalent annual cost" method. The minimum DCFROR is 15%. Use a 5 year evaluation life. The new D9L purchase price is $460,000 with an estimated $140,000 salvage value in 5 years, while the old D9 has a $90,000 fair market value now and zero book value with an estimated zero salvage value in 5 years. The new D9L would be depreciated starting in year 0 with the half year convention using 7 year life modified ACRS depreciation. The effective income tax rate is 40% and other income exists against which to use all deductions in the year incurred. Assume overhaul costs as well as operating costs given in the following table will be expensed in the year incurred. Assume the new D9L will give 130% of the service productivity given by the old D9 and that: a) the extra service cannot be utilized, b) the extra service can be utilized.

	Non-Operator Cost per Operating Hr.		Operating Hrs.	Overhaul Costs ($)	
Year	Old	New	Both	Old	New
0	-	-	-	100,000	-
1	25.0	22.0	4000	50,000	-
2	28.0	24.0	4000	125,000	125,000
3	31.0	27.0	4000	60,000	-
4	35.0	31.0	4000	150,000	150,000
5	39.0	35.0	4000	-	-

10-6 A firm is considering the economics of whether to lease or purchase a fleet of 10 trucks. The total purchase cost of the trucks is $100,000 and they will be depreciable over 5 years starting in year 0 with the half year convention, using modified ACRS depreciation. Take a writeoff on the remaining book value in the year the assets are sold. Salvage value of the trucks is expected to total $30,000 at year 3 when the trucks are expected to be sold. The operating, maintenance and insurance costs are considered to be the same whether the trucks are purchased or leased so they are left out of the analysis. The 10 trucks can be leased for $36,000 per year on a 3 year contract with monthly payments. To best account for the timing of the lease payments with annual periods, assume the first 6 months of lease payments, $18,000, are at year 0, $36,000 lease costs are at years 1 and 2 and $18,000 at year 3. The effective income tax rate is 40% and the firm has other taxable income and tax obligations against which to use tax deductions in any year.

A) Use present worth cost analysis and verify the results with incremental DCFROR analysis to determine if leasing or purchasing is economically better for a minimum DCFROR of 15%.

B) What uniform end-of-period annual equal revenues are required (UAERR) to cover the cost of leasing or purchasing and give the investor a 15% DCFROR on invested dollars?

C) Re-analyze the alternatives from the viewpoint of an investor that must carry negative taxable income forward to year 3 when other income is expected to exist. Use present worth cost analysis.

10-7   You have been asked to evaluate whether it is economically desirable
        to replace three existing machines with two new machines that would
        provide the same service over the next 3 years. The existing machines
        cost $300,000 5 years ago and have been fully depreciated. The
        second-hand value of the existing machines is $80,000 per machine
        at this time. Keeping and using the existing machines will result in
        estimated operating costs per machine of $120,000 at year 1, $130,000
        at year 2 and $140,000 at year 3. Year 3 existing machine salvage
        is estimated to be zero. Two new machines would cost $500,000 per
        machine. Operating costs per new machine are estimated to be $60,000
        at year 1, $80,000 at year 2 and $100,000 at year 3. Salvage value
        per new machine is estimated to be $125,000 in year 3. The new
        machines would be depreciable over 5 years starting at year 0 with
        the half year convention using modified ACRS depreciation. Other
        taxable income exists against which to use deductions in any year.
        The effective income tax rate is 40%, the minimum escalated dollar
        DCFROR is 15%. Use equivalent annual cost analysis to determine
        whether to replace the existing machines. Then calculate the uniform
        annual equivalent revenue required per machine to provide the service
        with the existing machines compared to the new machines.

10-8   A company is trying to evaluate the economic merits of purchasing
        or leasing a plant. It can be purchased installed on company land for
        $1,000,000 cash or leased for $200,000 per year at the beginning of
        each year on a ten year lease. Annual income is expected to be
        $800,000 with $200,000 annual operating costs at each of years 1
        through 10. The life of the plant is estimated to be 10 years. The net
        salvage value of the plant is estimated to be $400,000 at the end of
        its 10 year life. The effective federal plus state tax rate is 40%.
        Depreciation of the purchased plant cost would be straight line over
        10 years starting in year 0 with the half year convention. Determine
        the DCFROR that the company would receive on the $1,000,000
        year 0 investment that must be made to purchase rather than lease.
        If 10% is the minimum DCFROR, should the company lease or
        purchase? Verify the result with NPV and equivalent annual cost
        analysis.

10-9   A firm is considering the acquisition of a Caterpillar D9L tractor
        complete with dozer, ripper and cab. The list price is $454,328 and
        sales tax of 7.1% is capitalized into the depreciation basis. Based on

historical information the firm can expect to realize 30% of the list price in salvage in 5 years. Salvage will be taxed as ordinary income. Expected machine life is 15,000 hours: 4,000 hours each in years 1 and 2, 3,000 hours in year 3 and 2,000 hours in year 4 and 5. The machine will be depreciated using the modified ACRS depreciation for a 7 year life starting in year 0 with the half year convention. State ownership taxes and permits are tax deductible as operating expenses and are estimated to be 2.3% of the list price of the machine in year 1, 1.5% in year 2, 1.25% in year 3, 1.0% in year 4 and .75% in year 5. (In practice, the state tax is based on 75% of cost, but to cover miscellaneous fees and permits in various counties, 100% of the list price is used.) Insurance is $.55 per $100 invested in year 1, escalating 6% per annum. Major repairs of $100,000 at the end of year 2, $75,000 at the end of year 3 and $125,000 at the end of year 4 will be necessary. Minor repairs will be $15,000 in year 1 escalating by 6% per annum. In addition, $20,000 will be spent at the end of year 5 to prepare the unit for auction. For tax purposes, major and minor repairs should be expensed as operating costs in the year incurred since these expenditures are not expected to add to the life of the machine or cause significant modifications to the unit.

Determine the before-tax standard cost per hour necessary to cover costs for a 15% after-tax minimum DCFROR. The effective state and federal income tax rate is 40%. It will be assumed that other income exists against which to use all deductions in the year incurred. Then measure the impact to the standard cost per hour of a variation to the production schedule. Assume the machine will operate 3,000 hours per year for 5 years with all other costs remaining constant.

Summary of Data Cost

Cost	$454,328				
Sales Tax	$ 32,257				

Year	0	1	2	3	4	5
Insurance	-	2,498	2,649	2,808	2,976	3,155
Taxes, Permits	-	10,450	6,815	5,679	4,543	3,407
Major Repairs	-	-	100,000	75,000	125,000	-
Minor Repairs	-	15,000	15,900	16,954	17,865	38,937
Salvage	-	-	-	-	-	136,298
Hours/Year	-	4,000	4,000	3,000	2,000	2,000
Alt. Hours/Year	-	3,000	3,000	3,000	3,000	3,000

CHAPTER 11

LEVERAGE CONCEPTS:
EVALUATIONS INVOLVING BORROWED MONEY

11.1 Introduction of Leverage Applications

Most major investment projects that are undertaken anywhere in the world today involve at least some borrowed money. This makes the analysis of investments involving borrowed money a very important economic evaluation situation. The terms "leverage and "gearing" often are used in referring to the economic effects on investments involving a combination of borrowed money and equity capital. The dictionary defines leverage as "increased means of accomplishing some purpose." We use a lever and fulcrum to get leverage to raise a heavy object such as a large rock, and we use someone else's money in addition to our own equity capital to leverage investment dollars to increase the profit we can generate with our equity. To illustrate this effect with a common example, consider that you have $10,000 to invest and that you pay cash for 1,000 shares of XYZ stock at $10 per share. Assume that the stock increases in price to $15 per share within a few months and you sell the 1,000 shares for $15,000. Neglecting stock broker commissions, your profit is $5,000 giving you a 50% return on your $10,000 equity investment over the period of time involved. Now assume that instead of paying cash for the stock, that you use your $10,000 cash as margin equity and borrowed another $10,000, enabling you to purchase 2,000 shares of XYZ at $10 per share. Now you have $20,000 working for you instead of just your $10,000 equity. If the stock price goes to $15 per share and you sell the 2,000 shares, you receive $30,000 income of which $10,000 is used to repay the borrowed money, leaving $10,000 profit above recovery of your $10,000 equity. Neglecting stock broker commissions and also the borrowed money interest, this gives you a 100% return on your $10,000 initial equity investment over the period of time involved. The effect of 50% borrowed money or leverage has enabled us to double the profit we would receive per equity dollar invested. At this point it is appropriate and relevant to state a basic law of economics which is: "There ain't no free lunch." You are not getting something for nothing with borrowed money. Leverage can work against you in exactly the same manner that it works for you. To illustrate this, consider that the shares of XYZ stock drop in price to $5 per share from their initial $10 per share. If we paid cash for 1,000 shares, this is a $5,000 loss or a -50% return on our $10,000 equity investment. If we had used $10,000 borrowed money together with our $10,000 equity, we would have lost $5 per share on 2,000 shares or $10,000. This means we would have lost all of our equity because the $10,000 income from selling 2,000 shares at $5 per share would be needed in its entirety to repay the $10,000 borrowed money and we would have a -100% return on our equity investment. So, note that leverage can and will work against us as well as for us in different situations.

We now want to demonstrate the handling of borrowed money in DCFROR and NPV analysis of various types of projects. As with the XYZ stock illustration just discussed, including leverage in analyses means we are calculating the rate of return or NPV based on our equity investment in a project rather than on the total investment value. All of the examples and problems presented in the text to this point have been for cash investment situations. *There are three basic differences between the analysis of cash investment alternatives and investment alternatives involving borrowed money. First, interest on borrowed money is an additional operating expense tax deduction that must be accounted for each evaluation period that mortgage payments are made. Second, loan principal payments are additional non-tax deductible capital costs that must be accounted for as after-tax outflows of money each evaluation period that mortgage payments are made. Third, investment capital costs must be adjusted for borrowed money inflows of money each evaluation period that loans are made.* These three adjustments are the basic evaluation considerations that must be accounted for in leveraged investment analyses that are not present in cash investment analyses as the following example illustrates.

EXAMPLE 11-1 Analysis of a Leveraged Investment

An investment project requires the year 0 investment of $100,000 for depreciable assets and $15,000 for working capital. The depreciable assets will be depreciated straight line for a 5 year life starting in year 0 with the half year convention. Annual project income is expected to be $65,000 with annual operating costs of $25,000, assuming a washout of escalation of annual income and operating costs. Year 4 asset salvage value and working capital return are estimated to be $35,000. The effective tax rate is 40% and other income exists against which to use tax deductions in any year.

A) Calculate project DCFROR assuming cash investments (100% Equity).
B) Calculate project DCFROR assuming $100,000 of the $115,000 investment will be borrowed at an interest rate of 10% per year with a four year loan to be paid off with uniform and equal mortgage payments at years 1, 2, 3 and 4.
C) Evaluate the sensitivity of the cash investment and leveraged investment DCFROR results to ±$10,000 per year change in year 1 through 4 revenues.

Solution: All Values in Thousands of Dollars:

$100 borrowed at 10% annual interest on a 4 year loan gives annual mortgage payments of $100(A/P_{10,4})$ = $31.547

Each mortgage payment must be broken into interest and principal components since only the interest portion of mortgage payments is tax deductible.

Year 1: Interest = .10($100) = $10
        Loan Principal Repaid = $31.547 − $10.00 = $21.547
        New Loan Principal Balance = $100 −$21.547 = $78.453

Year 2: Interest = .10($78.453) = $7.8453
        Loan Principal Repaid = $31.547 − $7.8453 = $23.702
        New Loan Principal Balance = $78.453 − $23.702 = $54.751

Year 3: Interest = .10($54.751) = $5.4751
        Loan Principal Repaid = $31.547 − $5.4751 = $26.072
        New Loan Principal Balance = $54.751 − $26.072 = $28.679

        Year 4: Interest = .10($28.679) = $2.8679
        Loan Principal Repaid = $31.547 − $2.8679 = $28.679
        New Loan Principal Balance = $28.679 − $28.679 = $0

I = Income, C = Capital Cost, OC = Operating Cost, Int = Interest,
P = Principal Payments, L = Salvage and Working Capital Return

Before-Tax Cash Investment Diagram

	I=65	I=65	I=65	I=65	
C=115	OC=25	OC=25	OC=25	OC=25	
					L=35
0	1	2	3	4	

Borrowed Money Diagram (or Loan Amortization Schedule)

```
         Int=10    Int= 7.8  Int= 5.5  Int= 2.9
I=100    P=21.5    P=23.7    P=26.1    P=28.7

0        1         2         3         4
```

Sum of Cash Investment and Loan Amortization Diagrams

```
          I=65      I=65      I=65      I=65
          OC=25     OC=25     OC=25     OC=25
          Int=10    Int= 7.8  Int= 5.5  Int= 2.9
C=15      P=21.5    P=23.7    P=26.1    P=28.7
                                                  L=35
0         1         2         3         4
```

Notice that exactly the same cumulative equity cost of $115,000 is paid for the borrowed money case "B" and the cash investment case "A" since the leveraged investment year 0 equity cost of $15,000 plus loan principal payments add up to $115,000. However, the use of borrowed money enables us to defer a significant portion of our equity cost into the future. With borrowed money the cost we pay for deferring equity costs is the interest charged each year. If the interest cost is less than the profit generated by the borrowed money, leverage works for us and our leveraged economic analysis results look better than the corresponding cash investment results.

A) Cash Investment Analysis

Year	0	1	2	3	4
Revenue		65	65	65	100[*]
-Oper Costs		-25	-25	-25	-25
-Depreciation	-10	-20	-20	-20	-20[**]
-Writeoff					-25
Taxable	-10	20	20	20	30
-Tax @ 40%	4	-8	-8	-8	-12
Net Income	-6	12	12	12	18
+Depreciation	10	20	20	20	20
+Writeoffs					25
-Capital Costs	-115				
Cash Flow	-111	32	32	32	63

*Includes Salvage Value
**Includes $15 Working Capital and $10 Depreciable

PW Eq: $0 = -111 + 32(P/A_{i,3}) + 63(P/F_{i,4})$

   i = Cash Investment DCFROR = 14.2%

At this point in the analysis we can tell whether the effect of borrowed money leverage will work for us or against us by comparing the cash investment DCFROR to the after-tax cost of borrowed money. Since interest is tax deductible every dollar of interest saves $0.40 in tax for a 40% income tax rate. This makes borrowing at 10% before-tax equivalent to an after-tax borrowed money interest rate of 6%. Borrowing money at an after-tax interest rate of 6% and putting it to work at the cash investment DCFROR of 14.2% makes leverage work for us. We expect the leveraged economic analysis results to look better than the cash investment results, and the following leveraged analysis calculations verify this expectation. Borrowing money at an after-tax interest rate that is less than the cash investment DCFROR of a project will always give a leveraged project DCFROR that is greater than the corresponding cash investment project DCFROR.

B) Leveraged Investment Analysis

Year	0	1	2	3	4
Revenue		65.00	65.00	65.00	100.00
-Oper Costs		-25.00	-25.00	-25.00	-25.00
-Depreciation	-10.00	-20.00	-20.00	-20.00	-20.00
-Writeoff					-25.00
-Interest		-10.00	-7.85	-5.48	-2.87
Taxable	-10.00	10.00	12.15	14.52	27.13
-Tax payment	4.00	-4.00	-4.86	-5.81	-10.85
Net Income	-6.00	6.00	7.29	8.71	16.28
+Depreciation	10.00	20.00	20.00	20.00	20.00
+Writeoff					25.00
-Principal		-21.55	-23.70	-26.07	-28.68
-Capital Costs	-115.00				
+Borrowed	100.00				
Cash Flow	-11.00	4.45	3.59	2.64	32.60

PW Eq: $0 = -11.00 + 4.45(P/F_{i,1}) + 3.59(P/F_{i,2}) + 2.64(P/F_{i,3})$

$+ 32.60(P/F_{i,4})$

   i = Leveraged Investment DCFROR = 53.6%

This leveraged DCFROR represents after-tax rate of return on investor equity investments. Note that the leveraged DCFROR of 53.6% is much larger than the cash investment DCFROR of 14.2% although the leveraged positive cash flow is significantly smaller than the cash investment cash flow for each project year. The reason leverage works for us in this analysis is because borrowing money at an after-tax cost of 6% and putting it to work in this project which has a 14.2% cash investment DCFROR causes the negative leveraged cash flow at year 0 to be reduced proportionally more by the year 0 borrowed money than the positive leveraged cash flows are reduced in the revenue generating years by loan interest and principal payment costs. Leverage always works for an investor when the after-tax borrowed money interest rate is less than the cash investment project DCFROR.

To summarize this discussion, deferring equity cost by using borrowed money is always economically desirable as long as the borrowed money is earning more than it costs on an after-tax basis. However, the optimum amount of leverage for a given investor is really a financial decision rather than an economic decision. More leverage always makes the economics of investments look better if the after-tax cost of borrowed money is less than the cash investment DCFROR. Financially, an investor must consider the magnitude of mortgage payments that can be handled if investment economics turn bad. Bankruptcy proceedings are an unpleasant experience and getting over-extended on investment loans for investments that turn bad can have very negative financial as well as economic results.

People often talk about greater risk and uncertainty being associated with achieving leveraged investment results in comparison with cash investment results. What they usually mean is that leveraged results are more sensitive to changes in evaluation parameters than cash investment results are, because leveraged results in general always relate to smaller equity investment values. In other words, a given change in any evaluation parameter such as revenue or operating costs will cause a bigger magnitude change in leveraged evaluation results than in cash investment evalution results. The Case "C" sensitivity analysis illustrates this consideration by showing that a given increase or decrease in project revenue for this example causes bigger magnitude change and percent change in leveraged DCFROR than in cash investment analysis DCFROR.

C) Sensitivity Analysis of Cash and Leveraged Investments

The effect of increasing or decreasing revenue by $10,000 per year will be analyzed. Since tax deductions for this investment are the same regardless of revenue, increasing or decreasing revenue by $10,000 in years 1 through 4 will increase or decrease income tax at the 40% tax rate by $4,000 each year. The net effect of revenue and tax changes will increase or decrease cash flow by $6,000 each year for either the cash investment or leverage analysis. Making the $6,000 per year cash flow adjustment is an easy way of obtaining the sensitivity analysis cash flows that lead to the DCFROR results.

Cash Investment Sensitivity Analysis

						DCFROR
	-111	32	32	32	63	
Base Case Cash Flows						14.2%
	0	1	2	3	4	

	-111	38	38	38	69	
$10,000 Revenue						21.0%
Increase Per Year	0	1	2	3	4	

	-111	26	26	26	57	
$10,000 Revenue						7.2%
Decrease Per Year	0	1	2	3	4	

The changes in cash investment DCFROR due to increasing or decreasing revenue by $10,000 each year amount to ±50% changes from the base case 14.2% DCFROR.

Leveraged Investment Sensitivity Analysis

						DCFROR
Base Case	-11.0	4.45	3.59	2.64	32.60	
Cash Flows						53.7%
	0	1	2	3	4	

	-11.0	10.45	9.59	8.64	38.60	
$10,000 Revenue						101.0%
Increase Per Year	0	1	2	3	4	

	-11.0	-1.55	-2.41	-3.36	26.60	
$10,000 Revenue						12.4%
Decrease Per Year	0	1	2	3	4	

The changes in leveraged investment DCFROR due to increasing or decreasing revenue by $10,000 each year amount to +88% to -77% changes from the base case 53.7% DCFROR. The physical range of variation in leveraged DCFROR results from 101% to 12.4% is much greater than the 7.2% to 21% variation in cash investment results caused by the same ±$10,000 change in revenue. This greater range of variation in leveraged versus cash investment results relates to the greater risk and uncertainty that some people mention in discussing the attainment of leveraged results compared to the attainment of cash investment results.

EXAMPLE 11-2 A Land Investment Analysis With Leverage

Assume you have a chance to buy 20 acres of land for $11,000 with a $1,000 down-payment and annual end-of-year mortgage payments of $2,000 principal plus 10% interest on the unpaid principal. Assume further that you think the land can be sold for $16,000 cash three years from now and that the loan would be paid off at the time of the sale. The effective income tax rate is 30%. Calculate the DCFROR based upon:

A) Your equity investment in the land
B) Paying cash for the land
C) Land selling price is $14,000 instead of $16,000
D) Calculate the breakeven sale value at year 3 that would give you a 25% escalated dollar leveraged DCFROR (use Case A values).

Solution, C = Equity Capital Cost, i = interest, p = principal:

Case A, Before Tax Diagram

```
               i=$1,000    i= $800     i= $600
C=$1,000       p=$2,000    p=$2,000    p=$6,000
                                                 L = $16,000
0              1           2           3
```

Assume that the interest is used as a tax writeoff against other investment income each year, saving you $0.30 in tax per $1 of interest deduction. (Loan principal payments are not allowable tax deductions.) The sale price of $16,000 less $11,000 cost gives a capital gain of $5,000 taxed as ordinary income at the 30% ordinary income tax rate. The tax would be .30(5,000) or $1,500 so sale cash flow at year 3 would be $16,000 − $1,500 tax or $14,500. The cost of acquiring land is not depreciable or tax deductible in any way except against the sale value.

```
Cash Flow = -$1,000    -$2,700    -$2,560    -$6,420+14,500
                                              Net = $8,080

            0          1          2          3
```

PW Eq: $0 = -1,000 - 2,700(P/F_{i,1}) - 2,560(P/F_{i,2}) + 8,080(P/F_{i,3})$

i = Leveraged Investment DCFROR = 15.3%

Case B, Cash Investment

If we assume a cash investment, no interest or principal payments are needed and the after-tax salvage value at the end of year 3 is the same, $14,500.

After-Tax Diagram

```
Cash Flow = -$11,000          -            -          $14,500

             0          1          2          3
```

PW Eq: $0 = -\$11,000 + \$14,500(P/F_{i,3})$

i = Cash Investment DCFROR = 9.6%

In this case, leverage has increased by a factor of about 60% the DCFROR that you would receive on the equity you have invested at any time. The total final profit is the same in both the leveraged and cash investment cases, but it takes less of your dollars to achieve the profit when borrowed money is used. However, you can't get something for nothing, and the increased profits that leverage can give you are offset by the increased risk of using borrowed money. Quantitatively, this means that a given change in any parameter that affects the economic analysis will cause a larger variation in the leveraged DCFROR than in the cash investment DCFROR, i.e., leverage can dissipate profits quicker just as it can build them quicker. To illustrate this consider the part "C" analysis that the land in this example is sold for $14,000 instead of $16,000 and calculate the percent variation in DCFROR from the results just calculated.

C) Reduced Sale Price of $14,000

For the leveraged case yearly interest and principal costs are the same, while the new after-tax salvage is $14,000 – $3,000(.30) tax or $13,100.

Leveraged Investment

PW Eq: $0 = -1,000 - 2,700(P/F_{i,1}) - 2,560(P/F_{i,2}) + 6,680(P/F_{i,3})$

The new leveraged investment DCFROR is 3.7%

Percent variation from base case result (15.3 – 3.7)/15.3 x 100 = 76%

Cash Investment

PW Eq: $0 = -\$11,000 + \$13,100(P/F_{i,3})$

The new cash investment DCFROR is 6.0%

Percent variation from base case result (9.6 – 6.0)/9.6 x 100 = 37%

The 76 percent decrease in the leveraged DCFROR is greater than the 37 percent decrease in the cash investment analysis results, showing that investors can lose money faster with leverage just like they can make money faster with leverage.

D) Breakeven Analysis

To achieve a 25% leveraged DCFROR on equity invested dollars, let "X" equal the breakeven required after-tax cash flow.

PW Eq: $0 = -1,000 - 2,700(P/F_{i,1}) - 2,560(P/F_{i,2}) + X(P/F_{i,3})$

Solving for "X" gives X = $9,372 for $i^* = 25\%$. What before-tax sale value will give this cash flow? Let "Y" equal the breakeven before-tax sale value.

$Y - (Y - 11,000)(.30$ tax rate$) - \$6,420$ principal and interest $= \$9,372$

Solving for Y: $Y = (9,372 - 3,300 + 6,420)/0.70 = \$17,845$

If you sell for $17,845:

Year 3 income tax $= (\$17,845 - 11,000)(.30) = \$2,053$
Year 3 after-tax interest and loan principal $= \$6,420$

So, year 3 cash flow equals $\$17,845 - \$2,053 - \$6,420 = \$9,372$. This is the cash flow that gives the investor a 25% DCFROR on leveraged equity investments.

11.2 Considerations Related to Leveraged Investment Analysis

We have seen in Examples 11-1 and 11-2 that both the meaning of economic analysis results and the risk and uncertainty associated with leveraged and cash investment project economic analysis results are very different. This brings up the question concerning, "how should leveraged investments be evaluated for investment decision making purposes?" To reach a conclusion concerning the best answer to that question, consider the following comments:

1) Whenever possible always compare evaluation alternatives with the same or similar leverage, including the project alternatives that determine the minimum ROR. As will be shown in section 11.4 your minimum ROR will be higher for leveraged project evaluations than for cash investment evaluations. Since the risks and uncertainties and meaning of economic results with different amounts of leverage are not the same, it is not reasonable for investment decision-making purposes to compare project analysis results based on different amounts of leverage.

2) Since more and more leverage gives higher and higher DCFROR results, the use of leveraged economic analysis results for decision making purposes can sometimes mislead the decision-maker into thinking a marginal project is a better project than it actually is. For this reason there is considerable merit in making zero leverage, the cash investment case as the common basis for comparing all investment opportunities. This approach is based on analyzing all projects from the viewpoint, "Would I be willing to invest my cash in any or all of the projects considered if I had the money?" If the

answer is yes, "Which projects would be best?" The cash investment analysis approach is used by a majority of companies. Another advantage of this approach is that it does not require knowing the financing conditions when the analysis is made. Since financing arrangements often are not finalized until just before initiation of a project, using cash investment economic analysis eliminates the need to guess and make sensitivity analysis for different borrowed money assumptions. Remember if the after-tax cost of borrowed money is less than the cash investment DCFROR, leverage will work for you and the leveraged DCFROR on your equity investment will be greater than the cash investment DCFROR for any and all investment projects. If the cash investment economic analysis results look satisfactory, the leveraged results will look even better if the after-tax borrowed money interest rate is less than the cash investment DCFROR.

3)   There are exceptions to every rule. In cases where interest free non-recourse loans are made available by another company to be repaid out of production product, or revenue if a project is successful, the leverage considerations are not the same as we have been discussing. To illustrate this concept, in past years some companies needing natural gas reserves have funded drilling companies in this manner. If the obligation to repay the loan does not exist if the project fails, the risk and uncertainty conditions obviously are very different than when repayment of the loan must be made whether we succeed or fail. In the non-recourse loan analysis case we would want to verify that the net present value that we could get by tying up our equipment and employees in the leveraged interest free loan project would be at least as great as the net present value we could generate by putting our employees and equipment on other projects being considered. Comparing DCFROR results is of little or no value in this case because you get an infinite percent DCFROR with 100% borrowed money.

4)   Different projects attract better financing than others because of relative risks and uncertainties involved with different projects in the eyes of the lender. Cash investment analysis does not take this consideration into account. Looking at projects on a cash investment basis is going to give you a good and probably the best basis for evaluating how a lender will view the economic potential and risk and uncertainty associated with projects, but it may be necessary to make a leveraged analysis comparison to take into account financing differences. Remember, the number one concern of a lender is, "Will there be sufficient project cash flow to cover the mortgage payments over the life of the project?" Usually a banker likes to see at least

a 2 to 1 ratio of cash flow to debt mortgage payments each year, but obviously this ratio, which is sometimes called the "debt service ratio," varies widely with the risks and uncertainties that are felt to exist with regard to project cash flow.

5)   Finally, the use of borrowed money relates to a finance decision as well as having an effect on economic evaluation results with and without leverage. Remember, we have been discussing how to determine the best projects from an economic viewpoint regardless of where the money is coming from to finance these projects. Now after it has been determined that given projects look satisfactory from a cash investment viewpoint, if we have the money to spend, it may also be necessary to analyze the projects from a leveraged viewpoint for financial as well as economic reasons if the financing terms are different for the different projects. This was mentioned in the previous paragraph. Remember to use the same leverage in all analysis cases and use incremental analysis if the alternatives are mutually exclusive. For non-mutually exclusive alternatives use cumulative NPV or use Growth DCFROR or Present Value Ratio to rank the projects that will maximize the profit on your available equity capital.

11.3 1986 Tax Law Change Regarding Interest Deductions

Under the new 1986 Tax Reform Law, individual and corporate taxpayers may still, as before, deduct interest on business debts incurred for the purpose of generating investment or business income. However, the new tax bill puts significant new restrictions on the kind of income that individuals can use interest deductions against and limits or eliminates the deductibility of certain interest by individuals. *Two major changes in the new tax bill for non-corporate taxpayers (to be phased in between 1987 and 1991) are 1) interest on personal loans is becoming non-deductible except for home mortgage loans on principal and second homes to the extent the debt does not exceed the purchase price plus improvements, which is the same restriction that applies to trade or business loans, 2) new limitations apply to the deduction of investment interest, limiting this deduction to the amount of net investment income for the year.* Discussion of these items follows.

Interest on personal loans becomes non-deductible by non-corporate taxpayers over a five year phase-in period between 1987 and 1991 when the new law is in full force. Until 1991, taxpayers may deduct the full amount of interest allowed under the old law minus an increasing percentage of the interest that is disallowed under new law as follows:

For Tax Years Beginning In:	The Percentage of Interest Disallowed Is:
1987	35%
1988	60%
1989	80%
1990	90%
1991 and later	100%

This new category of non-deductible interest, referred to as "personal interest," includes all interest other than:

1) Interest incurred in connection with a trade or business.

2) Investment interest (there are restrictions on investment interest that are discussed in the next paragraph).

3) Qualified first and second home mortgage interest mentioned earlier.

4) Certain specialized interest categories such as deferred estate tax interest.

Investment interest limitations that limit investment interest deductions to the amount of net investment income for the year will be phased in over 1987 to 1991 using the same percentages applicable to non-deductible personal interest. Net investment income is defined as the excess of investment income over investment expense. Investment expense will be calculated using actual operating expenses, tax depreciation, depletion and amortization deductions. Investment income includes the taxpayers share of income or loss attributable to any business interest and to include gain on investment property. Interest that is subject to the new investment interest limitations is defined as interest on debt incurred or continued to purchase or carry property held for investment. Property held for investment includes any property that produces income of the following types: interest, dividends, annuities or royalties not derived in the ordinary course of a trade or business. Investment interest does not include qualified residence interest or interest from a passive activity such as real estate rental property or limited partnerships which by definition are passive investments. Passive investment deductions may only be used against passive investment income. You should be getting the idea that the new tax law is very complicated with respect to the deductibility of different types of interest by different investors, so consultation with a good tax accountant is advisable before making new investments involving borrowed money.

EXAMPLE 11-3 A Leveraged Real Estate Investment Analysis

An individual investor is considering the purchase of an apartment house priced at $400,000. The property appraises at a high enough value to enable the investor to finance 95% of cost ($380,000) with a 10% annual interest loan repayable with uniform and equal mortgage payments over ten years. The investor plans to reinvest rental revenues each year for major repairs to fix up the property which is in a run down condition. It is expected that the property can and will be sold two years from now for $600,000. The investor considers that this investment will be treated as a passive investment for tax purposes and no other passive investment income exists. The investor has taxable income exceeding $150,000 in normal years, so does not expect to qualify for the special $25,000 passive investment deduction against other non-passive income. Rental revenues are expected to be $70,000 at year 1 and $75,000 at year 2 with corresponding operating costs including major repairs expensed as operating costs of $75,000 in each of years 1 and 2. Consider that the apartment house goes into service in the first month of year 1 and straight line, 27.5 year life depreciation is applicable to $360,000 of the $400,000 cost with $40,000 allocated for land. Calculate the investor's leveraged DCFROR assuming the investor's effective income tax rate is 31%. Analyze the sensitivity of DCFROR to reducing the year 2 sale value to $500,000 from $600,000.

Solution:

Loan Amortization Schedule:

Mortgage Payments $= \$380,000(A/P_{10,10}) = \$61,845$
Year 1 Interest $= \$380,000(.10) = \$38,000$
Year 1 Principal $= \$61,845 - \$38,000 = \$23,845$

New Loan Principal $= \$380,000 - \$23,845 = \$356,155$

Year 2 Interest $= \$356,155(.10) = \$35,615$
Year 2 Principal $= \$61,845 - \$35,615 = \$26,230$

New Loan Principal $= \$356,155 - \$26,230 = \$329,925$

Depreciation Schedule, Half Month Convention Applies

Year 1: $\$360,000(1/27.5)(11.5/12) = \$12,545$
Year 2: $\$360,000(1/27.5) = \$13,091$

Remaining Book Value $= \$360,000 - 25,636 = \$334,364$

Cash Flows

Year	0	1	2
Revenue		70,000	675,000*
-Oper Cost		-75,000	-75,000
-Interest		-38,000	-35,615
-Depreciation		-12,545	-13,091
-Writeoff			-334,364
-Loss Forward			-55,545
Taxable Income		-55,545	161,385
Tax @ 31%			-50,029
Net Income		-55,545	111,356
+Depreciation		12,545	13,091
+Writeoff			334,364
+Loss Forward			55,545
-Loan Principal	380,000	-23,845	-356,155
-Capital Costs	-400,000		
Leveraged Cash Flow	-20,000	-66,845	158,201

*Includes terminal sale value revenue.

Leveraged PW Eq: $0 = -20,000 - 66,845(P/F_{i,1}) + 158,201(P/F_{i,2})$

$$i = \text{Leveraged DCFROR} = 60.0\%$$

Reducing salvage value revenue to $500,000 from $600,000 at year 3 will reduce cash flow by $69,000 since all deductions remain the same and 31% of the reduced $100,000 revenue would be reduced tax. Reducing year 3 cash flow by $69,000 from $158,201 to $89,201 yields the following:

Leveraged PW Eq: $0 = -20,000 - 66,845(P/F_{i,1}) + 89,201(P/F_{i,2})$

$$i = \text{Leveraged DCFROR} = 2.20\%$$

The leveraged DCFROR is very sensitive to changes in the final sale value.

11.4 Minimum Rate of Return and Leverage

NPV analysis at first glance seems to offer a leveraged analysis advantage over DCFROR analysis since NPV results, for a given minimum DCFROR, vary over a finite range as you go from zero to 100% borrowed money instead of the infinite range over which DCFROR results vary. However, *for leveraged NPV results to be valid for decision-making purposes, the minimum DCFROR used in NPV calculations must be based on the same or a similar amount of leverage as the project being analyzed as discussed in this section. This means that you need a different minimum DCFROR for every NPV calculation based on different amounts of borrowed money.* More leverage makes DCFROR economics of projects look better as long as the after-tax cost of borrowed money is less than the cash investment DCFROR of the project in which the borrowed money is being used. *Since the minimum DCFROR represents the analysis of other opportunities for the investment of capital, it should be evident that it is desirable and necessary for valid economic analysis to evaluate the "other opportunities" on the same leverage basis as the project or projects being analyzed.*

It has been emphasized throughout this text that the opportunity cost of capital, which is the return on investment forgone if a new investment is accepted, is the appropriate "minimum rate of return" or "hurdle rate" to use in economic evaluations. In this section we want to examine the effect of leverage (borrowed money) on opportunity cost of capital. It will be shown that opportunity cost of capital is still the appropriate minimum rate of return (or discount rate), with leverage as with cash investments, but that the opportunity cost or discount rate increases as the proportion of borrowed dollars incorporated into the analysis of other opportunities increases. This assumes that the after-tax cost of borrowed funds is less than the cash investment DCFROR of the project or projects representing other investment opportunities so that leverage enhances the economic potential of these other investment opportunities.

To illustrate the effect of leverage on opportunity cost of capital, assume that the best alternative use of funds, or an investment typical of other cash investment opportunities, is represented by the initial investment of $100,000 in non-depreciable property that will generate revenues of $70,000 per year and operating costs of $20,000 per year in each of the following years. Assume a 40% effective tax rate and zero salvage value. Calculate cash investment DCFROR.

```
Year                      0          1 - 5
==================================================
Revenue                              70,000
-Oper. Costs                        -20,000
--------------------------------------------------
Taxable                              50,000
-Tax @ 40%                          -20,000
--------------------------------------------------
Net Income                           30,000
-Capital Costs        -100,000
--------------------------------------------------
Cash Flow             -100,000       30,000
```

PW Eq: 0 = -100,000 + 30,000(P/A$_{i,5}$)

    i = DCFROR = 15%

This 15% DCFROR becomes our cash investment opportunity cost of capital, minimum DCFROR, hurdle rate, or discount rate if it represents our other investment opportunities.

If the investor was able to borrow 25% of the initial $100,000 capital cost at a 10% annual interest rate, the leveraged project DCFROR would be greater than 15% because the cash investment project DCFROR is greater than the after-tax cost of borrowed money devoted to it. (Borrowing at 10% interest before-tax gives 6% interest after-tax for a 40% tax rate.) Assuming that a $25,000, 5 year loan at 10% interest per year is amortized with 5 equal mortgage payments of $6,600, the leveraged DCFROR is calculated as follows:

All Values are in Thousands of Dollars

Year	0	1	2	3	4	5
Revenue		70	70	70	70	70
-Oper. Costs		-20	-20	-20	-20	-20
-Interest		-2.5	-2.09	-1.64	-1.14	-0.6
Taxable		47.5	47.91	48.36	48.86	49.4
-Tax @ 40%		-19.00	-19.16	-19.34	-19.54	-19.76
Net Income		28.50	28.75	29.02	29.32	29.64
±Loan Principal	25.00	-4.10	-4.51	-4.96	-5.46	-6.00
-Capital Costs	-100.00					
Lever Cash Flow	-75.00	24.40	24.24	24.06	23.86	23.64

An alternate reasonably quick way of getting the leveraged cash flows for different amounts of borrowed money is to adjust the cash investment cash flows for, 1) loan income in the year or years of borrowing, 2) after-tax interest cost which is before-tax interest multiplied by one minus the tax rate, 3) loan principal payments. This is illustrated for the 25% borrowed money cash flows just calculated the long way.

```
Cash Investment
Cash Flow        -100.00   30.00   30.00   30.00   30.00   30.00
+Loan Income       25.00
-After-Tax
 Interest                   -1.50   -1.25   -0.98   -0.68   -0.36
-Loan Principal
 Payments                   -4.10   -4.51   -4.96   -5.46   -6.00
-----------------------------------------------------------------
Lever Cash Flow   -75.00   24.40   24.24   24.06   23.86   23.64
```

PW Eq: $0 = -75 + 24.40(P/F_{i,1}) + 24.24(P/F_{i,2}) + 24.06(P/F_{i,3})$

$$+ 23.86(P/F_{i,4}) + 23.64(P/F_{i,5})$$

i = Leveraged Investment DCFROR = 18.2%

This result is 3.5% higher than the 15% cash investment DCFROR. Increasing the borrowed money leverage proportion increases the leveraged DCFROR as Table 11-1 summarizes for this specific illustration.

Table 11-1 Loan Repayment with Uniform and Equal Mortgage Payments

Cash Investment	Leveraged Proportion	Leveraged Equity Investment	Leveraged DCFROR
$100,000	0%	$100,000	15.2%
$100,000	25%	$ 75,000	18.2%
$100,000	50%	$ 50,000	24.1%
$100,000	75%	$ 25,000	41.1%
$100,000	100%	$ 0	∞%

These results demonstrate that the opportunity cost that defines the after-tax minimum rate of return is a function of the leverage proportion associated with the investment. Because the use of leverage will increase the project DCFROR, the minimum rate of return or hurdle rate that the project investment must equal or exceed for acceptance must also be increased to reflect the increased leverage incorporated in the investment. If the minimum DCFROR is not increased to reflect the increased leverage proportion, almost any project can be made to look economically attractive simply by increasing the proportion of borrowed money devoted to the project. Also, as discussed earlier in Example 11-1, leveraged DCFROR results have different uncertainty associated with their meaning compared to the meaning of cash investment DCFROR results. This is because cash investment DCFROR results relate to larger unamortized investments every year compared to the corresponding meaning of leveraged DCFROR results, which always relate to smaller unamortized investments each year. This always causes sensitivity analysis of any project parameter to give greater total variations in leveraged results compared to cash investment results. This means that both the physical meaning and the uncertainty meaning are different for DCFROR results based on different amounts of leverage. One of the most important considerations in economic analysis work is to be consistent in the assumptions and handling of different investment analyses. With leverage this means using the same amount of leverage in all economic analyses, including the ones used to determine the minimum rate of return. Relating this to the analysis of projects compared with other investment opportunities summarized in Table 11-1, new projects evaluated based on 25% borrowed money at 10% interest would have to beat the 18.2% minimum DCFROR associated with a 25% leveraged investment in the alternative use of funds. If 50% leverage is contemplated at a 10% borrowing rate, projects considered must beat a 24.1% minimum DCFROR. With 100% leverage no equity investment exists and leveraged DCFROR results become effectively meaningless because you determine that all projects have an infinite percent return on zero dollars invested, hardly useful results on which to base economic decisions. If the after-tax cost of borrowed money exceeds what it earns in the project into which it is invested, the 100% leverage gives a negative infinite percent DCFROR.

The general conclusion that the minimum DCFROR is a function of the proportion of leverage involved in the investment is complicated by the fact that a leveraged project will yield different DCFROR results as a function of the terms of the loan repayment schedule associated with a given leverage proportion. To illustrate, consider the project described earlier to obtain the Table 11-1 results, that is a $100,000 non-depreciable cash investment project generating revenues of $70,000 per year and operating costs of $20,000 per year for 5 years with zero salvage and a 40% tax rate. With 50% borrowed money ($50,000) at 10% interest paid off with 5 equal year 1 through 5 mortgage payments of $13,200 each, Table 11-1 shows a 24% leveraged DCFROR. The borrower, however, may be able to arrange for the $50,000 loan on different repayment terms, such as paying interest each year with two equal $25,000 balloon loan principal payments at the end of year 4 and 5. Here the repayment schedule has changed but the lender is still receiving 10% interest (on different unamortized loan principal values) and the borrower is still using 50% leverage as a proportion of the initial project cost. The leveraged cash flow calculations follow.

All Values in Thousands of Dollars.

Year	0	1	2	3	4	5
Revenue		70	70	70	70	70
-Oper. Costs		-20	-20	-20	-20	-20
-Interest		-5	-5	-5	-5	-2.5
Taxable		45	45	45	45	47.5
-Tax @ 40%		-18.0	-18.0	-18.0	-18.0	-19.0
Net Income		27.0	27.0	27.0	27.0	28.5
±Loan Principal	50.00				-25.0	-25.0
-Capital Costs	-100.00					
Lever Cash Flow	-50.00	27.0	27.0	27.0	2.0	3.5

PW Eq: $0 = -50.00 + 27.0(P/F_{i,1}) + 27.0(P/F_{i,2}) + 27.0(P/F_{i,3})$
$$+ 2.0(P/F_{i,4}) + 3.5(P/F_{i,5})$$
$$i = \text{Leveraged (50\% Borrowed) DCFROR} = 30.9\%$$

This is a larger minimum leveraged DCFROR result than the 24% DCFROR based on repaying the $50,000 loan with 5 equal mortgage payments.

Finally, the lender may insist on accelerated repayment of loan principal and interest out of 100% of project cash flows in the early years. Analysis of the 50% leveraged case for these loan repayment terms follows:

All Values in Thousands of Dollars.

Year	0	1	2	3	4	5
Revenue		70	70	70	70	70
-Oper. Costs		-20	-20	-20	-20	-20
-Interest		-5	-2.3			
Taxable		45	47.7	50	50	50
-Tax @ 40%		-18.0	-19.1	-20	-20	-20
Net Income		27.0	28.6	30	30	30
±Loan Principal	50.00	-27.0	-23.0			
-Capital Costs	-100.00					
Lever Cash Flow	-50.00	0.0	5.6	30	30	30

PW Eq: $0 = -50 + 5.6(P/F_{i,2}) + 30(P/A_{i,3})(P/F_{i,2})$

   i = Leveraged (50% Borrowed) DCFROR = 18.5%

This is a very different DCFROR result compared to the 24% and 30.9% results previously calculated for different loan repayment schedules for 50% borrowed money.

The conclusion to be drawn from this exercise is the need to *recognize that the minimum DCFROR or opportunity cost of capital is a function not only of other available investment opportunities and the proportion of leverage employed in evaluating those investment opportunities but also is a function of the loan repayment schedule.* It is necessary to be consistent in evaluating different investment opportunities with the same leverage proportion and the same type of loan repayment schedule for economic analysis results to be comparable. However, the question "what is proportional leverage?" often is very difficult to answer in comparing projects with different lives and different distributions of costs. To avoid these difficulties, most companies and individuals make zero leverage, the cash investment case, the basis for the economic comparison of projects. Cash investment analysis will give the same economic decision as leveraged analysis that is based on using the proper leveraged analysis procedures described in this section.

11.5 Capitalization of Interest in Certain Leveraged Investments

A capitalized cost is deductible for tax purposes over a period of time greater than a year by deductions such as depreciation, amortization or depletion, while an expensed cost is deductible in the year incurred as an operating cost type of expense. *Capitalization of interest payments on borrowed money means deducting the interest over the tax deductible life of the asset to which the interest relates by allowable tax deductions such as depreciation, amortization or writeoffs against a terminal sale or liquidation value.* The rational for capitalization of interest is that it is required under U.S. tax law in certain instances discussed in the next paragraph.

Under special interest capitalization rules, interest on a debt must be capitalized if the debt is incurred or continued to finance the construction, building, installation, manufacture, development, or improvement of real or tangible personal property that is produced by the taxpayer and that has,

1) a long useful life, which means a depreciable life of 15 years or more under the 1986 tax reform act, 2) an estimated production period exceeding two year, or, 3) an estimated production period exceeding one year and a cost exceeding one million dollars.

The following example illustrates capitalization of borrowed money interest during the construction period of a project to be deducted by depreciation over the allowable project depreciation life.

EXAMPLE 11-4 Capitalization of Construction Interest in Investment Analysis

A natural gas pipeline is to be constructed over a right-of-way that will cost $500,000 at year 0 with construction costs of $600,000 at year 0, $700,000 at year 1 and $800,000 at year 2. The pipeline is expected to go into service at the beginning of year 3, so straight line depreciation for a 15 year life will start in year 3 with the half year convention. Borrowed money interest will be capitalized and depreciated with pipeline cost. 100% of the year 0, 1 and 2 construction costs (not the right-of-way cost) will be borrowed at 10% annual interest with all loan interest and principal capitalized to year 2 to be paid off by ten equal mortgage payments at years 3 through 12. However, it is expected that the pipeline will be sold at year 4 for $4 million with a writeoff on remaining book value taken at year 4 against the sale income. The loan will also be paid off in year 4. Pipeline revenues are projected to be $400,000 at year 3 and $450,000 at year 4 with operating costs of $150,000 at year 3 and $160,000 at year 4. Other income exists against which to use deductions in the years incurred and the effective income tax rate is 40%.

Solution, All Values in Thousands of Dollars:

Loan Amortization Schedule

Year 1 Interest $= .10(\$600) = \$60$
Year 2 Interest $= .10(\$600 + \$700 + \$60) = \$136$
Year 2 Capitalized Interest and Cost
  $= \$600 + \$700 + \$800 + \$60 + \$136 = \$2,296$
Year 3-12 Mortgage Payments $= \$2,296(A/P_{10,10}) = \$373.67$
Year 3 Interest $= .10(\$2,296) = \$229.60$
Year 3 Principal $= \$373.67 - \$229.60 = \$144.07$
Year 4 Principal Owed $= \$2,296 - \$144.07 = \$2,151.93$
Year 4 Interest $= .10(\$2,151.93) = \$215.19$

Depreciation Schedule

Year 3 $= (\$2,296)(1/15)(1/2) = \$ 76.53$
Year 4 $= (\$2,296)(1/15) = \$ 153.06$
Remaining Book Value Writeoff $= \$2,066.44$

Cash Flow Calculations

Year	0	1	2	3	4
Income				400.0	4,460.0
-Oper Costs				-150.0	-160.0
-Post Prod. Interest				-229.6	-215.2
-Depreciation				-76.5	-153.1
-Writeoff					-2,066.4
Taxable Income				-56.1	1,865.3
-Tax a 40%				22.4	-746.1
Net Income				-33.7	1,865.3
+Deprec/Writeoff				76.5	2,219.5
-Loan Principal	600	760	936	-141.1	-2,151.9
-Capital Costs	-1,100	-760	-936		
Cash Flow	-500	0	0	-101.3	1,186.8

PW Eq: $0 = -500 - 101.3(P/F_{i,3}) + 1,186.8(P/F_{i,4})$

i = Leveraged DCFROR = 20.8%

11.6 Lease Versus Purchase and Leveraged lease Analysis

Comparison of leasing versus purchasing of assets and facilities from an economic analysis viewpoint is the same as the analysis of any service-producing alternatives as was illustrated previously in Chapter 10. However, lease versus purchase analysis is such a common important analysis to people in all types of industries and organizations that it merits special attention.

Many people consider leasing as an alternative method of financing to borrowing money and from a financial viewpoint it certainly is. However, from an economic analysis viewpoint, the dollar values on lease compared to purchase time diagrams may look similar to or identically the same as dollar values for automated equipment compared to a labor intensive approach to providing a service or for new equipment compared to old. Staying with old equipment or a labor intensive service-producing approach, like leasing, may be thought of as an alternative financing approach to purchasing a new asset. However, in all of these analyses, including lease versus purchase, the time value of money must be handled using a minimum rate of return that represents other opportunities felt to exist for the use of capital and not the cost of borrowed money, unless borrowed money is considered to be unlimited. In other words, the minimum rate of return in lease versus purchase analyses must be the same as in all other analyses if you want to get valid, comparable results for economic decision making purposes.

Some of the often repeated advantages and disadvantages of leasing compared to purchasing are as follows:

Advantages of Leasing

1. Leasing charges for equipment may be written off for tax purposes in the year in which they occur, whereas first cost of purchased equipment must be depreciated over its useful life.
2. Leasing offers an added line of credit over and above a company's normal line of credit and it permits intermediate term financing without bond, debenture, or stock offerings.
3. Leasing gives added "leverage" to potential return on investment by creating the potential to increase profits without increasing capital investment.
4. Leasing reduces the risk of purchasing equipment and suffering a sunk cost because a speculative project proves unsuccessful. Changes generally are easier to make with leased equipment than purchased equipment. Flexibility is a word that describes this advantage.

Disadvantages of Leasing

1. The dollar cost of leasing may be more than the dollar cost of buying the same equipment; therefore, profitability often favors ownership.
2. At the end of the lease, the leasing company still owns the equipment.

Leveraged leases are leases where the lessor (the asset owner) uses borrowed money to purchase the property which is then leased to the lessee. Leveraged leases must satisfy lease provisions described in Section 10.7 for cash investment leases plus some additional provisions that follow. Investors in leveraged lease assets must make an equity investment of at least 20% of asset value and be at risk for that amount. The lessee may not make a loan to the lessor to cover any part of the purchase price. Basically the lessor must be able to show that he can profit from the lease and not strictly from tax benefits related to the lease. It is possible for an investor in a leveraged lease to get an advance ruling from the U.S. Internal Revenue Service concerning whether a proposed leveraged lease transaction will be considered to be a lease or a conditional sale (a capital lease with lease payments capitalized and depreciated). The following example illustrates a typical leveraged operating lease analysis.

EXAMPLE 11-5 Breakeven Leveraged Lease Payment Analysis

Company "A" is considering the purchase of equipment costing $200,000 to lease to Company "B" on a 4 year lease agreement. Company A would acquire the equipment using $40,000 cash equity and $160,000 borrowed money at a 12% annual interest rate, so this is a leveraged lease analysis. The borrowed money will be repaid over 4 years with annual end-of-year mortgage payments of $40,000 loan principal plus interest due each year. Modified ACRS 5 year life depreciation will be taken starting in year 0 with the half year convention. Company "A" has other income and tax obligations against which to use tax deductions in any year and the effective tax rate is 40%. The sale value of the equipment is estimated to be $60,000 at the end of year 4 and Company "B" will be given an option to buy the equipment at year 4 at the $60,000 price. Determine the four uniform and equal breakeven beginning-of-year lease payments each year starting in year 0 for a 25% escalated dollar leveraged minimum DCFROR on equity investment dollars. Then make the analysis for a 10% minimum escalated dollar DCFROR.

Solution, All Values in Thousands of Dollars:

The analysis is from the viewpoint of Company A (lessor).

Year	0	1	2	3	4
Lease Revenue	X	X	X	X	60.0
-Loan Interest		-19.2	-14.4	-9.6	-4.8
-Depreciation	-40	-64.0	-38.4	-28.8	-28.8
Taxable Income	X-40	X-83.2	X-52.8	X-38.4	26.4
-Tax @ 40%	-.4X+16	-.4X+33.3	-.4X+21.1	-.4X+15.4	-10.6
Net Income	.6X-24	.6X-49.9	.6X-31.7	.6X-23.0	15.8
+Depreciation	40	64.0	38.4	28.8	28.8
-Loan Principal	160	-40.0	-40.0	-40.0	-40.0
-Capital Costs	-200				
Leveraged CF	.6X-24	.6X-25.9	.6X-33.3	.6X-34.2	4.6

For $i^* = 25\%$

PW Eq: $0 = (.6X-24) + (.6X-25.9)(P/F_{25,1}) \overset{.8000}{} + (.6X-33.3)(P/F_{25,2}) \overset{.6400}{}$

$$+ (.6X-34.2)(P/F_{25,3}) \overset{.5120}{} + 4.6(P/F_{25,4}) \overset{.4096}{}$$

$0 = 1.77X - 81.66$

$X = \$46.14$ year 0, 1, 2, and 3 lease payments

Note that this breakeven cash flow of $46,140 each year gives positive cash flow at years 0 and 1 followed by negative cash flow at years 2 and 3 followed by positive cash flow at year 4. This income, cost, income analysis situation causes the 25% minimum DCFROR meaning to change from rate of reinvestment requirement meaning in the early years to rate of return meaning in the later years. You need to keep in mind that a big minimum DCFROR discount rate is good from the investor viewpoint when it means rate of return, but it is bad when rate of reinvestment requirement meaning applies. Highly leveraged projects sometimes generate positive cash flow in early years, as in this analysis, giving rate of reinvestment requirement rather than rate of return meaning to the discount rate over at least part of the project evaluation life. An economic analyst unfamiliar with these leverage effects can become confused and possibly misled from an economic investment decision making viewpoint by this type of leveraged analysis situation if it is not recognized. In this analysis the rate of return meaning of the discount rate is stronger than rate of reinvestment requirement meaning, so lowering the discount rate to 10% from 25% lowers, rather than increases the breakeven lease payments as the following calculations show.

For $i^* = 10\%$

$$\text{PW Eq:} \quad 0 = (.6X\text{-}24) + (.6X\text{-}10.9)\underset{.9091}{(P/F_{10,1})} + (.6X\text{-}33.3)\underset{.8264}{(P/F_{10,2})}$$

$$+ (.6X\text{-}34.2)\underset{.7513}{(P/F_{10,3})} + 4.6\underset{.6830}{(P/F_{10,4})}$$

$$0 = 2.09X - 83.98$$

$$X = \$40.18 \text{ year } 0, 1, 2, \text{ and } 3 \text{ lease payments}$$

11.7 Summary

In summarizing this chapter on leverage, the following point is considered to be pertinent. Do not borrow money when you have a sufficient treasury to finance investments on a 100% equity basis unless the portion of your treasury not invested in the investment can be put to work at a DCFROR which is more than the after-tax cost of borrowed money.

PROBLEMS

11-1 Your corporation is considering the purchase of mountain recreation land for a cost of $60,000 and you estimate that 5 years from now it will be possible to sell the land for $150,000. Assume that your corporation is in the 40% effective ordinary tax bracket and that profit from the sale of the land in 5 years will be taxed as ordinary income. Determine your corporation DCFROR on its equity in the investment for:

A) Paying cash for the land,

B) Borrowing $50,000 of the $60,000 purchase cost at 10% interest per year with a mortgage agreement to pay back $10,000 principal plus interest on the unpaid principal at each of years 1 through 5. Assume interest costs each year are expenses against other income.

11-2 An investor purchased land 2 years ago for $1 million and the land has since been zoned for a commercial shopping center development. The investor has received an offer of $7 million cash for the land now at year zero and gain would be taxed as an individual long term capital gain. Assume the individual ordinary income effective tax rate is 35%. Keeping the property and developing it starting now at time zero will involve costs and revenues shown on the following diagram.

All values are in millions of dollars.

```
C Bldgs.=30      Income/Yr.=65     70      75
C Equip.= 5      OpCost/Yr.=25     30      35
                                                   L=40
    0 (Now)                     1       2       3
```

To finance the development, $5 million of cash equity will be invested at year zero and $30 million will be borrowed at year zero at 12% annual interest with the loan set up to be repaid over 5 years with equal mortgage payments at the end of years 1 through 5. However, if the property is sold at year 3 the remaining loan principal will be paid off at that time. The buildings will be depreciated over a 31.5 year life using straight line depreciation starting in month 1 of year 1 with the mid-month convention. The equipment will be depreciated using 7 year life modified ACRS depreciation starting in year 1 with the half year convention. Assume any taxable gain on the terminal value (L) is taxed as ordinary income. For a leveraged minimum DCFROR of 20% determine whether selling or developing is economically better.

11-3   A major petroleum company spent $3 million last year acquiring the
mineral rights to a property surrounded by producing oil wells. Probability of successful development is considered to be 100%. An offer
of $5 million cash now at time zero has been received for the property
from another investor and gain from the sale would be taxed as
ordinary income. It is projected that if we fully develop the property
and produce it over the next 3 years that a sale value of $6.5 million
for the property and all production assets can be realized 3 years from
now with any sale taxable gain assumed to be taxed as ordinary
income. To develop the property the company must borrow $4 million
at 12% annual interest now (at time zero) to be paid off over 5 years
with 5 equal end-of-year mortgage payments. However, if the property
is sold at the end of year 3, the remaining loan principal will be paid
off then. The minimum DCFROR is 25% for leveraged investments
of this type. Make a DCFROR analysis to determine whether it is
better to sell now or develop and sell 3 years from now based on the
development data given on the following diagram.

All values are in millions of dollars.

```
                              Revenue  =7.0   11.0      9.0
                              Op. Costs=1.2    2.5      2.1
Cost Tangibles  =1.5          Tangibles=1.0
Cost Intangibles=2.0          Intang   =2.0
                              _____
                                                          L=6.5
     0                           1         2         3
```

Royalties are 15% of revenues each year. Operating costs include all
severance and excise tax. 10% of total initial reserves are produced
in year 1, 16% in year 2 and 14% in year 3. Assume intangible well
costs are incurred in the first month of the year in which they occur.
Tangible well costs are depreciated over 7 years using the modified
ACRS rates starting in the year tangible costs are incurred with the
half year convention. Use a 40% effective income tax rate.

11-4   You are to evaluate for a corporation the economics of purchasing a
silver property now at year 0 for a $2 million mineral rights acquisition
cost. Mining equipment costs of $3 million will be incurred at year
0 but put into service in year 1 with mineral development costs of
$1.5 million spent during year 1. Consider that the mineral develop-
ment costs are incurred in the seventh month of year 1 for tax deduction
purposes. Other income exists against which to use negative taxable

income in any year so credit the project with tax savings in the year deductions are taken. Mining equipment will be depreciated starting in year 1 with the half year convention using modified ACRS depreciation for a 7 year life. Production is estimated to be 300,000 ounces of silver per year with silver prices projected to be $15 per ounce in year 1, $20 per ounce in year 2 and $25 per ounce in year 3. Total silver reserves are estimated to be 3,000,000 ounces. Operating costs are estimated to be $10 per ounce in year 1, $11.25 per ounce in year 2 and $12.50 per ounce in year 3. The effective income tax rate is 40%. Assume the mine will be sold at the end of year 3 for $6 million and that any taxable gain from the sale will be taxed as ordinary income. Calculate the leveraged project DCFROR assuming $4 million is borrowed at year 0 at a 10% annual interest rate. Loan mortgage payments will be uniform and equal over year 1 to 10. Assume the remaining unpaid loan principal will be paid off at the end of year 3 when the mine is sold.

11-5 An investor is evaluating the purchase of 200 acres of land for a $200,000 purchase price now with plans to sell the land for a profit one year from now. The investor plans to pay for the property with $40,000 cash equity and $160,000 borrowed money at a 10% annual interest rate with the loan to paid in full when the property is sold. What escalated dollar sale value must the land have one year after purchase to give the investor a constant dollar leveraged DCFROR of 30% on investor equity if the annual inflation rate is projected to be 10%? Assume that the capital gain from the land sale will be taxed as ordinary income with an effective ordinary income tax rate of 34%.

11-6 A business is considering the purchase of an excavating machine for a cost of $150,000 at year 0. An additional $10,000 working capital investment will be required at time 0 for spare parts inventory. It is projected that rental of the machine will generate annual escalated dollar sales revenues of $150,000, $180,000 and $210,000 in years 1, 2 and 3 and escalated dollar operating costs of $50,000, $70,000 and $90,000 for years 1, 2 and 3 respectively. The machine will be depreciated using 7 year life modified ACRS depreciation starting at year 0 with the half year convention. It is estimated that the machine will be used for 3 years and sold for a $50,000 escalated dollar salvage value. To pay for the machine $120,000 will be borrowed from a bank at time 0 at 10% interest per year on unpaid principal amounts with equal principal payments of $40,000 plus interest made at the end of years 1, 2 and 3. Consider the effective tax rate to be 40%. Assuming an average annual inflation rate of 10% per year calculate the constant dollar DCFROR on the business equity investment over the 3 year evaluation life for the leverage conditions stated. What is the leveraged escalated dollar DCFROR that corresponds to the leveraged constant dollar DCFROR?

11-7   A depreciable investment of $100,000 is required at time 0 to develop a new product with an expected 5 year market life. A development cost of $10,000, to be expensed against other income, is also required at time 0 along with $30,000 for working capital. Sales of $150,000 per year are expected in year 1 with operating costs of $118,000. Escalation of sales and operating costs are expected to be a washout in year 2 through 5. Working capital return of $30,000 and equipment salvage of $0 are expected to be realized at the end of year 5 when the project is terminated. The effective income tax rate is 40%. Depreciation is straight line over 5 years starting in year 0 with the half year convention. Compare the cash investment DCFROR with the leveraged DCFROR for borrowing $100,000 at time 0 at 12% interest per year with $20,000 principal plus interest paid off each year.

CHAPTER 12

VALUATION OF PROPERTY, PROJECTS AND BUSINESSES

12.1 Approaches to Valuation of Investments

Placing correct value on investment property and projects is extremely important to investors, bankers and sellers alike. Again and again, how much a property is worth at a given time under a given set of market conditions must be determined. Sometimes financial considerations such as the maximum mortgage loan that can be obtained on an investment and the loan terms will affect or determine the sale value of a property. However, projected future earnings usually determine the market value of assets. Lending institutions are just as anxious as buyers and sellers to know the answers to valuation problems. Often they depend upon a professional class of 'rule-of-thumb' appraiser rules to develop the guidelines on which to base their commitments. Investment bankers perform the same appraiser service in relation to putting value on companies, projects and investment situations.

There are three basic approaches that appraisers, investment bankers and investors take in determining the market value of investment property. These approaches are, 1) replacement cost, 2) market valuation based on comparable sales, and 3) discounted cash flow analysis valuation of projected future positive and negative cash flows.

The replacement cost approach to valuation is based on analyzing cost for land, mineral rights, buildings and equipment, roads, development, and other costs to replace an existing facility, production operation, real estate investment or general investment project. You need to be very careful to include all costs that are relevant for this type of analysis and that can be a difficult task sometimes. Different projects that on the surface seem similar or identical may have significantly different development or operating costs for subtle reasons that an inexperienced evaluator might overlook.

The comparable sales approach to valuation is based on looking at recent sale prices for properties or investments similar to the one being valued. This approach works very well in housing real estate where many transactions occur regularly for similar properties over any given period of time in given locations. To a lesser degree this approach is applicable to apartment house, office building and land real estate investments. The consideration that you must be very careful about in making comparable sales analysis is the comparable equivalence of properties being analyzed. When you get into the analysis of income producing projects, business and general investments, subtle differences in location, property taxes, operating costs such as energy costs, development or needed improvement costs, size of operation (which may affect efficiency of operation), existing product sale contracts and many other factors can cause significant differences in investment valuations. Comparable sales is often a poor approach to valuation of natural resource properties. The value of mineral, petroleum and timber rights varies significantly with size of reserves, projected timing for development of reserves, expected rate of production of reserves, expected cost for development and production of reserves, projected product price at different future points in time related to production, and, future salvage value of the assets are some of the significant parameters to be considered. Usually at least several of these parameters differ significantly for different properties, making comparable sales a very poor approach to valuation of natural resource properties. Different size and quality of natural resource reserves affects the timing and cost of production, which generally makes it imperative to go to discounted cash flow valuation of these types of investments rather than trying to utilize the comparable sales approach.

Discounted cash flow analysis for valuation purposes relates directly to after-tax net present value analysis of investments to be valued. This requires projecting the magnitude and timing of project capital investment costs and operating costs to produce product at a given rate with projected future product selling prices. All expected inflows and outflows of money including salvage values or abandonment costs need to be taken into account. Proper tax effects and any risk of failure need to be accounted for properly in a valid discounted cash flow valuation. These calculations and concepts have been the subject of emphasis in the previous eleven chapters of this text, so we will conclude this discussion by emphasizing the importance of the magnitude and timing of input cost and revenue data and the income tax and evaluation assumptions applied to these data to obtain valid discounted cash flow valuation results. Section 12.3 in this chapter further emphasizes that after-tax NPV of a project in general does not represent the maximum price that an investor can pay to receive the minimum DCFROR discount rate on invested dollars. Because acquisition costs of various types are tax deductible through depreciation, amortization, depletion or writeoffs upon sale or abandonment of a project, the value of an investment usually is bigger than its NPV. Example 12-4 illustrates these considerations in detail so they will not be discussed further here.

All three of the valuation approaches just discussed have valuation importance in various situations. The following are three simple example illustrations of typical applications of these approaches to valuation.

EXAMPLE 12-1 Valuation Based on Cost

A man pays $10,000 for a lot on which he builds a house costing $40,000. Landscaping costs $3,000. By not leaving his money in the bank, bank interest of $2,500 was lost over the 8 month period between the investment in the lot and the finished construction of the house. Based on cost valuation, what price must the man receive for the house to break even with the return on his money he would have received from the bank?

Solution:

In this case the sum of the costs is $55,500 so this is the value that represents breakeven with the bank interest on the invested dollars. In non-income producing investment valuations such as home cost valuation, replacement cost and the comparable sales approach are the two approaches used most commonly.

EXAMPLE 12-2 Valuation Based on Comparable Sales

The man in Example 12-1 has just completed building his home for the $55,500 in costs specified when a large company announces it is going to build a new plant nearby greatly increasing the demand for homes in the area. Comparable homes start selling for $75,000. How should the man value his new home?

Solution:

Over the short term dislocations in supply and demand due to situations like the one described in this problem can cause significant differences between cost value and market value from comparable sales. It seems obvious that if the market will bear a $75,000 asking price, then $75,000 is the value the man should place on the property even though cost valuation is only $55,500.

EXAMPLE 12-3 Valuation Based on Discounted Cash Flow Analysis

The truest test of proper valuation of an income producing investment is to calculate the present worth of projected future positive and negative cash flow at a satisfactory minimum rate of return. Market conditions may permit you to purchase the property cheaper or to sell it for more but you should always calculate what it is actually worth in order to judge whether the market price is high or low relative to actual value. This is how good investments are found. You do not have to buy everything you evaluate. Risk and uncertainty often make the projection of cash flow difficult but it must be done.

Apply this approach to determine the share value of 3,000,000 shares of common stock in XYZ Corporation if the following future positive and negative cash flows are projected: $50,000,000 will be borrowed this year to build a plant that is projected to generate $12,000,000 annual after-tax cash flow for each of the next 10 years. Note that the valuation technique is the same if we want to determine the value of a mineral lease or real estate property instead of common stock value. The minimum DCFROR is 12% in escalated dollars. Using a 12% after-tax discount rate implicitly assumes that any annual cash flow paid out in dividends to the investor can be invested elsewhere at 12% by the investor, and any cash flow not paid out in dividends can and will be invested at a 12% annually compounded DCFROR by the XYZ Corporation.

Solution:

PW Cash Flow $= \$12,000,000(P/A_{12,10}) = \$67,800,000$

PW Debt $= \$50,000,000$

PW Valuation $=$ PW Cash Flow $-$ PW Debt $= \$17,800,000$

Value Per Common Share $= 17.8 / 3 = \$5.93$

If the project life is extended to 15 and 20 years we get:

15 Years: PW Cash Flow $= \$12,000,000(P/A_{12,15}) = \$81,730,000$

Value Per Common Share $= 31.73 / 3 = \$10.58$

20 Years: PW Cash Flow $= \$12,000,000(P/A_{12,20}) = \$89,630,000$

Value Per Common Share $= 39.63 / 3 = \$13.21$

Changing the minimum rate of return would change the valuation results just like changing project life affected the results. It becomes easy to see why there is seldom unanimity concerning investment values in the marketplace.

Note in Example 12-3 that the value of present assets of the XYZ Corporation has no effect on the determination of present value. This assumes that existing assets are owned by the corporation and are necessary to generate the projected cash flow. If existing assets can be liquidated and we can still generate the given cash flow stream then the value of the assets that are not needed to generate cash flow should be added to the total valuation of the business.

12.2 Valuation of Public Projects and Investments

Valuation of public and governmental investment projects and properties requires the same sound valuation approaches that are necessary for private companies and individuals. The big difference between public and private valuation is lack of taxation of public investments so before-tax analysis is appropriate. The profit motive should exist in public investments the same as it does in private investments except the profits usually are received as benefits to the public rather than dividends or profit distribution. Good use of public investment funds minimizes our tax costs and maximizes public benefits we receive per public dollar invested.

In public investment evaluations it is just as important as in private evaluations to (1) clearly define investment alternatives, (2) convert intangible considerations to tangible dollar values when possible and (3) use an investment decision method based upon proper handling of the time value of money at a satisfactory minimum rate of return to compare alternative investments. In general the same methods of analysis used in the evaluation of mutually exclusive and non-mutually exclusive private investment alternatives are valid and necessary for the correct evaluation of public projects.

Public projects, whether funded at the local, state or national government level, inevitably are funded by an agency that has limited resources because citizens make far more requests and demands for service than monetary resources permit carrying out. Therefore, it is very important that the best possible use is made of available funds and it is necessary to use an opportunity cost of capital minimum rate of return in evaluating public projects the same as in evaluating private investment projects.

Determination of benefits that will accrue to the public from investment in various government projects such as roads, bridges, airports, dams and recreation areas is necessary to establish the relative desirability of projects under consideration. It is, of course, a tough job to determine all the public benefits that may be derived from a given investment situation. However, as in evaluating private investments, someone must take the responsibility to attempt to reduce intangible considerations to tangible values that can be handled in an orderly fashion using a given evaluation method to compare various alternatives. Comparing benefits to costs and accounting for the time value of money is the correct basis for valid economic analysis of public or private investments. This means that a suitable minimum rate of return must be selected. As in private enterprise the minimum rate of return should reflect the other opportunities which are available for investment of existing capital. As in private enterprise determination of a suitable minimum rate of return is a difficult task because it is hard to know for sure what ROR other opportunities might yield unless putting money in the bank is the other alternative. This is seldom the case in public projects. Certainly the minimum rate of return should be greater that the cost of public money or the projects should not be undertaken. If it will cost the public a ten percent interest rate on bonds for a project the minimum rate of return must be at least ten percent. How much greater than ten percent it really should be depends on what alternative projects would yield that may have to be passed over if a particular project is carried out. This opportunity cost of capital for public project analysis is directly analogous to private investment opportunity cost of capital.

12.3 NPV Use For Acquisition Cost Valuation

Net present value (NPV) represents the additional after-tax cost that can be incurred at the point in time NPV is calculated and still give the investor the minimum DCFROR on invested dollars. The key words here are "after-tax costs" because that is what NPV represents. Acquisition costs are before-tax costs. You must account for the tax deductibility of acquisition costs to determine tax savings from acquisition cost tax deductions. Netting the present worth of these tax savings against the acquisition cost give us the "after-tax acquisition cost", which equals the project NPV. In general, if an acquisition cost is to be incurred for assets that are tax deductible, an investor can pay more than the NPV value of the project and still get the minimum DCFROR on invested dollars. Whether acquisition costs are for assets that are depreciable, amortizable, depletable or non-deductible except as a writeoff against sale value like land is very important, necessary input information for valid acquisition cost analysis. The following example illustrates these concepts.

EXAMPLE 12-4 NPV Related to Breakeven Acquisition Cost Analysis

Consider a project with an equipment cost of $15 million and a development cost of $10 million at year 0. Uniformly equal escalated dollar revenues of $20 million per year for years 1 through 5 are expected to be generated with escalated dollar operating costs of $5 million per year. Salvage value at year 5 is expected to be 0. Expense the full development cost in year 0 and assume other taxable income exists against which to use the deduction. Depreciate the equipment straight line over 5 years starting in year 0 with the half-year convention. Use a 40% effective income tax rate. For a minimum escalated dollar DCFROR of 20%, calculate project NPV. Then make the following acquisition cost analyses.

Case 1: Prior to starting this project what could an investor pay to acquire the right to develop the project if a 20% DCFROR is satisfactory? Assume the acquisition cost would be treated as a patent or business agreement cost for tax purposes that can be amortized straight line over 5 years (years 1 through 5).

Case 2: After developing the project and realizing the year 1 revenue and operating cost what could an investor pay to acquire the project at the beginning of year 2 to get a 20% DCFROR on invested dollars? Assume this acquisition cost would be specified so that 60% of the cost is considered to be for depreciable assets and 40% of the cost is for 5 year life amortizable business agreement or patent costs.

Solution, All Values in Thousands of Dollars:

Case 1

Year	0	1-4	5
Revenue		20,000	20,000
-Oper Costs		-5,000	-5,000
-Development	-10,000		
-Depreciation	-1,500	-3,000	-1,500
Taxable	-11,500	12,000	13,500
-Tax a 40%	4,600	-4,800	-5,400
Net Income	-6,900	7,200	8,100
+Depreciation	1,500	3,000	1,500
-Capital Costs	-15,000		
Cash Flow	-20,400	10,200	9,600

$$NPV = 10,200(P/A_{20,4}) + 9,600(P/F_{20,5}) -20,400 = +\$9,860$$

If you pay $9.86 million to acquire the property and the acquisition cost is tax deductible as a patent cost as described in Case 1 of the problem statement, NPV will still be positive. You can afford to pay more than the NPV of

$9.86 million and still get a 20% DCFROR on invested dollars. This is illus-
trated now for an assumed $10 million amortizable acquisition cost.

Year	0	1-4	5
Revenue		20,000	20,000
-Oper Costs		-5,000	-5,000
-Development	-10,000		
-Depreciation	-1,500	-3,000	-1,500
-Amortization		-2,000	-2,000
Taxable	-11,500	10,000	11,500
-Tax @ 40%	4,600	-4,000	-4,600
Net Income	-6,900	6,000	6,900
+Depreciation	1,500	5,000	3,500
-Capital Costs	-25,000		
Cash Flow	-30,400	11,000	10,400

$$NPV = -30,400 + 11,000(P/A_{20,4}) + 10,400(P/F_{20,5}) = +2,250$$

Although the NPV of the initial project was $ 9.86 million, spending 10
million to acquire the patent rights has still left the project with positive NPV
because of the patent tax deduction effects. We can calculate the amount
that can be paid for the patent to make project NPV zero as follows:

Let "X" equal the unknown patent cost that will reduce the year 0 NPV by
$9.86 million. X/5 is the annual amortization tax deduction from this cost.

$(X/5)(.4$ tax rate$) = .08X$ tax savings per year.

Reduce the acquisition cost, "X", by the present worth of tax savings:

$$X - .08X \overset{2.991}{(P/A_{20,5})} = 9.86$$

X = $12.97 or approximately $13 million

Now verify that the acquisition cost of $13.0 million for patent rights makes
the project NPV equal to zero.

Year	0	1-4	5
Revenue		20,000	20,000
-Oper Costs		-5,000	-5,000
-Development	-10,000		
-Depreciation	-1,500	-3,000	-1,500
-Amortization		-2,600	-2,600
Taxable	-11,500	9,400	10,900
-Tax @ 40%	4,600	-3,700	-4,300
Net Income	-6,900	5,700	6,600
+Depreciation	1,500	5,600	4,100
-Capital Costs	-28,000		
Cash Flow	-33,400	11,300	10,700

$$NPV = -33,400 + 11,300(P/A_{20,4}) + 10,700(P/F_{20,5}) = 0$$

Therefore, the project DCFROR is equal to 20%

Case 2

After the year 0 costs and year 1 revenues and operating cost have been incurred they are sunk. Even the cash flows calculated for the initial project are not relevant to our analysis because the investor cash flow will be based on tax deductions related to acquisition cost paid for the project assets.

To make the Case 2 analysis calculate the year 2 through 5 revenue cash flow after-tax without accounting for any capital costs or tax deductions other than operating expenses. Using these cash flow results, calculate year 1 NPV and equate to year 1 after-tax acquisition cost, similar to the Case 1 analysis.

Year 2 through 5 revenue cash flow without accounting for depreciation or amortization tax deductions is $20 - $5 - .4($15)$ tax or $+$9.0$. Year 1 NPV from this cash flow is $9.0(P/A_{20,4})$ or $+$23.30$. We want to calculate the before-tax acquisition cost that is 60% depreciable and 40% amortizable that would give us this after-tax acquisition cost equal to the NPV of $23.30 at year 1.

Let X = Acquisition Cost, 60% Depreciable, 40% Amortizable

Year 2 Depreciation = .6X(1/5)(1/2) = 0.06X
Year 2 Amortization = .4X(1/5)   = 0.08X

Year 3, 4 & 5 Deprec = .6X(1/5)   = .12X
Year 3, 4 & 5 Amort = .4X(1/5)   = .08X

Year 5 Writeoff = .18X for Depreciation and 0.08X for Amortization

Year 2   Tax Savings = 0.14X(.4 tax rate) = 0.056X
Year 3,4 Tax Savings = 0.20X(.4 tax rate) = 0.08X
Year 5   Tax Savings = 0.46X(.4 tax rate) = 0.184X

Year 1 PW Tax Savings

$$= .056X((P/F_{20,1}) + .08X(P/F_{20,2}) + .08X(P/F_{20,3}) + .184X(P/F_{20,1})$$

$$= .2373X$$

X - .2373X = After-Tax Acquisition Cost = NPV = 23.30

X = \$30.55 is the acquisition cost that, 60% depreciable, 40% amortizable makes NPV = 0 for a minimum DCFROR of 20%. The cash flow calculation proof is left to the reader.

This example was designed to illustrate the importance that the type of asset being acquired has on acquisition cost analysis results. Whether assets being acquired are depreciable, amortizable, depletable, expensed or not deductible except as a writeoff against terminal value (land and inventory asset costs) must be taken into account in proper acquisition cost analysis.

12.4 Capital Cost Estimates

Capital cost estimation is a vital component of investment analysis. Before economic analysis of different investment alternatives can be made it is necessary to estimate the total capital required for the individual alternatives. Various types of capital costs are present in different evaluations but the following is a checklist of general capital costs that may be relevant for any general investment situation whether it be a mineral or non-mineral project.

1. Land
2. Working Capital
3. Mineral Rights Acquisition/Lease
4. Research/Development
5. Exploration/Development
6. Intangible Drilling Costs in Oil and Gas Projects
7. Depreciable Assets or "Fixed Capital Assets"
8. Indirect Supervision/Construction/Contractor Expenses

Direct costs that should be considered when estimating costs for a general plant or production facility include purchased equipment, instrumentation and controls, piping, electrical equipment and materials, buildings for production and services including utilities, site development, service facilities and land. For all of these items the estimate must include the cost of installation, allowance for escalation of costs to occur at some future point in time, freight charges, taxes, insurance, duties and other fees related to preparing the assets for service.

Indirect costs that should be considered when estimating the cost for a general plant or production facility include engineering and supervision, construction expenses, contractor's fees and a contingency fee.

There are two basic approaches that can be used to estimate capital costs for projects depending an the accuracy required. The first approach involves a rough estimate of project capital costs which often can be obtained rapidly by what is called the "ratio method". The ratio method involves taking published data giving the total capital investment per unit of annual production for given processes and production operations at a given point in time and using capacity ratio indices together with cost escalation indices to estimate the cost of a new facility for a specified production rate. The second approach involves basing the capital cost estimate on facility design criteria by estimating the costs of the individual components that go into developing a physical facility that is ready to operate. There are many variations of this estimating approach that give varying degrees of accuracy in capital cost estimate results but the final detailed cost estimate for a new project is generally this type of estimate because it offers the potential of giving the best cost estimate accuracy of maybe plus or minus five percent. There are many excellent cost estimation textbooks and the reader who wants specific details on different cost estimation methods should refer to the selected references by Chilton, Peters and Timmerhaus, Popper, and Ostwald. These books provide basic cost estimation procedures, details and many other references.

Escalation of capital costs obviously is a very significant thorn in the side of capital cost estimation and economic evaluation personnel. The past is no guarantee of what the future will hold but analysis of past, especially recent, trends in the costs of equipment and facilities similar to those you are considering may provide information that will be useful in projecting actual escalated costs that must be incurred for a new facility at some future point in time. Some common indices used for this purpose are:

1. U.S. Bureau of Labor Statistics, Labor and Material price Indexes
2. "Chemical Engineering", Plant Cost Index
3. "Engineering News Record", Construction and Building Indexes
4. Marshall and Swift Equipment Cost Index

5. Various special indices related to specific industries such as the Nelson Refinery Construction Index

In summary, estimation of the capital costs for a project along with the annual revenues, operating costs, final salvage value, working capital return and project life is critical to obtain valid economic evaluation results. "Garbage in, garbage out" is a saying that is valid for economic analysis as well as all kinds of technical and managerial analyses. The purpose of an investment analysis must be known before determining whether a rough capital cost estimate based on ratio analysis giving maybe plus or minus thirty percent accuracy is sufficient or whether a more detailed cost estimate with plus or minus five or ten percent accuracy is needed. It costs more money to get more accuracy and reliability in cost estimation results and there is no need to spend a large sum of money on a detailed estimate if a rough estimate will do the job. On the other hand it is imperative that a decision-maker not make a final decision on economic analysis results that are based on rough capital estimates which the decision-maker thinks are accurate cost estimates. In the final analysis the degree of accuracy needed in cost estimation work at different stages of evaluating a project must be determined using the same common sense and good judgement vital to all management and engineering decision-making.

PROBLEMS

12-1 The following data relate to a petroleum project.

Costs are in thousands of dollars
Production is in thousands

Year	0	1	2	3	4	5
Production, (Bbls)		62	53	35	24	17
Intangibles, (IDC's)	750	250				
Tangible (Completion)		670				
Mineral Rights. Acq.	100					
Operating Costs		175	193	212	233	256
Price, ($/Bbl)		26.0	26.0	26.0	27.3	28.7

Royalties, (14.0% of Revenue)
The crude oil percentage depletion rate is 15%
Initial reserves for cost depletion equal cumulative production.
Effective Federal/State Income Tax Rate is 40.0%
Liquidation value in year 5 is zero.
Tangibles are depreciated using 7 year modified ACRS rates, starting depreciation in year 1 with the half year convention. Writeoff remaining depreciable tangible asset book value at year 5. Assume intangible costs are incurred in the first month of the year in which they are shown.

1) Calculate the after-tax escalated dollar DCFROR, NPV and PVR for a minimum DCFROR of 15% from the viewpoint of:

   A) Integrated (major) petroleum producer with other income against which to use deductions in the year incurred.
   B) Integrated (major) petroleum producer that does not have other income against which to use deductions in the year incurred so project economics must "stand alone".

2) Risk adjust the expense against other income Part 1A analysis results assuming 40% probability of success with the year 0 costs and 60% probability of failure with failure resulting in a year 1 net abandonment cost of $70,000 to be expensed in that year against other income. If failure occurs, a writeoff of remaining book values on mineral rights acquisition cost and 30% of year 0 mineral development cost not deducted at year 0 will be taken at year 1.

3) Make the analyses in Parts 1 and 2 for an independent producer.

4) Analyze the breakeven crude oil price per barrel that received uniformly from years 1 through 5, would make this project yield a 15% DCFROR for the investor and tax scenario in Part 1A.

5) What additional year 0 mineral rights acquisition cost (above the $100,000 cost built into this analysis) could be incurred and still give the project a 15% DCFROR for the data and assumptions for Part 1A.

12-2 The following data relate to a mining project with increasing waste rock or overburden to ore ratio as mine life progresses, giving declining production per year.

Costs are in thousands of dollars.
Production is in thousands.

Year	0	1	2	3	4	5
Production in Tons		62	53	35	24	17
Mineral Development	750	250				
Mining Equipment		670				
Mineral Rights. Acq.	100					
Operating Costs		175	193	212	233	256
Price, $ Per Ton		26.0	26.0	26.0	27.3	28.7

Royalties, (14.0% of Revenue)
The mineral percentage depletion rate is 15%.
Initial reserves for cost depletion equal cumulative production.
Effective Federal/State Income Tax Rate is 40.0%
Liquidation Value in Year 5 is Zero.
Mining equipment is depreciated using 7 year modified ACRS rates, starting in year 1 with the half year convention. Writeoff remaining depreciable equipment book value at year 5. Assume mineral development costs are incurred in the first month of the year in which they are shown.

1) Calculate the after-tax escalated dollar DCFROR, NPV and PVR for a minimum DCFROR of 15% from the viewpoint of:

A) Corporate mineral producer with other income against which to use deductions in the year incurred.
B) Corporate mineral producer that does not have other income

against which to use deductions in the year incurred so project economics must "stand alone".

2) Risk adjust the expense against other income Part 1A analysis results assuming 40% probability of success with the year 0 costs and 60% probability of failure with failure resulting in a year 1 net abandonment cost of $70,000 to be expensed in year 1 against other income. If failure occurs, a writeoff of remaining book values on mineral rights acquisition cost and 30% of year 0 mineral development cost not deducted at year 0 will be taken at year 1.

3) Make the analyses in Parts 1 and 2 for an individual mineral producer.

4) Analyze the breakeven price per ton of ore that received uniformly from years 1 through 5, would make this project yield a 15% DCFROR for the investor and tax scenario in Part 1A.

5) What additional year 0 mineral rights acquisition cost (above the $100,000 cost built into this analysis) could be incurred and still give the project a 15% DCFROR for the data and assumptions for Part 1A.

APPENDICES

A: Discrete Compounding Interest Factors, $i = \frac{1}{2}\%$ to $i = 200\%$.

B: Continuous Interest With End of Period Payments: Formalas and Applications

C: Continuous Interest With Continuous Flow of Funds: Formulas and Applications

D: Glossary of Investment Terminology

E: Arithmetic Gradient Series Factor Development

F: Geometric Gradient Series Factor Development and Applications

APPENDIX A

DISCRETE COMPOUNDING INTEREST FACTORS

Discrete Compounding Interest Factors, i=1/2% to i=200%.

Single Payment Compound
Amount Factor
$$= F/P_{i,n} = (1+i)^n$$

Single Payment Present
Worth Factor
$$= P/F_{i,n} = \frac{1}{(1+i)^n}$$

Uniform Series Compound
Amount Factor
$$= F/A_{i,n} = \frac{(1+i)^n - 1}{i}$$

Sinking Fund Factor
$$= A/F_{i,n} = \frac{i}{(1+i)^n - 1}$$

Capital Recovery Factor
$$= A/P_{i,n} = \frac{i(1+i)^n}{(1+i)^n - 1}$$

Uniform Series Present
Worth Factor
$$= P/A_{i,n} = \frac{(1+i)^n - 1}{i(1+i)^n}$$

Arithmetic Gradient
Series Factor
$$= A/G_{i,n} = \frac{1}{i} - \frac{n}{i}(A/F_{i,n})$$

$i=1/2\%$

n	$F/P_{i,n}$	$P/F_{i,n}$	$F/A_{i,n}$	$A/F_{i,n}$	$A/P_{i,n}$	$P/A_{i,n}$	$A/G_{i,n}$
1	1.005	0.9950	1.000	1.0000	1.0050	0.995	0.000
2	1.010	0.9901	2.005	0.4988	0.5038	1.985	0.499
3	1.015	0.9852	3.015	0.3317	0.3367	2.970	0.997
4	1.020	0.9803	4.030	0.2481	0.2531	3.950	1.494
5	1.025	0.9754	5.050	0.1980	0.2030	4.926	1.990
6	1.030	0.9705	6.076	0.1646	0.1696	5.896	2.485
7	1.036	0.9657	7.106	0.1407	0.1457	6.862	2.980
8	1.041	0.9609	8.141	0.1228	0.1278	7.823	3.473
9	1.046	0.9561	9.182	0.1089	0.1139	8.779	3.967
10	1.051	0.9514	10.228	0.0978	0.1028	9.730	4.459
11	1.056	0.9466	11.279	0.0887	0.0937	10.677	4.950
12	1.062	0.9419	12.336	0.0811	0.0861	11.619	5.440
13	1.067	0.9372	13.397	0.0747	0.0797	12.556	5.930
14	1.072	0.9326	14.464	0.0691	0.0741	13.489	6.420
15	1.078	0.9279	15.537	0.0644	0.0694	14.417	6.907
16	1.083	0.9233	16.614	0.0602	0.0652	15.340	7.394
17	1.088	0.9187	17.697	0.0565	0.0615	16.259	7.880
18	1.094	0.9141	18.786	0.0532	0.0582	17.173	8.365
19	1.099	0.9096	19.880	0.0503	0.0553	18.082	8.850
20	1.105	0.9051	20.979	0.0477	0.0527	18.988	9.334
21	1.110	0.9006	22.084	0.0453	0.0503	19.888	9.817
22	1.116	0.8961	23.194	0.0431	0.0481	20.784	10.299
23	1.122	0.8916	24.310	0.0411	0.0461	21.676	10.781
24	1.127	0.8872	25.432	0.0393	0.0443	22.563	11.261
25	1.133	0.8828	26.559	0.0377	0.0427	23.446	11.741
26	1.138	0.8784	27.692	0.0361	0.0411	24.324	12.220
27	1.144	0.8740	28.830	0.0347	0.0397	25.198	12.698
28	1.150	0.8697	29.975	0.0334	0.0384	26.068	13.175
29	1.156	0.8653	31.124	0.0321	0.0371	26.933	13.651
30	1.161	0.8610	32.280	0.0310	0.0360	27.794	14.127
35	1.191	0.8398	38.145	0.0262	0.0312	32.035	16.491
40	1.221	0.8191	44.159	0.0227	0.0277	36.172	18.836
45	1.252	0.7990	50.324	0.0199	0.0249	40.207	21.160
50	1.283	0.7793	56.645	0.0177	0.0227	44.143	23.462
55	1.316	0.7601	63.126	0.0159	0.0209	47.981	25.745
60	1.349	0.7414	69.770	0.0143	0.0193	51.726	28.006
65	1.383	0.7231	76.582	0.0131	0.0181	55.377	30.247
70	1.418	0.7053	83.566	0.0120	0.0170	58.939	32.468
75	1.454	0.6879	90.727	0.0110	0.0160	62.414	34.668
80	1.490	0.6710	98.068	0.0102	0.0152	65.802	36.847
85	1.528	0.6545	105.594	0.0095	0.0145	69.107	39.006
90	1.567	0.6384	113.311	0.0088	0.0138	72.331	41.145
95	1.606	0.6226	121.222	0.0083	0.0133	75.476	43.263
100	1.647	0.6073	129.334	0.0077	0.0127	78.543	45.361

$$i = 1\%$$

n	$F/P_{1,n}$	$P/F_{1,n}$	$F/A_{1,n}$	$A/F_{1,n}$	$A/P_{1,n}$	$P/A_{1,n}$	$A/G_{1,n}$
1	1.010	0.9901	1.000	1.00000	1.01000	0.990	--
2	1.020	0.9803	2.010	0.49751	0.50751	1.970	0.497
3	1.030	0.9706	3.030	0.33002	0.34002	2.941	0.993
4	1.041	0.9610	4.060	0.24628	0.25628	3.902	1.487
5	1.051	0.9515	5.101	0.19604	0.20604	4.853	1.980
6	1.062	0.9420	6.152	0.16255	0.17255	5.795	2.471
7	1.072	0.9327	7.214	0.13863	0.14863	6.728	2.960
8	1.083	0.9235	8.286	0.12069	0.13069	7.652	3.448
9	1.094	0.9143	9.369	0.10674	0.11674	8.566	3.923
10	1.105	0.9053	10.462	0.09558	0.10558	9.471	4.418
11	1.116	0.8963	11.567	0.08645	0.09645	10.368	4.900
12	1.127	0.8874	12.683	0.07885	0.08885	11.255	5.381
13	1.138	0.8787	13.809	0.07241	0.08241	12.134	5.861
14	1.149	0.8700	14.947	0.06690	0.07690	13.004	6.338
15	1.161	0.8613	16.097	0.06212	0.07212	13.865	6.814
16	1.173	0.8528	17.258	0.05794	0.06794	14.718	7.288
17	1.184	0.8444	18.430	0.05426	0.06426	15.562	7.761
18	1.196	0.8360	19.615	0.05098	0.06098	16.398	8.232
19	1.208	0.8277	20.811	0.04805	0.05805	17.226	8.702
20	1.220	0.8195	22.019	0.04542	0.05542	18.046	9.169
21	1.232	0.8114	23.239	0.04303	0.05303	18.857	9.635
22	1.245	0.8034	24.472	0.04086	0.05086	19.660	10.100
23	1.257	0.7954	25.716	0.03889	0.04889	20.456	10.562
24	1.270	0.7876	26.973	0.03707	0.04707	21.243	11.024
25	1.282	0.7798	28.243	0.03541	0.04541	22.023	11.483
26	1.295	0.7720	29.526	0.03387	0.04387	22.795	11.941
27	1.308	0.7644	30.821	0.03245	0.04245	23.560	12.397
28	1.321	0.7568	32.129	0.03112	0.04112	24.316	12.851
29	1.335	0.7493	33.450	0.02990	0.03990	25.066	13.304
30	1.348	0.7419	34.785	0.02875	0.03875	25.808	13.756
35	1.417	0.7059	41.660	0.02400	0.03400	29.409	15.987
40	1.489	0.6717	48.886	0.02046	0.03046	32.835	18.177
45	1.565	0.6391	56.481	0.01771	0.02771	36.095	20.327
50	1.645	0.6080	64.463	0.01551	0.02551	39.196	22.436
55	1.729	0.5785	72.852	0.01373	0.02373	42.147	24.505
60	1.817	0.5504	81.670	0.01224	0.02224	44.955	26.533
65	1.909	0.5237	90.937	0.01100	0.02100	47.627	28.522
70	2.007	0.4983	100.676	0.00993	0.01993	50.169	30.470
75	2.109	0.4741	110.913	0.00902	0.01902	52.587	32.379
80	2.217	0.4511	121.672	0.00822	0.01822	54.888	34.249
85	2.330	0.4292	132.979	0.00752	0.01752	57.078	36.080
90	2.449	0.4084	144.863	0.00690	0.01690	59.161	37.872
95	2.574	0.3886	157.354	0.00636	0.01636	61.143	39.626
100	2.705	0.3697	170.481	0.00587	0.01587	63.029	41.342

i=2%

n	$F/P_{i,n}$	$P/F_{i,n}$	$F/A_{i,n}$	$A/F_{i,n}$	$A/P_{i,n}$	$P/A_{i,n}$	$A/G_{i,n}$
1	1.020	0.9804	1.000	1.00000	1.02000	0.980	--
2	1.040	0.9612	2.020	0.49505	0.51505	1.942	0.495
3	1.061	0.9423	3.060	0.32675	0.34675	2.884	0.987
4	1.082	0.9238	4.122	0.24262	0.26262	3.808	1.475
5	1.104	0.9057	5.204	0.19216	0.21216	4.713	1.960
6	1.126	0.8880	6.308	0.15853	0.17853	5.601	2.442
7	1.149	0.8706	7.434	0.13451	0.15451	6.472	2.921
8	1.172	0.8535	8.583	0.11651	0.13651	7.325	3.396
9	1.195	0.8368	9.755	0.10252	0.02252	8.162	3.868
10	1.219	0.8203	10.950	0.09133	0.11133	8.983	4.337
11	1.243	0.8043	12.169	0.08218	0.10218	9.787	4.802
12	1.268	0.7885	13.412	0.07456	0.09456	10.575	5.264
13	1.294	0.7730	14.680	0.06812	0.08812	11.348	5.723
14	1.319	0.7579	15.974	0.06260	0.08260	12.106	6.179
15	1.346	0.7430	17.293	0.05783	0.07783	12.849	6.631
16	1.373	0.7284	18.639	0.05365	0.07365	13.578	7.080
17	1.400	0.7142	20.012	0.04997	0.06997	14.292	7.526
18	1.428	0.7002	21.412	0.04670	0.06670	14.992	7.968
19	1.457	0.6864	22.841	0.04378	0.06378	15.678	8.407
20	1.486	0.6730	24.297	0.04116	0.06116	16.351	8.843
21	1.516	0.6598	25.783	0.03878	0.05878	17.011	9.276
22	1.546	0.6468	27.299	0.03663	0.05663	17.658	9.705
23	1.577	0.6342	28.845	0.03467	0.05467	18.292	10.132
24	1.608	0.6217	30.422	0.03287	0.05287	18.914	10.555
25	1.641	0.6095	32.030	0.03122	0.05122	19.523	10.974
26	1.673	0.5976	33.671	0.02970	0.04970	20.121	11.391
27	1.707	0.5859	35.344	0.02829	0.04829	20.707	11.804
28	1.741	0.5744	37.051	0.02699	0.04699	21.281	12.214
29	1.776	0.5631	38.792	0.02578	0.04578	21.844	12.621
30	1.811	0.5521	40.568	0.02465	0.04465	22.396	13.025
35	2.000	0.5000	49.994	0.02000	0.04000	24.999	14.996
40	2.208	0.4529	60.402	0.01656	0.03656	27.355	16.888
45	2.438	0.4102	71.893	0.01391	0.03391	29.490	18.703
50	2.692	0.3715	84.579	0.01182	0.03182	31.424	20.442
55	2.972	0.3365	98.587	0.01014	0.03014	33.175	22.106
60	3.281	0.3048	114.052	0.00877	0.02877	34.761	23.696
65	3.623	0.2761	131.126	0.00763	0.02763	36.197	25.215
70	4.000	0.2500	149.987	0.00667	0.02667	37.499	26.663
75	4.416	0.2265	170.792	0.00586	0.02586	38.677	28.043
80	4.875	0.2051	193.772	0.00516	0.02516	39.745	29.375
85	5.383	0.1858	219.144	0.00456	0.02456	40.711	30.606
90	5.943	0.1683	247.157	0.00405	0.02405	41.587	31.793
95	6.562	0.1524	278.085	0.00360	0.02360	42.380	32.919
100	7.245	0.1380	312.232	0.00320	0.02320	43.098	33.986

i = 3%

n	$F/P_{i,n}$	$P/F_{i,n}$	$F/A_{i,n}$	$A/F_{i,n}$	$A/P_{i,n}$	$P/A_{i,n}$	$A/G_{i,n}$
1	1.030	0.9709	1.000	1.00000	1.03000	0.971	--
2	1.061	0.9426	2.030	0.49261	0.52261	1.913	0.493
3	1.093	0.9151	3.091	0.32353	0.35353	2.829	0.980
4	1.126	0.8885	4.184	0.23903	0.26903	3.717	1.463
5	1.159	0.8626	5.309	0.18835	0.21835	4.580	1.941
6	1.194	0.8375	6.468	0.15460	0.18460	5.417	2.414
7	1.230	0.8131	7.662	0.13051	0.16051	6.230	2.882
8	1.267	0.7894	8.892	0.11246	0.14246	7.020	3.345
9	1.305	0.7664	10.159	0.09843	0.12843	7.786	3.803
10	1.344	0.7441	11.464	0.08723	0.11723	8.530	4.256
11	1.384	0.7224	12.808	0.07808	0.10808	9.253	4.705
12	1.426	0.7014	14.192	0.07046	0.10046	9.954	5.145
13	1.469	0.6810	15.618	0.06403	0.09403	10.635	5.587
14	1.513	0.6611	17.086	0.05853	0.08853	11.296	6.021
15	1.558	0.6419	18.599	0.05377	0.08377	11.938	6.450
16	1.605	0.6232	20.157	0.04961	0.07961	12.561	6.874
17	1.653	0.6050	21.762	0.04595	0.07595	13.166	7.294
18	1.702	0.5874	23.414	0.04271	0.07271	13.754	7.708
19	1.754	0.5703	25.117	0.03981	0.06981	14.324	8.118
20	1.806	0.5537	26.870	0.03722	0.06722	14.877	8.523
21	1.860	0.5375	28.676	0.03487	0.06487	15.415	8.923
22	1.916	0.5219	30.537	0.03275	0.06275	15.937	9.319
23	1.974	0.5067	32.453	0.03081	0.06081	16.444	9.709
24	2.033	0.4919	34.426	0.02905	0.05905	16.936	10.095
25	2.094	0.4776	36.459	0.02743	0.05743	17.413	10.477
26	2.157	0.4637	38.553	0.02594	0.05594	17.877	10.853
27	2.221	0.4502	40.710	0.02456	0.05456	18.327	11.266
28	2.288	0.4371	42.931	0.02329	0.05329	18.764	11.593
29	2.357	0.4243	45.219	0.02211	0.05211	19.188	11.956
30	2.427	0.4120	47.575	0.02102	0.05102	19.600	12.314
35	2.814	0.3554	60.462	0.01654	0.04654	21.487	14.037
40	3.262	0.3066	75.401	0.01326	0.04326	23.115	15.650
45	3.782	0.2644	92.720	0.01079	0.04079	24.519	17.156
50	4.384	0.2281	112.797	0.00887	0.03887	25.730	18.557
55	5.082	0.1968	136.072	0.00735	0.03735	26.774	19.860
60	5.892	0.1697	163.053	0.00613	0.03613	27.676	21.067
65	6.830	0.1464	194.333	0.00515	0.03515	28.453	22.184
70	7.918	0.1263	230.594	0.00434	0.03434	29.123	23.215
75	9.179	0.1089	272.631	0.00367	0.03367	29.702	24.136
80	10.641	0.0940	321.363	0.00311	0.03311	30.201	25.035
85	12.336	0.0811	377.857	0.00265	0.03265	30.631	25.855
90	14.300	0.0699	443.349	0.00226	0.03226	31.002	26.567
95	16.578	0.0603	519.272	0.00193	0.03193	31.323	27.235
100	19.219	0.0520	607.288	0.00165	0.03165	31.599	27.844

$$i = 4\%$$

n	$F/P_{i,n}$	$P/F_{i,n}$	$F/A_{i,n}$	$A/F_{i,n}$	$A/P_{i,n}$	$P/A_{i,n}$	$A/G_{i,n}$
1	1.040	0.9615	1.000	1.00000	1.04000	0.962	--
2	1.082	0.9246	2.040	0.49020	0.53020	1.886	0.490
3	1.125	0.8890	3.122	0.32035	0.36035	2.775	0.974
4	1.170	0.8548	4.246	0.23549	0.27549	3.630	1.451
5	1.217	0.8219	5.416	0.18463	0.22463	4.452	1.922
6	1.265	0.7903	6.633	0.15076	0.19076	5.242	2.386
7	1.316	0.7599	7.898	0.12661	0.16661	6.002	2.843
8	1.369	0.7307	9.214	0.10853	0.14853	6.733	3.294
9	1.423	0.7026	10.583	0.09449	0.13449	7.435	3.739
10	1.480	0.6756	12.006	0.08329	0.12329	8.111	4.177
11	1.539	0.6496	13.486	0.07415	0.11415	8.760	4.609
12	1.601	0.6246	15.026	0.06655	0.10655	9.385	5.034
13	1.665	0.6006	16.627	0.06014	0.10014	9.986	5.453
14	1.732	0.5775	18.292	0.05467	0.09467	10.563	5.866
15	1.801	0.5553	20.024	0.04994	0.08994	11.118	6.272
16	1.873	0.5339	21.825	0.04582	0.08582	11.652	6.672
17	1.948	0.5134	23.698	0.04220	0.08220	12.166	7.066
18	2.026	0.4936	25.645	0.03899	0.07899	12.659	7.453
19	2.107	0.4746	27.671	0.03614	0.07614	13.134	7.834
20	2.191	0.4564	29.778	0.03358	0.07358	13.590	8.209
21	2.279	0.4388	31.969	0.03128	0.07128	14.029	8.578
22	2.370	0.4220	34.248	0.02920	0.06920	14.451	8.941
23	2.465	0.4057	36.618	0.02731	0.06731	14.857	9.297
24	2.563	0.3901	39.083	0.02559	0.06559	15.247	9.648
25	2.666	0.3751	41.646	0.02401	0.06401	15.622	9.993
26	2.772	0.3607	44.312	0.02257	0.06257	15.983	10.331
27	2.883	0.3468	47.084	0.02124	0.06124	16.330	10.664
28	2.999	0.3335	49.968	0.02001	0.06001	16.663	10.991
29	3.119	0.3207	52.966	0.01888	0.05888	16.984	11.312
30	3.243	0.3083	56.085	0.01783	0.05783	17.292	11.627
35	3.946	0.2534	73.652	0.01358	0.05358	18.665	13.120
40	4.801	0.2083	95.026	0.01052	0.05052	19.793	14.476
45	5.841	0.1712	121.029	0.00826	0.04826	20.720	15.705
50	7.107	0.1407	152.667	0.00655	0.04655	21.482	16.812
55	8.646	0.1157	191.159	0.00523	0.04523	22.109	17.807
60	10.520	0.0951	237.991	0.00420	0.04420	22.623	18.697
65	12.799	0.0781	294.968	0.00339	0.04339	23.047	19.491
70	15.572	0.0642	364.290	0.00275	0.04275	23.395	20.196
75	18.945	0.0528	448.631	0.00223	0.04223	23.680	20.821
80	23.050	0.0434	551.245	0.00181	0.04181	23.915	21.372
85	28.044	0.0357	676.090	0.00148	0.04148	24.109	21.857
90	34.119	0.0293	827.983	0.00121	0.04121	24.267	22.283
95	41.511	0.0241	1012.785	0.00099	0.04099	24.398	22.655
100	50.505	0.0198	1237.624	0.00081	0.04081	24.505	22.980

i=5%

n	$F/P_{i,n}$	$P/F_{i,n}$	$F/A_{i,n}$	$A/F_{i,n}$	$A/P_{i,n}$	$P/A_{i,n}$	$A/G_{i,n}$
1	1.050	0.9524	1.000	1.00000	1.05000	0.952	--
2	1.103	0.9070	2.050	0.48780	0.53780	1.859	0.488
3	1.158	0.8638	3.153	0.31721	0.36721	2.723	0.967
4	1.216	0.8227	4.310	0.23201	0.28201	3.546	1.439
5	1.276	0.7835	5.526	0.18097	0.23097	4.329	1.902
6	1.340	0.7462	6.802	0.14702	0.19702	5.076	2.358
7	1.407	0.7107	8.142	0.12282	0.17282	5.786	2.805
8	1.477	0.6768	9.549	0.10472	0.15472	6.463	3.244
9	1.551	0.6446	11.027	0.09069	0.14069	7.108	3.676
10	1.629	0.6139	12.578	0.07950	0.12950	7.722	4.099
11	1.710	0.5847	14.207	0.07039	0.12039	8.306	4.514
12	1.796	0.5568	15.917	0.06283	0.11283	8.863	4.922
13	1.886	0.5303	17.713	0.05646	0.10646	9.394	5.322
14	1.980	0.5051	19.599	0.05102	0.10102	9.899	5.713
15	2.079	0.4810	21.579	0.04634	0.09634	10.380	6.097
16	2.183	0.4581	23.657	0.04227	0.09227	10.838	6.474
17	2.292	0.4363	25.840	0.03870	0.08870	11.274	6.842
18	2.407	0.4155	28.132	0.03555	0.08555	11.690	7.203
19	2.527	0.3957	30.539	0.03275	0.08275	12.085	7.553
20	2.653	0.3769	33.066	0.03024	0.08024	12.462	7.903
21	2.786	0.3589	35.719	0.02800	0.07800	12.821	8.242
22	2.925	0.3418	38.505	0.02597	0.07597	13.163	8.573
23	3.072	0.3256	41.430	0.02414	0.07414	13.489	8.897
24	3.225	0.3101	44.502	0.02247	0.07247	13.799	9.214
25	3.386	0.2953	47.727	0.02095	0.07095	14.094	9.524
26	3.556	0.2812	51.113	0.01956	0.06956	14.375	9.827
27	3.733	0.2678	54.669	0.01829	0.06829	14.643	10.112
28	3.920	0.2551	58.403	0.01712	0.06712	14.898	10.411
29	4.116	0.2429	62.323	0.01605	0.06605	15.141	10.694
30	4.322	0.2314	66.439	0.01505	0.06505	15.372	10.969
35	5.516	0.1813	90.320	0.01107	0.06107	16.374	12.250
40	7.040	0.1420	120.800	0.00828	0.05828	17.159	13.377
45	8.985	0.1113	159.700	0.00626	0.05626	17.774	14.364
50	11.467	0.0872	209.348	0.00478	0.05478	18.256	15.233
55	14.636	0.0683	272.713	0.00367	0.05367	18.633	15.966
60	18.679	0.0535	353.584	0.00283	0.05283	18.929	16.606
65	23.840	0.0419	456.798	0.00219	0.05219	19.161	17.154
70	30.426	0.0329	588.529	0.00170	0.05170	19.343	17.621
75	38.833	0.0258	756.654	0.00132	0.05132	19.485	18.018
80	49.561	0.0202	971.229	0.00103	0.05103	19.596	18.353
85	63.254	0.0158	1245.087	0.00080	0.05080	19.684	18.635
90	80.730	0.0124	1594.607	0.00063	0.05063	19.752	18.871
95	103.035	0.0097	2040.694	0.00049	0.05049	19.806	19.069
100	131.501	0.0076	2610.025	0.00038	0.05038	19.848	19.234

i=6%

n	$F/P_{i,n}$	$P/F_{i,n}$	$F/A_{i,n}$	$A/F_{i,n}$	$A/P_{i,n}$	$P/A_{i,n}$	$A/G_{i,n}$
1	1.060	0.9434	1.000	1.00000	1.06000	0.943	--
2	1.124	0.8900	2.060	0.48544	0.54544	1.833	0.485
3	1.191	0.8396	3.184	0.31411	0.37411	2.673	0.961
4	1.262	0.7921	4.375	0.22859	0.28859	3.465	1.427
5	1.338	0.7473	5.637	0.17740	0.23740	4.212	1.883
6	1.419	0.7050	6.975	0.14336	0.20336	4.917	2.330
7	1.504	0.6651	8.394	0.11914	0.17914	5.582	2.768
8	1.594	0.6274	9.897	0.10104	0.16104	6.210	3.195
9	1.689	0.5919	11.491	0.08702	0.14702	6.802	3.613
10	1.791	0.5584	13.181	0.07587	0.13587	7.360	4.022
11	1.898	0.5268	14.972	0.06679	0.12679	7.887	4.421
12	2.012	0.4970	16.870	0.05928	0.11928	8.384	4.811
13	2.133	0.4688	18.882	0.05296	0.11296	8.853	5.192
14	2.261	0.4423	21.015	0.04758	0.10758	9.295	5.564
15	2.397	0.4173	23.276	0.04296	0.10296	9.712	5.926
16	2.540	0.3936	25.673	0.03895	0.09895	10.106	6.279
17	2.693	0.3714	28.213	0.03544	0.09544	10.477	6.624
18	2.854	0.3503	30.906	0.03236	0.09236	10.828	6.960
19	3.026	0.3305	33.760	0.02962	0.08962	11.158	7.287
20	3.207	0.3118	36.786	0.02718	0.08718	11.470	7.605
21	3.400	0.2942	39.993	0.02500	0.08500	11.764	7.915
22	3.604	0.2775	43.392	0.02305	0.08305	12.042	8.217
23	3.820	0.2618	46.996	0.02128	0.08128	12.303	8.510
24	4.049	0.2470	50.816	0.01968	0.07968	12.550	8.795
25	4.292	0.2330	54.865	0.01823	0.07823	12.783	9.072
26	4.549	0.2198	59.156	0.01690	0.07690	13.003	9.341
27	4.822	0.2074	63.706	0.01570	0.07570	13.211	9.603
28	5.112	0.1956	68.528	0.01459	0.07459	13.406	9.857
29	5.418	0.1846	73.640	0.01358	0.07358	13.591	10.103
30	5.743	0.1741	79.058	0.01265	0.07265	13.765	10.342
35	7.686	0.1301	111.435	0.00897	0.06897	14.498	11.432
40	10.286	0.0972	154.762	0.00646	0.06646	15.046	12.359
45	13.765	0.0727	212.744	0.00470	0.06470	15.456	13.141
50	18.420	0.0543	290.336	0.00344	0.06344	15.762	13.796
55	24.650	0.0406	394.172	0.00254	0.06254	15.991	14.341
60	32.998	0.0303	533.128	0.00188	0.06188	16.161	14.791
65	44.145	0.0227	719.083	0.00139	0.06139	16.289	15.160
70	59.076	0.0169	967.932	0.00103	0.06103	16.385	15.461
75	79.057	0.0126	1300.949	0.00077	0.06077	16.456	15.706
80	105.796	0.0095	1746.600	0.00057	0.06057	16.509	15.903
85	141.579	0.0071	2342.982	0.00043	0.06043	16.549	16.062
90	189.465	0.0053	3141.075	0.00032	0.06032	16.579	16.189
95	253.546	0.0039	4209.104	0.00024	0.06024	16.601	16.290
100	339.302	0.0029	5638.368	0.00018	0.06018	16.618	16.371

$i=7\%$

n	$F/P_{i,n}$	$P/F_{i,n}$	$F/A_{i,n}$	$A/F_{i,n}$	$A/P_{i,n}$	$P/A_{i,n}$	$A/G_{i,n}$
1	1.070	0.9346	1.000	1.00000	1.07000	0.935	0.000
2	1.145	0.8734	2.070	0.48309	0.55309	1.808	0.483
3	1.225	0.8163	3.215	0.31105	0.38105	2.624	0.955
4	1.311	0.7629	4.440	0.22523	0.29523	3.387	1.416
5	1.403	0.7130	5.751	0.17389	0.24389	4.100	1.865
6	1.501	0.6663	7.153	0.13980	0.20980	4.767	2.303
7	1.606	0.6227	8.654	0.11555	0.18555	5.389	2.730
8	1.718	0.5820	10.260	0.09747	0.16747	5.971	3.147
9	1.838	0.5439	11.978	0.08349	0.15349	6.515	3.552
10	1.967	0.5083	13.816	0.07238	0.14238	7.024	3.946
11	2.105	0.4751	15.784	0.06336	0.13336	7.499	4.330
12	2.252	0.4440	17.888	0.05590	0.12590	7.943	4.703
13	2.410	0.4150	20.141	0.04965	0.11965	8.358	5.065
14	2.579	0.3878	22.550	0.04434	0.11434	8.745	5.417
15	2.759	0.3624	25.129	0.03979	0.10979	9.108	5.758
16	2.952	0.3387	27.888	0.03586	0.10586	9.447	6.090
17	3.159	0.3166	30.840	0.03243	0.10243	9.763	6.411
18	3.380	0.2959	33.999	0.02941	0.09941	10.059	6.722
19	3.617	0.2765	37.379	0.02675	0.09675	10.336	7.024
20	3.870	0.2584	40.995	0.02439	0.09439	10.594	7.316
21	4.141	0.2415	44.865	0.02229	0.09229	10.836	7.599
22	4.430	0.2257	49.006	0.02041	0.09041	11.061	7.872
23	4.741	0.2109	53.436	0.01871	0.08871	11.272	8.137
24	5.072	0.1971	58.177	0.01719	0.08719	11.469	8.392
25	5.427	0.1842	63.249	0.01581	0.08581	11.654	8.639
26	5.807	0.1722	68.676	0.01456	0.08456	11.826	8.877
27	6.214	0.1609	74.484	0.01343	0.08343	11.987	9.107
28	6.649	0.1504	80.698	0.01239	0.08239	12.137	9.329
29	7.114	0.1406	87.346	0.01145	0.08145	12.278	9.543
30	7.612	0.1314	94.461	0.01059	0.08059	12.409	9.749
35	10.677	0.0937	138.237	0.00723	0.07723	12.948	10.669
40	14.974	0.0668	199.635	0.00501	0.07501	13.332	11.423
45	21.002	0.0476	285.749	0.00350	0.07350	13.606	12.036
50	29.457	0.0339	406.528	0.00246	0.07246	13.801	12.529
55	41.315	0.0242	575.929	0.00174	0.07174	13.940	12.921
60	57.946	0.0173	813.520	0.00123	0.07123	14.039	13.232
65	81.273	0.0123	1146.755	0.00087	0.07087	14.110	13.476
70	113.989	0.0088	1614.134	0.00062	0.07062	14.160	13.666
75	159.876	0.0063	2269.657	0.00044	0.07044	14.196	13.814
80	224.234	0.0045	3189.063	0.00031	0.07031	14.222	13.927
85	314.500	0.0032	4478.576	0.00022	0.07022	14.240	14.015
90	441.103	0.0023	6287.185	0.00016	0.07016	14.253	14.081
95	618.670	0.0016	8823.854	0.00011	0.07011	14.263	14.132
100	867.716	0.0012	12381.662	0.00008	0.07008	14.269	14.170

i=8%

n	$F/P_{i,n}$	$P/F_{i,n}$	$F/A_{i,n}$	$A/F_{i,n}$	$A/P_{i,n}$	$P/A_{i,n}$	$A/G_{i,n}$
1	1.080	0.9259	1.000	1.00000	1.08000	0.926	--
2	1.166	0.8573	2.080	0.48077	0.56077	1.783	0.481
3	1.260	0.7938	3.246	0.30803	0.38803	2.577	0.949
4	1.360	0.7350	4.506	0.22192	0.30192	3.312	1.404
5	1.469	0.6806	5.867	0.17046	0.25046	3.993	1.846
6	1.587	0.6302	7.336	0.13632	0.21632	4.623	2.276
7	1.714	0.5835	8.923	0.11207	0.19207	5.206	2.694
8	1.851	0.5403	10.637	0.09401	0.17401	5.747	3.098
9	1.999	0.5002	12.488	0.08008	0.16008	6.247	3.491
10	2.159	0.4632	14.487	0.06903	0.14903	6.710	3.871
11	2.332	0.4289	16.645	0.06008	0.14008	7.139	4.240
12	2.518	0.3971	18.977	0.05270	0.13270	7.536	4.596
13	2.720	0.3677	21.495	0.04652	0.12652	7.904	4.940
14	2.937	0.3405	24.215	0.04130	0.12130	8.244	5.273
15	3.172	0.3152	27.152	0.03683	0.11683	8.559	5.594
16	3.426	0.2919	30.324	0.03298	0.11298	8.851	5.905
17	3.700	0.2703	33.750	0.02963	0.10963	9.122	6.204
18	3.996	0.2502	37.450	0.02670	0.10670	9.372	6.492
19	4.316	0.2317	41.446	0.02413	0.10413	9.604	6.770
20	4.661	0.2145	45.762	0.02185	0.10185	9.818	7.037
21	5.034	0.1987	50.423	0.01983	0.09983	10.017	7.294
22	5.437	0.1839	55.457	0.01803	0.09803	10.201	7.541
23	5.871	0.1703	60.893	0.01642	0.09642	10.371	7.779
24	6.341	0.1577	66.765	0.01498	0.09498	10.529	8.007
25	6.848	0.1460	73.106	0.01368	0.09368	10.675	8.225
26	7.396	0.1352	79.954	0.01251	0.09251	10.810	8.435
27	7.988	0.1252	87.351	0.01145	0.09145	10.935	8.636
28	8.627	0.1159	95.339	0.01049	0.09049	11.051	8.829
29	9.317	0.1073	103.966	0.00962	0.08962	11.158	9.013
30	10.063	0.0994	113.283	0.00883	0.08883	11.258	9.190
35	14.785	0.0676	172.317	0.00580	0.08580	11.655	9.961
40	21.725	0.0460	259.057	0.00386	0.08386	11.925	10.570
45	31.920	0.0313	386.506	0.00259	0.08259	12.108	11.045
50	46.902	0.0213	573.770	0.00174	0.08174	12.233	11.411
55	68.914	0.0145	848.923	0.00118	0.08118	12.319	11.690
60	101.257	0.0099	1253.213	0.00080	0.08080	12.377	11.902
65	148.780	0.0067	1847.248	0.00054	0.08054	12.416	12.060
70	218.606	0.0046	2720.080	0.00037	0.08037	12.443	12.178
75	321.205	0.0031	4002.557	0.00025	0.08025	12.461	12.266
80	471.955	0.0021	5886.935	0.00017	0.08017	12.474	12.330
85	693.456	0.0014	8655.706	0.00012	0.08012	12.482	12.377
90	1018.915	0.0010	12723.939	0.00008	0.08008	12.488	12.412
95	1497.121	0.0007	18701.507	0.00005	0.08005	12.492	12.473
100	2199.761	0.0005	27484.516	0.00004	0.08004	12.494	12.455

$i = 9\%$

n	$F/P_{i,n}$	$P/F_{i,n}$	$F/A_{i,n}$	$A/F_{i,n}$	$A/P_{i,n}$	$P/A_{i,n}$	$A/G_{i,n}$
1	1.090	0.9174	1.000	1.00000	1.09000	0.917	0.000
2	1.188	0.8417	2.090	0.47847	0.56847	1.759	0.478
3	1.295	0.7722	3.278	0.30505	0.39505	2.531	0.943
4	1.412	0.7084	4.573	0.21867	0.30867	3.240	1.393
5	1.539	0.6499	5.985	0.16709	0.25709	3.890	1.828
6	1.677	0.5963	7.523	0.13292	0.22292	4.486	2.250
7	1.828	0.5470	9.200	0.10869	0.19869	5.033	2.657
8	1.993	0.5019	11.028	0.09067	0.18067	5.535	3.051
9	2.172	0.4604	13.021	0.07680	0.16680	5.995	3.431
10	2.367	0.4224	15.193	0.06582	0.15582	6.418	3.798
11	2.580	0.3875	17.560	0.05695	0.14695	6.805	4.151
12	2.813	0.3555	20.141	0.04965	0.13965	7.161	4.491
13	3.066	0.3262	22.953	0.04357	0.13357	7.487	4.818
14	3.342	0.2992	26.019	0.03843	0.12843	7.786	5.133
15	3.642	0.2745	29.361	0.03406	0.12406	8.061	5.435
16	3.970	0.2519	33.003	0.03030	0.12030	8.313	5.724
17	4.328	0.2311	36.974	0.02705	0.11705	8.544	6.002
18	4.717	0.2120	41.301	0.02421	0.11421	8.756	6.269
19	5.142	0.1945	46.018	0.02173	0.11173	8.950	6.524
20	5.604	0.1784	51.160	0.01955	0.10955	9.129	6.767
21	6.109	0.1637	56.764	0.01762	0.10762	9.292	7.001
22	6.659	0.1502	62.873	0.01591	0.10590	9.442	7.223
23	7.258	0.1378	69.532	0.01438	0.10438	9.580	7.436
24	7.911	0.1264	76.790	0.01302	0.10302	9.707	7.638
25	8.623	0.1160	84.701	0.01181	0.10181	9.823	7.832
26	9.399	0.1064	93.324	0.01072	0.10072	9.929	8.016
27	10.245	0.0976	102.723	0.00973	0.09973	10.027	8.191
28	11.167	0.0895	112.968	0.00885	0.09885	10.116	8.357
29	12.172	0.0822	124.135	0.00806	0.09806	10.198	8.515
30	13.268	0.0754	136.307	0.00734	0.09734	10.274	8.666
35	20.414	0.0490	215.710	0.00464	0.09464	10.567	9.308
40	31.409	0.0318	337.882	0.00296	0.09296	10.757	9.796
45	48.327	0.0207	525.857	0.00190	0.09190	10.881	10.160
50	74.357	0.0134	815.081	0.00123	0.09123	10.962	10.430
55	114.408	0.0088	1260.092	0.00082	0.09084	11.014	10.626
60	176.031	0.0057	1944.792	0.00051	0.09051	11.048	10.768
65	270.846	0.0037	2998.288	0.00033	0.09032	11.070	10.870
70	416.730	0.0024	4619.223	0.00022	0.09022	11.084	10.943
75	641.191	0.0016	7113.232	0.00014	0.09023	11.094	10.994
80	986.552	0.0010	10950.574	0.00009	0.09011	11.100	11.030
85	1517.932	0.0007	16854.800	0.00006	0.09010	11.104	11.055
90	2335.527	0.0004	25939.184	0.00004	0.09004	11.106	11.073
95	3593.497	0.0003	39916.635	0.00003	0.09002	11.108	11.085
100	5529.041	0.0002	61422.675	0.00002	0.09000	11.109	11.093

$i=10\%$

n	$F/P_{i,n}$	$P/F_{i,n}$	$F/A_{i,n}$	$A/F_{i,n}$	$A/P_{i,n}$	$P/A_{i,n}$	$A/G_{i,n}$
1	1.100	0.9091	1.000	1.00000	1.10000	0.909	--
2	1.210	0.8264	2.100	0.47619	0.57619	1.736	0.476
3	1.331	0.7513	3.310	0.30211	0.40211	2.487	0.937
4	1.464	0.6830	4.641	0.21547	0.31547	3.170	1.381
5	1.611	0.6209	6.105	0.16380	0.26380	3.791	1.810
6	1.772	0.5645	7.716	0.12961	0.22961	4.355	2.224
7	1.949	0.5132	9.487	0.10541	0.20541	4.868	2.622
8	2.144	0.4665	11.436	0.08744	0.18744	5.335	3.004
9	2.358	0.4241	13.579	0.07364	0.17364	5.759	3.372
10	2.594	0.3855	15.937	0.06275	0.16275	6.144	3.726
11	2.853	0.3505	18.531	0.05396	0.15396	6.495	4.064
12	3.138	0.3186	21.384	0.04676	0.14676	6.814	4.388
13	3.452	0.2897	24.523	0.04078	0.14078	7.103	4.699
14	3.797	0.2633	27.975	0.03575	0.13575	7.367	4.996
15	4.177	0.2394	31.772	0.03147	0.13147	7.606	5.279
16	4.595	0.2176	35.950	0.02782	0.12782	7.824	5.549
17	5.054	0.1978	40.545	0.02466	0.12466	8.022	5.807
18	5.560	0.1799	45.599	0.02193	0.12193	8.201	6.053
19	6.116	0.1635	51.159	0.01955	0.11955	8.365	6.286
20	6.727	0.1486	57.275	0.01746	0.11746	8.514	6.508
21	7.400	0.1351	64.002	0.01562	0.11562	8.649	6.719
22	8.140	0.1228	71.403	0.01401	0.11401	8.772	6.919
23	8.954	0.1117	79.543	0.01257	0.11257	8.883	7.108
24	9.850	0.1015	88.497	0.01130	0.11130	8.985	7.288
25	10.835	0.0923	98.347	0.01017	0.11017	9.077	7.458
26	11.918	0.0839	109.182	0.00916	0.10916	9.161	7.619
27	13.110	0.0763	121.100	0.00826	0.10826	9.237	7.770
28	14.421	0.0693	134.210	0.00745	0.10745	9.307	7.914
29	15.863	0.0630	148.631	0.00673	0.10673	9.370	8.049
30	17.449	0.0573	164.494	0.00608	0.10608	9.427	8.176
35	28.102	0.0356	271.024	0.00369	0.10369	9.644	8.709
40	45.259	0.0221	442.593	0.00226	0.10226	9.779	9.096
45	72.890	0.0137	718.905	0.00139	0.10139	9.863	9.374
50	117.391	0.0085	1163.909	0.00086	0.10086	9.915	9.570
55	189.059	0.0053	1880.591	0.00053	0.10053	9.947	9.708
60	304.482	0.0033	3034.816	0.00033	0.10033	9.967	9.802
65	490.371	0.0020	4893.707	0.00020	0.10020	9.980	9.867
70	789.747	0.0013	7887.470	0.00013	0.10013	9.987	9.911
75	1271.895	0.0008	12708.954	0.00008	0.10008	9.992	9.941
80	2048.400	0.0005	20474.002	0.00005	0.10005	9.995	9.961
85	3298.969	0.0003	32979.690	0.00003	0.10003	9.997	9.974
90	5313.023	0.0002	53120.226	0.00002	0.10002	9.998	9.983
95	8556.676	0.0001	85556.760	0.00001	0.10001	9.999	9.989

i=12%

n	$F/P_{i,n}$	$P/F_{i,n}$	$F/A_{i,n}$	$A/F_{i,n}$	$A/P_{i,n}$	$P/A_{i,n}$	$A/G_{i,n}$
1	1.120	0.8929	1.000	1.00000	1.12000	0.893	--
2	1.254	0.7972	2.120	0.47170	0.59170	1.690	0.472
3	1.405	0.7118	3.374	0.29635	0.41635	2.402	0.925
4	1.574	0.6355	4.779	0.20923	0.32923	3.037	1.359
5	1.762	0.5674	6.353	0.15741	0.27741	3.605	1.775
6	1.974	0.5066	8.115	0.12323	0.24323	4.111	2.172
7	2.211	0.4523	10.089	0.09912	0.21912	4.564	2.552
8	2.476	0.4039	12.300	0.08130	0.20130	4.968	2.913
9	2.773	0.3606	14.776	0.06768	0.18768	5.328	3.257
10	3.106	0.3220	17.549	0.05698	0.17698	5.650	3.585
11	3.479	0.2875	20.655	0.04842	0.16842	5.938	3.895
12	3.896	0.2567	24.133	0.04144	0.16144	6.194	4.190
13	4.363	0.2292	28.029	0.03568	0.15568	6.424	4.468
14	4.887	0.2046	32.393	0.03087	0.15087	6.628	4.732
15	5.474	0.1827	37.280	0.02682	0.14682	6.811	4.980
16	6.130	0.1631	42.753	0.02339	0.14339	6.974	5.215
17	6.866	0.1456	48.884	0.02046	0.14046	7.120	5.435
18	7.690	0.1300	55.750	0.01794	0.13794	7.250	5.643
19	8.613	0.1161	63.440	0.01576	0.13576	7.366	5.838
20	9.646	0.1037	72.052	0.01388	0.13388	7.469	6.020
21	10.804	0.0926	81.699	0.01224	0.13224	7.562	6.191
22	12.100	0.0826	92.503	0.01081	0.13081	7.645	6.351
23	13.552	0.0738	104.603	0.00956	0.12956	7.718	6.501
24	15.179	0.0659	118.155	0.00846	0.12846	7.784	6.641
25	17.000	0.0588	133.334	0.00750	0.12750	7.843	6.771
26	19.040	0.0525	150.334	0.00665	0.12665	7.896	6.892
27	21.325	0.0469	169.374	0.00590	0.12590	7.943	7.005
28	23.884	0.0419	190.699	0.00524	0.12524	7.984	7.110
29	26.750	0.0374	214.583	0.00466	0.12466	8.022	7.207
30	29.960	0.0334	241.333	0.00414	0.12414	8.055	7.297
35	52.800	0.0189	431.663	0.00232	0.12232	8.176	7.658
40	93.051	0.0107	767.091	0.00130	0.12130	8.244	7.899
45	163.988	0.0061	1358.230	0.00074	0.12074	8.283	8.057
50	289.002	0.0035	2400.018	0.00042	0.12042	8.304	8.160
55	509.321	0.0020	4236.005	0.00024	0.12024	8.317	8.225
60	897.597	0.0011	7471.641	0.00013	0.12013	8.324	8.266
65	1581.872	0.0006	13173.937	0.00008	0.12008	9.328	8.292
70	2787.800	0.0004	23223.332	0.00004	0.12004	8.330	8.308
75	4913.056	0.0002	40933.799	0.00002	0.12002	8.332	8.318
80	8658.483	0.0001	72145.692	0.00001	0.12001	8.332	8.324

i=15%

n	$F/P_{i,n}$	$P/F_{i,n}$	$F/A_{i,n}$	$A/F_{i,n}$	$A/P_{i,n}$	$P/A_{i,n}$	$A/G_{i,n}$
1	1.150	0.8696	1.000	1.00000	1.15000	0.870	--
2	1.322	0.7561	2.150	0.46512	0.61512	1.626	0.465
3	1.521	0.6575	3.472	0.28798	0.43798	2.283	0.907
4	1.749	0.5718	4.993	0.20027	0.35027	2.855	1.326
5	2.011	0.4972	6.742	0.14832	0.29832	3.352	1.723
6	2.313	0.4323	8.754	0.11424	0.26424	3.784	2.097
7	2.660	0.3759	11.067	0.09036	0.24036	4.160	2.450
8	3.059	0.3269	13.727	0.07285	0.22285	4.487	2.781
9	3.518	0.2843	16.786	0.05957	0.20957	4.772	3.092
10	4.046	0.2472	20.304	0.04925	0.19925	5.019	3.383
11	4.652	0.2149	24.349	0.04107	0.19107	5.234	3.655
12	5.350	0.1869	29.002	0.03448	0.18448	5.421	3.908
13	6.153	0.1625	34.352	0.02911	0.17911	5.583	4.144
14	7.076	0.1413	40.505	0.02469	0.17469	5.724	4.362
15	8.137	0.1229	47.580	0.02102	0.17102	5.847	4.565
16	9.358	0.1069	55.717	0.01795	0.16795	5.954	4.752
17	10.761	0.0929	65.075	0.01537	0.16537	6.047	4.925
18	12.375	0.0808	75.836	0.01319	0.16319	6.128	5.084
19	14.232	0.0703	88.212	0.01134	0.16134	6.198	5.231
20	16.367	0.0611	102.444	0.00976	0.15976	6.259	5.365
21	18.822	0.0531	118.810	0.00842	0.15842	6.312	5.488
22	21.645	0.0462	137.632	0.00727	0.15727	6.359	5.601
23	24.891	0.0402	159.276	0.00628	0.15628	6.399	5.704
24	28.625	0.0349	184.168	0.00543	0.15543	6.434	5.798
25	32.919	0.0304	212.793	0.00470	0.15470	6.464	5.883
26	37.857	0.0264	245.712	0.00407	0.15407	6.491	5.961
27	43.535	0.0230	283.569	0.00353	0.15353	6.514	6.032
28	50.066	0.0200	327.104	0.00306	0.15306	6.534	6.096
29	57.575	0.0174	377.170	0.00265	0.15265	6.551	6.154
30	66.212	0.0151	434.745	0.00230	0.15230	6.566	6.207
35	133.176	0.0075	881.170	0.00113	0.15113	6.617	6.402
40	267.864	0.0037	1779.090	0.00056	0.15056	6.642	6.517
45	538.769	0.0019	3585.128	0.00028	0.15028	6.654	6.583
50	1083.657	0.0009	7217.716	0.00014	0.15014	6.661	6.620
55	2179.622	0.0005	14524.148	0.00007	0.15007	6.664	6.641
60	4383.999	0.0002	29219.992	0.00003	0.15003	6.665	6.653
65	8817.787	0.0001	58778.583	0.00002	0.15002	6.666	6.659

i=20%

n	$F/P_{i,n}$	$P/F_{i,n}$	$F/A_{i,n}$	$A/F_{i,n}$	$A/P_{i,n}$	$P/A_{i,n}$	$A/G_{i,n}$
1	1.200	0.8333	1.000	1.00000	1.20000	0.833	--
2	1.440	0.6944	2.200	0.45455	0.65455	1.528	0.455
3	1.728	0.5787	3.640	0.27473	0.47473	2.106	0.879
4	2.074	0.4823	5.368	0.18629	0.38629	2.589	1.274
5	2.488	0.4019	7.442	0.13438	0.33438	2.991	1.641
6	2.986	0.3349	9.930	0.10071	0.30071	3.326	1.979
7	3.583	0.2791	12.916	0.07742	0.27742	3.605	2.290
8	4.300	0.2326	16.499	0.06061	0.26061	3.837	2.576
9	5.160	0.1938	20.799	0.04808	0.24808	4.031	2.836
10	6.192	0.1615	25.959	0.03852	0.23852	4.192	3.074
11	7.430	0.1346	32.150	0.03110	0.23110	4.327	3.289
12	8.916	0.1122	39.581	0.02526	0.22526	4.439	3.484
13	10.699	0.0935	48.497	0.02062	0.22062	4.533	3.660
14	12.839	0.0779	59.196	0.01689	0.21689	4.611	3.818
15	15.407	0.0649	72.035	0.01388	0.21388	4.675	3.959
16	18.488	0.0541	87.442	0.01144	0.21144	4.730	4.085
17	22.186	0.0451	105.931	0.00944	0.20944	4.775	4.198
18	26.623	0.0376	128.117	0.00781	0.20781	4.812	4.298
19	31.948	0.0313	154.740	0.00646	0.20646	4.843	4.386
20	38.338	0.0261	186.688	0.00536	0.20536	4.870	4.464
21	46.005	0.0217	225.026	0.00444	0.20444	4.891	4.533
22	55.206	0.0181	271.031	0.00369	0.20369	4.909	4.594
23	66.247	0.0151	326.237	0.00307	0.20307	4.925	4.648
24	79.497	0.0126	392.484	0.00255	0.20255	4.937	4.694
25	95.396	0.0105	471.981	0.00212	0.20212	4.948	4.735
26	114.475	0.0087	567.377	0.00176	0.20176	4.956	4.771
27	137.371	0.0073	681.853	0.00147	0.20147	4.964	4.802
28	164.845	0.0061	819.223	0.00122	0.20122	4.970	4.829
29	197.814	0.0051	984.068	0.00102	0.20102	4.975	4.853
30	237.376	0.0042	1181.882	0.00085	0.20085	4.979	4.873
35	590.668	0.0017	2948.341	0.00034	0.20034	4.992	4.941
40	1469.772	0.0007	7343.858	0.00014	0.20014	4.997	4.973
45	3657.262	0.0003	18281.310	0.00005	0.20005	4.999	4.988
50	9100.438	0.0001	45497.191	0.00002	0.20002	4.999	4.994

$$i = 25\%$$

n	$F/P_{i,n}$	$P/F_{i,n}$	$F/A_{i,n}$	$A/F_{i,n}$	$A/P_{i,n}$	$P/A_{i,n}$	$A/G_{i,n}$
1	1.250	0.8000	1.000	1.00000	1.25000	0.800	--
2	1.562	0.6400	2.250	0.44444	0.69444	1.440	0.444
3	1.953	0.5120	3.812	0.26230	0.51230	1.952	0.852
4	2.441	0.4096	5.766	0.17344	0.42344	2.362	1.225
5	3.052	0.3277	8.207	0.12185	0.37185	2.689	1.563
6	3.815	0.2621	11.259	0.08882	0.33882	2.951	1.868
7	4.768	0.2097	15.073	0.06634	0.31634	3.161	2.142
8	5.960	0.1678	19.842	0.05040	0.30040	3.329	2.387
9	7.451	0.1342	25.802	0.03876	0.28876	3.463	2.605
10	9.313	0.1074	33.253	0.03007	0.28007	3.571	2.797
11	11.642	0.0859	42.566	0.02349	0.27349	3.656	2.966
12	14.552	0.0687	54.208	0.01845	0.26845	3.725	3.114
13	18.190	0.0550	68.760	0.01454	0.26454	3.780	3.244
14	22.737	0.0440	86.949	0.01150	0.26150	3.824	3.356
15	28.422	0.0352	109.687	0.00912	0.25912	3.859	3.453
16	35.527	0.0281	138.109	0.00724	0.25724	3.887	3.537
17	44.409	0.0225	173.636	0.00576	0.25576	3.910	3.608
18	55.511	0.0180	218.045	0.00459	0.25459	3.928	3.670
19	69.389	0.0144	273.556	0.00366	0.25366	3.942	3.722
20	86.736	0.0115	342.945	0.00292	0.25292	3.954	3.767
21	108.420	0.0092	429.681	0.00233	0.25233	3.963	3.805
22	135.525	0.0074	538.101	0.00186	0.25186	3.970	3.836
23	169.407	0.0059	673.626	0.00148	0.25148	3.976	3.863
24	211.758	0.0047	843.033	0.00119	0.25119	3.981	3.888
25	264.698	0.0038	1054.791	0.00095	0.25095	3.985	3.905
26	330.872	0.0030	1319.489	0.00076	0.25076	3.988	3.921
27	413.590	0.0024	1650.361	0.00061	0.25061	3.990	3.935
28	516.988	0.0019	2063.952	0.00048	0.25048	3.992	3.946
29	646.235	0.0015	2580.939	0.00039	0.25039	3.994	3.955
30	807.794	0.0012	3227.174	0.00031	0.25031	3.995	3.963
35	2465.190	0.0004	9856.761	0.00010	0.25010	3.998	3.986
40	7523.164	0.0001	30088.655	0.00003	0.25003	3.999	3.995

i=30%

n	$F/P_{i,n}$	$P/F_{i,n}$	$F/A_{i,n}$	$A/F_{i,n}$	$A/P_{i,n}$	$P/A_{i,n}$	$A/G_{i,n}$
1	1.300	0.7692	1.000	1.00000	1.30000	0.769	--
2	1.690	0.5917	2.300	0.43478	0.73478	1.361	0.435
3	2.197	0.4552	3.990	0.25063	0.55063	1.816	0.827
4	2.856	0.3501	6.187	0.16163	0.46163	2.166	1.178
5	3.713	0.2693	9.043	0.11058	0.41058	2.436	1.490
6	4.827	0.2072	12.756	0.07839	0.37839	2.643	1.765
7	6.275	0.1594	17.583	0.05687	0.35687	2.802	2.006
8	8.157	0.1226	23.858	0.04192	0.34192	2.925	2.216
9	10.604	0.0943	32.015	0.03124	0.33124	3.019	2.396
10	13.786	0.0725	42.619	0.02346	0.32346	3.092	2.551
11	17.922	0.0558	56.405	0.01773	0.31773	3.147	2.683
12	23.298	0.0429	74.327	0.01345	0.31345	3.190	2.795
13	30.288	0.0330	97.625	0.01024	0.31024	3.223	2.890
14	39.374	0.0254	127.913	0.00782	0.30782	3.249	2.968
15	51.186	0.0195	167.286	0.00598	0.30598	3.268	3.034
16	66.542	0.0150	218.472	0.00458	0.30458	3.283	3.089
17	86.504	0.0116	285.014	0.00351	0.30351	3.295	3.135
18	112.455	0.0089	371.518	0.00269	0.30269	3.304	3.172
19	146.192	0.0068	483.973	0.00207	0.30207	3.311	3.202
20	190.050	0.0053	630.165	0.00159	0.30159	3.316	3.228
21	247.065	0.0040	820.215	0.00122	0.30122	3.320	3.248
22	321.184	0.0031	1067.280	0.00094	0.30094	3.323	3.265
23	417.539	0.0024	1388.464	0.00072	0.30072	3.325	3.278
24	542.801	0.0018	1806.003	0.00055	0.30055	3.327	3.289
25	705.641	0.0014	2348.803	0.00043	0.30043	3.329	3.298
26	917.333	0.0011	3054.444	0.00033	0.30033	3.330	3.305
27	1192.533	0.0008	3971.778	0.00025	0.30025	3.331	3.311
28	1550.293	0.0006	5164.311	0.00019	0.30019	3.331	3.315
29	2015.381	0.0005	6714.604	0.00015	0.30015	3.332	3.319
30	2619.996	0.0004	8729.985	0.00011	0.30011	3.332	3.322
35	9727.860	0.0001	32422.868	0.00003	0.30003	3.333	3.330

i=40%

n	$F/P_{i,n}$	$P/F_{i,n}$	$F/A_{i,n}$	$A/F_{i,n}$	$A/P_{i,n}$	$P/A_{i,n}$	$A/G_{i,n}$
1	1.400	0.7143	1.000	1.00000	1.40000	0.714	--
2	1.960	0.5102	2.400	0.41667	0.81667	1.224	0.417
3	2.744	0.3644	4.360	0.22936	0.62936	1.589	0.780
4	3.842	0.2603	7.104	0.14077	0.54077	1.849	1.092
5	5.378	0.1859	10.946	0.09136	0.49136	2.035	1.358
6	7.530	0.1328	16.324	0.06126	0.46126	2.168	1.581
7	10.541	0.0949	23.853	0.04192	0.44192	2.263	1.766
8	14.758	0.0678	34.395	0.02907	0.42907	2.331	1.919
9	20.661	0.0484	49.153	0.02034	0.42034	2.379	2.042
10	28.925	0.0346	69.814	0.01432	0.41432	2.414	2.142
11	40.496	0.0247	98.739	0.01013	0.41013	2.438	2.222
12	56.694	0.0176	139.235	0.00718	0.40718	2.456	2.284
13	79.371	0.0126	195.929	0.00510	0.40510	2.469	2.334
14	111.120	0.0090	275.300	0.00363	0.40363	2.478	2.373
15	155.568	0.0064	386.420	0.00259	0.40259	2.484	2.403
16	217.795	0.0046	541.988	0.00185	0.40185	2.489	2.426
17	304.913	0.0033	759.784	0.00132	0.40132	2.492	2.444
18	426.879	0.0023	1064.697	0.00094	0.40094	2.494	2.458
19	597.630	0.0017	1491.576	0.00067	0.40067	2.496	2.468
20	836.683	0.0012	2089.206	0.00048	0.40048	2.497	2.476
21	1171.356	0.0009	2925.889	0.00034	0.40034	2.498	2.482
22	1639.898	0.0006	4097.245	0.00024	0.40024	2.498	2.487
23	2295.857	0.0004	5737.142	0.00017	0.40017	2.499	2.490
24	3214.200	0.0003	8032.999	0.00012	0.40012	2.499	2.492
25	4499.880	0.0002	11247.199	0.00009	0.40009	2.499	2.494

i=50%

n	$F/P_{i,n}$	$P/F_{i,n}$	$F/A_{i,n}$	$A/F_{i,n}$	$A/P_{i,n}$	$P/A_{i,n}$	$A/G_{i,n}$
1	1.500	0.6667	1.000	1.00000	1.50000	0.667	--
2	2.250	0.4444	2.500	0.40000	0.90000	1.111	0.400
3	3.375	0.2963	4.750	0.21053	0.71053	1.407	0.737
4	5.062	0.1975	8.125	0.12308	0.62308	1.605	1.015
5	7.594	0.1317	13.188	0.07583	0.57583	1.737	1.242
6	11.391	0.0878	20.781	0.04812	0.54812	1.824	1.423
7	17.086	0.0585	32.172	0.03108	0.53108	1.883	1.565
8	25.629	0.0390	49.258	0.02030	0.52030	1.922	1.675
9	38.443	0.0260	74.887	0.01335	0.51335	1.948	1.760
10	57.665	0.0173	113.330	0.00882	0.50882	1.965	1.824
11	86.498	0.0116	170.995	0.00585	0.50585	1.977	1.871
12	129.746	0.0077	257.493	0.00388	0.50388	1.985	1.907
13	194.620	0.0051	387.239	0.00258	0.50258	1.990	1.933
14	291.929	0.0034	581.859	0.00172	0.50172	1.993	1.952
15	437.894	0.0023	873.788	0.00114	0.50114	1.995	1.966
16	656.841	0.0015	1311.682	0.00076	0.50076	1.997	1.976
17	985.261	0.0010	1968.523	0.00051	0.50051	1.998	1.983
18	1477.892	0.0007	2953.784	0.00034	0.50034	1.999	1.988
19	2216.838	0.0005	4431.676	0.00023	0.50023	1.999	1.991
20	3325.257	0.0003	6648.513	0.00015	0.50015	1.999	1.994

i=70%

n	F/P i,n	P/F i,n	F/A i,n	A/F i,n	A/P i,n	P/A i,n	A/G i,n
1	1.700	0.5882	1.000	1.0000	1.7000	.5882	--
2	2.890	0.3460	2.700	0.3704	1.0704	.9343	.3703
3	4.913	0.2035	5.590	0.1789	0.8789	1.1378	.6619
4	8.352	0.1197	10.503	0.0952	0.7952	1.2575	.8845
5	14.199	0.0704	18.855	0.0530	0.7530	1.3280	1.0497
6	24.138	0.0414	33.054	0.0302	0.7302	1.3694	1.1693
7	41.034	0.0244	57.191	0.0175	0.7175	1.3938	1.2537
8	69.758	0.0143	98.225	0.0102	0.7102	1.4081	1.3122
9	118.590	0.0084	167.980	0.0060	0.7060	1.4165	1.3520
10	201.600	0.0050	286.570	0.0035	0.7035	1.4215	1.3787
11	342.720	0.0029	488.170	0.0020	0.7020	1.4244	1.3964
12	582.620	0.0017	830.890	0.0012	0.7012	1.4261	1.4079
13	990.460	0.0010	1413.	0.0007	0.7007	1.4271	1.4154
14	1684	0.0006	2404.	0.0004	0.7004	1.4277	1.4203
15	2862	0.0003	4087.	0.0002	0.7002	1.4281	1.4233

i=90%

n	F/P i,n	P/F i,n	F/A i,n	A/F i,n	A/P i,n	P/A i,n	A/G i,n
1	1.900	0.5263	1.000	1.0000	1.9000	0.5263	--
2	3.610	0.2770	2.900	0.3448	1.2448	0.8033	0.3448
3	6.859	0.1458	6.510	0.1536	1.0536	0.9491	0.5991
4	13.032	0.0767	13.369	0.0748	0.9748	1.0259	0.7787
5	24.761	0.0404	26.401	0.0379	0.9379	1.0662	0.9007
6	47.046	0.0213	51.162	0.0195	0.9195	1.0875	0.9808
7	89.387	0.0112	98.208	0.0102	0.9102	1.0987	1.0319
8	169.84	0.0059	187.60	0.0053	0.9053	1.1046	1.0637
9	322.69	0.0031	357.43	0.0028	0.9028	1.1077	1.0831
10	613.11	0.0016	680.12	0.0015	0.9015	1.1093	1.0948
11	1165.	0.0009	1293.	0.0008	0.9008	1.1102	1.1017
12	2213.	0.0004	2458.	0.0004	0.9004	1.1106	1.1057
13	4205.	0.0002	4671.	0.0002	0.9002	1.1108	1.1080
14	7990.	0.0001	8877.	0.0001	0.9001	1.1110	1.1094
15	15181.	0.0001	16867.	0.0001	0.9001	1.1110	1.1101

i=110%

n	F/P i,n	P/F i,n	F/A i,n	A/F i,n	A/P i,n	P/A i,n	A/G i,n
1	2.100	0.4762	1.000	1.0000	2.100	0.4762	--
2	4.410	0.2268	3.100	0.3226	1.423	0.7029	0.3226
3	9.261	0.1080	7.510	0.1332	1.233	0.8109	0.5459
4	19.448	0.0514	16.771	0.0596	1.160	0.8623	0.6923
5	40.841	0.0245	36.219	0.0276	1.128	0.8868	0.7836
6	85.766	0.0117	77.060	0.0130	1.113	0.8985	0.8383
7	180.11	0.0055	162.83	0.0061	1.106	0.9040	0.8700
8	378.23	0.0026	342.93	0.0029	1.103	0.9067	0.8879
9	794.28	0.0013	721.16	0.0014	1.101	0.9079	0.8978
10	1668.	0.0006	1515.	0.0007	1.101	0.9085	0.9031
11	3503.	0.0003	3183.	0.0003	1.100	0.9088	0.9059
12	7356	0.0001	6686.	0.0001	1.100	0.9090	0.9075

$$i=130\%$$

n	$F/P_{i,n}$	$P/F_{i,n}$	$F/A_{i,n}$	$A/F_{i,n}$	$A/P_{i,n}$	$P/A_{i,n}$	$A/G_{i,n}$
1	2.300	0.4348	1.000	1.0000	2.300	0.4348	--
2	5.290	0.1890	3.300	0.3030	1.603	0.6239	0.3030
3	12.167	0.0822	8.590	0.1164	1.416	0.7060	0.5006
4	27.984	0.0357	20.757	0.0482	1.348	0.7417	0.6210
5	64.363	0.0155	48.741	0.0205	1.320	0.7573	0:6903
6	148.04	0.0068	113.10	0.0088	1.309	0.7640	0.7284
7	340.48	0.0029	261.14	0.0038	1.304	0.7670	0.7486
8	783.11	0.0013	601.62	0.0017	1.302	0.7682	0.7590
9	1801.	0.0006	1385.	0.0007	1.301	0.7688	0.7642
10	4143.	0.0002	3186.	0.0003	1.300	0.7690	0.7668
11	9528.	0.0001	7328.	0.0001	1.300	0.7691	0.7681
12	21915.	0.0001	16857.	0.0001	1.300	0.7692	0.7687

$$i=150\%$$

n	$F/P_{i,n}$	$P/F_{i,n}$	$F/A_{i,n}$	$A/F_{i,n}$	$A/P_{i,n}$	$P/A_{i,n}$	$A/G_{i,n}$
1	2.500	0.4000	1.000	1.0000	2.500	0.4000	--
2	6.250	0.1600	3.500	0.2857	1.785	0.5600	0.2857
3	15.625	0.0640	9.750	0.1026	1.602	0.6240	0.4615
4	39.062	0.0256	25.375	0.0394	1.539	0.6496	0.5616
5	97.656	0.0102	64.437	0.0155	1.515	0.6598	0.6149
6	244.14	0.0041	162.09	0.0062	1.506	0.6639	0.6420
7	610.35	0.0016	406.23	0.0025	1.502	0.6656	0.6552
8	1526.	0.0007	1017.	0.0010	1.501	0.6662	0.6614
9	3815.	0.0003	2542.	0.0004	1.500	0.6665	0.6643
10	9537.	0.0001	6357.	0.0002	1.500	0.6666	0.6656
11	23842.	0.0000	15894.	0.0001	1.500	0.6666	0.6662
12	59604.	0.0000	39736.	0.0000	1.500	0.6667	0.6665

$$i=200\%$$

n	$F/P_{i,n}$	$P/F_{i,n}$	$F/A_{i,n}$	$A/F_{i,n}$	$A/P_{i,n}$	$P/A_{i,n}$	$A/G_{i,n}$
1	3.000	.33333	1.000	1.000	3.000	0.3333	--
2	9.000	.11111	4.000	0.25000	2.250	0.4444	.2500
3	27.000	.03704	13.000	0.07692	2.077	0.4815	.3846
4	81.000	.01235	40.000	0.02500	2.025	0.4938	.4500
5	243.000	.00412	121.000	0.00826	2.008	0.4979	.4793
6	729.000	.00137	364.000	0.00275	2.003	0.4993	.4917
7	2187.000	.00046	1093.000	0.00092	2.001	0.4998	.4968
8	6561.000	.00015	3280.000	0.00030	2.000	0.4999	.4987
9	19683.000	.00005	9841.000	0.00010	2.000	0.5000	.4995
10	59049.000	.00002	29524.000	0.00003	2.000	0.5000	.4998

APPENDIX B

CONTINUOUS INTEREST WITH END OF PERIOD PAYMENTS: FORMULAS AND APPLICATIONS

B.1 Formula Development

In Chapter 2 it was shown that compounding interest an infinite number of times per year leads to what is called "continuous compounding of interest." In this appendix, the compound interest formulas are derived for continuous interest with end of period payments. In the next appendix the formulas are developed for continuous interest with the continuous flow of money.

The following symbols will be used in the formulas to be developed:

r = the nominal annual continuous interest rate

n = the number of years

P, A, and F are defined as used throughout the text.

If a principal, P, is drawing continuous compound interest, an incremental interest amount, ΔP, is accumulated in incremental time, Δt. Writing an incremental dollar balance as shown in equation B-1 gives P at time $t + \Delta t$ — P at time t equals P times r times the incremental time, Δt.

$$P|t+\Delta t - P|t = Pr\Delta t \quad \text{or} \quad \frac{P|t+\Delta t - P|t}{\Delta t} = Pr \qquad \text{B-1}$$

Taking the limit as Δt approaches zero gives

$$\lim_{\Delta t \to 0} \frac{P|t+\Delta t - P|t}{\Delta t} = \frac{dP}{dt} = Pr \qquad \text{B-2}$$

since the left side of Equation B-2 is the definition of the derivative of P with respect to t.

Separating the variables and integrating Equation B-2 yields

$$\int_{P=P}^{P=F} \frac{dP}{P} = \int_{t=0}^{t=n} rdt \qquad\qquad\qquad \text{B-3}$$

$$\ln P\Big|_{P}^{F} = rt\Big|_{o}^{n} \text{ or } \ln F/P = rn \qquad\qquad \text{B-4}$$

Taking the antilog of Equation B-4 gives

$$F = Pe^{rn} = P(F/P_{r,n}) \qquad\qquad\qquad \text{B-5}$$

The factor e^{rn} is the continuous interest single payment compound amount factor.

$$\text{Since} \quad P = F(1/e^{rn}) = F(P/F_{r,n}) \qquad\qquad \text{B-6}$$

the factor $1/e^{rn}$ is the continuous interest single payment present worth factor.

As we did in Chapter 2 for discrete period compound interest, we can now develop a uniform series compound amount factor for continuous interest with equal end of period payments. Treating each term of the series of payments individually yields the equation

$$F = A + Ae^{r} + Ae^{2r} + \text{---} + Ae^{r(n-2)} + Ae^{r(n-1)} \qquad \text{B-7}$$

Multiplying each side of Equation B-7 by e_r yields

$$Fe^{r} = Ae^{r} + Ae^{2r} + Ae^{3r} + \text{---} + Ae^{r(n-1)} + Ae^{rn} \qquad \text{B-8}$$

Subtracting Equation B-7 from B-8 gives

$$Fe^{r} - F = Ae^{rn} - A$$

or

$$F = A\left[\frac{e^{rn}-1}{e^{r}-1}\right] = A(F/A_{r,n}) \qquad\qquad \text{B-9}$$

where the factor $(e^{nr}-1)/(e^{r}-1)$ is the continuous interest end of period payment uniform series compound amount factor.

Rearranging Equation B-9 gives

$$A = F\left[\frac{e^{r}-1}{e^{rn}-1}\right] = F(A/F_{r,n}) \qquad\qquad \text{B-10}$$

where the factor $(e^{r}-1)/(e^{rn}-1)$ is the continuous interest end of period payment sinking fund deposit factor.

Formulas relating A and P result by combining Equations B-5 and B-9 to eliminate F.

$$P = A \left[\frac{e^{rn}-1}{(e^r-1)e^{rn}}\right] = A(P/A_{r,n})$$ B-11

where $(e^{rn}-1)/(e^r-1)e^{rn}$ is the continuous interest end of period payment uniform series present worth factor.

Rearranging Equation B-11 gives

$$A = P \left[\frac{(e^r-1)e^{rn}}{e^{rn}-1}\right] = P(A/P_{r,n})$$ B-12

where $(e^r-1)e^{rn}/(e^{rn}-1)$ is the continuous interest end of period payment capital recovery factor.

Table B1 gives tabulated values of commonly needed values of e^{ϕ} (where $\phi = r$ or nr) to calculate the continuous interest factors developed in this section. These factors ordinarily are not used frequently enough to justify tabulating complete tables in this text.

B.2 Applications

EXAMPLE B-1   Continuous Interest Compared to Annual and Effective Interest

Calculate the future worth 6 years from now of a present sum of $1000 if interest is:

a) 10% per year compounded continuously
b) 10% per year compounded annually
c) an effective annual rate for 10% compounded continuously.

Solution:

a) $1000

$$\vdash\!\!-\!\!-\!\!-\!\!-\!\!-\!\!-\!\!-\!\!-\!\!-\!\!-\!\!\dashv \quad F=1000(F/P_{r,6}) \text{ for } r = .10$$
$$0 \quad 1 - - - - - 6$$

from Appendix B, $F/P_{r,6} = e^{6r} = e^{0.60} = 1.822$
therefore, $F = 1000(1.822) = \$1822$

b)
$$F = 1000 \overset{1.772}{(F/P_{i,6})} = 1772 \quad \text{for } i = 10\%$$

c) Same result as "a", i.e., effective continuous interest gives the identical result with continuous compounding of the nominal rate.

The effective rate is $\dot{E}=e^r-1 = e^{0.1}-1 = 1.1052-1 = 0.1052$ or 10.52%. This rate compounded annually gives the same result as 10% compounded continuously.

EXAMPLE B-2   Continuous Interest for Uniform Series

Determine the uniform series of end of year payments required to amortize a $10,000 loan in 10 years if interest is

a) $r = 6\%$ yer year compounded continuously
b) $i = 6\%$ per year compounded annually
c) $E = $ An effective annual rate for 6% compounded continuously.

Solution:

a)
$$
\begin{array}{ccc}
\$10,000 & A & A \\
\vdash\!\!\!-\!\!\!-\!\!\!-\!\!\!-\!\!\!-\!\!\!-\!\!\!-\!\!\!-\!\!\!-\!\!\dashv \\
0 & 1 - - - - - - 10
\end{array}
\qquad \text{so } A = 10,000\,(A/P_{r,10}^{.1370})=\$1370
$$

where $A/P_{r,10} = (e^{.06}-1)\,e^{.60}/e^{.60}-1 = \dfrac{(.0618)\,(1.8221)}{.8221}$

b) $A = 10,000\,(A/P_{i,10}^{.1359}) = \$1359.$

c) Same result as "a", since compounding "r" continuously gives the same total annual interest as compounding the effective rate, $E = e^r-1$, annually.

Continuous Interest Factors for Lump Sum End of Period Payments:

$F/P_{r,n} = e^{rn}$

$P/F_{r,n} = 1/e^{rn}$

$F/A_{r,n} = (e^{rn}-1)/(e^r-1)$

$A/F_{r,n} = (e^r-1)/(e^{rn}-1)$

$P/A_{r,n} = (e^{rn}-1)/(e^r-1)e^{rn}$

$A/P_{r,n} = (e^r-1)e^{rn}/(e^{rn}-1)$

e^ϕ Factors

ϕ	e^ϕ	ϕ	e^ϕ	ϕ	e^ϕ
.01	1.0101	.68	1.9739	1.85	6.3598
.02	1.0202	.69	1.9937	1.90	6.6859
.03	1.0305	.70	2.0138	2.00	7.3891
.04	1.0408	.72	2.0544	2.10	8.1662
.05	1.0513	.75	2.1170	2.20	9.0250
.06	1.0618	.76	2.1383	2.25	9.4877
.07	1.0725	.77	2.1598	2.30	9.9742
.08	1.0833	.80	2.2255	2.40	11.023
.09	1.0942	.81	2.2479	2.50	12.182
.10	1.1052	.84	2.3164	2.55	12.807
.12	1.1275	.85	2.3396	2.60	13.464
.14	1.1503	.88	2.4109	2.70	14.880
.15	1.1618	.90	2.4596	2.75	15.643
.16	1.1735	.91	2.4843	2.80	16.445
.18	1.1972	.95	2.5857	2.85	17.288
.20	1.2214	.96	2.6117	2.90	18.174
.21	1.2337	.98	2.6645	3.00	20.086
.22	1.2461	.99	2.6912	3.10	22.198
.24	1.2712	1.00	2.7183	3.20	24.533
.25	1.2840	1.02	2.7732	3.25	25.790
.26	1.2969	1.05	2.8577	3.30	27.133
.27	1.3100	1.06	2.8864	3.40	29.964
.28	1.3231	1.08	2.9447	3.50	33.115
.30	1.3499	1.10	3.0042	3.60	36.598
.32	1.3771	1.12	3.0649	3.70	40.447
.33	1.3910	1.14	3.1268	3.80	44.701
.34	1.4049	1.15	3.1582	3.90	49.402
.35	1.4191	1.17	3.2220	4.00	54.598
.36	1.4333	1.19	3.2871	4.20	66.686
.38	1.4623	1.20	3.3201	4.25	70.105
.39	1.4700	1.25	3.4903	4.40	81.451
.40	1.4918	1.26	3.5254	4.50	90.017
.42	1.5220	1.28	3.5966	4.75	115.18
.44	1.5527	1.30	3.6693	4.80	121.51
.45	1.5683	1.33	3.7810	5.00	148.41
.46	1.5841	1.36	3.8962	5.10	164.02
.48	1.6161	1.40	4.0552	5.40	221.41
.50	1.6487	1.44	4.2207	5.70	298.87
.52	1.6820	1.50	4.4817	6.00	403.43
.54	1.7160	1.52	4.5722	6.40	601.85
.55	1.7333	1.53	4.6182	6.50	665.14
.56	1.7507	1.55	4.7115	6.80	897.85
.57	1.7683	1.60	4.9530	7.00	1096.6
.60	1.8221	1.62	5.0531	7.20	1339.4
.63	1.8776	1.70	5.4739	7.50	1808.0
.64	1.8965	1.71	5.5290	7.60	1998.2
.65	1.9155	1.75	5.7546	8.00	2981.0
.66	1.9348	1.80	6.0496	8.50	4914.8
				9.00	8103.1
				9.50	13360.
				10.00	22026.

TABLE B-1: e^ϕ Factors (where ϕ = r or nr) for Use in Calculating Continuous Compound Interest Factors for End of Period or Funds Flow Payments.

APPENDIX C

CONTINUOUS INTEREST WITH CONTINUOUS FLOW OF FUNDS: FORMULAS AND APPLICATIONS

C.1 Formula Development

Since receipts and disbursements flow somewhat continuously in many real business situations, to account for this situation as realistically as possible, it sometimes is deemed to be desirable to have compound interest formulas based upon the continuous flow of funds rather than end of period lump sums. Since the interest rate compounding must correspond to the periods used, continuous interest must be used with the continuous flow of funds, i.e., an infinite number of payment periods require an interest rate with an infinite number of compounding periods.

The following symbols will be used in the formulas to be developed:

r = the nominal continuous interest rate

n = the number of years

$\bar{A}$ = the single total amount of funds flowing continuously during a period, in a uniform series of n equal payments. In the equations developed in this text, it is assumed that $\bar{A}$ is an input. $\bar{A}$ is often called a "funds flow" term.

P and F are defined as used throughout the text.

F^* = the single total amount of funds flowing continuously during a period in a single equivalent payment for the year occurring at the end of the funds flow payment period.

Writing an incremental dollar balance shows that money accumulates from two sources: interest on invested principal, and the continuous inflow from $\bar{A}$. The incremental equation is:

$$P|_{t+\Delta t} - P|_t = Pr\Delta t + \overline{A}\Delta t \qquad \text{C-1}$$

Dividing by Δt and taking the limit as Δt approaches zero yields

$$\frac{dP}{dt} = Pr + \overline{A}$$

Separating the variables and integrating gives

$$\int_{P=P}^{P=F} \frac{rdP}{Pr+\overline{A}} = \int_{t=0}^{t=n} rdt \quad \text{or} \quad \ln(Pr+\overline{A})\Big|_P^F = rt\Big|_o^n \qquad \text{C-2}$$

Substituting the limits gives

$$\ln(Fr+\overline{A})/(Pr+\overline{A}) = rn \qquad \text{C-3}$$

so

$$\frac{Fr+\overline{A}}{Pr+\overline{A}} = e^{rn} \qquad \text{C-4}$$

When there are no continuous uniform annual payments, $\overline{A}=0$ and $F=Pe^{rn}$, the same as Equation B-5 developed in Appendix B for continuous interest with lump sum payments. The present worth equation $P=F(1/e^{rn})$ is the same as Equation B-6.

The four factors for $F/\overline{A}_{r,n}$; $\overline{A}/F_{r,n}$; $P/\overline{A}_{r,n}$; and $\overline{A}/P_{r,n}$ all differ from the factors developed in Chapter 14. These factors result from the following developments:

1. To relate F and $\overline{A}$, assume $P = O$ in Equation C-4. This makes Equation C-4 yield

$$F = \overline{A}(e^{rn}-1)/r = \overline{A}(F/\overline{A}_{r,n}) \qquad \text{C-5}$$

where $(e^{rn}-1)/r$ is the funds flow uniform series compound amount factor. Rearranging

$$\overline{A} = Fr/(e^{rn}-1) = F(\overline{A}/F_{r,n}) \qquad \text{C-6}$$

where $r/(e^{rn}-1)$ is the funds flow sinking fund deposit factor. Note that F, $\overline{A}$, and the $F/\overline{A}_{r,n}$ and $\overline{A}/F_{r,n}$ factors are positive.

2. To relate P and $\overline{A}$, assume $F = O$ in Equation C-4. This makes Equation C-4 yield

$$\overline{A} = Pre^{rn}/(1-e^{rn}) = P(\overline{A}/P_{r,n}) \qquad \text{C-7}$$

where $re^{rn}/(1-e^{rn})$ is the funds flow capital recovery factor. Note that it is negative since $(1-e^{rn})$ will always be negative for all real values of r and n. $\overline{A}$ is negative in Equation C-7 since it is an output of money (a payment) required to recover the initial principal, P, plus interest due. Since $\bar{A}$ is the annual mortgage payment necessary to repay P in n years, we can see that this sign convention is consistent and logical.

Rearranging Equation C-7 gives

$$P = \bar{A}(1-e^{rn})/re^{rn} = \bar{A}(P/\bar{A}_{r,n}) \qquad \text{C-8}$$

where $(1-e^{rn})/re^{rn}$ is the funds flow uniform series present worth factor. Note that both $\bar{A}$ and $P/\bar{A}_{r,n}$ are negative in Equation C-8 to give a positive present value, P. It is normal to switch $1-e^{rn}$ to $e^{rn}-1$ so that funds flow factors are always positive. This is done in the remainder of this text.

These factors based on the funds flow concept find relatively wide usage by companies in making economic analyses of alternative investment possibilities. It is felt by many economic analysts that because receipts and disbursements flow somewhat continuously, that the funds flow assumption is better than the end of period payments assumption with discrete compound interest. This is true in some cases, but in most practical evaluation cases, both lump sum payments and continuous receipts and disbursements are involved. Therefore, using either method alone gives some error and the best result would come from a combination of the methods. Computer programming gets complicated when funds flow and discrete payments are both considered in the same problem, so it is common for companies to use one method or the other, but not a combination of both. Typical percent differences that result between using the two methods are illustrated by the following examples.

C.2 Applications

EXAMPLE C-1 Funds Flow Compared to End of Period Payments

Calculate the present worth of 10 uniform $1000 payments if

a) interest is 10% per year compounded continuously and payments are end of year

b) interest is 10% per year compounded continuously and payments are continuous

c) what is the percent change in results from a) to b)?

Solution:

a) P=?   A=1000   A=1000

      |———————+—————————————————|
      0   1 - - - - - - - n=10

                    6.00
so $P=1000(P/A_{r,10})$ = $6000   for   r = 0.10

where $PR_{r,10} = (e^{1.0}-1)/(e^{.1}-1)e^{1.0}$

$= 1.7183/(0.1052)(2.718) = 6.00$

b)

P=? $\bar{A}$=1000 $\bar{A}$=1000

├─────────┼───────────────┤
0   1 - - - - - - - n=10

so $P=1000(P/\bar{A}_{r,10}) = \$6325.$ for $r = 0.10$

(over $P/\bar{A}_{r,10}$: 6.325)

where $P/\bar{A}_{r,10} = (e^{1.0}-1)/.1\ e^{1.0} = (1.7183)/0.27183 = 6.325$

c)   % change a) to b) $= \dfrac{6325-6000}{6000} \times 100 = 5.41\%$ deviation between results.

EXAMPLE C-2   Analysis Involving Both Lump Sum and Funds Flow Payments

Development of an investment project involves the following cash outlays: three lump sum payments of \$70,000 at time zero and at the end of the first and second years, and uniform funds flow payments of \$50,000 during each of the first three years. Assume a nominal annual continuous interest rate of 10% and calculate the present worth of all payments:

a) assuming the funds flow payments to be end of year payments
b) assuming the lump sum payments to be funds flow payments during the prior year
c) properly combining both lump sum and funds flow calculations as appropriate.

Solution:

C=70000   C=50000   C=70000   C=50000   C=70000   C=50000

├─────────────────────┼─────────────────────┼─────────────────────┤
0   1   2   3

$r = 10\%$

a) Assume all costs are end of period costs.

Present Worth $= 70000 + 120,000\underset{1.720}{(P/A_{r,2})} + 50000\underset{.741}{(P/F_{r,3})}$

$= \$313,500$

where $P/A_{r,2} = (e^{.2}-1)/(e^{.1}-1)e^{.2} = (.2214)/(.1052)(1.2214) = 1.720$

$P/F_{r,3} = 1/e^{.3} = 1/1.3499 = .741$

b) Assume all costs are funds flow.

$$\text{Present Worth} = 70,000 + 50,000 \overset{2.594}{(P/\overline{A}_{r,3})} + 70,000 \overset{1.810}{(P/\overline{A}_{r,2})}$$

$$= \$326,200$$

where $P\overline{A}_{r,3} = (e^{.3}-1)/.1e^{.3} = (.3499)/.13499 = 2.594$

$P/\overline{A}_{r,2} = e^{.2}-1/.1e^{.2} = (2214)/.12214 = 1.810$

Alternate Solution for b):

$$\text{P.W.} = 70,000 + 120,000(P/\overline{A}_{r,2}) + 50,000 \overset{.952}{(P/\overline{A}_{r,1})} \overset{.818}{(P/F_{r,2})}$$

$$= \$326,200$$

where $P/\overline{A}_{r,1} = (e^{.1}-1)/.1 \ e^{.1} = .1052/.11052 = 0.952$

$P/F_{r,2} = 1/e^{.2} = 1/1.2214 = .818$

c) $\text{P.W.} = 70,000 + 70,000 \overset{1.720}{(P/\text{a}_{r,2})} + 50,000 \overset{2.594}{(P/\overline{A}_{r,3})} = 320,100$

Note that a) and b) results both differ from c), with the correct result, "c", between the results for "a" and "b".

C.3 Discount Factors to Time Zero for Single Funds Flow Payments

To find the present worth of a funds flow single cash payment or receipt which we will call F*, made during the nth year as illustrated

```
P=?                        | - F* - |
|----------+- - - - - - +--------+
0          1 - - - - - n-1       n
```

on the diagram, it is common to combine the appropriate funds flow factor and end of period continuous interest factor as follows:

The sum of money at time n-1 equivalent to F* is

$$F^* (P/\overline{A}_{r,1})$$

The present worth, P, of the sum of money $F^* (P/\overline{A}_{r,1})$ is

$$P = (P/F_{r,n-1})(F^*)(P/\overline{A}_{r,1}) = (\frac{F^*}{e^{r(n-1)}})(\frac{e^r-1}{re^r})$$

$$= F^* (\frac{e^r-1}{re^{rn}}) = F^* (P/F^*_{r,n}) \text{ where } P/F^*_{r,n} = \frac{e^r-1}{re^{rn}}$$

The factor $(e^r-1)/re^{rn}$ can be used to find the present worth at time zero of a one-year funds flow payment made during the nth year. It is tabulated in the following Table C1.

TABLE C-1   Discount factors to time zero for cash effects, F*, which occur uniformly over one-year periods after time zero, at various nominal annual continuous interest rates, r, where n = the end of year period.

$$\text{Factor} = (e^r-1)/re^{rn} = P/F^*_{r,n}$$

Year	r=5%	r=10%	r=15%	r=20%	r=25%	r=30%	r=40%	r=50%
0-1	.9754	.9516	.9286	.9063	.8848	.8640	.8242	.7869
1-2	.9278	.8611	.7993	.7421	.6891	.6400	.5525	.4773
2-3	.8826	.7791	.6879	.6075	.5367	.4741	.3703	.2895
3-4	.8395	.7050	.5921	.4974	.4179	.3513	.2482	.1756
4-5	.7986	.6379	.5096	.4072	.3255	.2602	.1664	.1065
5-6	.7596	.5772	.4386	.3334	.2535	.1928	.1115	.0646
6-7	.7226	.5223	.3775	.2730	.1974	.1428	.0748	.0392
7-8	.6874	.4726	.3250	.2235	.1538	.1058	.0501	.0238
8-9	.6538	.4276	.2797	.1830	.1197	.0784	.0336	.0144
9-10	.6219	.3869	.2407	.1498	.0933	.0581	.0225	.0087
10-11	.5916	.3501	.2072	.1227	.0726	.0430	.0151	.0053
11-12	.5628	.3168	.1783	.1004	.0566	.0319	.0101	.0032
12-13	.5353	.2866	.1535	.0822	.0441	.0236	.0068	.0020
13-14	.5092	.2593	.1321	.0673	.0343	.0175	.0045	.0012
14-15	.4844	.2347	.1137	.0551	.0267	.0130	.0030	.0007
15-16	.4608	.2123	.0979	.0451	.0208	.0096	.0020	.0004
16-17	.4383	.1921	.0842	.0369	.0162	.0071	.0014	.0003
17-18	.4169	.1739	.0725	.0303	.0126	.0053	.0009	.0002
18-19	.3966	.1573	.0624	.0248	.0098	.0039	.0006	.0001
19-20	.3772	.1423	.0537	.0203	.0077	.0029	.0004	.0001
20-21	.3588	.1288	.0462	.0166	.0060	.0021	.0003	--
21-22	.3413	.1165	.0398	.0136	.0046	.0016	.0002	--
22-23	.3247	.1054	.0343	.0111	.0036	.0012	.0001	--
23-24	.3089	.0954	.0295	.0091	.0028	.0009	.0001	--
24-25	.2938	.0863	.0254	.0075	.0022	.0007	.0001	--
25-30	.2535	.0646	.0165	.0043	.0011	.0003	--	--
30-35	.1974	.0392	.0078	.0016	.0003	.0001	--	--
35-40	.1538	.0238	.0037	.0006	.0001	--	--	--
40-45	.1197	.0144	.0017	.0002	--	--	--	--
45-50	.0933	.0087	.0008	.0001	--	--	--	--

GLOSSARY OF
INVESTMENT TERMINOLOGY
(New York Stock Exchange and Other Terms)

1. ACCRUED INTEREST—Interest accrued on a bond since the last interest payment was made. The buyer of the bond pays the market price plus accrued interest. Exceptions include bonds that are in default and income bonds. (See: Flat)

2. ALL OR NONE ORDER—A market or limited price order which is to be executed in its entirety or not at all, but, unlike a fill or kill order, is not to be treated as cancelled if not executed as soon as it is represented in the Trading Crowd. Bids or offers on behalf of all or none orders may not be made in stocks, but may be made in bonds when the number of bonds is fifty or more.

3. ALTERNATIVE ORDER-EITHER/OR ORDER—An order to do either of two alternatives—such as, either sell (buy) a particular stock at a limit price or sell (buy) on stop. If the order is executed on the happening of one alternative, the order on the other alternative is treated as cancelled. If the order is for an amount larger than one unit of trading, the number of units executed determines the amount of the alternative order to be treated as cancelled.

4. AMORTIZE—To pay off a debt, or cost; normally, gradual retirement of a debt with a series of payments. "Amortization" is an IRS approved tax deduction method (for certain special investment costs) which is similar to straight line depreciation.

5. ANNUAL REPORT—The formal financial statement issued yearly by a corporation to its shareowners. The annual report shows assets, liabilities, earnings—how the company stood at the close of the business year and how it fared profit-wise during the year.

6. ARBITRAGE—A technique employed to take advantage of differences in price. If, for example, XYZ stock can be bought in New York for $10 a share and sold in London at $10.50, an arbitrageur may simultaneously purchase XYZ stock here and sell the same amount in London, making a profit of 50 cents a share, less expenses. Arbitrage may also involve the purchase of rights to subscribe to a security, or the purchase of a convertible security—and the sale at or about the same time of the security obtainable through exercise of the rights or of the security obtainable through conversion. (See: Convertible, Rights)

7. ASSETS—Everything a corporation owns or due to it: Cash, investments, money due it, materials and inventories, which are called current assets; buildings and machinery, which are known as fixed assets; and patents and goodwill, called intangible assets. (See: Liabilities)

8. AT THE CLOSE ORDER—A market order which is to be executed at or as near to the close as practicable.

9. AT THE OPENING OR AT THE OPENING ONLY ORDER—A market or limited price order which is to be executed at the opening of the stock or not at all, and any such order or portion thereof not so executed is treated as cancelled.

10. BALANCE SHEET—A condensed statement showing the nature and amount of a company's assets, liabilities and capital on a given date. In dollar amounts the balance sheet shows what the company owned, what it owed, and the ownership interest in the company of its stockholders. (See: Assets, Earnings Report)

11. BEAR—Someone who believes the market will decline. (See: Bull)

12. BEAR MARKET—A declining market. (See: Bull Market)

13. BEARER BOND—A bond which does not have the owner's name registered on the books of the issuing company and which is payable to the holder. (See: Coupon Bond, Registered Bond)

14. BIDS AND ASKED—Often referred to as a quotation or quote. The bid is the highest price anyone has declared that he wants to pay for a security at a given time, the asked is the lowest price anyone will take at the same time. (See: Quotation)

15. BOND—Basically an IOU or promissory note of a corporation usually issued in multiples of $1,000, although $100 and $500 denominations are not uncommon. A bond is evidence of a debt on which the issuing company usually promises to pay the bond-holders a specified amount of interest for a specified length of time, and to repay the loan on the expiration date. In every case a bond represents debt—its holder is a creditor of the corporation and not a part owner as is the shareholder.

16. BOOK VALUE—The value of a capitalized investment that has not been written off for tax purposes by depreciation, depletion, or amortization. Book value is often referred to as "adjusted basis" in U.S. Internal Revenue Service literature.

17. BULL—One who believes the market will rise. (See: Bear)
    A Bull Market is an advancing market.

18. CALL—(See: Puts and Calls)

19. CALLABLE—A bond issue, all or part of which may be redeemed by the issuing corporation under definite conditions before matur-ity. The term also applies to preferred shares which may be re-deemed by the issuing corporation.

20. CAPITAL GAIN OR CAPITAL LOSS—Profit or loss from the sale of a capital asset. A capital gain, under current Federal income tax laws, may be either short-term (12 months or less) or long-term (more than 12 months). A short-term capital gain is taxed at the reporting individual's full income tax rate. A long-term capital gain is taxed at the appropriate long-term tax rate.

21. CAPITALIZE—Investment costs that are not expensed for tax purposes in the year in which they are incurred but that are written off for tax purposes by depreciation, depletion or amortization over a period of time greater than one year are said to be "capitalized."

22. CAPITALIZATION—Total amount of the various securities is-sued by a corporation. Capitalization may include bonds, deben-tures, preferred and common stock and surplus. Bonds and deben-tures are usually carried on the books of the issuing company in terms of their par or face value. Preferred and common shares may be carried in terms of par or stated value. Stated value may be an arbitrary figure decided upon by the directors or may represent

the amount received by the company from the sale of the securities at the time of issuance. (See: Par)

23. CASH FLOW—Reported net income of a corporation plus amounts charged off for depreciation, depletion, amortization, extraordinary charges to reserves, which are bookkeeping deductions and not paid out in actual dollars and cents. A yardstick used in recent years because of the larger non-cash deductions appearing to offer a better indication of the ability of a company to pay dividends and finance expansion from self-generated cash than the conventional reported net income figure.

24. COLLATERAL—Securities or other property pledged by a borrower to secure repayment of a loan.

25. COMMON STOCK—Securities which represent an ownership interest in a corporation. If the company has also issued preferred stock, both common and preferred have ownership rights, but the preferred normally has prior claim on dividends and, in the event of liquidation, assets. Claims of both common and preferred stockholders are junior to claims of bondholders or other creditors of the company. Common stockholders assume the greater risk, but generally exercise the greater control and may gain the greater reward in the form of dividends and capital appreciation. (See: Preferred Stock)

26. CONGLOMERATE—A corporation seeking to diversify its operations by acquiring enterprises in widely varied industries.

27. CONVERTIBLE—A bond, debenture or preferred share which may be exchanged by the owner for common stock or another security, usually of the same company, in accordance with the terms of the issue.

28. CORNER—Buying of a stock or commodity on a scale large enough to give the buyer, or buying group, control over the price. A person who must buy that stock or commodity, for example one who is short, is forced to do business at an arbitrarily high price with those who obtained the corner. (See: Short Position, Short Sale)

28. COUPON BOND—Bond with interest coupons attached. The coupons are clipped as they come due and are presented by the

holder for payment of interest. (See: Bearer Bond, Registered Bond)

30. COVERING—Buying a security previously sold short. (See: Short Sale, Short Covering)

31. CUMULATIVE PREFERRED—A stock having a provision that if one or more dividends are omitted, the omitted dividends must be paid before dividends may be paid on the company's common stock.

32. CURRENT ASSETS—Those assets of a company which are reasonably expected to be realized in cash, or sold, or consumed during the normal operating cycle of the business. These include cash, U.S. Government bonds, receivables and money due usually within one year, and inventories.

33. CURRENT LIABILITIES—Money owed and payable by a company, usually within one year.

34. DAY ORDER—An order to buy or sell which, if not executed expires at the end of the trading day on which it was entered.

34. DEBENTURE—A promissory note backed by the general credit of a company and usually not secured by a mortgage or lien on any specific property. (See: Bond)

36. DEPLETION—Recovery of an owner's economic interest in mineral (including oil and gas) reserves through federal tax deductions related to removal of the mineral over the economic life of the property. The greater tax deduction from separate cost depletion and percent depletion calculations is selected each year. Tax deductions from percent depletion over project life often exceed the value of an owner's original economic interest in a property.

37. DIVERSIFICATION—Spreading investments among different companies in different fields. Another type of diversification is also offered by the securities of many individual companies because of the wide range of their activities. (See: Investment Trust)

38. DOUBLE TAXATION—Short for Double Taxation of Dividends. The federal government taxes corporate profits once as corporate income; any part of the remaining profits distributed as dividends to stockholders is taxed again as income to the recipient stockholder.

39. DOWN TICK—(See: Up Tick)

40. EARNINGS REPORT—A statement also called an income state-ment—issued by a company showing its earnings or losses over a given period. The earnings report lists the income earned, expenses and the net result. (See: Balance Sheet)

41. EQUITY—The ownership interest of common and preferred stock-holders in a company. Also refers to excess of value of securities over the debit balance in a margin account.

42. EX-DIVIDEND—A synonym for "without dividend." The buyer of a stock selling ex-dividend does not receive the recently declared dividend. Ex-rights similarly means "without rights."

43. EXPENSED—Costs written off for tax deduction purposes in the year in which they are incurred. The converse of "expensed" is "capitalized."

44. EXTRA—The short form of "extra dividend." A dividend in the form of stock or cash in addition to the regular or usual dividend the company has been paying.

45. FILL OR KILL—A market or limited price order is to be executed in its entirety as soon as it is represented in the Trading Crowd. If not so executed, the order is treated as cancelled. For purposes of this definition a "stop" is considered an execution.

46. FISCAL YEAR—A corporation's accounting year. Due to the nature of their particular business, some companies do not use the calendar year for their bookkeeping. A typical example is the de-partment store which finds December 31 too early a date to close its books after the Christmas rush. For that reason many stores wind up their accounting year January 31. Their fiscal year, there-fore, runs from February 1 of one year through January 31 of the next. The fiscal year of other companies may run from July 1 through the following June 30. Most companies, though, operate on a calendar year basis.

47. FLAT—This term means that the price at which a bond is traded includes consideration for all unpaid accruals of interest. Bonds which are in default of interest or principal are traded flat. Income bonds, which pay interest only to the extent earned are usually traded flat. All other bonds are usually dealt in "and interest,"

which means that the buyer pays to the seller the market price plus interest accrued since the last payment date. When applied to a stock loan, flat means without premium or interest. (See: Short Sale)

48. FUNDED DEBT—Usually interest-bearing bonds or debentures of a company. Could include long-term bank loans. Does not include short-term loans, preferred or common stock.

49. GOOD 'TIL CANCELLED ORDER (GTC) OR OPEN ORDER —An order to buy or sell which remains in effect until it is either executed or cancelled.

50. GROWTH STOCK—Stock of a company with prospects for future growth—a company whose earnings are expected to increase at a relatively rapid rate.

51. HEDGE—(See: Arbitrage, Puts & Calls, Selling Against the Box, Short Sale)

52. INDENTURE—A written agreement under which debentures are issued, setting forth maturity date, interest rate, and other terms.

53. INVESTMENT BANKER—Also known as an underwriter. He is the middleman between the corporation issuing new securities and the public. The usual practice is for one or more investment bankers to buy outright from a corporation a new issue of stocks or bonds. The group forms a syndicate to sell the securities to individuals and institutions. Investment bankers also distribute very large blocks of stocks or bonds—perhaps held by an estate. Thereafter the market in the security may be over-the-counter, on a regional stock exchange, the American Exchange or the New York Stock Exchange. (See: Over-the-Counter, Primary Distribution)

54. INVESTMENT TRUST—A company or trust which uses its capital to invest in other companies. There are two principal types: the closed-end and the open-end, or mutual fund. Shares in closed-end investment trusts, some of which are listed on the New York Stock Exchange, are readily transferable in the open market and are bought and sold like other shares. Capitalization of these companies remains the same unless action is taken to change, which is seldom. Open-end funds sell their own new shares to investors, stand ready to buy back their old shares, and are not listed. Open-end funds are

so called because their capitalization is not fixed; they issue more shares as people want them.

55. LEVERAGE—The effect on the per-share earnings of the common stock of a company when large sums must be paid for bond interest or preferred stock dividends, or both, before the common stock is entitled to share in earnings. Leverage may be advantageous for the common when earnings are good but may work against the common stock when earnings decline. Example: Company A has 1,000,000 shares of common stock outstanding, no other securities. Earnings drop from $1,000,000 to $800,000 or from $1 to 80 cents a share, a decline of 20 per cent. Company B also has 1,000,000 shares of common but must pay $500,000 annually in bond interest. If earnings amount to $1,000,000, there is $500,000 available for the common or 50 cents a share. But earnings drop to $800,000 so there is only $300,000 available for the common, or 30 cents a share—a drop of 40 per cent. Or suppose earnings of the company with only common stock increased from $1,000,000 to $1,500,000 —earnings per share would go from $1 to $1.50, or an increase of 50 per cent. But if earnings of the company which had to pay $500,000 in bond interest increased that much—earnings per common share would jump from 50 cents to $1 a share, or 100 per cent. When a company has common stock only, no leverage exists because all earnings are available for the common, although relatively large fixed charges payable for lease of substantial plant assets may have an effect similar to that of a bond issue.

56. LIABILITIES—All the claims against a corporation. Liabilities include accounts and wages and salaries payable, dividends declared payable, accrued taxes payable, fixed or long-term liabilities such as mortgage bonds, debentures and bank loans. (See: Assets, Balance Sheet)

57. LIMIT, LIMITED ORDER OR LIMITED PRICE ORDER—An order to buy or sell a stated amount of a security at a specified price, or at a better price, if obtainable after the order is represented in the Trading Crowd.

58. LIQUIDATION—The process of converting securities or other property into cash. The dissolution of a company, with cash remaining after sale of its assets and payment of all indebtedness being distributed to the shareholders.

59. LIQUIDITY—The ability of the market in a particular security to absorb a reasonable amount of buying or selling at reasonable price changes. Liquidity is one of the most important characteristics of a good market.

60. LOAD—The portion of the offering price of shares of open-end investment companies which covers sales commissions and all other costs of distribution. The load is incurred only on purchase, there being, in most cases, no charge when the shares are sold (redeemed).

61. LOCKED IN—An investor is said to be locked in when he has a profit on a security he owns but does not sell because his profit would immediately become subject to the capital gains tax. (See: Capital Gain)

62. LONG—Signifies ownership of securities: "I am long 100 U.S. Steel" means the speaker owns 100 shares. (See: Short Position, Short Sale)

63. MARGIN—The amount paid by the customer when he uses his broker's credit to buy a security. Under Federal Reserve regulations, the initial margin required in the past 20 years has ranged from 40 per cent of the purchase price all the way to 100 per cent.

64. MARGIN CALL—A demand upon a customer to put up money or securities with the broker. The call is made when a purchase is made; also if a customer's equity in a margin account declines below a minimum standard set by the Exchange or by the firm. (See: Margin)

65. MARKET ORDER—An order to buy or sell a stated amount of a security at the most advantageous price obtainable after the order is represented in the Trading Crowd. (See: Good 'til Cancelled Order, Limit Order, Stop Order)

66. MINIMUM RATE OF RETURN (i*)—The rate of return that an investor feels he has opportunities in which to invest available investment capital with reasonable risk. An investor normally is looking for alternative investments that yield a rate of return better than i*.

67. NEGOTIABLE—Refers to a security, title to which is transferable by delivery.

68. NONCUMULATIVE—A preferred stock on which unpaid dividends do not accrue. Omitted dividends are, as a rule, gone forever. (See: Cumulative Preferred)

69. ODD-LOT—An amount of stock less than the established 100-share unit or 10-share unit of trading: from 1 to 99 shares for the great majority of issues, 1 to 9 for so-called inactive stocks. (See: Round Lot)

70. OFFER—The price at which a person is ready to sell. Opposed to bid, the price at which one is ready to buy. (See: Bid and Asked)

71. OPEN ORDER—(See: Good 'til Cancelled Order)

72. OPTION—A right to buy or sell specific securities or properties at a specified price within a specified tme. (See: Puts and Calls)

73. ORDERS GOOD UNTIL A SPECIFIED TIME—A market or limited price order which is to be represented in the Trading Crowd until a specified time, after which such order or the portion thereof not executed is to be treated as cancelled.

74. OVERBOUGHT—An opinion as to price levels. May refer to a security which has had a sharp rise or to the market as a whole after a period of vigorous buying, which it may be argued, has left prices "too high." (See: Technical Position)

75. OVERSOLD—An opinion—the reverse of overbought. A single security or a market which, it is believed, has declined to an unreasonable level. (See: Technical Position)

76. OVER-THE-COUNTER—A market for securities made up of securities dealers who may or may not be members of a securities exchange. Over-the-counter is mainly a market made over the telephone. Thousands of companies have insufficient shares outstanding, stockholders, or earnings to warrant application for listing on the N.Y. Stock Exchange. Securities of these companies are traded in the over-the-counter market between dealers who act either as principals or as brokers for customers. The over-the-counter market is the principal market for U.S. Government bonds and municipals and stocks of banks and insurance companies.

77. PAR—In the case of a common share, par means a dollar amount assigned to the share by the company's charter. Par value may also

be used to compute the dollar amount of the common shares on the balance sheet. Par value has little significance so far as market value of common stock is concerned. Many companies today issue no-par stock but give a stated per share value on the balance sheet. Par at one time was supposed to represent the value of the original investment behind each share in cash, goods or services. In the case of preferred shares and bonds, however, par is important. It often signifies the dollar value upon which dividends on preferred stocks, and interest on bonds, are figured. The issuer of a 3 per cent bond promises to pay that percentage of the bond's par value annually.

78. PARTICIPATING PREFERRED—A preferred stock which is entitled to its stated dividend and, also, to additional dividends on a specified basis upon payment of dividends on the common stock.

79. PREFERRED STOCK—A class of stock with a claim on the company's earnings before payment may be made on the common stock and usually entitled to priority over common stock if company liquidates. Usually entitled to dividends at a specified rate—when declared by the Board of Directors and before payment of a dividend on the common stock—depending upon the terms of the issue. (See: Cumulative Preferred, Participating Preferred)

80. PRICE-EARNINGS RATIO—The current market price of a share of stock divided by earnings per share for a twelve-month period. For example, a stock selling for $100 a share and earning $5 a share is said to be selling at a price-earning ratio of 20 to 1.

81. PRIMARY DISTRIBUTION—Also called primary offering. The original sale of a company's securities. (See: Investment Banker, Secondary Distribution)

82. PROXY—Written authorization given by a shareholder to someone else to represent him and vote his shares at a shareholders' meeting.

83. PUTS AND CALLS—Options which give the right to buy or sell a fixed amount of a certain stock at a specified price within a specified time. A put gives the holder the right to sell the stock; a call the right to buy the stock. Puts are purchased by those who think a stock may go down. A put obligates the seller of the contract to take delivery of the stock and pay the specified price to the owner of the option within the time limit of the contract. The price specified in

a put or call is usually close to the market price of the stock at the time the contract is made. Calls are purchased by those who think a stock may rise. A call gives the holder the right to buy the stock from the seller of the contract at the specified price within a fixed period of time. Put and call contracts are written for 30, 60 or 90 days, or longer. If the purchaser of a put or call does not wish to exercise the option, the price he paid for the option becomes a loss.

84. QUOTATION—Often shortened to "quote." The highest bid to buy and the lowest offer to sell a security in a given market at a given time. If you ask your broker for a "quote" on a stock, he may come back with something like "45¼ to 45½." This means that $45.25 is the highest price any buyer wanted to pay at the time the quote was given on the floor of the Exchange and that $45.50 was the lowest price which any seller would take at the same time. (See: Bid and Asked)

85. REGISTERED BOND—A bond which is registered on the books of the issuing company in the name of the owner. It can be transferred only when endorsed by the registered owner. (See: Bearer Bond, Coupon Bond)

86. REGISTRATION—Before a public offering may be made of new securities by a company, or of outstanding securities by controlling stockholders—through the mails or in interstate commerce—the securities must be registered under the Securities Act of 1933. Registration statement is filed with the SEC by the issuer. It must disclose pertinent information relating to the company's operations, securities, management and purpose of the public offering. Securities of railroads under jurisdiction of the Interstate Commerce Commission, and certain other types of securities, are exempted. On security offerings involving less than $300,000, less information is required.

Before a security may be admitted to dealings on a national securities exchange, it must be registered under the Securities Exchange Act of 1934. The application for registration must be filed with the exchange and the SEC by the company issuing the securities. It must disclose pertinent information relating to the company's operations, securities and management. Registration may become effective 30 days after receipt by the SEC of the certification by the exchange of approval of listing and registration, or sooner by special order of the Commission.

87. RIGHTS—When a company wants to raise more funds by issuing additional securities, it may give its stockholders the opportunity, ahead of others, to buy the new securities in proportion to the number of shares each owns. The piece of paper evidencing this privilege is called a right. Because the additional stock is usually offered to stockholders below the current market price, rights ordinarily have a market value of their own and are actively traded. In most cases they must be exercised within a relatively short period. Failure to exercise or sell rights may result in actual loss to the holder. (See: Warrant)

88. ROUND LOT—A unit of trading or a multiple thereof. On the NYSE the unit of trading is generally 100 shares in stocks and $1,000 par value in the case of bonds. In some inactive stocks, the unit of trading is 10 shares.

89. SEAT—A traditional figure-of-speech for a membership on an exchange. Price and admission requirements vary.

90. SEC—The Securities and Exchange Commission, established by Congress to help protect investors. The SEC administers the Securities Act of 1933, the Securities Exchange Act of 1934, the Trust Indenture Act, the Investment Company Act, the Investment Advisers Act, and the Public Utility Holding Company Act.

91. SECONDARY DISTRIBUTION—Also known as a secondary offering. The redistribution of a block of stock some time after it has been sold by the issuing company. The sale is handled off the NYSE by a securities firm or group of firms and the shares are usually offered at a fixed price which is related to the current market price of the stock. Usually the block is a large one, such as might be involved in the settlement of an estate. The security may be listed or unlisted.

92. SELLING AGAINST THE BOX—A method of protecting a paper profit. Let's say you own 100 shares of XYZ which has advanced in price, and you think the price may decline. So you sell 100 shares short, borrowing 100 shares to make delivery. You retain in your security box the 100 shares which you own. If XYZ advances, the loss on your short sale is exactly offset by the loss

in the market value of the stock you own. You can close out your short sale by buying 100 shares to return to the person from whom you borrowed, or you can send them the 100 shares which you own. Selling against the box differs from short selling sales in that the seller is protecting a profit rather than selling to profit from declining share prices. (See: Hedge, Short Sale)

93. SHORT COVERING—Buying stock to return stock previously borrowed to make delivery on a short sale.

94. SHORT POSITION—Stocks sold short and not covered as of a particular date. On the NYSE, a tabulation is issued a few days after the middle of the month listing all issues on the Exchange in which there was a short position at the mid-month settlement date of 5,000 or more shares, and issues in which the short position had changed by 2,000 or more shares in the preceding month. This tabulation is based on reports of positions on member firms' books. Short position also means the total amount of stock an individual has sold short and has not covered, as of a particular date. Initial margin requirements for a short position are the same as for a long position. Proceeds from short sales are excluded entirely from this report. The initial margin required of the short seller, however, and profits and losses on short sales are reflected in stock margin debt.

95. SHORT SALE—A person who believes a stock will decline and sells it though he does not own any has made a short sale. For instance: You instruct your broker to sell short 100 shares of ABC. Your broker borrows the stock so he can deliver the 100 shares to the buyer. The money value of the shares borrowed is deposited by your broker with the lender. Sooner or later you must cover your short sale by buying the same amount of stock you borrowed for return to the lender. If you are able to buy ABC at a lower price than you sold it for, your profit is the difference between the two prices—not counting commissions and taxes. But if you have to pay more for the stock than the price you received, that is the amount of your loss. Stock exchange and federal regulations govern and limit the conditions under which a short sale may be made on a national securities exchange.

96. SINKING FUND—Money regularly set aside by a company to redeem its bonds, debentures or preferred stock from time to time as specified in the indenture or charter.

97. SPECIALIST—A member of the New York Stock Exchange who has two functions: First, to maintain an orderly market, insofar as reasonably practicable, in the stocks in which he is registered as a specialist. In order to maintain an orderly market, the Exchange expects the specialist to buy or sell for his own account, to a reasonable degree, when there is a temporary disparity between supply and demand. Second, the specialist acts as a broker's broker. When a commission broker on the Exchange on the Exchange floor receives a limit order, say, to buy at $50 a stock then selling at $60—he cannot wait at the post where the stock is traded until the price reaches the specified level. So he leaves the order with the specialist, who will try to execute it in the market if and when the stock declines to the specified price. At all times the specialist must put his customers' interests above his own. There are about 350 specialists on the NYSE.

98. SPLIT—The division of the outstanding shares of a corporation into a larger number of shares. A 3-for-1 split by a company with 1 million shares outstanding results in 3 million shares outstanding. Each holder of 100 shares before the 3-for-1 split would have 300 shares, although his proportionate equity in the company would remain the same; 100 parts of 1 million are the equivalent of 300 parts of 3 million. Ordinarily splits must be voted by directors and approved by shareholders. (See: Stock Dividends)

99. STOCK DIVIDEND—A dividend paid in securities rather than cash. The dividend may be additional shares of the issuing company, or in shares of another company (usually a subsidiary) held by the company. (See: Ex-Dividend, Split)

100. STOP LIMIT ORDER—A stop limit order to buy becomes a limit order executable at the limit price, or at a better price, if obtainable, when a transaction in the security occurs at or above the stop price after the order is represented in the Trading Crowd. A stop limit order to sell becomes a limit order executable at the limit price or at a better price, if obtainable, when a transaction in the security occurs at or below the stop price after the order is represented in the Trading Crowd.

101. STOP ORDER—A stop order to buy becomes a market order when a transaction in the security occurs at or above the stop price

after the order is represented in the Trading Crowd. A stop order to sell becomes a market order when a transaction in the security occurs at or below the stop price after the order is represented in the Trading Crowd. A stop order may be used in an effort to protect a paper profit, or to try to limit a possible loss to a certain amount. Since it becomes a market order when the stop price is reached, there is no certainty that it will be executed at that price. (See: Limited Order, Market Order)

102. TAX-EXEMPT BONDS—The securities of states, cities and other public authorities specified under federal law, the interest on which is either wholly or partly exempt from federal income taxes.

103. TECHNICAL POSITION—A term applied to the various internal factors affecting the market; opposed to external forces such as earnings, dividends, political considerations and general economic conditions. Some internal factors considered in appraising the market's technical position include the size of the short interest, whether the market has had a sustained advance or decline without interruption, a sharp advance or decline on small volume and the amount of credit in use in the market.

104. THIN MARKET—A market in which there are comparatively few bids to buy or offers to sell or both. The phrase may apply to a single security or to the entire stock market. In a thin market, price fluctuations between transactions are usually larger than when the market is liquid. A thin market in a particular stock may reflect lack of interest in that issue or a limited supply of or demand for stock in the market. (See: Bid and Asked, Liquidity, Offer)

105. TIME ORDER—An order which becomes a market or limited price order at a specified time.

106. TRADING POST—One of 18 horseshoe-shaped trading locations on the floor of the New York Stock Exchange at which stocks assigned to that location are bought and sold. About 75 stocks are traded at each post.

107. UP TICK—A term used to designate a transaction made at a price higher than the preceding transaction. Conversely, a down tick, is a term used to designate a transaction made at a price lower than the preceding trade.

108. VOTING RIGHT—The stockholder's right to vote his stock in the affairs of his company. Most common shares have one vote each. Preferred stock usually has the right to vote when preferred dividends are in default for a specified period. The right to vote may be delegated by the stockholder to another person.

109. WARRANT—A certificate giving the holder the right to purchase securities at a stipulated price within a specified time limit or perpetually. Sometimes a warrant is offered with securities as an inducement to buy. (See: Rights)

APPENDIX E

ARITHMETIC GRADIENT SERIES FACTOR DEVELOPMENT

Represent a gradient series of payments which has a first term of B and constant positive gradient g between terms as the sum of the two series of payments as shown in Figure E-1.

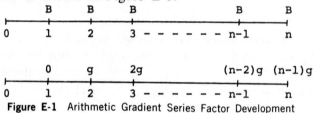

Figure E-1 Arithmetic Gradient Series Factor Development

B is spread uniformly each period over the project life. Now if we can spread the arithmetic gradient payments uniformly over each period of the project life we will have converted the gradient series to an equivalent series of equal period payments. The future worth of the gradient terms at year n is: $F = g(F/P_{i,(n-2)}) + 2g(F/P_{i,(n-3)}) + ---$

$$+ (n-2)g(F/P_{i,1}) + (n-1)g \qquad \text{E-1}$$

Multiplying this equation by $F/P_{i,1}$ gives

$$F(F/P_{i,1}) = g(F/P_{i,(n-1)}) + 2g(F/P_{i,(n-2)}) + ---$$

$$+ (n-2)g(F/P_{i,2}) + (n-1)g(F/P_{i,1}) \qquad \text{E-2}$$

Subtracting Equation E-1 from Equation E-2 yields

$$F-F(F/P_{i,1}) = -g(F/P_{i,(n-1)}) - g(F/P_{i,(n-2)}) -$$

$$\ldots - g(F/P_{i,2}) - g(FP_{i,1}) + (n-1)g =$$

$$-g[\underbrace{1 + F/P_{i,1} + F/P_{i,2} + \ldots + F/P_{i,(n-2)} + F/P_{i,(n-1)}}_{F/A_{i,n}}] + ng \qquad \text{E-3}$$

$$F - F(1+i) = -g[F/A_{i,n}] + ng$$

or $Fi = +g[F/A_{i,n}] - ng$

Dividing by i gives

$$F = g[\frac{F/A_{i,n}}{i} - \frac{n}{i}] \qquad \text{E-4}$$

Our objective is to calculate the uniform series of end of period payments, A, that is equivalent to the arithmetic gradient series. Recall that $F(A/F_{i,n}) = A$ and multiply each side of Equation E-4 by $A/F_{i,n}$

$$A = F(A/F_{i,n}) = g[\frac{1}{i} - \frac{n}{i}(A/F_{i,n})] = g(A/G_{i,n}) \qquad \text{E-5}$$

The arithmetic series factor (also called a gradient conversion factor in engineering economy literature) is bracketed. Adding the first term in a gradient series, B, to Equation E-5 gives the total arithmetic gradient series equation presented in chapter 2 as Equation 2-12

$$A = B \pm g(A/G_{i,n}) \qquad \text{2-12}$$

APPENDIX F

GEOMETRIC GRADIENT SERIES FACTOR DEVELOPMENT AND APPLICATIONS

When values vary by a constant percentage from period to period instead of by a constant dollar amount, a geometric gradient series is generated instead of an arithmetic gradient series. The following development generates a factor that permits calculation of the future value, F, or the equivalent uniform series of equal values, A', for a geometric gradient series of values that has the first term in the gradient represented by A and each subsequent term increasing or decreasing by a geometric ratio, r, which is one plus or minus the constant percent change from period to period. Mr. Ed Dallin, Senior Systems Analyst for Texasgulf in Raleigh, North Carolina, deserves credit for the following development and example illustrations.

$$
\begin{array}{cccccc}
A & Ar & Ar^2 & & Ar^{n-1} & \\
\hline
0 & 1 & 2 & 3 & n & \quad F=?
\end{array}
$$

$$F=A(1+i)^{n-1}+Ar(1+i)^{n-2}+Ar^2(1+i)^{n-3}+Ar^{n-3}(1+i)^2+Ar^{n-2}(1+i)+Ar^{n-1} \qquad \text{F-1}$$

Multiply both sides of Equation F-1 by $1+i$

$$F(1+i)=A(1+i)^n+Ar(1+i)^{n-1}+Ar^2(1+i)^{n-2}+\ldots+Ar^{n-2}(1+i)+Ar^{n-1}(1+i) \qquad \text{F-2}$$

Multiply both sides of Equation F-1 by r

$$Fr = Ar(1+i)^{n-1}+Ar^2(1+i)^{n-2}+\ldots+Ar^{n-2}(1+i)+Ar^{n-1}(1+i)+Ar^n \qquad \text{F-3}$$

subtract Equation F-3 from Equation F-2

$$F(1+i)-Fr = A(1+i)^n-Ar^n = F(1+i-r)$$

$$F = A\left[\frac{(1+i)^n-r^n}{1+i - r}\right] = Ar^{n-1}\left[\frac{(\frac{1+i}{r})^n - 1}{\frac{1+i}{r} - 1}\right] \qquad \text{F-4}$$

Now define a new interest rate "x"

$$x = \frac{1+i-r}{r} \qquad \text{F-5}$$

$$\text{therefore } F = Ar^{n-1} \left[\frac{(x+1)^n - 1}{x}\right] = Ar^{n-1}(F/A_{x,n}) \qquad \text{F-6}$$

where F is the future worth of a geometric gradient series of values. To get the equivalent series of uniform and equal end of period values, A', multiply both sides of the equation by $A/F_{i,n}$.

$$A' = F(A/F_{i,n}) = Ar^{n-1}(F/A_{x,n})(A/F_{i,n}) \qquad \text{F-7}$$

where A' is the series of equal values that is equivalent to a geometric series of values.

Note: if r = 1, then x = i

$$\text{and } F = A\left[\frac{(i+1)^n - 1}{i}\right] = A(F/A_{i,n})$$

which is the normal equation for calculating the future worth of a uniform series of equal values.

Steps to calculate A' for a geometric series:
1. Find x by equation F-5.
2. Look up F/A(x,n) in tables (and $A/F_{i,n}$ to get A').
3. Compute F from Equation F-6 or A' from Equation F-7
   Note: if r = 1, F/A(x,n) = F/A(i,n)
   if r = 0, F/A(i,n) = A(1 + i)^{n-1}
   which confirms the validity of the equations for these cases.

The following examples illustrate the use of the gradient series equations.

EXAMPLE F-1   Geometric Series Illustration

What is the value at the end of a 3 year annuity with an investment of 2 at year 1, 1.8 ar year 2, and 1.62 at year 3 with interest of 25%?

Solution:
2, 1.8, and 1.62 are a geometric series with a ratio r = 0.90.

Time Diagram

	2	1.8	1.62
0	1	2	3

$$x = \frac{1 + .25 - .9}{.9} = .38888 \text{ or } 38.888\%$$

$$F/A_{38.88\%,3} = 4.3179$$

$$F = 2 \times .9^2 \times F/A_{38.88\%,3} = 6.995 \text{(check by conventional calculation)}$$

$$2(1.25)^2 + 1.8(1.25) + 1.62 = 6.995$$

EXAMPLE F-2   Geometric Series Illustration

A four year annuity has one dollar the first year, two the second, four the third, and eight the fourth year. Interest is 25%. What is the value of the annuity at the end of the fourth year? The geometric ratio is 2.

Time Diagram

–	1	2	4	8
0	1	2	3	4

$$x = \frac{1 + .25 - 2}{2} = -.375 \text{ or } -37.5\%$$

$$F/A_{-37.5\%,4} = \frac{(1-.375)^4 - 1}{-.375} = 2.25976$$

$$F = (1)(2^3)(2.25976) = 18.078$$

As a check

$$F = (1)(1.25^3) + (2)(1.25^2) + (4)(1.25) + 8 = 18.078$$

EXAMPLE F-3   Geometric Series Illustration

This interesting case involves calculating the future worth, F, of a geometric series for
$$r = 1 + i \quad \text{or} \quad x = 0$$
Solution:
In this case, $F/A(o,n) = n$ as a limiting case. The interest increase just cancels out with the geometric ratio and the sum F is just Anr^{n-1} as can be seen from the original defining equation of F, Equation F-6.

EXAMPLE F-4   Future Value of Geometrically Declining Oil or Gas Revenue

A new oil or gas well is projected to generate revenue of $200,000 the first year of production with a 10% constant percentage decrease in revenues in each following year for 10 years. What is the future worth of generated revenues if the revenues are reinvested at $i^* = 15\%$ as received?

Solution:

Use Equation F-6 for $r = 0.90$ and $x = \dfrac{1+.15-0.9}{0.9} = 0.3777$

$$F = \$200,000 \underbrace{(0.9^9)}_{0.3874} \underbrace{(F/A_{27.77,10})}_{38.168} = \$2,957,257$$

EXAMPLE F-5   Geometric Escalation of Operating Costs

Project operating costs are estimated to be \$200,000 in year 1 and to increase 10% per year in each subsequent year. If $i^* = 15\%$, what uniform equivalent annual cost can be used in lieu of the geometric gradient series of costs?

Solution:

$$r = 1.10, \quad x = \dfrac{1+.15-1.10}{1.10} = 0.04545$$

$$\text{Using Eq. F-6,} \quad F = (200,000) \underbrace{(1.1^9)}_{2.3579} \underbrace{(F/A_{4.545\%,10})}_{12.314} = \$5,807,036$$

$$\text{Using Eq. F-7,} \quad A' = \$5,807,036 \underbrace{(A/F_{15,10})}_{0.04925} = \$285,996$$

A uniform series of equal values of \$285,996 at the end of years 1 to 10 is equivalent to the geometric gradient series.

SELECTED REFERENCES

Barish, Norman N., "Economic Analysis for Engineering and Managerial Decision Making," McGraw-Hill Book Company, New York, 1978.

Bennett, H. J., Thompson, J. G., Quiring, H. J., and Toland, J. E., "Financial Evaluation of Mineral Deposits Using Sensitivity and Probabilistic Analysis Methods," (I.C. 8495), U.S. Bur. Mines, Washington, D.C., 1970.

Bierman, H. J., and Smidt, S., "The Capital Budgeting Decision," Third Edition, Macmillan Company, New York, 1971.

Bullinger, C. E., "Engineering Economy," McGraw-Hill Book Company, Inc., New York, 1958.

Chilton, Cecil, "Cost Engineering in the Process Industries," McGraw-Hill Book Company, New York, 1960.

Churchman, C. W., Ackoff, R. L., and Arnoff, E. L., "Introduction to Operations Research," John Wiley and Sons, Inc., New York, 1957.

Commerce Clearing House, Explanation of Tax Reform Act of 1986, Chicago, 1986.

DeGarmo, E. P. and Canada, J. R., "Engineering Economy," Seventh Edition, Macmillan Company, New York, 1984.

Drucker, Peter F., "The Practice of Management," Harper & Row, New York, 1954.

Drucker, Peter F., "Managing for Results," Harper & Row, New York, 1964.

Gass, S. I., "Linear Programming—Methods and Applications," Second Edition, McGraw-Hill Book Company, New York, 1964.

Grant, E. L., Ireson, W. G., and Leavenworth, R. S., "Principles of Engineering Economy," Seventh Edition, Ronald Press Co., New York, 1982.

Hillier, F. S., and Lieberman, G. J., "Introduction to Operations Research," Third Edition, Holden-Day, Inc., San Franciso, 1980.

Hughes, Richard V., "Oil Property Valuation," John Wiley & Sons, Inc., New York, 1967.

McConkey, Dale D., "How to Manage by Results," American Management Association, New York, 1967.

McCray, Arthur W., "Petroleum Evaluations and Economic Decisions," Prentice-Hall, Englewood Cliffs, N.J., 1975.

Merrett, A. J., and Sykes, A., "Capital Budgeting and Company Finance," Longmans, Green and Co. Ltd., London, 1966.

Merrett, A. J., and Sykes, A., "The Finance and Analysis of Capital Projects," Longmans, Green and Co. Ltd., London, 1966.

Middleton, K. A., "The Economics of Capital Expenditure," Australian Society of Accountants, Melbourne, 1971.

Ostwald, Phillip F., "Cost Estimating for Engineering and Management," Prentice-Hall, Englewood Cliffs, N.J., 1974.

Newendorp, Paul D., "Decision Analysis for Petroleum Exploration," Petroleum Publishing Company, Tulsa, Ok., 1976.

Newman, Donald G., "Engineering Economic Analysis," Engineering Press, San Jose, Calif., 1983.

Peters, Max S. and Timmerhaus, Klaus D., "Plant Design and Economics for Chemical Engineers," Third Edition, McGraw-Hill Book Co., New York, 1983.

Popper, Herbert, "Modern Cost Engineering Techniques," McGraw-Hill Book Company, New York, 1970.

Riggs, James L., "Economic Decision Models," McGraw-Hill Book Company, New York, 1970.

Rudd, D. F. and Watson, C. C., "Strategy of Process Engineering," John Wiley & Sons, Inc., New York, 1968.

Samuelson, Paul A., "Economics," Tenth Edition, McGraw-Hill, New York, 1976.

Sandretto, Peter C., "The Economic Management of Research and Engineering," John Wiley & Sons, Inc., New York, 1968.

Schweyer, Herbert E., "Managerial and Engineering Economics," Reinhold Publishing Corporation, New York, 1964.

Smith, Gerald W., "Engineering Economy: Analysis of Capital Expenditures," Third Edition, The Iowa State Univ. Press, Ames, Iowa, 1979.

Stermole, J. M., Master of Science Thesis, "Breakeven Discounted Cash Flow Applied to Equipment Standard Costs," Colorado School of Mines, 1984.

Stermole, F. J., Stermole, J. M. and Bisque, S. M. "Software for Economic Evaluation," (SEE), Investment Evaluations Corp., 2000 Goldenvue Drive, Golden, Colo., 1986.

Taylor, George A., "Managerial and Engineering Economy," D. Van Nostrand Company, Inc., New York, 1975.

Terborgh, George, "Business Investment Management," Machinery and Allied Products Institute, Washington, D.C., 1967.

Thuesen, H. G., Fabrycky, W. J., and Thuesen, G. J., "Engineering Economy," Fifth Edition, Prentice-Hall, Inc., Englewood Cliffs, N.J., 1977.

Weston, J. Fred and Brigham, Eugene F., "Managerial Finance," Seventh Edition, The Dryden Press, 1981.

Woolsey, R.E.D. and Swanson, H.S., "Operations Research for Immediate Application," Harper and Row, New York, 1975.

INDEX